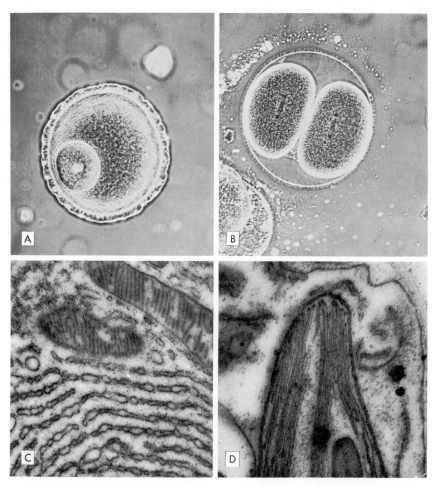

Examples of structures visible in cells by newer microscopical techniques:
A and B, phase microscopy; C and D, electron microscopy.

A, Unfertilized living egg of *Pateria miniata*, a West Coast starfish ($\times$ 185). Note the large germinal vesicle and nucleolus. B, A live dividing egg of the same species, showing the fertilization membrane ($\times$ 185). Note the spindles preparing for another division. C, Mitochondria (at the top, the structures with lamellae) and the endoplasmic reticulum of an acinar cell of the pancreas ($\times$ 20,000). D, Algal chloroplast, showing lamellar arrangement of constituents ($\times$ 65,000). (A and B courtesy of Dr. Richard Boolootian, University of California at Los Angeles. C and D courtesy of Dr. G. E. Palade, the Rockefeller Institute for Medical Research.)

CELL PHYSIOLOGY

ARTHUR C. GIESE, Ph.D.

PROFESSOR OF BIOLOGY
STANFORD UNIVERSITY

SECOND EDITION / **ILLUSTRATED**

W. B. Saunders Company   Philadelphia
London

To Raina

PREFACE TO THE SECOND EDITION

It is gratifying that "Cell Physiology" has stimulated sufficient interest to justify a second edition. This permits me to make some necessary changes and to attempt to bring the material up to date as far as possible. In a sense a textbook of such a rapidly growing field of study can never be entirely up to date, for new progress is being made even as these pages come off the press. "Cell Physiology" is based on the belief that the basic principles and techniques, systematically introduced in connection with a selection of material made over a period of years, will show the relationship between the two and will appeal to the reason of the student rather than to his memory. The new facts and ideas with which he may later come in contact he should be able himself to fit into the framework presented here.

I have not hesitated to introduce new material and new ideas when they are sound and helpful, but have made a conscious effort to avoid controversial issues. The addition of all this new material has necessitated some reorganization of the text and has limited it entirely to material focusing on the cell only. This was thought desirable in order to conserve space and gain greater unity. It will be noted, however, that almost two thirds of the material of the second edition remains essentially the same as the first. It would, in fact, be disturbing if the foundations of the subject were so frail as to require a complete rewriting.

For more extensive comments I am particularly indebted to Dr. C. J. Brokaw (Minnesota), Dr. R. Iverson (Miami), Dr. C. Manwell (Illinois), Dr. W. Jacobson (Cambridge University) and to my colleagues, Dr. S. Kalman, Dr. D. Kennedy and Dr. C. Yanofsky. I note with appreciation also the help of Mrs. M. Lusignan on the new figures and Mrs. B. McCaw for a careful reading of the finished copy.

I am indebted also to my many critics who have pointed out certain errors or deficiencies. I have tried to incorporate as many of their requests as possible. Some were, however, suggestions for modifications of the book in diametrically opposite directions, while others were considered outside the scope and intentions of the book.

ARTHUR C. GIESE

Stanford, California

PREFACE TO THE
FIRST EDITION

"Cell Physiology" as presented here is patterned after a set of lectures as they are given in my class at Stanford University. Although several excellent textbooks in cellular physiology are available and a number of good books bordering on the field have appeared, there exists no single book which gives a brief account of the subject. Students have asked repeatedly that this need be fulfilled; that a book be written which describes in simple language and in bold outline the major problems of cellular physiology, explaining their interrelationships and the current status of each of them without confusing the beginner with details or taking him into controversies upon which even the experts cannot agree.

Introducing a topic in cellular physiology by presenting controversial issues has often left students without an anchorage of fact by which to evaluate anything at all. On the other hand, I have been impressed by the tendency of many students to accept uncritically and to memorize anything written in a textbook. It is certainly not possible to avoid conflicting information on some subjects, since an open mind must be maintained on all real issues; but controversies on less important points can be minimized so that the major achievements in cellular physiology are not completely obscured. To help the student understand the scientific approach and develop an attitude of critical evaluation, I have found it extremely useful to include fundamental laboratory work and to conduct weekly discussions focusing on more specific controversial problems. And it is expected that after this primary orientation in the subject, students may become interested enough to turn to the more complete and analytical studies cited in references at the end of each chapter.

I have, moreover, confined the subject matter in this book to that dealing primarily with the cell, since this is basic to studies on multicellular organisms. By avoiding treatment of problems which relate to the organization of cells into organisms, it is possible to develop a more closely-knit body of information, such as could be presented to a class in the course of a quarter or a semester. Classes in plant physiology, comparative animal physiology, mammalian physiology and bacterial physiology are logical sequels to the course in cellular physiology.

At Stanford a one quarter course in cellular physiology is required of biology majors, most of whom take it at the junior or senior level. The student will have taken elementary botany, zoology, physics and introductory and organic chemistry. He is, therefore, unprepared for a rigorous physical-chemical treatment of the subject. However, the experience of the department over the years seems to have justified the premise that an introduction to cellular physiology at the elementary level is more beneficial than restriction of the course to a handful of graduate students with a broader background. Consequently, derivations of equations on physical-chemical principles or more extended chemical discussions, if included at all, are put in appendices because this makes the material available to those students who are really interested without impeding the flow of the subject for those who are not.

I am indebted to Miss Ruth Ogren, scientific illustrator, for preparing many of the illustrations, and to Professor Hadley Kirkman of Stanford University, Professor David Waugh of Massachusetts Institute of Technology, and Dr. Richard Boolootian of the Hopkins Marine Station for use of the photographs from which Figures 2.2, 14.6, and 7 and 14.2, respectively, were made. The courtesy of numerous publishers who have permitted copying of figures from books or periodicals is also acknowledged with gratitude. I am also indebted to Dr. George Palade of the Rockefeller Institute for Medical Research for electron micrographs used in the frontispiece, and to Dr. John Bennett, Stanford University, for the figure of the metabolic mill.

I wish to express my appreciation for many helpful comments and criticisms made by my colleagues and assistants, and especially to Professor J. P. Baumberger of Stanford University, Professor Jack Myers of the University of Texas, Professor John Spikes of the University of Utah, and to my students, Dr. Ray Iverson, Dr. David Shepard and Dr. Raymond Sanders, for a critical reading of the manuscript or parts of it. However, I must assume responsibility for opinions expressed and for omissions or errors which may still remain after proofreading. My main hope is that students will find this account interesting and stimulating.

ARTHUR C. GIESE

Stanford, California

CONTENTS

Chapter 9

Chapter 10

Chapter 22

Chapter 23

Chapter 24

SECTION

I

FUNCTIONAL ORGANIZATION OF THE CELL

Although the cell was recognized as a unit of structure and function of all living things in 1839 when Schleiden and Schwann formulated the Cell Doctrine, the nature of the cell and many details of cellular organization remained yet to be determined. For example, the origin and continuity of the nucleus were not recognized in 1839. Since then these and many other details of cellular organization have been clarified, but the functions of many of these structures have been effectively studied only recently.

A discussion of the scope of cell physiology appears in Chapter 1, the organization of different kinds of cells and some techniques for the study of cell structure are given in Chapter 2, followed by a discussion of the biochemistry of the cell in Chapter 3 and of the colloidal behavior of chemical constituents of the cell in Chapter 4. The functional organization of cell organelles is considered in Chapter 5 and the organization and functioning of the nucleus in Chapter 6.

THE SCOPE OF
CELL PHYSIOLOGY

Life Activities

It is desirable at the outset to establish the place which cell physiology occupies in the scientific scheme and to discuss briefly the ways in which the cell physiologist approaches the problems of cell functions.

Cell physiology is the study of the fundamental activities of plant cells, animal cells and microorganisms. These activities might be enumerated as follows: (1) Nutrition, including in its broadest sense the uptake and preparation of food and oxygen for use in the cells, the release of energy in cells and the elimination of the wastes produced, (2) response to the environment, (3) growth and (4) reproduction or cell division and differentiation.

The briefest comparison of plants, animals and microorganisms serves to show the fundamental similarities of their functions despite differences in structure. The body of a seed plant is composed of cells organized into a number of complex organs: root, stem, leaf, flower and, in the mature plant, the fruit with the developing seed. Through the root hairs water

and nutrient salts pass into the vascular tissue and are carried through the stem to the leaves. Carbon dioxide enters through the stomata of the leaves, and during the light of day carbohydrates are synthesized from carbon dioxide and water in the chlorophyll-bearing cells. From the carbohydrates and salts the plant later synthesizes other compounds such as amino acids, fatty acids and water-soluble vitamins. These manufactured foodstuffs are then distributed in a solution (the sap) to cells in all parts of the plant, and the excess may be stored in the seed, fruit, root, stem or, less frequently, in the leaf. The vascular system and the surrounding woody fibers serve as a skeleton supporting the entire plant.

Although photosynthesis occurs only in some special cells of the seed plant, all cells of the plant body must be supplied with cell foods, and they must be freed of cell wastes. Plants grow, using part of the food manufactured, and after reaching maturity they reproduce, using more of it. Growing plants respond to gravity, to light and to chemical and other factors in their environment. Thus the root grows downward in response to gravity, whereas the stem grows upward; the root grows away from the light while the stem grows toward it (for instance, everyone has seen the sunflower follow the sun). The response of plants to tactile stimuli is seen in the twining tendrils which fasten some plants to a support. Movements of plants are mainly growth movements, and although they are too slow for us to see, they can be readily demonstrated in time-lapse photography. The more rapid turgor movements can be seen in the sensitive plant, *Mimosa*.

The essential architectural plan of a vertebrate, a triploblastic form (embryonically three-layered), consists of an outer tube, the body wall, enclosing an inner tube, the gut, and supported by an internal skeleton consisting of bones. The head constitutes the anterior end and contains many of the sense organs or receptors. The trunk, consisting of a body wall and the internal organs in it, is supported by the appendages. The internal organs are organized into various organ systems. For example, the organs of the digestive system prepare food for use in the body, and the digested food is absorbed into the blood and is distributed over the entire body by the organs of the circulatory system. As in the plant, regardless of the organ in which it is found, the individual cell requires the same essential cell foods. The respiratory system takes up the oxygen which is distributed to all cells by way of the circulatory system, and it voids to the air the carbon dioxide brought to it by the circulatory system. The blood flushes wastes from cells in all parts of the body, carrying these wastes to the kidneys where they are extracted from the blood and voided to the exterior. The animal may be considered to have developed a set of services of supply—digestive, respiratory, circulatory and excretory—which maintain the cellular environment. The needed supplies of oxygen and food are brought to the cells, and the wastes of cellular activity are removed from the cells and voided to the exterior. By way of receptor organs (such as the eyes, ears, etc.) sensitive to light, sound, pressure, gravity, heat or chemicals, the animal receives information about the environment. Response to the information so gathered is made possible by a nervous and muscular system supported by a bony skeletal system. After reaching sexual maturity the animal reproduces.

As can be seen from above, the same fundamental activities of life—nutrition, response, growth and reproduction—are therefore performed by plants and animals, though in somewhat different ways.

However, complex organs like those found in higher plants and animals are not necessary for the performance of the fundamental biological functions in all organisms. Respiration takes place in bacteria, protozoa and unicellular plants, all without a respiratory system; likewise, digestion can occur without the aid of a digestive system and excretion, without the aid of an excretory system. Microorganisms get food and oxygen directly from the environment and void their wastes directly to it. They respond to the environment, and if conditions are favorable, they grow and reproduce.

The common denominator required for the performance of these fundamental activities of plants, animals and microorganisms is clearly the cell, not the complex organs or systems which have developed in multicellular plants and animals. These systems are concerned primarily with maintaining the internal environment in contact with the cells of the organisms. It is through the cell of the multicellular animal and plant that all the flow of matter and flux of energy occurs. The cell is a fundamental unit, not only of structure but also of function of all living things. A study of cellular physiology is, therefore, basic to an understanding of the fundamental activities of life.

Vitalistic and Mechanistic Interpretation of Life Activities

The mind of man demands an explanation for the phenomena of nature. Primitive peoples developed mythologies which conceived of the earth and man as being controlled by various supernatural forces. Such forces were later suggested to explain biologic phenomena and the functions of the human body. Accounts of these early conceptions may be found in various histories of biology.[1, 2, 3]*

As information was accumulated from observation and experimentation, it eventually became clear that the grosser functions in the animal and plant, such as digestion, respiration, circulation and excretion, are subject to the laws of physics and chemistry. Some persons, the "vitalists," however, maintain that although digestion, respiration, excretion and circulation might be interpreted in terms of chemical and physical laws, more complex processes such as the orderly development of the embryo and the complex mental life of man can be interpreted best in terms of something apart from and in addition to the physical-chemical laws. They postulate a vital force, categorically equivalent to matter and energy, to perform this role. Others, the "mechanists," think that all phenomena of life are ultimately describable in terms of chemical and physical laws. The cell physiologist finds it profitable to operate on the working hypothesis that the physiologic activities of the cell are the consequence of the operation of a physical-chemical system which constitutes the cell.

If the functions of the cell are the consequences of the operation of a physical-chemical system performing work, then the cell may be likened to a machine. It is the purpose of the cell physiologist, first, to determine the nature of the machinery of the cell and, second, to determine the principles which govern its operation, with the hope of better understanding its functioning. This hypothesis has been fruitful in stimulating experimentation in the past. The extent to which it will be fruitful in the future remains to be seen.[4, 5]

Experimental Approach in Cell Physiology

Cell physiology employs the experimental method. The student who reads the original literature soon finds that the solution to a problem in science is often achieved by slow and laborious collection of data. Pertinent observations are made and data already available are focused on the problem in question and a possible explanation, a hypothesis, is formulated. Carefully planned experiments are then prepared for testing it, and it may happen that after much work an investigator finds that the attempted explanation is inadequate and that he has only cleared the ground for further analytical work. An alternative hypothesis is then constructed and tested. Occasionally decisive experiments result in dramatic advances in knowledge and understanding.[6, 7] Such decisive experiments have occurred more frequently in physics and chemistry, where the total number of variables is fewer. In the biological system, where there are a great number of variables, similar progress in theoretical knowledge may be expected only as the physiologist gains control of these factors.

As an example of the scientific approach to problems, consider the question, "Is yeast fermentation a vital process: i.e., does yeast fermentation require the entire cell or will the enzymes derived from yeast cells ferment sugar apart from the cell?" This question was posed at the beginning of the twentieth century. On the hypothesis that enzymes alone can ferment sugar outside of the cell, experi-

---

* References to the literature are given in the back of each chapter as "literature cited." General references covering the material of the chapter precede the literature cited.

mental tests were made by Buchner, and fermentation of cell-free juice with autolyzed yeast was achieved, thus proving the hypothesis.[6] Many other examples of the experimental approach to physiological problems will be considered in later chapters.

Experimentation makes possible selection of the most likely explanation for a phenomenon. As the unlikely explanations are eliminated, the remaining one becomes more probable. It will become evident later, when various cellular functions are discussed, that many explanations suggested are only tentative ones, subject to revision as more decisive data become available.

The Relation of Cell Physiology to Various Fields of Physiology

Much of *animal physiology* deals with the work of the various organs of the body and of the coordination of the various organs in the integrated behavior of the animal as a whole. For example, the nutrition of the animal, the response of the animal and, to some extent, its reproduction are studied by the animal physiologist. Since he is concerned with organ function his study might be called organ physiology. Medical men in the past have been primarily concerned with vertebrate organ physiology, especially of mammals, because the information gained can be more directly applied to the physiology of man in health and disease. Therefore, medical physiology most often meant mammalian organ physiology. However, to interpret organ physiology, research workers in medical physiology have often found it necessary to work at the cellular level as well. Therefore much overlapping occurs at the present time.

Comparative animal physiology is a study of organ functions in various types of animals, vertebrate and invertebrate, in an attempt to find fundamental relations not recognized when the function is studied in only one group of animals.

Each function and the different ways in which it may be performed in various animals are therefore viewed in the perspective of the whole animal kingdom.

Plant Physiology concerns itself with the response, nutrition, growth and reproduction of various types of plants. Because many of these problems first required solution at the cell level, plant physiologists have contributed greatly to the development of cell physiology.

Since functioning of animals and plants depends ultimately upon the functioning of their component cells, an understanding of cell physiology is basic to all the other physiological studies. This has been recognized by researchers, many of whom, interested primarily in the higher organisms, have worked at the cell level as a background for solution of problems at the organ level.

By the use of the experimental method, the following cellular problems have been studied:

1. The nature of the organization of cells of plants, animals and microorganisms as a key to an understanding of cellular activities.

2. The nature of the cell environment and the resistance and adjustment of the cell to the variations of the environment.

3. The nature of the cell membrane and the regulation of transport of materials into and out of the cell across the membrane.

4. The nature of cell foods and their interconversions and the mechanism by which the process of respiration releases energy from cell foods.

5. Use of the energy liberated in respiration for performing the various types of work done by the cell; e.g., for the maintenance of irritability or readiness to respond, for motility required for the responses, for osmotic work and for the manufacture of secretions and of new constituents leading to cell growth and cell division.

A consideration of each of these problems in turn constitutes the major portion of this book. This approach leads from the problems of organization of the cell to cellular dynamics. It also leads from the more descriptive aspects of cell physiology to the more complex studies of respiration, irritability, growth and cell division. It has the advantage that much of the descriptive information is already available when the more difficult problems are analyzed. At the end, a brief chapter on the history of cell physiology brings into perspective some of the major trends of research in the field.

The Literature of Cell Physiology

The most recent achievements in cell physiology and data on current studies are presented at scientific meetings and are recorded in current issues of such periodicals as *Science, Nature*, the *Journal of General Physiology, The Journal of Cellular and Comparative Physiology*, the *Journal of Experimental Biology, Experimental Cell Research, Physiological Zoology, Biochimica et Biophysica Acta, Proceedings of the National Academy of Sciences, U.S., Archiv für die gesampte Physiologie, Compte Rendu de la Société de Biologie, Doklady Academii Nauk SSSR* (Biological Sciences Division), *Biofizika* and many others.

Reviews or summaries of recent advances on subjects of interest to the cell physiologist appear in such journals as the *Quarterly Review of Biology, Physiological Reviews, Biological Reviews of the Cambridge Philosophical Society, Annual Review of Physiology*, etc. Some reviews will be cited in the subsequent chapters.

There are many good monographs on various special subjects of interest to the cell physiologist; e.g., on protoplasmic structure, permeability, oxidation-reduction and respiratory enzymes, bioluminescence, muscle chemistry and physiology. In this book reference will be made to such monographs when they are pertinent to the subject matter being discussed in a given chapter.

Compendia and textbooks cover much larger fields than monographs, and consequently their treatment of specific topics is usually less complete. Reference is given below to textbooks of this kind which have been found most useful. Most of them will not be specifically cited again in this book, but they are fruitful sources of additional material, especially in the fields designated.

If a bibliography is to be compiled on a subject of interest, journals which abstract periodicals are helpful. The most useful abstract journals for the cell physiologist are *Biological Abstracts* and *Chemical Abstracts, International Abstracts of Biological Sciences, Berichte über die gesampte Physiologie, Berichte über die Wissenschaftliche Biologie, Inhaltsverzeichnisse sowjetscher Fachzeitschriften: III B, Chemie und Biologie* and *Bulletin de l'Institut Pasteur*. These journals not only give references to recent original papers, reviews and monographs, but they also furnish abstracts of the contents.

At the end of each chapter are general references in which the reader may find additional information covering the general field of the chapter, usually from a different point of view. Citations to other literature, indicated by superior numbers, support views expressed on subjects of lesser scope. They are included as an aid to those who may wish to get a more complete treatment of some topic which interests him especially.

GENERAL REFERENCES FOR CELL PHYSIOLOGY

Barnes, T. C., 1945: Textbook of General Physiology, Blakiston, New York. Interesting discussions of models of living systems.

Bayliss, L. E., 1959–60: Principles of General Physiology. I. The Physico-Chemical Background. II. General Physiology. Longmans, Green and Company, New York. A recent revision of a great classic.

Brachet, J., and Mirsky, A. E., 1959 to 1961: The Cell, 5 volumes, Academic Press, New York.

Davson, H., 1959: 2nd Ed. A Textbook of General Physiology. Blakiston, New York. Especially useful for considerations of permeability, muscular activity and nervous action.

De Robertis, E. L. P., Nowinski, W. W., and Saez, F. A., 1960: 3rd Ed. General Cytology. Saunders, Philadelphia. Especially useful for studies on the structure of cells.

Florkin, M., and Mason, H. (eds): Comparative Biochemistry. 6 volumes planned, some of which have appeared. Academic Press, New York.

Haas, J., 1955: Physiologie der Zelle, Verlag von Gebrüder Borntraeger, Berlin.

Heilbrunn, L. V., 1952: An Outline of General Physiology. 3rd Ed. Saunders, Philadelphia. A good general reference on all subjects in cellular physiology.

Heilbrunn, L. V., and Weber, F. (eds.), 1953–1959: Protoplasmatologia, Handbuch der Protoplasmaforschung. Springer, Vienna. 14 volumes (in English, French and German).

Höber, R., and others, 1945: Physical Chemistry of Cells and Tissues. Blakiston, New York. Useful for most problems in cell physiology.

Mitchell, P. H., 1956: 5th Ed. A Textbook of General Physiology. McGraw-Hill, New York. Especially useful for discussion of colloidal chemistry of cells, but containing useful discussion of a number of other topics.

Protoplasma Monographien, 1928 to the present.

Scheer, B. T., 1953: General Physiology, Wiley, New York.

Uber, F. (ed.), 1950: Biophysical Research Methods. Interscience Publishers, New York.

LITERATURE CITED*

1. Dawes, B., 1952: One Hundred Years of Biology. Macmillan, New York.
2. Nordenskiold, E., 1936: The History of Biology. Tudor, New York.
3. Singer, C., 1950: A History of Biology. Schuman, New York.
4. Reichenbach, H., 1953: The Rise of Scientific Philosophy. Univ. California Press, Berkeley, California.
5. Sinnott, E., 1953: Two Ways to Truth. Viking, New York.
6. Gabriel, M. L., and Fogel, S., 1955: Great Experiments in Biology. Prentice-Hall, New York.
7. Suñer, A. P., 1955: Classics of Biology. Pitman, London.
8. Pledge, H. T., 1959: Science since 1500. Harper, New York.

* Most references are in English because in our experience undergraduate students do not read papers in other languages. More readily available sources are often cited here in preference to the primary sources. References to primary sources may be obtained within the monographs cited.

CELL ORGANIZATION

It is common knowledge that the cell is differentiated into *nucleus* and *cytoplasm,* each of which is surrounded by a membrane, the nucleus by the *nuclear membrane* and the cytoplasm by the *cell* or *plasma membrane.* The outer portion of the cytoplasm, called the *ectoplasm,* is generally more finely granular and of a stiffer consistency than the inner portion, called the *endoplasm.* It is also familiar to all who have studied plants and animals that the cells of which they are composed are diverse in size and form. A brief summary of the range in size of cells is given in Table 2.1 and of the range in form in Table 2.2.

Although diverse in size and form, cells have a similar intracellular organization and usually possess the same formed structures or organelles[1] (see Fig. 2.1). The presence of most of the organelles in all cells suggests that each organelle performs some fundamental role in the economy of the cell. Determination of the functions of these organelles is one of the ultimate aims of the cell physiologist.

Organelles Seen in Fixed and Stained Cells

Under the microscope, a nucleus is seen

TABLE 2.1. *Range in Size of Cells*

MASS IN GRAMS	ORGANISM OR CELL
10^3 to 10^2	Dinosaur eggs, ostrich eggs, cycad ovules
10^1	*Valonia macrophysa* (mature)
10^0	*Valonia ventricosa* (mature)
10^{-1}	*Nitella* (large internode)
10^{-2} to 10^{-3}	Frog eggs
10^{-4}	Striated muscle of man
10^{-5}	Human ovum
10^{-6}	Large *Paramecium*
	Large sensory neuron of dog
10^{-7}	Average *Vorticella*
	Human smooth muscle fiber
	Human liver cell
10^{-8}	Dysentery ameba
10^{-9}	Frog erythrocyte
	Malarial parasite
	Human sperm
	Smallest Protozoa (*Monas*)
10^{-11}	Anthrax bacillus
10^{-12}	Tubercle and pus bacteria
10^{-14}	Smallest bacteria
	(Limit of microscopic vision)
10^{-15}	Filter passing viruses, etc.

From table of comparative masses in Haldane and Huxley, 1927: Animal Biology; data on Valonia from L. R. Blinks, personal communication; on Nitella, original; on frog egg, calculated from diameters. All values are orders of magnitude.

TABLE 2.2. *Types of Cells and Their Uses in the Study of Cell Physiology*

NAME	TYPICAL SHAPE	EXAMPLES	USE IN THE STUDY OF CELL PHYSIOLOGY
		ANIMAL	
Epithelial	Cuboidal or brick-like	Epidermis, glandular lining	Permeability, properties of protoplasm
Muscular	Spindle	Smooth, striated	Contractility, metabolism
Nervous	Cell body with long fibers	Sensory neuron, motor neuron,	Irritability, structure of protoplasm
Connective	Spheroid cells in a mass of extra-cellular material	Cartilage cells, cells in bone and connective tissue	Production of extra-cellular secretions
Blood	Disk-shaped or ameboid cells in fluid	Red blood cell, leucocyte	Permeability, ameboid move-ment, response to chemicals
Eggs	Usually spherical	Sea urchin egg, frog egg	Structure of proto-plasm, properties of protoplasm, permeability, function of nucleus
Sperm	Usually flagellated cells	Sea urchin sperm	Function of nucleus, nucleoprotein
Protozoans	Diverse	*Amoeba, Paramecium*	Ameboid and ciliary movement, nuclear function, permeability, effects of environ-ment
		PLANT	
Epidermal	Cuboidal or brick-like	Epidermis	Permeability
Vascular	Elongate (some strengthened by spirals, discs, etc.)	Phloem (in xylem only cell walls remain)	Structure of proto-plasm (phloem)
Supporting	Elongate, heavy walls	Bast fibers	
Undifferentiated (parenchyma)	Spheroidal	Mesophyll, inter-stitial cells of stem, root, etc.	Photosynthesis, structure of protoplasm
Unicellular algae	Diverse	*Chlorella*	Photosynthesis

NAME	TYPICAL SHAPE	EXAMPLES	USE IN THE STUDY OF CELL PHYSIOLOGY
PLANT			
Unicellular fungi	Diverse	Yeast	Metabolism
Filamentous fungi	Elongate cells	*Neurospora*	Biosynthesis
Bacteria	Diverse	The colon bacillus	Biosynthesis, metabolism

in every stained* cell although in bacteria and blue-green algae it lacks a membrane and is less well organized than in true cells of higher forms of plant and animal life. Within the nucleus a *nucleolus* is commonly present and so is a *linin* network bearing the *chromatin.* Between these materials is the *nucleoplasm.* The entire nucleus is surrounded by a nuclear membrane. Just outside the nucleus of animal cells is a *centriole,* a small granule which separates into two before mitosis (cell division). At mitosis the two centrioles move apart and form the poles of the spindles and the centers of the asters.

* See the appendix to this chapter for an account of methods of staining and for a description of microscopes.

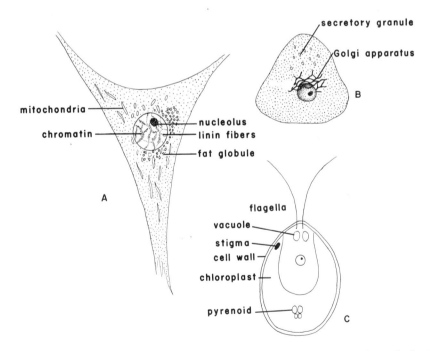

Fig. 2.1. Cells and cell organelles. *A* is a fibroblast, *B* is a cell of the pancreas, and *C* is the flagellate, *Chlamydomonas,* at the center of which is a nucleus.

Scattered in the cytoplasm are *mitochondria,* or chondriosomes, which have been seen in all kinds of cells examined. The appearance of mitochondria depends upon the handling of the tissues before preparation; they may appear as long rods, short rods or small granules.

The *Golgi apparatus,* named after its discoverer, is particularly prominent in nervous and secretory cells of animals and seems to be closely associated with secretory activities. In fixed and stained preparations (see Fig. 2.2) it appears to be a canalicular system closely associated with the mitochondria. Its presence is questionable in higher plants and it is absent from bacteria, algae and fungi. Its true structure and function have been the subject of long controversy which is not yet resolved.

Plastids are cytoplasmic organelles which may or may not contain pigment (for example, chlorophyll is the green pigment in chloroplasts, one of the kinds of plastids in green plants). *Vacuoles,* such as the contractile vacuoles of protozoans, and the large central sap vacuoles which are characteristic of plant cells, are often seen in cells.

When a cell is cleared by centrifugation of visible granules, oil globules and various organelles, a clear *ground substance* remains which is thought to represent the fundamental architecture of the cell. In fixed and stained preparations under the ordinary microscope this substance is devoid of structure, but under the electron microscope, which resolves much finer detail (see Appendix 2.2), the ground substance appears to contain a network called the *endoplasmic reticulum.*[2,51] Upon this reticulum can be seen fine granules called the *ribosomes.* Intercellular cytoplasmic connections called *plasmodesmata* are also found between cells in a tissue.[47]

It is of interest to note that while a cell contains but one nucleus it may have about 500 mitochondria, 5×10^5 microsomes and probably 5×10^8 enzyme molecules. A green plant cell will probably have about 50 chloroplasts. This multiplicity of units is a characteristic feature of cell organization. Even the nucleus of a diploid organism has two chromosomes of a kind and two genes of a kind, one in each of the members of a homologous pair of chromosomes.

As most of the organelles listed above were first described in fixed and stained preparations (see Appendix 2.1), the possibility was suggested that the fixing process, by precipitating the proteins, produces artificial structures, or *artifacts,* which do not represent the true structures of the cell. At the turn of the century Hardy and Fisher showed that some of these organelles could be duplicated

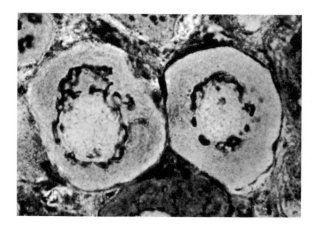

Fig. 2.2. The Golgi apparatus in cervical spinal ganglion cells of a female guinea pig. Kolatchev-Nassanov fixation ($\times$ 2000). (By courtesy of Professor Hadley Kirkman.)

by adding to gelatin such fixing agents as tannic acid, chromic acid or the salts of heavy metals. Therefore, it became necessary to determine whether the structures observed in fixed preparations were actually present in living cells. Many new and ingenious techniques were devised to demonstrate them, and the evidence for each organelle is presented below.

Experimental Evidence for Cell Organelles in Living Cells

When a living cell is examined under an ordinary light microscope, its main organization (nucleus, cytoplasm, plastids, granules, edges of membranes) is visible in outline because of differences in refraction of light by these structures.

When the living cell is centrifuged and observed during the process through the centrifuge microscope (see Fig. 2.4), the organelles, differing in specific gravity and size, are seen to move as discrete units. For example, in centrifuged eggs of the sea urchin *Arbacia*, the red pigment granules are thrown to the bottom of the cell; above them the yolk is deposited, then a layer of mitochondria, and finally the oil droplets are collected at the top of the egg, forming an oil cap. Between the zone of the mitochondria and the oil cap is a clear zone of fine granular protoplasm called the ground substance,[4] within which the nucleus of the egg comes to lie (see Fig. 2.3). Clearly, the specific gravity of the nucleus is less than that of some of the other cellular constituents.

The ground substance represents the cytoplasm cleared by centrifugation of the extraneous structures suspended in it. No structure in the ground substance of a living cell is visible under the ordinary light microscope, the ultraviolet microscope or the phase microscope. However, if cells are first fragmented and then centrifuged, the fragments of higher specific gravity settle more rapidly than those of lower specific gravity, other factors being equal, while larger particles settle more

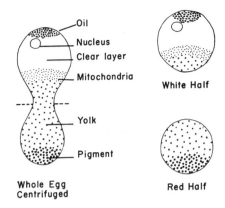

White Half

Red Half

Whole Egg Centrifuged

Fig. 2.3. Stratification in a centrifuged egg of the sea urchin, *Arbacia punctulata*. (After Harvey, E. B.: Biol. Bull., *81*:114, 1941.)

rapidly than smaller ones of the same specific gravity. Thus various particulates within the cell can then be segregated from one another. Large structures such as nuclei are readily separated from other constituents as are also mitochondria and large granules. After all these structures have been removed, minute submicroscopic bodies remain which can be

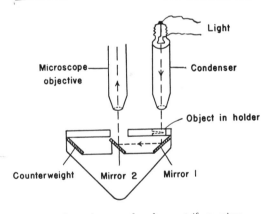

Fig. 2.4. Optical system for ultracentrifuge microscope. The condenser throws an image of the incandescent light on the object. The object is under the light for a fraction of a second during each revolution of the disk, but the image on mirror 1 reflected to mirror 2 is seen as a continuous moving picture because the eye, over the microscope in the axis of rotation of the centrifuge, fuses the many images coming to it per second. (From Harvey: J. Appl. Physics 9:73, 1938.)

centrifuged down at very high speeds. These are called the *microsomes,*[12] and some of them are believed to be the granules seen under the electron microscope[2] in the endoplasmic reticulum of the ground substance. Others are fragments of the endoplasmic reticulum (see Chapter 5).

The Nucleus and Its Constituents. The internal organization of the resting nucleus in a living cell is difficult to discern by ordinary microscopy, and even during mitosis and meiosis the chromosomes are seen only under rare circumstances. However, under the phase microscope (see Appendix 2.2), where slight differences in refractive index between diverse cellular constituents are exaggerated, the chromosomes of some cells may be seen quite clearly. In fact, time-lapse photography permits continuous observation of a single chromosome preparation throughout a cycle of meiosis or mitosis, corroborating what was previously deduced from a random sampling of many fixed and stained preparations. Furthermore, chromosomes are seen without the distortion which usually attends fixation. Time-lapse photography makes evident not only the sequence of events, but also the dynamic nature of the process—the movements of cell organelles such as mitochondria, and the changes in shape of the entire cells. (The possible meanings of these movements and the role each of the various organelles may play during mitosis and meiosis will be considered in Chapters 6 and 26.)

Chromosomes are also discerned in ultraviolet photomicrographs of cells in mitosis or meiosis, because the chromosomes absorb short wavelengths of these radiations more strongly than does the cytoplasm.[6] Much has been learned by the use of this technique (see Chapter 6) but it is not as generally useful as phase microscopy because cells are damaged by these radiations, and prolonged examination is thus impossible.

Chromosomes when visible may be reached by micromanipulator needles and moved about in the nucleus or in the cell (see Appendix 2.3), indicating that they are discrete units.[7] Moreover, fragmentation and irregularities in the partition of chromosomes can be observed in cells irradiated with ionizing radiations. Chromosomes have also been released from a suspension of nuclei (obtained by fractional centrifugation) and they maintain their identity through a variety of manipulations. No doubt now exists that chromosomes are real structural units, even though they are difficult to identify in the resting stages of cells.

Mitochondria. Mitochondria are visible in living cells under the phase microscope. They are seen to undergo active movements during mitosis and meiosis. Mitochondria may also be seen in living cells stained with the vital dye, Janus green B, which though not entirely harmless, permits the cell to remain alive for a long time so that one can observe how the mitochondria change in shape and size as the conditions vary.

Further evidence of the identity of mitochondria is provided by their movement as units during centrifugation of a whole cell[9] and by their discreteness after cell fragmentation. They may be separated from other particles in fragmented cells by washing in salt solutions followed by differential centrifugation. In suspension they maintain their identity if adequate conditions are provided. Such suspensions of mitochondria have been subjected to biochemical analyses, and many enzymes concerned with aerobic respiration, energy transfer and storage have been identified in them (see Chapter 17). Perhaps for this reason mitochondria are concentrated in regions of greatest cellular activity: at the secretory surface of a glandular cell, near the nodes of a nerve cell at which propagation is believed to occur, and in active muscle fibers. In these locations mitochondria might supply most readily the energy needed for the activities of the cells.

When cells divide, the mitochondria orient themselves relatively symmetrically on each side of the division figure, partition between the two cells being fairly equal. In some cases mitochondria have been seen to fragment after division. It is possible that the fragments then increase in size, thus reconstituting the amount of mitochondrial material needed in each daughter cell. However, mitochondria may also develop from minute bodies in the cytoplasm.

The origin of the mitochondria of the cell is still controversial. As mentioned earlier, mitochondria may be concentrated in one end of an *Arbacia* egg by centrifugation, and the centrifugal and centripetal halves of the egg may be pulled apart by further centrifugation, leaving one half of the egg free of mitochondria as viewed with the light microscope. In this half they appear to arise anew.[9-11] However, electronmicroscopic studies indicate the presence of minute bodies which appear to be precursors of mitochondria in the halves of eggs freed of large mitochondria by centrifugation.[12]

The Golgi Apparatus. In the living cell under favorable conditions the Golgi apparatus may be stained with methylene blue and observed for a limited time. It is also visible by means of phase microscopy. That it is fluid in consistency is suggested by the ease with which a microneedle moves through it.[7] It seems to be closely connected to the endoplasmic reticulum but its outlines are smooth (ribosomes being lacking) and it is chemically different from the reticulum, containing much more lipid. It can be separated from other constituents of the cell by differential centrifugation.[27] Some question exists whether the Golgi apparatus really constitutes a true organelle. Cytologists are inclined to look upon the Golgi apparatus as an assembly area for different kinds of secretions, especially lipids, rather than as a structural unit.[27, 38, 39] Into the Golgi area flow high energy compounds from the mitochondria and various secretions, probably including nucleic acids, from the nucleus.[10]

Plastids. The identity of chloroplasts as discrete structures has not been doubted because they are so readily seen in living cells of green plants. They have been separated by maceration of cells and fractional separation of the constituents (see Chapter 20). The internal structure of chloroplasts has also been studied by electron microscopy.[1]

Other plastids, however, have been less thoroughly studied, perhaps because their functions in plant cells are not as clearly evident as those of the chloroplast.[14] Leucoplasts, within which starch grains are formed, are organized bodies in the cytoplasm and they contain enzymes which synthesize starch from the glucose formed during photosynthesis.[14] Perhaps other synthetic functions are also localized in the plastids of plant cells.

Miscellaneous Cell Inclusions. Occasionally oil droplets and oil globules are seen in the protoplasm, particularly in cells in tissue culture, in marine eggs and in the marine protozoans known as radiolarians. These oil droplets are probably stores of nutrient or in some cases devices for reducing the specific gravity of the cell, thus making floating easier. In some cells glycogen granules occur, presumably representing stores of nutrient for the cell.

At present, workers have accepted the reality of the major cell organelles and are now concerned mainly with determination of their chemical constitution, physicochemical organization and function.

Variation in Organization of Animal Cells

In multicellular organisms, all of the cells are not exactly alike. They have become differentiated and adapted to perform some particular function of the organism.

A *tissue* is a mass of similar cells, usually continuous, performing a common function and usually forming a part of an *organ*. Intercellular fluid is almost always found in tissues. This is to be expected since every cell must have water frontage from which it obtains supplies and into which it pours its wastes. But because this intercellular fluid is not easily removed or modified, tissues as such used in experiments cannot be considered the equivalent of suspensions of cells.[16] Both animal and plant tissues are used in a variety of researches in cell physiology. Animal tissues are usually classified as epithelial, connective, muscular, nervous and blood.

Epithelial cells are generally closely packed, like bricks in a pavement, and form solid protective layers on the outside.[15] They also line cavities and tubules, produce secretions and proliferate cells. Epithelial cells may be isodiametric (having equal diameters in all directions), flattened, or elongated and columnar (often the columnar cells are glandular). From the epithelial cells of glands exude various secretions. Germinal cells, which give rise to gametes, spring from the epithelial cells of gonads. In epithelial cells are found the typical organelles expected in a cell. In glandular epithelial cells the mitochondria and Golgi apparatus are likely to be particularly well developed. While epithelial tissue consists primarily of cells, the external epithelium may secrete a cuticle, as in the earthworm, or a skeleton, as in arthropods.

Connective tissue, in contrast to epithelial tissue, is to a large extent composed of extracellular material and may contain relatively few cells. During early development of the embryo the cells lie close together, but during later development they secrete a gelatinous material which separates the cells. In this gelatinous matrix are laid the fibers of connective tissue and the salts of bone. Some connective tissues are cartilage, tendon, bone and adipose or fatty tissue. The composition of connective tissue in tendon is diagrammatically represented in Figure 2.5.

The cells in several types of muscular tissue (smooth, cardiac and skeletal) are considerably modified for the function of contraction. They are elongated cells and in all cases contain contractile fibrils, these being characteristic of muscle tissue and of no other tissue. The cells of the smooth or visceral musculature of vertebrates are spindle-shaped units containing a single nucleus in the center and have fine elongate fibrillae which represent the contractile elements. The skeletal musculature of vertebrates is highly differentiated for its function. Its unit of organization is the muscle fiber, consisting of the confluent bodies of numerous cells, each of which is indicated by a spindle-shaped nucleus. Elongate striated fibrils pack the cytoplasm of the skeletal muscle fiber, and large mitochondria are present, being especially conspicuous in the highly active flight muscles of vertebrates and insects. In the cardiac muscle of vertebrates, striated fibers are found and the unit is somewhat different in organization from that of skeletal muscle. Muscular tissues of invertebrates are very diverse, but in all cases contractile fibrils are found (see Fig. 23.7, 23.16, and 24.1).

The cells of the nervous system are highly specialized for conduction of nervous impulses. From the nerve cell body containing the nucleus extend the long fibers called *axons* and the short fibers called *dendrites* (see Fig. 21.1). The nerve cell with all of its processes is called a *neuron*. A well-developed Golgi apparatus appears in the cell body of a neuron, and mitochondria occur chiefly at the nodes. In the fibers are found granular deposits of nucleic acids which probably serve as nutrient in the activities of the nerve. The axon of a vertebrate nerve is called a *myelinated fiber* when it is covered with

FUNCTIONAL ORGANIZATION OF THE CELL

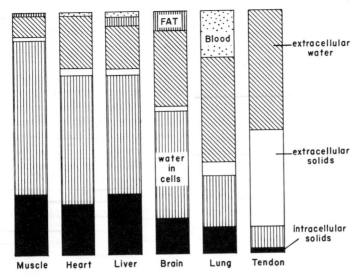

Fig. 2.5. Extracellular material in animal tissues. (Adapted from Lowry: Biol. Symposia, *10*:239, 1943.)

a fatty material enclosed by sheath cells. The sheath cells secrete the fatty material (myelin) about the nerve fiber. The myelin sheath may add much bulk to the vertebrate nervous system and, because of it, nervous tissue like the brain contains a considerable amount of extracellular material (see Fig. 2.5). However, the outgoing fibers from autonomic nerve ganglia located outside the cord are not myelinated. Invertebrate nerve fibers have little if any myelin.

Blood cells are also highly specialized. For instance, in vertebrate blood the red cells (erythrocytes) are mainly composed of the oxygen-carrying pigment, hemoglobin. In mammals the mature erythrocytes even lose their nuclei and have none of the characteristic cell organelles. The white cells of vertebrates and invertebrates —both granular ameboid cells called leucocytes, and the more or less spherical clear lymphocytes—are much more typical cells than the red cells since they have nuclei and the other cell organelles such as the mitochondria and the Golgi apparatus.

Variation in Organization of Plant Cells

Little agreement exists on classification of plant tissues, but the following might be cited as one possible classification: epidermal, undifferentiated, vascular (xylem and phloem), sclerenchyma and supporting or bast fibers (see Table 2.2).

Plant cells usually lack the Golgi apparatus but, unlike cells of animals, they usually possess plastids and vacuoles and are covered by a cell wall. Mitochondria, ribosomes and a nucleus are present as in animal cells.[17] The cells of epidermal tissues of plants line external surfaces of plant structures. Embryonic cells of plants, e.g., the *cambium*, are made up of cells similar in appearance and function to epithelial cells of animals. Undifferentiated plant cells, called *parenchyma*, exist in large numbers in the cortex of the stem, filling the spaces between conducting or supporting tissues. They also make up the mesophyll and the palisade cell layer of the leaf, in which photosynthesis occurs. Vascular tissue of plants consists of the *phloem* and the *xylem*. The phloem is constituted of long cells which contain living material and abut upon one another. It distributes the manufactured food throughout the entire plant. The xylem distributes water and salts to the cells of the plant. Cells with thickened walls, like the gritty stone cells in the pear, are representatives of *sclerenchyma* tissue. Supporting "cells" or bast fibers, consisting largely of secretions of cellulose and lignin, occur along the vascular tissues and contribute to the skeleton of the plant. Supporting fibers and xylem ducts in the adult plant are entirely extracellular, the cellular material having disappeared. As a result, an organ which contains an abundance of ducts and supporting fibers, like a mature stem, has much extracellular material. In contrast, a bud or a leaf is made up largely of relatively undifferentiated cells, and, except for the cell walls, consists of living material. Unfortunately, no convenient summary of the intracellular and extracellular constituents of plant tissue comparable to that for animal tissues shown in Figure 2.5 is available, although it is highly desirable because plant tissues are extensively used in cellular research (see Table 2.2).

Variation in Organization of Bacterial Cells

Bacteria and blue-green algae, unlike all kinds of true cells of plants and animals, lack a distinct nucleus enclosed by a nuclear membrane, the nuclear material being scattered in the cytoplasm. For this reason plant and animal cells with true nuclei are called *eukaryotic cells* while bacteria and cells of blue-green algae are called *prokaryotic cells*. Also procaryotic cells either lack all the other cell organelles (so characteristic of eucaryotic cells) or possess them in a primitive, undifferentiated condition. Because bacteria have been extensively investi-

gated, they alone are considered here, but much of what is said is applicable to blue-green algae as well.[48] On the other hand, the blue-green algae contain chlorophyll and a characteristic auxiliary pigment and differ from most bacteria in being photosynthetic.

Bacterial cells are covered with a protective *cell wall* which usually consists of carbohydrates and polypeptides but may contain protein and lipids. The bacteria can be made to retract from this wall by being placed in concentrated solutions of sugar or salt, the cell membrane now forming the outer boundary of the living material of the cell called the *protoplast* (Fig. 2.6). The cell wall may be digested with the enzyme lysozyme, exposing the protoplast which can now be made to swell or shrink like any other cell by decreasing or increasing the concentration of salts dissolved in the medium. The cell wall evidently plays some important role in addition to protection, since protoplasts formed by digesting the cell walls do not divide* or form new cell walls.[37]

In gram-positive bacteria, ribonucleic acid present in the surface takes up a stain made up of crystal violet and iodine; gram-negative bacteria lack such ribonucleic acid in the surface. Bacteria which are gram-negative (e.g., *Escherichia coli*, the colon bacterium) differ from gram-positive bacteria (e.g., *Bacillus megatherium*) in possessing cell walls heavily impregnated with lipids. Thick-walled resting stages called *spores* which resist high temperature and other unfavorable conditions are formed by some bacteria (bacilli).

Bacteria lack mitochondria and Golgi apparatus although they generally are filled with bodies resembling the microsomes of true cells. The plasma membrane which is rich in oxidative enzymes probably performs the function usually carried out by the mitochondria of plant

* Yeast protoplasts also fail to divide or conjugate.[49]

and animal cells. It is of interest that the plasma membrane of the large bacterium, *Thiovulvum majus*, sinks deep into the cytoplasm. In the tubercle bacillus, concentric membranes, suggesting incipient mitochondria, have been discovered in the cytoplasm with the aid of electron microscopy.

Many bacteria have been shown to possess large granules which grow and divide and are stained with the same dyes which affect chromosomes of true cells. These bodies appear to condense before division and become more diffuse thereafter.

Rickettsias,[36] which cause Rocky Mountain spotted fever, endemic typhus and murine typhus, are of about the size of small bacteria and in general their organization clearly places them among the bacteria. However, to some workers they appear to be escaped mitochondria and to others, a stage between viruses and bacteria. Like bacteria they possess a number of respiratory enzymes which are lacking in viruses. They have not yet been cultured except in cells of a host they infect.

Organization of Viruses

Some viruses[28, 40] are larger than bacteria; for example, the psittacosis virus measures 750 mμ in diameter while the pleuropneumonia bacterium measures only 150 mμ in diameter.[53] However, most virus particles are smaller than bacteria and the virus causing hoof and mouth disease is estimated to be only 10 mμ in diameter. The distinguishing character of viruses is that they are intracellular parasites of specific hosts. This is probably a consequence of their lack of energy-yielding and synthetic enzyme systems. The only enzymes demonstrated in viruses enable the bacterial virus to enter a bacterium, presumably by digesting the cell wall.

Most viruses consist of a protein coat over a nucleic acid core, but lipids and

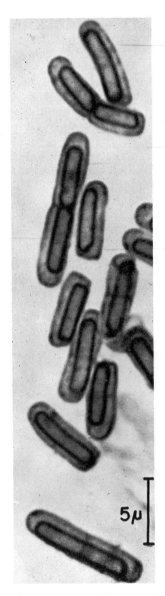

Fig. 2.6. Retraction of the cell contents (protoplast) from the cell wall induced by exposure to ether vapor and drying on glass before fixation. Stained with Victoria blue. [From Robinow, C. F. *In* vol. IV., "The Cell," (Brachet, J., and Mirsky, A. E., eds.). Academic Press, Inc., N. Y.]

lipoproteins have been claimed from some animal viruses. Viruses contain only one kind of nucleic acid, ribonucleic acid in plant and animal viruses, and deoxyribonucleic acid in bacterial viruses, while cells of animals and plants have both (see Chapters 3 and 6).[40] In general, animal viruses appear to be of a more complex nature than viruses of plants and bacteria (bacteriophages), but less is known of them because they present so many experimental difficulties. All viruses lack cell walls and the other organelles characteristic of bacteria, and thus viruses represent an entirely different category of organization.[40]

Most extensively studied are bacteriophages (bacteria-eaters as the name implies; see Figure 2.7). Only the nucleic acid portion of a phage enters (infects) a bacterium, as can be shown by radioactive markers on the nucleic acid (P^{32}) and on the protein (S^{35}). After the phage nucleic acid enters the bacterium, the suspension of bacteria and phage can be agitated violently to detach the phage particles. Infection occurs nonetheless, even though it can be demonstrated that only about 1 per cent of the labeled phage protein still adheres to the bacteria. Furthermore, nucleic acid–free "ghosts" containing all of the protein of bacteriophages are not infectious to bacteria although they attach themselves firmly. The bacteriophage nucleic acid particle once inside the bacterium loses its identity (eclipse period), but after half an hour phages can again be identified (by electron microscopy).

It can be demonstrated by various marker techniques that, once inside, the nucleic acid of the phage takes command of the synthetic activities of the bacterium, suspending the normal synthetic activities of the bacterium, hydrolyzing its nucleic acids and directing the synthesis

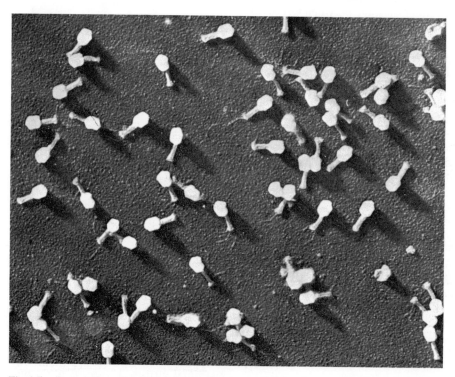

Fig. 2.7.   Bacteriophage T_2 of the colon bacillus seen under the electron microscope ($\times$ 37,000). Each of the particles can produce a plaque in a growth of bacteria and so become visible. (From Herriott, R. M., and Barlow, J. L., J. Gen. Physiol. *36*:17, 1953.)

FUNCTIONAL ORGANIZATION OF THE CELL

of the virus type of nucleic acid and protein. The protein coat of the virus is synthesized anew from materials taken in by the bacterial cell. About ten minutes after infection, packaging of the virus nucleic acid in protein coats begins (as shown by electronmicrography in disrupted virus-infected bacteria) and continues for another twenty minutes, when the process is complete. At this time the bacterium is ruptured (lysed), liberating between 40 and 100 or more complete phage particles.

The effect of a bacteriophage in a suspension of bacteria (*in vitro*) plated on nutrient medium can be detected by spots of lysis—clear areas produced by liquefaction of the layer of bacteria. This occurs only after a number of life cycles of the phage. The number of particles or the *titer* in the initial suspension can thus be assayed by the number of lysed spots. Phages which cause lysis are called virulent or *lytic phages*.

Phages may affect bacteria in either of two ways—they may grow and lyse the bacteria as described above, or they may become incorporated into the genetic material of the bacterium and remain in an inactive "masked" form. That they have altered the hereditary characteristics of the bacteria is shown by the resistance of the bacteria so infected to attacks by homologous phages which would otherwise lyse these bacteria. Phages which "hide" in this manner, dividing only when the bacterium divides, are spoken of as temperate or *lysogenic phages* (i.e., giving rise to lytic phages). An occasional masked lysogenic phage particle multiplies, perhaps because its host has become weakened and no longer holds it in check.[52]

Damaging the bacteria infected with lysogenic phages by radiations or other unfavorable agents leads to a rapid development of the phage into an active lytic form. The particles are then released in infectious form much as in other strains of phage. Lysis of an occasional bacterium in an undamaged population can spread the infection to many previously uninfected members of the population, in this way maintaining a mild infection. Lysogeny, as the phenomenon is called, indicates the intimate relationship formed by the phage and the bacterium, a conception having great influence on microbial genetics (see Chapter 6).

APPENDIX

2.1 Staining Technique for Living and Fixed Cells

Vital dyes penetrate living cells and color certain structures without seriously injuring the cells.[18] For example, neutral red may be used to stain the cytoplasm, although in some cells it accumulates in vacuoles instead. Janus green B stains mitochondria selectively. Methylene blue selectively stains the Golgi apparatus. Vital dyes are not entirely harmless, but they kill only after cells have been exposed to them for a long time. Sometimes the poisonous constituent (e.g., the heavy metals in Janus green B) may be removed from a vital dye solution, making the dye much less toxic than the original sample. While helpful, the vital dye technique has only limited use because many of the cell organelles are not stained by such dyes and, in all cases, scattering of light obscures boundaries of structures. However, dyes have been used to demonstrate that some cell organelles such as the mitochondria, Golgi apparatus and vacuoles are real structures present in the living cell.

Most of the early work on the nature of cell organelles was done with fixed and stained preparations. *Fixing agents* such as formalin, alcohol, acids, salts of heavy metals, or mixtures of these, precipitate the proteins and render them insoluble. Next, water is removed from the fixed tissues by *dehydrating agents,* such as alcohol, and the tissues are embedded in paraffin and sectioned with a microtome. The sections are affixed to slides and the paraffin is removed with xylol and washed in xylol-alcohol. By washing in decreasing concentrations of alcohol the sections are partially hydrated and the proteinaceous material of the cell is then differentially stained to distinguish the structures present. Natural dyes (e.g., hematoxylin) or basic anilin dyes (e.g., safranin and basic fuchsin) stain the nucleus selectively, and acid dyes (e.g., orange G, eosin and fast green) stain the cytoplasm. The sections are then dehydrated with alcohol. To reduce scattering of light, it is necessary to replace the alcoholic medium with a substance having the same refractive index as that of the protein particles. This is accomplished with a *clearing agent,* such as xylol, which infiltrates among the protein particles. The preparation is then mounted in balsam, which has a refractive index about equal to that of the cell proteins. As a result, it is possible to look at the cell and see clearly the stained structures which are within.[18]

2.2 Microscopical Techniques

The ordinary light microscope (see Fig. 2.8) makes it possible to see stained structures so long as they are larger than the limit of resolution.[19] The smallest object, d, resolved (seen clearly and distinctly from similar sized objects separated by like small distances) by the light microscope may be determined from the following equation:

$$d = \frac{\lambda}{NA + na} \qquad (2.1)$$

In this equation λ is the wavelength of light used, NA is the numerical aperture of the objective and na the numerical aperture of the condenser. Since for critical study the numerical aperture of the condenser is chosen equal to that of the objective, the equation is often written:

$$d = \lambda/2NA \qquad (2.2)$$

The numerical aperture is given by the equation:

$$NA = n \sin \alpha \qquad (2.3)$$

Here n is the refractive index of the light path in the formation of the microscopical image, and α is half the angular aperture of the light beam entering the condenser. When immersion oil is used between condenser and slide, and slide and objective, the numerical aperture may be as large as 1.6, although in practice it is seldom over 1.4. The factor which limits resolution with the light

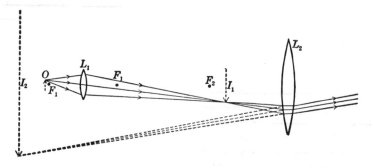

Fig. 2.8. Light path in the ordinary light compound microscope. The group of ocular lenses is diagrammatically represented by L_2, the group of objective lenses by L_1. The object (O) on a microscope slide is placed just outside the principal focus of the objective lens (L_1), which has a short focus. This lens produces a real image at I_1 which is formed inside the principle focus of the eyepiece lens (L_2). The eye, looking through the lens L_2, sees a magnified virtual image (I_2) of the image I_1. The eyepiece lens is thus used as a magnifying glass to view the real image (I_1). (From *Physics*, by Stewart and Gingrich. Fifth Edition. Ginn and Company.)

FUNCTIONAL ORGANIZATION OF THE CELL

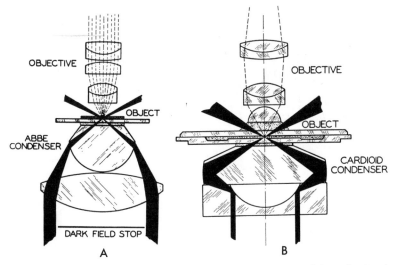

Fig. 2.9. Dark field microscopy. The dark field stop shown in *A* is much less effective than the dark field condenser shown in *B*. (By permission of the Bausch and Lomb Company.)

microscope is therefore the wavelength of light. Under optimal conditions the smallest object seen is theoretically about one-third the wavelength of visible light or about 0.13 μ in blue light. Usually the limit is set at about 0.2 μ because the eye is most sensitive in the yellow-green part of the spectrum (0.55 μ) and a maximal numerical aperture of 1.6 is seldom achieved. An object of this size is visible only if the structure shows maximal contrast. In order to increase the contrast between unstained structures and to obtain greater resolution of details of cell organelles, various types of microscopes have been developed, each of which is considered in turn below.

The *dark field microscope* is an ordinary microscope with a special condenser.[19] By use of a dark stop in the condenser the light from the center of the field is removed and the object is illuminated only by an oblique beam of light as seen in Figure 2.9. The object is therefore seen by light reflected and scattered from interfaces in the object. With dark field microscopy the outlines of the cell, the nucleus, mitochondria, oil droplets, vacuoles and various inclusions may be readily identified. Moreover, in cells undergoing division, the centrosomes, asters, spindles and chromosomes may be observed. Objects smaller than those seen with the ordinary light microscope may be detected with dark field microscopy but not resolved.

The *polarizing microscope* has a polarizer in the condenser and an analyzer in the ocular. A polarizer is a prism or polaroid plate which transmits plane polarized light. If polarizer and analyzer are crossed at an angle of 90° no light is transmitted. An object viewed through the microscope with this setting is invisible unless it too rotates the plane of polarization of the light. Such additional polarization occurs under certain circumstances—for instance, during division when constituents of spindles and other structures are aligned precisely.[20] For observation of such processes polarized light is valuable. It also gives clues to the arrangement of molecules in structures of the cell (see Chapter 14).

The *phase contrast microscope*, which has the same resolving power as the ordinary light microscope, enables one to see structures in the living cell by taking ad-

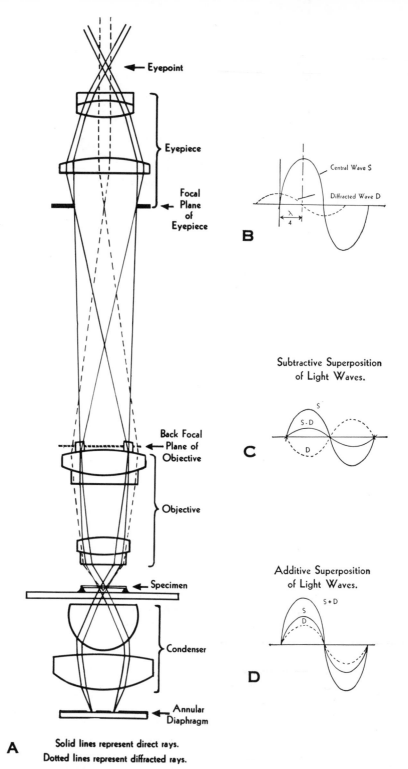

Eyepoint

Eyepiece

Focal
Plane
of
Eyepiece

B

Central Wave S

Diffracted Wave D

$\frac{\lambda}{4}$

Back Focal
Plane of
Objective

C

Subtractive Superposition
of Light Waves.

S
S - D
D

Objective

Specimen

Condenser

Additive Superposition
of Light Waves.

S + D
S
D

D

Annular
Diaphragm

A   Solid lines represent direct rays.
Dotted lines represent diffracted rays.

Fig. 2.10. *A*, shows the light path in a phase microscope. *B*, shows the normal retardation by ¼ wavelength of light diffracted by an object and its difference in phase from the light passing through the surrounding medium. By phase optics the two waves are superimposed to reinforce each other in bright contrast phase as shown in *D* or to subtract from each other as in dark contrast phase shown in *C*. (By permission of the American Optical Company.)

vantage of the slight differences in refractive index between any two structures to improve their visibility.[21] The phase contrast microscope does this by the use of a special diaphragm in the condenser and a phase plate in the objective. The annular diaphragm used in the condenser of the phase microscope permits light to pass through the condenser as a hollow cone, the remaining light being absorbed. (See Fig. 2.10.) This cone is focused on the object. The phase plate placed at the back focal plane of the objective is a transparent disk containing a groove (or elevation) of such a size and shape as to coincide with the direct image of the substage annular diaphragm formed at the back focal plane when no object is viewed. If an object is placed between the condenser and the objective, in addition to the direct image a number of overlapping diffracted images of the diaphragm then appear at the back focal plane of the objective. The depth of the groove (or the elevation) in the phase plate of the objective is so made that the two sets of rays forming the direct image and the diffracted image differ in optical path by a quarter wavelength of the illuminating beam of light (Fig. 2.10B). Under these conditions the phase difference which is not seen by the eye is converted to an intensity difference which we see.[22, 23] In the bright contrast phase optical system the two sets of rays are added to make a brighter image as in Figure 2.10 at D, whereas in dark contrast phase they partially cancel one another making a more contrasting darker image as in Figure 2.10 at C.

The phase contrast microscope (bright or dark contrast may be used), in which a small difference of refractive index is exaggerated, enabling one to distinguish adjacent structures, has made it possible to observe structures previously very difficult or impossible to see. The behavior of chromosomes of living cells during mitosis or meiosis can be followed with ease, and many of the other organelles may be studied. The phase contrast microscope

has furnished the most convincing evidence that many of the organelles identified in fixed and stained preparations of the cell are real and not artifacts.

With the use of the *interference microscope* the residual halo which accompanies the image seen under a phase microscope is avoided because the aperture of the objective of such a microscope is not restricted by a phase plate, the same area of the objective being used for the two interfering beams.[43] The relative phase of the two beams is continuously variable so that any part of an object can be given maximum or minimum contrast at will.

As observed in Figure 2.11 a horizontal glass plate, L, nearly parallel to a similar plate above the object, intercepts the illuminating cone of light from the condenser (both surfaces of this plate are partially aluminized). Part of the illuminating cone traverses the plate and is focused on the object, while part is reflected downward at the upper surface of Plate L and is then reflected upward by its lower surface. While only one beam traverses the object, two beams traverse the object plane. The beam failing to pass through the object, the *comparison beam*, is internally reflected twice within the plate and has a diameter much larger than that of the field.

A second horizontal plate, U, identical to the first and almost parallel to it, is situated above the plane of the object. Both of its surfaces are also partially aluminized, but in addition its upper surface carries an axial opaque spot somewhat larger than the maximum field of the microscope. This spot prevents the direct vertical light beam from the source which traverses the object from reaching the objective, but allows the light from the beam which has traversed the object and then enters the plate to the side of the spot to reach the objective.

Part of the illuminating beam which has passed through the object is reflected twice in plate U and part of the comparison beam passes through this plate with-

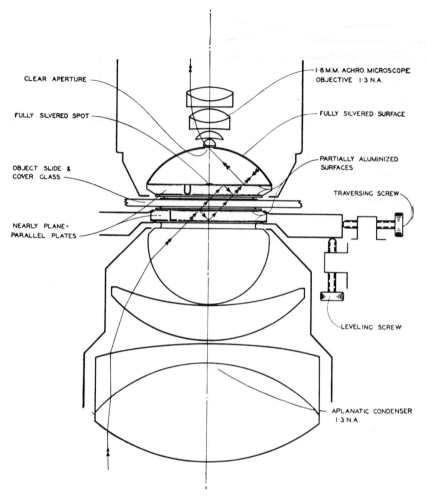

CLEAR APERTURE

FULLY SILVERED SPOT

OBJECT SLIDE & COVER GLASS

NEARLY PLANE-PARALLEL PLATES

1·8 M.M. ACHRO. MICROSCOPE OBJECTIVE 1·3 N.A.

FULLY SILVERED SURFACE

PARTIALLY ALUMINIZED SURFACES

TRAVERSING SCREW

LEVELING SCREW

APLANATIC CONDENSER 1·3 N.A.

Fig. 2.11. Dyson interferometer microscope, light path. For explanation see accompanying text. (By permission of Cooke, Troughton and Simms, Ltd.)

out reflection, the two beams emerging from the upper surface in coincidence when the plates are correctly aligned. The observer above the upper plate sees two coincident fields of view, one comprising an image of the light source only and the other an image of the light source with the object superimposed. Apart from the interference due to the object, the phase difference between the two images will be zero. The combined images may be viewed by a normal microscope objective. The interferometer plates L

and U are movable so that the path difference between the two coincident fields can be varied at will over the whole area of vision. Ideal conditions for maximum contrast cannot be obtained for objects much larger than the field of view, because the object is then traversed by a portion of the background beam.

Because an object such as a cell contains various substances, it has an optical path different from that of the surrounding water. For this reason when the background is adjusted to maximum light intensity (bright field), the cell appears darker and it is possible at a glance to note the distribution of structures in the cell much as if a stained preparation were being observed in an ordinary light microscope. More than this, it is possible to determine the average amount of dry material (dry mass) present in a given area of the cell by the use of the interference microscope, because the greater the amount of material present in the cell, the greater will be the difference between its optical path (refractive index times thickness) and that of the surrounding fluid. The difference in optical path is determined by the difference between interference bands in the surrounding fluid and in the object when the upper wedge plate is rotated so that the wedge axes are no longer parallel. The field is then crossed by parallel interference fringes. These fringes are seen as lighter and darker bands of the same color when monochromatic light is used, or bands of color on either side of white bands when white light is used. For example, one tenth wavelength displacement for monochromatic green light (5460 Å) is equivalent to a dry mass of 10^{-13} gm/μ^2.

The *ultraviolet microscope* looks like the ordinary light microscope but its lenses are made of quartz to permit transmission of wavelengths of invisible ultraviolet as short as 2200 Å (visible light covers the range from blue at 3900 Å to the far red at 7800 Å). The invisible ultraviolet light is then projected upon a screen which fluoresces in the visible spectrum. Usually, however, it is recorded photographically. Because chromosomes absorb more short ultraviolet radiation than cytoplasm does,[6] they are readily seen in photographs taken with ultraviolet light at 2600 Å. Under the ultraviolet microscope resolution of fine structure is about twice that obtained with the ordinary light microscope as may be judged from application of equations 2.1 and 2.2, the wavelength of short ultraviolet light being about half that of the

visible.[24, 25] Unfortunately ultraviolet radiation damages the cells, so that prolonged observation of cells so illuminated is not possible.

An instrument which may serve as a valuable adjunct to all of the microscopes considered above is the *television camera attachment*. Since the electron tube used in it "sees" at low light intensities and can be made sensitive to a restricted part of the spectrum (a narrow band in the green, blue or ultraviolet), much clearer pictures can be obtained than with ordinary microscopy.[26] Furthermore, a prolonged illumination is avoided since the image may be viewed on a phosphorescent screen which retains the image for a minute or two after exposure. Momentary illumination with light of low intensity suffices. This attachment, therefore, is especially useful for viewing living cells under ultraviolet light.[29, 35]

The *electron microscope*, which was developed on the eve of World War II, has proved a powerful tool for analysis of large chemical molecules, viruses and, to some extent, of cellular structures.[30] In the electron microscope the beams of electrons are focused by magnets which serve as lenses (see Fig. 2.12). The object must be viewed on a fluorescent screen or photographed. The electron microscope has a resolving power 50 to 200 times that of the light microscope. Greater resolution was anticipated, but while the wavelengths accompanying the electron beams are short (e.g., a 60,000 volt electron beam is accompanied by a wavelength of 0.05 Å), the numerical aperture of the electron microscope is only about 0.0005. Substitution of these values in equation 2.1 gives the best resolution achieved on biological materials at the present time.

The main disadvantages attendant upon use of the electron microscope are the required thinness of sections and the necessity of studying them dry (in a vacuum).[31] The first difficulty has been overcome largely by the development of

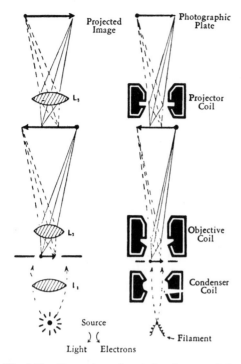

Fig. 2.12. Comparison of optical pathways in light and electron microscopes. (From Thompson: Endeavour, 2:125, 1943.)

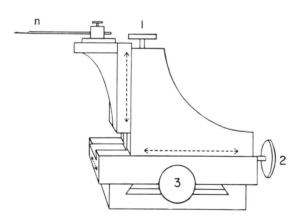

Fig. 2.13. One type of micromanipulator. It consists essentially of a microlathe enabling movements of the needle (n) in the three coordinates of space by manipulation of screws 1, 2, and 3. Another instrument (a mirror image of the one shown) stands on the other side of the microscope, all mounted on a heavy stand. (After Taylor: Zool., Univ. of Cal. Publ., 26:443, 1925.)

microtomes which can make sections 0.1 to 0.2 μ in thickness.[44, 46] However, removal of salts and water is likely to alter structure; therefore, membranes, cytoplasm or formed structural components seen by electron microscopy must be interpreted with some caution. Notwithstanding these facts, it will become apparent in studies presented later that much has been learned about the cell by electron microscopy, and about structural elements such as the cuticle and the cell wall. The possibility of using an electron microscope for investigation of living materials is being effectively explored by Gaston Dupouy, who encloses the live, wet bacteria in collodion films which resist the vacuum surrounding the minute capsule.

2.3 Micromanipulators

Since the end of the last century micromanipulators of one kind or another have been in use, first for handling single cells and later for microsurgery upon them.[32, 33, 34] Some of the earlier models were essentially microlathes which made possible slow but precise movements in the three coordinates of space (see Fig. 2.13). Pneumatic models have been developed which make possible quick and easy movements for microsurgery. The pneumatic micromanipulator of De Fonbrunne (Fig. 2.14) has had wide usage because of its ease of operation and sensitivity of response. Essentially it consists of three pumps, two horizontal and one vertical, which connect by way of rubber tubes to the pneumatic capsules of the instrument holder (for needle or pipette).[41] The movements in the horizontal plane of a single lever or joy stick are reflected at a ratio of anywhere from 1:50 to 1:2,500, according to the setting decided upon. The vertical plane level is set by the screw on the lever. An electric micromanipulator utilizing thermal expansion wires has been described but has not had

FUNCTIONAL ORGANIZATION OF THE CELL

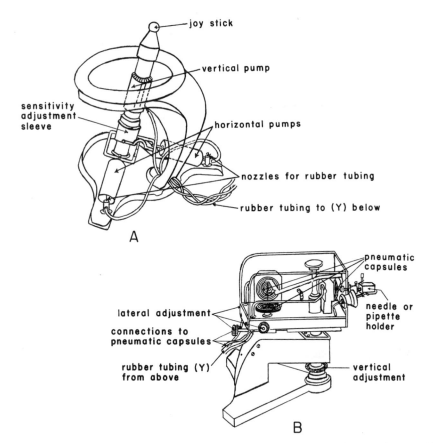

joy stick

vertical pump

sensitivity
adjustment
sleeve

horizontal pumps

nozzles for rubber tubing

rubber tubing to (Y) below

A

pneumatic
capsules

lateral adjustment

connections to
pneumatic capsules

needle or
pipette
holder

rubber tubing (Y)
from above

vertical
adjustment

B

Fig. 2.14. The deFonbrunne pneumatic micromanipulator. A movement of the control or joy stick is duplicated by the needle (or other instrument) with a reduction in magnitude of ⅟₅₀ to ½,₅₀₀, set at the sensitivity adjustment sleeve. This is achieved through passage of the pressure change through three pumps, two horizontal and one vertical, attached to three pneumatic capsules with rubber tubing, the capsules in turn controlling the needle or instrument holder. Two such micromanipulators are often used together, one to hold, the other to cut or manipulate a structure viewed under the microscope. (By courtesy of A. S. Aloe Co., St. Louis, Mo.)

much use.[42] Production of microforges for the controlled manufacture of microtools has also facilitated microdissection. Important information on the function of the nucleus of cells has been gained by the use of such tools for transplantation of nuclei between cells (see Chapter 6). The micromanipulator thus makes the microscope more than an observational tool, and properties of many of the cell organelles have been explored by its use. Even bacteria have been dissected under high power.[34]

GENERAL REFERENCES

Andrew, W., 1959: Textbook of Comparative Histology. Oxford Univ. Press, New York.

Bourne, G. H., 1951: Cytology and Cell Physiology. 2nd Ed. Oxford Univ. Press, London.

Brachet, J., and Mirsky, A. E., 1959 to 1961: The Cell. Five volumes, Academic Press, New York.

Burnet, F. (ed.), 1959 (vol. I): The Viruses. Academic Press, New York.

Copenhaver, W. M., and Johnson, D. D., 1958: Bailey's Textbook of Histology. 14th Ed. Williams & Wilkins, Baltimore.

Danielli, J. F., 1953: Cytochemistry, A Critical Approach. Wiley, New York.

Danielli, J. F. (ed.), 1958: General Cytological Methods. Academic Press, New York.

Davenport, H. A., 1960: Histological and Histochemical Technics. Saunders, Philadelphia.

De Robertis, E. D. P., Nowinski, W. W., and Saez, F. A., 1960: General Cytology. 3rd Ed. Saunders, Philadelphia.

Esau, K., 1953: Plant Anatomy. Wiley, New York.

Gabriel, M. L., and Fogel, S. (eds.), 1955: Great Experiments in Biology, Part I, The Cell Theory. Prentice-Hall, Englewood Cliffs, N. J.

Heilbrunn, L. V., and Weber, F. (eds.) 1953–1959: Protoplasmatologia, Handbuch der Protoplasmaforschung. 14 volumes. Springer, Vienna.

Picken, L., 1960: The Organization of Cells. Clarendon, Oxford.

Robinow, G. F., 1960: Outline of the visible organization of bacteria, in The Cell, vol. 3 (Brachet, J., and Mirsky, A. E., eds.). Academic Press, New York.

Roelefsen, P. A., 1959: The Plant Cell. Gebruder Borntraeger, Berlin-Nikolassee.

Thomas, R., 1960: Viruses, in The Cell, vol. 3 (Brachet, J., and Mirsky, A. E., eds.) Academic Press, New York.

* * * *

The Journal of Cell Biology, formerly The Journal of Biophysical and Biochemical Cytology, and the Journal of Ultrastructure Research contain current articles especially on electron microscopy of cells.

LITERATURE CITED

1. De Robertis, E. D. P., Nowinski, W. W., and Saez, F. A., 1960: General Cytology. 3rd Ed. Saunders, Philadelphia.

2. Palade, G. E., and Siekevitz, P., 1956: J. Biophys. Biochem. Cyt. 2:171.

3. Picken, L., 1960: The Organization of Cells. Clarendon, Oxford.

4. Harvey, E. N., 1938: J. Appl. Physics 9:73.

5. Bennett, A. H., Jupnik, H., Osterberg, H., and Richards, O. W., 1946: Trans. Am. Micros. Soc. 65:99.

6. Caspersson, T., 1950: Cell Growth and Cell Function. Norton, New York.

7. Chambers, R., and Kopac, M. J., 1950: pp. 492–543 in McClung's Handbook of Microscopical Technique. 3rd Ed. Hoeber, New York.

8. Foot, N. C., 1950: pp. 564–570 in McClung's Handbook of Microscopical Technique. 3rd Ed. Hoeber, New York.

9. Harvey, E. N., 1951: Ann. N. Y. Acad. Sci. 51:1336.

10. Lindberg, O., and Ernster, L., 1954: Chemistry and Physiology of Mitochondria and Microsomes. Protoplasmatologia, Springer-Verlag, Vienna.

11. Bourne, G. H., 1951: Cytology and Cell Physiology. Oxford Univ. Press, London.

12. Novikoff, A. B., 1961: Mitochondria in The Cell (Brachet, J., and Mirsky, A. E., eds.). 2:299.

13. Palade, G. E., and Porter, K. R., 1954: J. Exp. Med. 100:641.

14. Sager, R., and Palade, G. E., 1954: Exp. Cell. Res. 7:584.

15. Copenhaver, W. M., and Johnson, D. D., 1958: Bailey's Textbook of Histology. 14th Ed. Williams and Wilkins, Baltimore.

16. Lowry, O. H., 1943: Biol. Symp. 10:233.

17. Roelefsen, P. A., 1959: The Plant Cell. Gebruder Borntraeger, Berlin-Nikolassee.

18. McClung, C. E., 1950: in McClung's Handbook of Microscopical Techniques. 3rd Ed. Hoeber, New York.

19. Needham, G. H., 1958: The Practical Use of the Microscope. Thomas, Springfield, Ill.

20. Inoue, S., 1951: Exp. Cell. Res. 2:513.

21. Zernike, F., 1955: Science 121:345, "How I discovered phase contrast."

22. Bennett, A. H., et al., 1951: Phase Microscopy. Principles and Application. Wiley, New York.

23. Richards, O. W., 1954: Science 120:631.

24. Blout, E. R., 1953: Ad. Biol. and Med. Physics 3:286.

25. Gottschewski, G. H. M., 1954: Mikroskopie 9:147.

26. Zworykin, V. K., Florey, L. E., and Shrader, R. E., Sept., 1952: Electronics 25:150.

27. Kuff, C. L., 1959: Ch. 7 in Subcellular Particles (Hayashi, T., ed.). Am. Physiol. Soc., Washington.

28. Thomas, R., 1960: Viruses, in The Cell, vol. 1, pp. 1–44. (Brachet, J., and Mirsky, A. E., eds.) Academic Press, New York.

29. Whipple, A. O., Parpart, A. K., and Chang, J. T., 1954: Ann. Surg. 140:266.

30. Zworykin, V. K., Morton, G. A., Ramberg, E. G., Hillier, J., and Vance, A. W., 1945: Electron Optics and the Electron Microscope. Wiley, New York.

31. Cosslett, V. E., 1951: Practical Electron Microscopy. Academic Press, New York.

32. Chambers, R., 1949: Biol. Rev., 24:246.

33. Kopac, M. J., 1955: Internat. Rev. Cyt. 4:1.

34. Marshak, A., 1955: Internat. Rev. Cyt. 4:103.

35. Montgomery, P. O., and Bonner, W. A., May, 1958: Sci. Am. 198:39–43.

36. Bovarick, M. R., Jan., 1955: Sci. Am. 192:74.

37. Robinow, C. F., 1960: in The Cell, vol. 4, pp. 45–108. (Brachet, J., and Mirsky, A. E., eds.), Academic Press, New York.

38. Hovasee, R., 1956: Le Vacuome Animal. Protoplasmatologia III, D, 2.

39. Danegeard, P., 1956: Le Vacuome de la Cellule Vegetale, Morphologie. Protoplasmatologia III, D, 1.

40. Weidel, W., 1959: Virus., Univ. Michigan Press, Ann Arbor.

41. De Fonbrunne, P., 1937: Micromanipulateur-pneumatique et micro-forge, pour la fabrication des micro-instruments. Soc. Industrielle d' imprimerie, 10, rue Vallier, Levallois-Perret.

42. Bush, V., Duryee, W. R., and Hastings, J. A., 1953: Rev. Sci. Instruments 24:487.

43. Hale, A. J., 1958: The Interference Microscope, in Biological Research, Livingstone, Edinburgh.

44. Pease, D. C., 1960: Histological Techniques for Electron Microscopy. Academic Press, New York.

45. Taylor, W. K., 1960: Flying Spot Microscope, in New Approaches in Cell Biology. (Walker, P. B., ed.). Symposium Imperial College, London, 1958.

46. Tokayasu, K., and Okamura, S., 1959: J. Biophys. Biochem. Cyt. 6:305.

47. Meeuse, A. D. J., 1957: Plasmodesmata (Vegetable Kingdom). Protoplasmatologia II, A, 1, c. Springer, Vienna.

48. Geitler, L., 1960. Schizophyzeen. Handbuch der Pflanzenanatomie. Abteilung: Spezieller Teil. vol. 4. Gebruder Borntraeger, Berlin.

49. Holter, H., and Ottolenghi, P., 1960: Compt. Rend. Lab. Carlsberg 31:409.

50. Dalton, A. J., 1961: in The Cell (Brachet, J. and Mirsky, A. E., eds.) 2:603.

51. Porter, K. R., 1961: Idem. 2:621.

52. Hogness, P. S., 1962: in The Molecular Control of Cellular Activity, p. 189. (Allen, J. M., ed.), McGraw-Hill, New York.

53. Morowitz, H. J., and Turtelotte, M. E., March, 1962: Sci. Am. 206:117.

BIOCHEMISTRY OF
THE CELL

Some early physiologists conceived of life as the result of the properties of molecules unique to protoplasm.[1] However, with the development of biochemistry as a science, it became evident that many different types of molecules are found in the cell and that while some of these are extremely complex, no one of them can be considered to confer the properties of life upon the cell. Many of these compounds have been extracted from tissues, organs or whole organisms, and analyzed and characterized. In recent years, with the development of procedures for fractionating organelles of the cell and of various micromethods, much information on the distribution of these compounds in cells and even in the parts of a single cell is now available.

Constituents of the Cell

The main classes of compounds in the cell are easy to demonstrate qualitatively. Water, proteins, lipids, salts and carbohydrates are readily identified by well-known tests for each. Other classes of compounds, both organic and inorganic,

are also present in small amounts (Table 3.1).

Quantitative determination of cell constituents is somewhat more difficult. It requires the exclusion of extracellular material in the analysis. For example, Table 3.2 gives data on the compounds present in per cent of wet weight in the body of an animal, a plant, a sea urchin egg and a jellyfish. At first glance one is led to believe that the relative amounts of cellular constituents are highly variable in different organisms. However, the data are not strictly comparable since in the first example they represent an analysis of the entire animal body,[2] in the second of the entire plant body, in the third of only the eggs of the sea urchin, *Paracentrotus*,[3] and in the fourth of the entire body of a jellyfish.[4]

Only in the sea urchin egg is there an approximation of the constituents of a cell, since it contains relatively little stored material and no skeleton. The figures (Table 3.2) for the animal body include the large amount of extracellular salt present in the skeleton, the extracellular solids of connective tissues and the

TABLE 3.1. *Compounds Found in Cells of Organisms**

CLASSES OF COMPOUNDS	SUBCLASSES	EXAMPLES	SOLUBILITY OF EXAMPLES
Protein	Albumin	Egg albumin	Dissolves in distilled water; coagulates on heating
	Histone	Thymus histone Globin	Water soluble; relatively low molecular weight; basic; forms scum on heating
	Protamin	Sperm protamin	Water soluble; relatively low molecular weight; basic
	Globulin	Serum globulin	Soluble in salt solution
	Prolamine	Gliadin (wheat)	Soluble in 80% alcohol
	Glutelin	Glutenin (wheat)	Soluble in acid or basic solution
	Scleroprotein (albuminoid)	Horns, nails, hair	Insoluble in most reagents
Lipids	Triglycerides	Tripalmitin, tristearin	Soluble in fat solvents
	Sterols	Cholesterol	Soluble in fat solvents
	Waxes	Beeswax	Soluble in fat solvents
	Phospholipids	Cephalin, lecithin	Soluble in both fat solvents and water to some degree
Carbohydrates	Monosaccharides		
	hexoses	Glucose Fructose	Water soluble
	pentoses	Ribose Deoxyribose	Water soluble
	Disaccharides	Sucrose Maltose Lactose	Water soluble
	Polysaccharides		
	pentosans	Xylans in wood	Insoluble in water or fat solvents
	hexosans	Starch, glycogen	May be prepared in colloidal state in water
		Cellulose	Insoluble in water or fat solvents
	Chitin	Insect chitin	Insoluble (glucosamine condensate)

* This table is included here primarily for purposes of handy reference. Many of the compounds are considered in the text.

TABLE **3.1.** *Compounds Found in Cells of Organisms* (Cont.)*

CLASSES OF COMPOUNDS	SUBCLASSES	EXAMPLES	SOLUBILITY OF EXAMPLES
Carbohydrates	Mucopoly-saccharides		
	hyaluronic acid	Intercellular cement	Insoluble (attacked by enzyme hyaluronidase)
	chondroitin sulfuric acid	In matrix of con-nective tissue	Insoluble in water or fat solvents
	Nitrogenous neutral hetero-polysaccharides	Blood group substances	
Conjugated compounds	Nucleoproteins	Nucleohistone	Soluble in strong salt solutions
	Chromoproteins	Hemoglobin	Soluble in water
	Lipoproteins	Rhodopsin (visual purple)	
	Phosphoproteins	Casein of milk	Water soluble
	Flavoproteins	Yellow enzyme	Water soluble
	Glycoproteins	Protein of connec-tive tissue matrix	Water soluble
	Adipocellulose	On plant cell walls	Insoluble

* This table is included here primarily for purposes of handy reference. Many of the compounds are considered in the text.

large amount of extracellular fatty material present in the sheaths of fibers of the nervous system. Most tissues of a multicellular animal or plant usually contain such extracellular material.[5] In a tendon, for example, cells make up an insignificant fraction of the tissue because most of the tissue solids and water are extra-cellular. On the other hand, analysis of muscular tissue, which is relatively free of extracellular solid (see Fig. 2.5), gives values much closer to those for the sea urchin egg. Muscle contains somewhat less than 80 per cent water, close to 20 per cent protein, about 1 per cent carbohydrate, and some lipid and salt.[6]

TABLE **3.2.** *Compounds in Organisms in Per Cent of Total Wet Weight*

COMPOUND	STEER* (33 MO.)	CORN PLANT* (MATURE)	SEA URCHIN EGG† (PARACENTROTUS)	JELLYFISH*
Proteins	16.73	1.8	15.18	0.67%
Lipids	24.62	0.5	4.81	trace
Carbohydrates	—	17.5	1.36	trace
Salts (ash)	5.24	1.2	0.34	3
Water	55.51	79	77.3	96

* Data from Burrell, 1947: Organic Chemistry for Students of Biological Sciences.
† Ephrussi, 1933: Arch. de Biol. 44:1.

The plant body contains much cellulose in cell walls and skeletal tissue. The jellyfish has an unusually large amount of water and a very small amount of protein and lipid, the total solid being about 4 per cent. However, a large proportion of the water is extracellular, being present in the mesogloea, a jelly-containing layer into which a small amount of protein is secreted by the cells. If the cells lining the mesogloea were to be analyzed, their composition would probably be found to resemble that of the sea urchin egg.

The protoplasm of any plant or animal cell is likely to contain approximately 75 to 85 per cent water, 10 to 20 per cent protein, 2 to 3 per cent lipid, 1 per cent carbohydrate and about 1 per cent salt and miscellaneous substances. Although the most prominent constituent of the cell is water, the substance which gives the cell its characteristic structure is protein. Lipids are important in all membranes, while carbohydrates serve as nutrient reserves.

It is instructive to compare the relative numbers of molecules of the different constituents in the cell (see Table 3.3). The relative numbers of molecules can be determined from the amount of each substance and from the average molecular weight of each class. For purposes of calculation deoxyribonucleic acid (DNA) is arbitrarily assigned a molecular weight of 10^6, ribonucleic acid (RNA) of 5×10^4, and protein 3.6×10^4. Such a calculation shows that more than a million water molecules are present for every DNA molecule and about 18,000 for every protein molecule. From the table one may observe that in spite of the comparatively large percentage of protein content of the cell, the number of protein molecules present is relatively small.[7] Nucleic acids (DNA and RNA together) constitute about 1 per cent of the wet weight of a cell (1.2 per cent of the liver cell, for example),[34] yet they have a profound effect on the functioning of the cell. The data in the table are useful since they indicate the availability of the various molecules for combination with protein or for osmotic action.

Water, Free and Bound

Cell foods reach the cell dissolved in water, and apparently all the chemical

TABLE 3.3. *Relative Number of Molecules of Various Types of Cellular Materials**

SUBSTANCE	PER CENT	AVERAGE MOLECULAR WEIGHT	MOLARITY IN CELL	NUMBER OF MOLE- CULES RELATIVE TO PROTEIN	NUMBER OF MOLE- CULES RELATIVE TO DNA
Water	85	18	47.2	1.7×10^4	1.2×10^7
Protein	10	36,000	0.0028	1	7.0×10^2
DNA†	0.4	10^6	0.000,004	—	1.0
RNA‡	0.7	4.0×10^4	0.000,175	—	4.4×10^1
Lipid	2	700	0.028	10^1	7.0×10^3
Other organic materials§	0.4	250	0.016	6	4.0×10^3
Inorganic	1.5	55	0.272	10^2	6.8×10^4

* Data on all but nucleic acids from Sponsler and Bath.[7] DNA and RNA data for rat liver cell taken from Euler and Hahn.[34]
  † Deoxyribonucleic acid; see section on nucleic acids.
  ‡ Ribonucleic acid.
  § Sponsler and Bath give 1.5 per cent, from which 1.1 per cent was subtracted for RNA and DNA, in making the calculations of numbers of molecules relative to DNA. The numbers of molecules relative to protein were calculated by Sponsler and Bath, using 1.5 per cent for "other organic molecules."

reactions of importance to life occur in aqueous solution. Water is present in large quantities in the more active tissues; for example, white matter of the brain contains about 68 per cent water, whereas the gray matter, made up of the constituents of the neurons, contains about 85 per cent.[27]

Water in the cell occurs in two forms—free and bound although the partition between the two forms is quite indefinite. *Free water* is that which is available for metabolic processes; *bound water* is that which is loosely held to a protein molecule by dipole attraction. The force of imbibition is the expression of such adsorption of water to the surface of protein molecules. Bound water is attached to protein molecules by the formation of hydrogen bonds and therefore forms part of the structure of protoplasm. Hydrogen bonds result from the attraction of two electronegative atoms for a proton, and only the most electronegative atoms such as fluorine, oxygen, nitrogen and chlorine are capable of forming them. Radicals with residual electronegativity forming hydrogen bonds in protoplasm are hydroxyl, carboxyl, keto, amino, imino, sulf-

hydryl and trivalent nitrogen. Each amino group of a gelatin molecule is capable of binding 2.6 molecules of water.[7] It is estimated that in general approximately 4.5 per cent of all the water available in the cell is bound,[8] the greater portion being free to act as a solvent in which metabolic reactants may dissolve (see also Chapters 4 and 7).

Salts

Salts are present in all cells and are necessary for life. If the salts are removed by placing tissues in distilled water, death ensues. The salt requirement of cells is strikingly illustrated by the occurrence of muscle cramps following excessive perspiration, which is attended by excessive salt loss. When salt is lost in perspiration, the potassium in muscle cells leaks into the extracellular fluid and cramps result. Since potassium re-enters the cells after intake of salt, the cramps are quickly relieved by ingestion of a salty drink or a salted food.

The salt content in cells of a representative tissue[5] is given in Figure 3.1. It will be noted that of the cations, potassium is

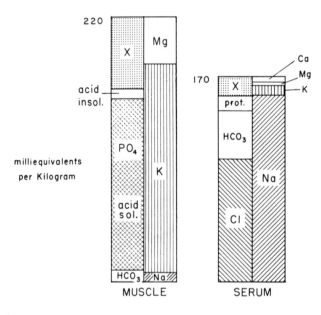

Fig. 3.1. Comparison of ion content of muscle tissue and blood serum. (After Lowry: Biol. Symp., *10*:241, 1943.)

TABLE 3.4. *Elements Found in Cells of Various Organisms (Primary and Invariable Elements Are Found in Cells of All Organisms.*)*

PRIMARY (1–60%)	INVARIABLE		VARIABLE	
	SECONDARY (0.05–1%)	MICROCON-STITUENTS (0.05%)	SECONDARY	MICROCON-STITUENTS
H	Na*	B	Ti	Li* St
C	Mg*	F*	V*	Be Mo*
N	S*	Si	Zn*	Al* Ag
O	Cl*	Mn*	Br	Cr Cd*
P*	K*	Cu*		Co* Sn
	Ca*	I*		Ni* Cs
	Fe*			Ge Ba*
				As Pb
				Ru

After Sverdrup, et al.[10]

* All elements marked with an asterisk have been found necessary for some type of enzyme action, according to Schweigart, 1951:Z. Pflanzenernähr *54*:36. Boron and silicon have been found necessary for plants. The unmarked variable elements may be only contaminants since no function for them has been found and they are found in only small quantities and not in all organisms.

present in highest concentration inside the cell, magnesium in lesser concentration, and sodium and calcium are present in relatively small amounts. The dominant anion of cells is phosphate, part of which is soluble in acid, part insoluble. A second important anion is bicarbonate. In some cells (erythrocytes and liver cells) chloride is also present. While these salts are the main ones in cells, small quantities of a large number of other elements also are found, probably as salts[39] (see Table 3.4). For example, iron is always present in relatively sizable amounts, while manganese and copper are found in very small amounts (microconcentrations, less than 0.05 per cent). Vanadium, zinc, nickel, molybdenum and even tin are found in variable but always minute quantities.[10, 39, 57] Some of these salts are necessary for the functioning of certain enzymes (see Chapters 16 and 17).

It is interesting that the cation present in the highest concentration in the body fluid (e.g., serum, Fig. 3.1) is sodium, only a small amount of potassium being found. Such a difference in concentration of sodium and potassium inside and outside cells is vital to their functioning as is most readily seen in studies on highly irritable tissues such as muscle and nerve (see Chapters 21 and 22). Sodium also appears to be necessary for syntheses occurring in the nucleus and potassium for those in the cytoplasm.[56]

Proteins

Proteins are responsible for the characteristic structure of the cell. They are molecules of large molecular weight, ranging from about 6,000 to many million. Their large size probably accounts for many of their peculiar properties.[46, 47]

All proteins contain carbon, hydrogen, oxygen, nitrogen and usually sulfur, and some in addition have phosphorus. Proteins are made up of amino acids, of which there exist some twenty kinds (see Fig. 3.4 and Table 3.5). The amino acids of a protein are united to one another by their respective amino and carboxyl

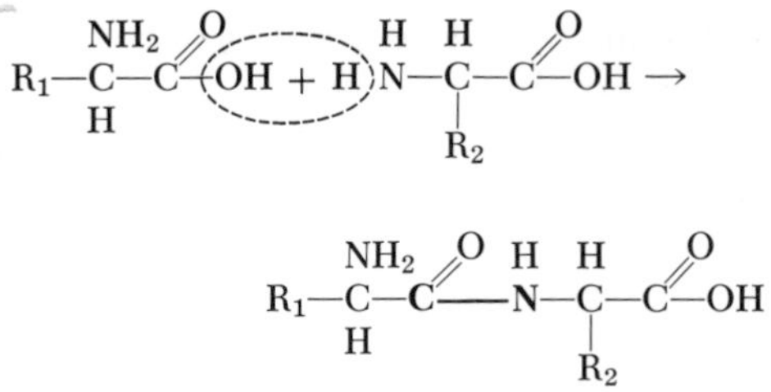

Fig. 3.2. Formation of a peptide bond between two amino acids. The N and C of the peptide bond are in bold type.

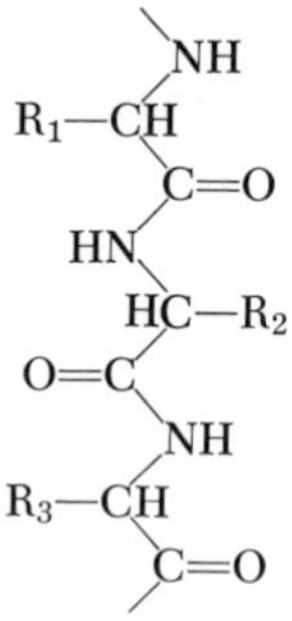

Fig. 3.3. The peptide backbone of a protein molecule.

groups, forming *peptide bonds* (see Fig. 3.2). In the cell only phosphorylated amino acids in the presence of appropriate enzymes apparently react to form peptide bonds. The chain of peptide bonds between successive amino acid residues forms the backbone of the protein molecule (see Fig. 3.3). However, other linkages occur as well and, in fact, are necessary to explain the native structure of a protein. These are considered later in connection with the helical structure of protein molecules.

Although there are some 20 kinds of amino acids in proteins (Table 3.5), not all the amino acids are present in all the proteins (Table 3.6), and those present occur in proportions characteristic of each protein. In Table 3.6 are given data for the amino acid composition of a few representative proteins.[44] It is evident that some proteins, such as gelatin, contain relatively few aromatic amino acids (e.g., tyrosine and phenylalanine) per molecule, whereas most others, such as albumin, contain relatively many. In histone a larger proportion of basic amino acids is present, while in myosin a larger proportion of acidic ones is found. Sulfur–containing amino acids are com-

TABLE 3.5.   *Types of Natural Amino Acids and Abbreviations Used for Them*

A. Monoamino-monocarboxylic	D. Hydroxyl-containing
Glycine (Gly)	Threonine (Thr)
Alanine (Ala)	Serine (Ser)
Valine (Val)	E. Sulfur-containing
Leucine (Leu)	Cystine (Cys or Cy-S)
Isoleucine (Ileu)	Methionine (Met)
B. Monoamino-dicarboxylic	F. Aromatic
Glutamic (Glu)	Phenylalanine (Phe)
Aspartic (Asp)	Tyrosine (Tyr)
C. Diamino-monocarboxylic	G. Heterocyclic
Arginine (Arg)	Tryptophan (Tryp)
Lysine (Lys)	Proline (Pro)
Hydroxylysine (Hlys)	Hydroxyproline (Hpro)
	Histidine (His)

A. Monoamino-monocarboxylic:
Glycine
$CH_2\overset{+}{N}H_3$
|
COO^-

D. Sulfur containing:
Cysteine
$HS—CH_2$
|
$CH\overset{+}{N}H_3$
|
COO^-

Methionine
$CH_2—S—CH_3$
|
CH_2
|
$CH\overset{+}{N}H_3$
|
COO^-

B. Monoamino-dicarboxylic:

D-Glutamic
$COOH$
|
CH_2
|
CH_2
|
$CH\overset{+}{N}H_3$
|
COO^-

E. Aromatic:
Phenylalanine
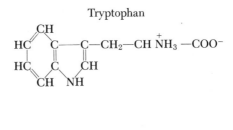

C. Diamino-monocarboxylic:
D-Arginine

F. Heterocyclic:

Tryptophan

Fig. 3.4. Representative amino acids. The amino acids probably occur in the cell in ionic forms, the ionization depending upon the pH or hydrogen ion concentration of the cell. They are here shown in zwitterion form, the proton being attached to the amino group.

pletely absent from histone, and few are present per molecule of gelatin. Although only 20 types of amino acids exist, the number of proteins which can be formed from them is large. This is not difficult to comprehend if we make an analogy between the amino acids and the letters of the alphabet, since the entire English language is derived from 26 letters combined in diverse ways.

When both the molecular weight of a protein and the relative proportions of its constituent amino acids are known, an empirical formula in terms of its amino acid content may be written for it.[13, 14] Thus the empirical formula for ribonuclease, an enzyme catalyzing digestion of ribonucleic acid, is:

Asp_4, $(AspNH_2)_{11}$, Glu_6, $(GluNH_2)_6$, Gly_3, Ala_{12}, Val_9, Leu_2, $Ileu_3$, Ser_{15}, Thr_{10}, Cys_8, Met_4, Pro_4, Phe_3, Tyr_6, His_4, Lys_{10}, Arg_{14}.

$AspNH_2$ and $GluNH_2$ refer to the amines of aspartic and glutamic acids respectively (see Table 3.5 for meaning of the abbreviations for amino acids). Ribonuclease

TABLE 3.6. *Amino Acid Composition of Several Proteins*
(The numerical values indicate the percentage of each type of amino acid present in the protein. The data illustrate the variability of amino acid constitution of different kinds of proteins.)

AMINO ACID	TYPE OF PROTEIN			
	GELATIN	RABBIT MYOSIN	CALF THYMUS HISTONE	HUMAN SERUM ALBUMIN
Alanine	9.3	6.5	6.94	—
Amide N	0.07	1.20	0.87	0.88
Arginine	8.55	7.36	17.4	6.20
Aspartic acid	6.7	8.9	5.71	8.95
Cysteine	0.0	—	0.0	0.70
Cystine/2	0.0	1.40	0.0	5.60
Glutamic acid	11.2	22.1	4.30	17.0
Glycine	26.9	1.9	5.07	1.60
Histidine	0.73	2.41	2.69	3.50
Isoleucine	1.8	} 15.6	20.5	1.70
Leucine	3.4		5.21	11.00
Lysine	4.60	11.92	10.23	12.30
Methionine	0.9	3.4	0.0	1.30
Phenylalanine	2.55	4.3	4.08	7.80
Proline	14.8	1.9	4.04	5.10
Serine	3.18	4.33	4.71	3.34
Threonine	2.2	5.1	4.80	4.60
Tryptophan	0.0	0.8	0.0	0.2
Tyrosine	1.0	3.4	3.30	4.70
Valine	3.3	2.6	3.22	7.70

(From Cantarow and Schepartz, 1962: Biochemistry. 3rd Ed. 1962)

consists of 124 amino acids of 19 different kinds.[38, 40] Relatively few proteins have been so analyzed to date.

In a few cases the analysis of protein structure has been pursued to the point where not only the empirical but also the structural formula has been determined.

For example, this was done for insulin (molecular weight 6000) illustrated in Figure 3.5. The procedure is long and difficult. It is necessary to determine first by end-group analysis how many polypeptide chains are present in the molecule. It is obvious that a polypeptide chain

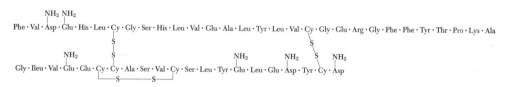

Fig. 3.5. Structure of the protein insulin. The abbreviations for the various amino acids are interpreted in Table 3.5. The residues indicated with NH_2 groups attached are amines of the corresponding amino acids. (From Sanger, 1959. Science *129*:1343.)

can have only one terminal α amino group and such an amino group can be made to react with dinitrofluorobenzene to form a bright yellow dinitrophenol derivative. When a known molar concentration of the protein is then hydrolyzed by acid or enzymatically, the marked peptide can be isolated and determined quantitatively. From the data the number of polypeptide chains per protein molecule can be determined. This can be checked by determination of the number of terminal carboxyl groups per protein molecule, using an enzyme specific to the terminal carboxyl groups (carboxypeptidase, see Chapter 16). Next the disulfide bonds linking the polypeptide chains are readily broken by performic acid. The polypeptides are then separated from one another by fractional precipitation with salts. Each polypeptide must then be hydrolyzed in such ways as to cleave it in certain places only. Fortunately, selective enzymes are available and these, combined with acid or alkaline hydrolysis, made it possible to shatter the chain in many places and to note the overlapping sequences in the chromatographed products (see appendix to Chapter 20). It thus proved possible to identify all of the amino acids in the two polypeptide chains making up the insulin molecule. Furthermore, it was possible to determine the order of the various amino acids in the two polypeptide chains. Determination of the positions of the cross linkages between the two chains by disulfide groups proved difficult, but successful methods were devised. This intensive analytical study,[42] continuing for ten years, won the Nobel prize for Sanger in 1958.

At present the amino acid sequences of insulin (from several species of animals), adrenocorticotropic hormone, bovine glucagon, bovine pigment–cell-stimulating hormone, tobacco mosaic virus and ribonuclease have been worked out.[38] The three dimensional arrangement has not been fully determined for any of the enzymes for which the amino acid sequence is known.

Solubility of Proteins. Proteins differ from one another in solubility. In the past, before much was known of their structure, solubility was one of the main criteria for classification of proteins. At present such a classification is interesting primarily from an operational point of view. For example, the *albumins* are soluble in neutral distilled water, whereas the *globulins* are soluble only in dilute neutral salt solution. Some proteins are soluble only in acid or basic solution (glutelins of cereals), and some are soluble in alcohol solutions (prolamines, e.g., gliadin of wheat). The *scleroproteins* or albuminoids are relatively insoluble and are hydrolyzed and degraded only under special conditions or by special reagents. They are resistant to digestive enzymes largely because disulfide linkages between respective sulfur–containing amino acids in these proteins must be reduced to sulfhydryls before the digestive enzymes can exert their influence on the peptide linkages. Reduction of disulfide occurs more readily under alkaline conditions. In the alkaline intestinal tracts of some insects (e.g., clothes moth larvae) these groups are reduced, following which the scleroproteins are digested.[15] The dermatophyte fungi which tolerate highly alkaline conditions (see Table 8.4) are also capable of using these proteins as food.[16]

Proteins as Zwitterions. All proteins show certain characteristics in common. Like amino acids (Fig. 3.4), proteins are zwitterions; that is, they are charged both positively and negatively and at the isoelectric pH they are electrically neutral. Therefore, at the isoelectric pH (see Chapter 8) they will not migrate toward the anode or the cathode of an electric field. As with amino acids, the isoelectric pH of a protein depends upon the relative number of basic and acidic groups present in the molecules. An excess of acid groups on a protein molecule—for example, a molecule with

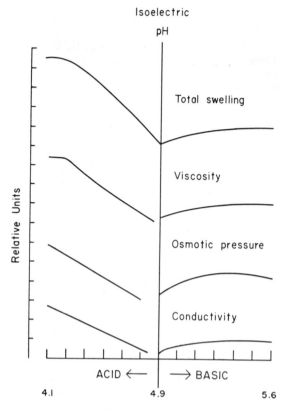

Isoelectric
pH

Total swelling

Viscosity

Osmotic pressure

Conductivity

Relative Units

ACID ⟵ | ⟶ BASIC

4.1   4.9   5.6

Fig. 3.6. Effect of pH on properties of gelatin. (After Loeb: Proteins and the Theory of Colloidal Behavior. New York, McGraw-Hill Book Company, 1924, p. 46.)

many polycarboxy amino acids—shifts the isoelectric point to the acid side of neutrality, as in serum albumin, which has an isoelectric pH of 4.7. An excess of basic groups on a protein—for example, one with many polyamino acids—shifts the isoelectric pH to the basic side, as in gliadin, which has an isoelectric pH of 9.0.

On the acid side of the isoelectric pH the protein dissociates primarily as a base and is predominantly positively charged. On the alkaline side the protein dissociates as an acid and is predominantly negatively charged. The charge on proteins can be readily demonstrated by their reactions with dyes. A positively charged protein reacts only with a negatively charged dye, forming a colored precipitate. Since the protein is positively charged only on the acid side of its isoelectric pH, the reaction with the negatively charged dye occurs only at a low pH. A negatively charged protein, on the other hand, reacts only with a positively charged dye, forming a colored precipitate.[17] The protein molecule is negatively charged only at a high pH on the alkaline side of its isoelectric pH (see Table 3.7).

In general, physical-chemical properties of a protein are at a minimum[18] at its *isoelectric pH* (see Fig. 3.6), at which it is electrically neutral:

1. The viscosity tends to be minimal; in other words, the protein offers least resistance to flow since there

TABLE 3.7. *Reaction of Proteins with Dyes in Relation to the Isoelectric pH of the Protein*

		CHARGE ON PROTEIN ON ACID SIDE OF THE ISOELECTRIC pH	CHARGE ON PROTEIN ON ALKALINE SIDE OF THE ISOELECTRIC pH
		+	−
Charge on dye molecule	+	0	Dye-protein complex formed
	−	Dye-protein complex formed	0

is less attraction between the molecules and less binding of water.

2. The osmotic pressure is lowest at this pH since the number of ions produced is least.
3. The least swelling occurs under these conditions since the electrically neutral protein molecules hold the least water of hydration.
4. The conductivity is at a minimum since the molecules are electrically neutral.
5. The solubility is also minimal under these conditions, and proteins become highly sensitive to small amounts of salts which combine with the proteins, precipitating them.

Globular and Fibrous Protein Molecules. Protein molecules may be either globular or fibrous in shape.[19] Some proteins may take either form, depending upon the prevailing conditions. For example, actin, an important protein of muscle, is present in either globular or fibrous form, depending upon the concentration of certain salts.

Two kinds of fibrous proteins have been found: (1) the keratin-myosin-elastin-fibrinogen group and (2) the collagen group. In the first are the proteins of the epidermis of mammals, amphibians and some fishes; of hair, horn, etc., growing from mammalian epidermis; of the myosin of muscle fibers; and of the clotting protein, fibrinogen. All of these give x-ray diffraction patterns related to that of natural unstretched mammalian hair (α keratin). These fibers can be stretched in hot water or alkali to a second form called β keratin. The latter form gives a simpler x-ray diffraction picture than the former. If the stretched fiber is released, it gradually reverts to its original size. If released immediately while still immersed, the fibers contract to two-thirds the length of the original fibers, giving a supercontracted form.

In the second or collagen group are the fibers found in tendons, cartilage and fish scales, and the partial hydrolysis product of collagen—gelatin. These fibers do not stretch on pulling, although they contract in hot water. The x-ray diffraction patterns of collagen fibers are quite distinct from those of the keratin-myosin-elastin-fibrinogen group.

Analyses of the α form of the keratin-myosin-elastin-fibrinogen proteins by monochromatic x-ray bombardment indicate a fundamental crystallite structure showing regular periodic distances between refracting units (see Fig. 3.7). The only arrangement of amino acids which could be in keeping with the x-ray diffraction pictures of such fibrous proteins is a helix. From a knowledge of the stereochemical requirements of the peptide backbone (Fig. 3.3), that is, of the distances between atoms and of the possible angles which they may make with one another, models have been made which summarize most of the existing data. For example, Pauling and Corey have found that the α helix, in which each turn contains 3.6 amino acid residues (see Fig. 3.8A), is most consistent with the facts. Agreement is still incomplete, however, unless in addition to the α helix there is postulated a large helix made up of α helices. If the radius of the large helix is 6 Å, three of these large helices would twist around one another in a model of the fiber[19] (Fig. 3.8B).

X-ray analysis of the β or stretched form of the keratin-myosin-elastin-fibrinogen proteins shows that the atomic arrangements are no longer spiral but may best be represented as a pleated ribbon polypeptide chain[19] (Fig. 3.8C).

From x-ray analysis of the collagen group of fibrous proteins, workers postulate that here the unit is a cylindric system parallel to the fiber axis and formed of three polypeptide chains, each coiled into a helix, all three helices having the same pitch and each chain being completely hydrogen bonded to the other two. Hydrogen bonds link glycine and hydroxyproline units in the molecule.[46]

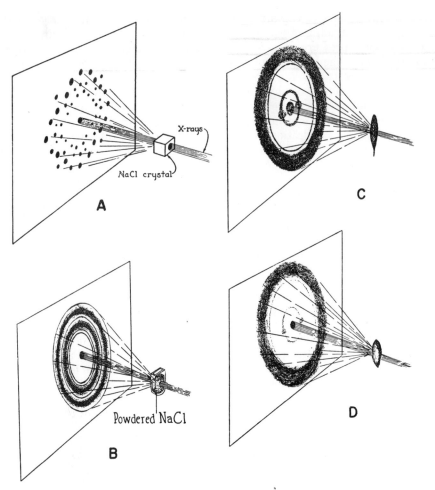

Fig. 3.7. X-ray diffraction diagrams for NaCl crystal (A), NaCl powder (B), resting muscle (C) and contracted muscle (D). (Modified from Amberson and Smith: Outline of Physiology. New York, Appleton-Century-Crofts, Inc., 1948, pp. 136–137.)

The banding seen in electronmicrographs is the result of regular orientation of amino acid residues in the fibers.[47]

The collagen molecule is an extremely long thin rodlet—the most asymmetrical molecule yet isolated. When collagen is warmed, it breaks down and forms a gel composed of gelatin, the molecules of which are one third of the molecular weight of the collagen. The collagen molecule has now been shown to consist of three peptide chains, each one incorporating considerable proline, hydroxypro-line and glycine (See gelatin, Table 3.6). Glycine, the smallest of the three, occurs every fourth position on each chain. This makes it possible for the bulkier units to fit into the links of the triple strand. The extra hydrogen bonds of hydroxyproline link it firmly to neighboring molecules in a fibril. As a consequence the collagen present in a tissue is more resistant to heat than the molecularly dispersed collagen in solution.

The main intent in presenting these examples of protein structure is to

FUNCTIONAL ORGANIZATION OF THE CELL

illustrate the possibility of explaining in terms of molecular arrangements the x-ray data and many of the facts known about the chemistry of proteins. The models at hand already help to interpret chemical and biological data with more consistency than was previously possible.

It thus appears that primary, second-

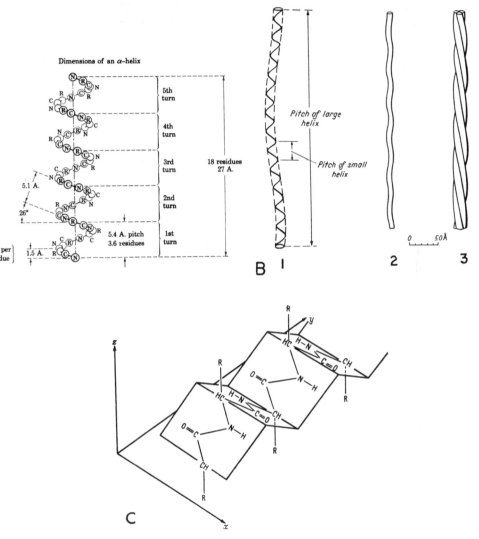

Fig. 3.8. A, the Pauling-Corey 3.6 residue α helix. R refers to a radical (methyl, phenyl, etc.), C stands for the carbon atom and N for the nitrogen atom. B, a compound helix made up of a succession of α helices which are shown inside the large helix delimited by the dotted border. In (1) the pitch of the large helix is marked between the long arrows. The pitch of one of the many individual α helices, of which the large helix is constructed, is shown between the short arrows. The compound helix is shown in a simplified way in (2). Three such helices coil together to form a rope (3) when the radius of the large helix is 6 Å. C, pleated ribbon polypeptide chain to represent the arrangement of the amino acids in the β or stretched fibers of the keratin-myosin-elastin-fibrinogen group of proteins. (A, from Anfinsen, The Molecular Basis of Evolution, Wiley, N. Y., 1959, p. 101. B and C from Springall, The Structural Chemistry of Proteins. Academic Press, N. Y., 1954.)

ary and tertiary structures occur within the protein molecule.[40, 60] The primary structure is that expressed by the structural chemical formula and depends entirely upon chemical valence bonds: the peptide bonds which unite amino acid residues in the peptide backbone of a protein and those covalent bonds that form fixed sites of cross linkage, such as the disulfide bonds between half-cystine residues and the phosphate diester linkages of certain phosphoproteins. Secondary structural bonds are the result of hydrogen bond formation as, for example, the amide (CONH) linkages between $C=O$ and NH groups on amino acid residues of the polypeptide chain. The α helix and pleated ribbon of Pauling shown in Figure 3.8 are results of such secondary bonds. The α helix has the maximal number of amide bonds for spirals of various pitch values considered and is, therefore, probably the most stable. Tertiary structure and disulfide linkages are considered necessary to stabilize the α helix in solution and it is probable that only those parts of proteins which are properly anchored by such bonds can maintain the helical configuration. The tertiary structure is the result of (1) van der Waals interactions between hydrophobic groups, agglomerated by mutual repulsion of solvent, and (2) those special hydrogen bonds which exist between hydroxyl groups of tyrosine and the ϵ amino groups of lysine and various electronegative groups along the peptide chain.[40]

Globular proteins such as albumin and globulin consist of one or several peptide chains folded up in some way and held in configuration by hydrogen bonds and cohesive forces of like-to-like radicals, e.g., methyl groups of neighboring amino acids. It is still somewhat uncertain whether an α helix represents the structure of a globular protein.[41] Globular proteins may unfold when the cohesive and hydrogen bonds are broken by heat or other agents which denature the proteins.

Denaturation. Denaturation of a protein is defined by Kauzmann[41] as a "process or a sequence of processes in which the spatial arrangement of the polypeptide chains within the protein molecule is changed from that typical of the native protein to a more disordered arrangement." As defined above, denaturation may involve breakage of some primary bonds along with some secondary and tertiary bonds. Such a modification of the unique structure of the protein molecule, gives rise to definite changes in chemical, physical or biological properties. For example, denatured protein binds water less readily and becomes less soluble. Similarly, denatured enzyme is no longer active catalytically. Both types of protein, fibrous and globular, are subject to denaturation.

Native and denatured protein may exist in equilibrium with one another in solution, but various factors may affect the equilibrium between them. For example, heat, acid, alkali, heavy metals, alkaloids, detergents, guanidine, urea, organic solvents, hydrostatic pressure, surface reactions, ultraviolet and ionizing radiations, all tend to favor denaturation. In many cases the denaturation is essentially irreversible, proceeding with an output of energy.

Denaturation sometimes may be undetectable to the eye although it is present in a latent condition. For instance, when albumin is heated to 60° C. at a pH far to one side of its isoelectric pH and in the virtual absence of salts, it will remain in solution even though it is denatured. Adjustment of the solution to the isoelectric pH results in the formation of a precipitate, a process for which the term *flocculation* is employed. Readjustment of the pH far to one side of the isoelectric pH results in dissolution of the flocculum; therefore, flocculation is reversible. However, if the flocculum is heated, flocculation is made irreversible and the process is then spoken of as *coagulation.*

Proteins unfold during denaturation. Since unfolding exposes hydrophobic groups which repel water, the denatured protein is less soluble in aqueous solution and more susceptible to precipitation from solution than the native protein. Unfolding during denaturation is accompanied, in some proteins, by an increased total volume of the solution, as measured by the method of dilatometry. The dilatometer is a flask with a finely calibrated capillary tip. The increase in volume of a protein during denaturation may amount to 0.2 ml. per 100 grams of protein. This increase may be accounted for in the following manner: The folded, native protein has its hydrophobic radicals hidden; the hydrophilic radicals, which are exposed, attract water molecules, holding them closely. Conversely, when the molecule is denatured and unfolded, the hydrophobic radicals are exposed, repelling the water; the capacity of the protein to bind water is reduced and the total volume of the solution is thus increased.[21]

When the volume of a protein solution increases during denaturation, the denaturation can be reversed by the application of pressure which reduces the volume. A typical experiment is shown in Figure 3.9. At 65° C., a temperature which denatures certain globular proteins at atmospheric pressure, higher pressures prevent the denaturation of the protein, and the percentage of protein remaining in solution—that is, in the native state—increases with increase in pressure.

When heat injury to a given biological process is reversed by pressure, the process is assumed to be one in which the enzyme of the limiting reaction under consideration is denatured with an increase in volume. Several such cases have been effectively studied, such as the quenching of luminescence in luminous bacteria by heat, heat-stoppage of cleavage in sea urchin eggs and the heat-induced loss of infectivity of virus, all of which are reversed by moderate pressure.

Conjugated Proteins. Proteins may

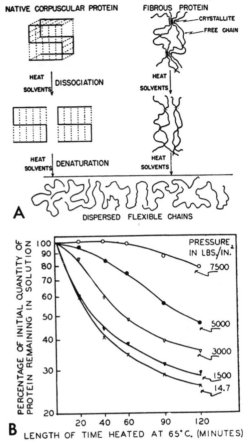

A

B

Fig. 3.9. *A*, Denaturation of globular and fibrous proteins. (From Cantarow and Schepartz: Biochemistry.) *B*, Degree of precipitation of protein at 65° C. when subjected to various pressures. (From Johnson and Campbell: J. Biol. Chem., *163*:644, 1946.)

combine with various other compounds in an organism to form compounds called conjugated proteins. An example of these is hemoglobin, a chromoprotein in which the protein *globin* is combined with the iron–containing porphyrin compound, *heme*. Hemoglobin has the unique property of loosely binding oxygen from the respiratory organ and releasing it to the tissue fluid where the oxygen tension is low. A porphyrin chromoprotein similar to hemoglobin and serving as an electron carrier in all aerobic cells is cytochrome (see Chapter 16). Of great importance to the

A. Purine nucleus   B. Pyrimidine nucleus

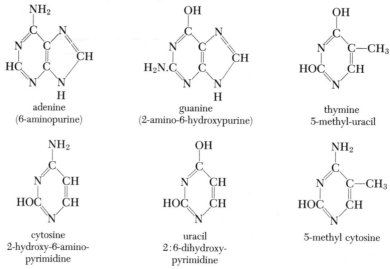

C. Purines and pyrimidines found in nucleic acids

adenine
(6-aminopurine)

guanine
(2-amino-6-hydroxypurine)

thymine
5-methyl-uracil

cytosine
2-hydroxy-6-amino-
pyrimidine

uracil
2:6-dihydroxy-
pyrimidine

5-methyl cytosine

D. Nucleotide units

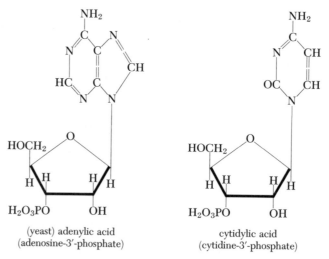

(yeast) adenylic acid
(adenosine-3′-phosphate)

cytidylic acid
(cytidine-3′-phosphate)

Fig. 3.10. *A* and *B*, purines and pyrimidines found in nucleic acids, *C. D*, nucleotide units.

cell is the class of conjugated proteins known as *nucleoproteins*. They are formed by a combination of basic proteins (protamines or histones) with nucleic acid. Nucleic acid is considered to be a large molecule and is essentially a polymer of several kinds of nucleotides. Each nucleotide unit is composed of phosphoric acid, a pentose sugar and a purine or pyrimidine base. The structures of the kinds of purines and pyrimidines found in nucleic acids are given in Figure 3.10 along with that of a representative nucleotide. A polymer of nucleotides is formed by bridges between pentose and phosphoric acid residues of successive nucleotide molecules, as well as by other secondary bonds which are best represented in the Watson and Crick spiral model of nucleic acid (Fig. 3.16).

Lipids

Lipids serve not only as food reserves but also as parts of structures of the cell. They have one property in common: they are all soluble in fat solvents. Lipids are a diverse chemical assembly which includes fats, waxes, phospholipids, carotenoids and sterols.[12] Fat is a triglyceride ester of gycerol and three fatty acid molecules. For instance, if three butyric acid molecules are linked to glycerin, the product is tributyrin; and if three palmitic acid molecules are linked to glycerin, the product is tripalmitin (see Fig. 3.11). The three fatty acid molecules in neutral fat may be of two or three kinds. The two most prevalent fatty acids are palmitic and oleic acids, both of which are almost always present in every natural fat. In fat depots these two acids often form the main components of the saturated and unsaturated fatty acid fractions, respectively. However the fatty acid mixture present is often distinctive of the species of plant or animal in question. Neutral fats (triglycerides) occur in cells primarily as food reserve.

Phospholipids, containing phosphorus,

$$
\begin{array}{l}
\text{H}\\
\text{HC}-\text{O}-\overset{\overset{\displaystyle O}{\|}}{\text{C}}-(\text{CH}_2)_{14}-\text{CH}_3\\[2pt]
\text{HC}-\text{O}-\overset{\overset{\displaystyle O}{\|}}{\text{C}}-(\text{CH}_2)_{14}-\text{CH}_3\\[2pt]
\text{HC}-\text{O}-\overset{\overset{\displaystyle O}{\|}}{\text{C}}-(\text{CH}_2)_{14}-\text{CH}_3\\
\text{H}
\end{array}
$$

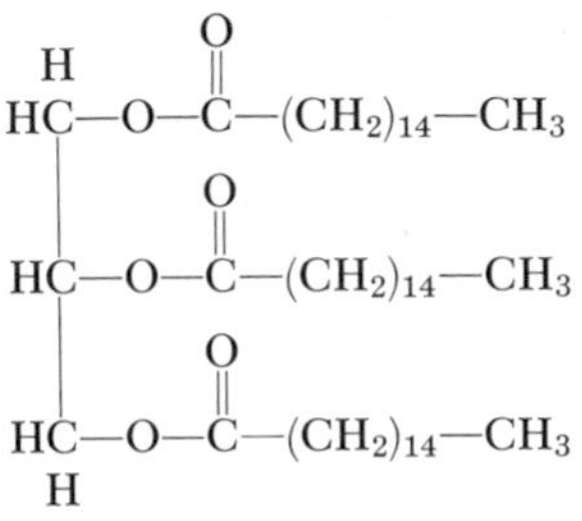

Fig. 3.11.   Tripalmitin, a triglyceride.

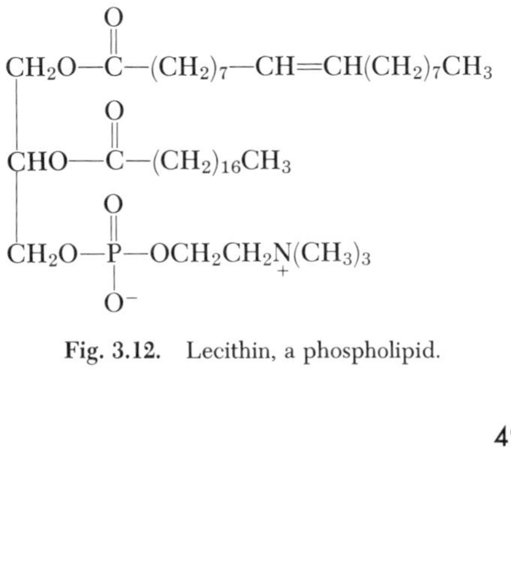

are of great importance in the cell. The simplest phospholipid is a phosphatidic acid in which two fatty acids and one phosphoric acid are attached to the three hydroxyl groups of glycerol. In most phospholipids the phosphoric acid, in turn, is combined with an organic base by another ester linkage, as shown in Fig. 3.12. Since phospholipids possess both acid and basic groups, they behave as zwitterions. Because of their ionic water-attracting (hydrophilic) groups and their fatty acid fat-attracting and water-repelling (lipophilic or hydrophobic) groups, phospholipids are somewhat soluble in both water and fats (or fat solvents) and therefore serve an important role in the cell in binding both types of compounds together. For example, lecithin, one of the phospholipids, is especially important as a structural material in the cell membrane since by its hydrophilic groups it maintains the continuity between the aqueous outside and the aqueous inside of the cell, yet fat-soluble materials dissolve in it and enter the cell

$$
\begin{array}{l}
\text{CH}_2\text{O}-\overset{\overset{\displaystyle O}{\|}}{\text{C}}-(\text{CH}_2)_7-\text{CH}=\text{CH}(\text{CH}_2)_7\text{CH}_3\\[2pt]
\text{CHO}-\overset{\overset{\displaystyle O}{\|}}{\text{C}}-(\text{CH}_2)_{16}\text{CH}_3\\[2pt]
\text{CH}_2\text{O}-\overset{\overset{\displaystyle O}{\|}}{\underset{\overset{\displaystyle |}{\text{O}^-}}{\text{P}}}-\text{OCH}_2\text{CH}_2\overset{+}{\text{N}}(\text{CH}_3)_3
\end{array}
$$

Fig. 3.12.   Lecithin, a phospholipid.

because of its hydrophobic groups. Some phospholipids are characteristic of the species in which they are found. For example, phosphatidyl-inositol, in which the phosphoric acid is esterified by inositol,[12] is unique to plant cells. Phospholipids containing large amounts of highly unsaturated $C_{20}-$ and $C_{22}-$ fatty acids are found in many animal cells but not in plant cells.

Waxes are esters of higher aliphatic alcohols and higher fatty acids of longer chain length than the fatty acids of other lipid classes (generally C_{24} to C_{30} or even to C_{36}). For example, beeswax is a mixture of cerotic acid with myricyl palmitate. Waxes generally form protective coatings. In only a few instances do they constitute a part of the depot lipid. For example, the depot lipid of the cells in seeds of the shrub *Simmondsia californica* consists of esterified wax, and 70 per cent of the depot lipid of the sperm whale is wax ester. Depot waxes have shorter chain fatty acids than cuticular waxes.[12]

Another important group of fatty compounds is the sterols, aromatic alcohols characterized by the presence of a free hydroxyl group. Sterols are found free as well as esterified with such fatty acids as palmitic or oleic. While cholesterol (see Fig. 3.13) is by far the most prominent sterol of cells of vertebrates, a large number of sterols is known. A characteristic sterol of plant cells is β sitosterol and one characteristic of fungi is ergosterol (one of the provitamins D). These differ from cholesterol only in the side chain attached to the top of the molecule as shown in Figure 3.13. The male and female sex hormones of vertebrates are sterols. The vitamins D also belong to this group. Sterols are found in the cell membrane and in other cell structures containing lipids.[48]

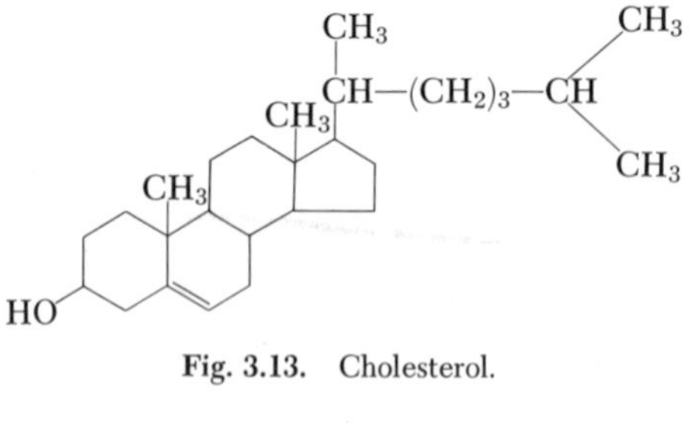

The sterols, being nonsaponifiable, are easily separated by saponification from most of the lipids generally found in cells. The other lipids, in turn, can be separated by chromatographic procedures.

Carotenoids (carotenes and xanthophylls), an important group of red and yellow plant pigments, are included among the lipids because of their solubility in fat solvents. Chemically they are tetraterpenes (a terpene has 10 carbon atoms), hydrocarbon in nature with alternate double bonds, and they may be acyclic (without a ring; for example, lycopene, the coloring matter of the tomato), or cyclic (e.g., carotene, a dicyclic tetraterpene). Carotenes consist of carbon and hydrogen only (see Fig. 20.10), while xanthophylls contain, in addition, oxygen (in the rings as hydroxy or carbonyl groups, or both). Lutein, the yellow xanthophyll of leaves, is a dihydroxy derivative of carotene. Chromatographic analysis indicates the existence of six carotenes and a number of xanthophylls. While carotenoids are synthesized in plants, they may accumulate in tissues of some animals. Vitamin A, which is important to growth and vision of some animals, is derived from carotene.

Carbohydrates[44]

Carbon, hydrogen and oxygen are present in carbohydrates in the proportions of one carbon to two hydrogens to one oxygen (CH_2O). Representatives of the main groups of carbohydrates are the monosaccharides, disaccharides, polysaccharides and mucopolysaccharides, a few of which are listed in Table 3.4.

The monosaccharides are known as hexoses if they have six carbons, pentoses if they have five (see Fig. 3.14). Glucose (dextrose, or grape sugar) and fructose

Fig. 3.13. Cholesterol.

FUNCTIONAL ORGANIZATION OF THE CELL

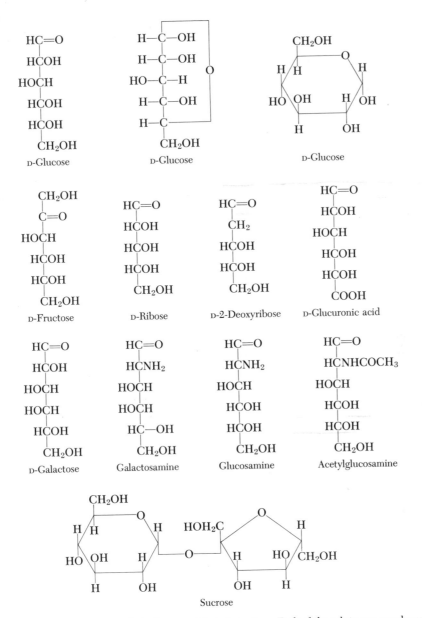

Fig. 3.14. Representative carbohydrates and their derivatives. Each of the substances may be represented in the three forms shown for glucose.

(levulose, or fruit sugar) are examples of hexoses, and ribose and deoxyribose, the sugars present in nucleic acids, are examples of pentoses. Glucose is of great importance in cellular metabolism and is discussed at length in Chapters 17 and 18.

While it may be stored as glucose, especially in fruits (e.g., grape), it is usually polymerized to an insoluble form such as glycogen (animal starch) in animal cells and starch in plant cells. In cells enzymes occur which are able to digest these insoluble food reserves, mobilizing them for use when the need arises.

The commonest and best known disaccharide is sucrose or table sugar, which is stored in cells of such plants as the sugar cane and the sugar beet. Another important disaccharide is lactose which is present in milk secreted by cells of the mammary gland.

Polysaccharides are important skeletal materials in the cells of xylem, phloem and bast fibers, as well as in all cell walls of plants. Cellulose is the main polysaccharide found in plant cell walls. The cell walls are cemented together by pectin, a D-galacturonic acid polymer.[45] Lignin, a complex ring compound, is also present in cell walls, especially in older cells.[37] D-Glucosamine acetylated on the amino group is polymerized to form part of the skeletal chitin of arthropods and several other invertebrate groups (Fig. 3.14). Chitin is occasionally present in some plant cell walls (e.g., yeast).

The mucopolysaccharides are of interest as structural materials secreted by cells of animals. Intercellular cement consists of hyaluronic acid. Hyaluronic acid is a polymer of glucuronic acid and acetylglucosamine. Invading microorganisms often secrete the enzyme hyaluronidase, which enables them to penetrate tissues more effectively because it digests the intercellular cement. The matrix of connective tissue and cartilage contains—in addition to some protein—chondroitin sulfuric acid, which is a polymer of galactosamine, glucuronic acid and sulfate.[44]

On human red cells are found blood group substances. These are nitrogenous, neutral heteropolysaccharides containing amino acids or peptides as well as carbohydrate groups. They are therefore related to the mucopolysaccharides containing, among other substances, N-acetyl-D-glucosamine. These substances act as agglutinogens and are highly specific. Two main agglutinogens and six minor ones are found. The blood group, or type, of an individual is determined by the na-ture of the hereditary blood group substance present on his red cells. A person having one type of blood substance has antibodies against other types but not against his own.[43]

Nucleic Acids—Deoxyribonucleic (*DNA*) and Ribonucleic (*RNA*)

About fifty years ago Miescher extracted nucleic acids and nucleoproteins from pus cells and fish sperm by the use of high concentrations of salt (1 to 2 molar NaCl).[50] He found that about 60 per cent of the solids in sperm were nucleic acids, 35 per cent were proteins and 5 per cent were other materials, such as lipids, salts and carbohydrates. Since then extensive information has accumulated on the chemistry of the nucleic acids. Because of their large content of nucleic acid, sperm have been widely used in such studies, but other types of cells have been employed as well. For example, nuclei can be easily isolated from ruptured red blood cells of birds or from other fragmented tissues. The nuclei usually remain intact and presumably may be washed free of cytoplasmic fragments by differential centrifugation.[51] Nucleic acid is readily extracted from such a suspension of nuclei.

Two types of nucleic acids have been extracted and identified by chemical means in all cells tested—deoxyribonucleic acid (DNA) and ribonucleic acid (RNA). Experiments show that DNA is the predominant nucleic acid in the nucleus, while RNA is predominant in the cytoplasm. Each is considered to be composed of nucleotides (Fig. 3.10). Differences between the two nucleic acids include differences in pentoses, pyrimidine bases and size of molecule (Table 3.8). The pentose called deoxyribose, or D-ribodesose, is present in DNA, whereas the pentose, D-ribose, is present in RNA (see Fig. 3.14). The pyrimidine thymine is found in DNA; its place is taken by uracil in RNA. The molecular weight of

TABLE 3.8. *Similarities and Differences between the Constitutions of DNA and RNA*

CONSTITUENT	DNA	RNA
Purine:		
adenine	+	+
guanine	+	+
Pyrimidine:		
cytosine	+	+
uracil	−	+
thymine	+	−
methyl cytosine*	+	−
Sugar:		
ribose	−	+
deoxyribose	+	−
Phosphoric acid	+	+

* Data from Davidson.[52] Methyl cytosine is not always present. Methyl adenine occurs in the RNA of some microorganisms, methyl guanine in the RNA of certain plant cells and especially in the soluble RNA of liver cells along with methyl cytosine. 6-methyl aminopurine has been found in the DNA of some strains of the colon bacillus.

DNA is very large (several millions) while that of RNA is usually considered to be smaller, although the molecular weight of neither is known with accuracy since it depends partly upon the method of preparation.[52] Thus, freshly isolated tobacco mosaic virus RNA has a molecular weight of 300,000 but decomposes spontaneously to units of molecular weight of 61,000. Alkaline hydrolysis decomposes these into units of molecular weight of 15,000.[52] Several types of RNA are found in every cell: ribosomal RNA of large molecular weight, transfer RNA of relatively low molecular weight and messenger RNA (see Chapter 6).[58, 59]

The structure of deoxyribonucleic acid has been the center of attention in a number of studies, especially with x-rays. X-ray diffraction patterns indicate that dried fibers of pure DNA have a crystalline structure, although moist fibers form a less perfect pattern (paracrystalline). It has been found that the refracting units are much farther apart than would have been anticipated on the basis of a simple linear arrangement of the known constituents of the nucleic acids (phosphoric acid, pentose and base). Watson and Crick[53, 54] found that they could interpret the diffraction pattern by proposing a double helix as the possible structure of a nucleic acid fiber, because when such a fiber was coiled, refraction occurred periodically only from those units which were in line at any one time, their periodicity depending upon the pitch of the helix. From the calculated distances between atoms of the constituents of nucleic acid, they decided that the backbone of the nucleic acid consists of phosphoric acid residues and pentose sugar, while the side chains consist of the purine and pyrimidine bases. When the purine base of one helix in the model is juxtaposed to the pyrimidine base of the other helix, the fit of the two helices in the model is excellent (Fig. 3.16). Calculation of the angles between units in the molecule predicted from x-ray diffraction data showed that this model fits the requirements for the structure of DNA best. Watson and Crick therefore propose that the two helices of DNA are linked through these bases by way of hydrogen bonds, adenine being linked to thymine, and cytosine being linked to guanine (see Fig. 3.15). In extracts of DNA the amount of adenine is always equal to that of thymine, and the amount of cytosine is equal to that of guanine[52] (see Table 3.9). The model, therefore, satisfactorily accounts for the content of bases in deoxyribonucleic acid. The puzzling change in the x-ray diffraction pattern between moist and dry DNA is also interpretable with the helical model as being the result of slippage between the two helices causing displacement of the perfect crystalline pattern of the dry fiber.

While it has been considered likely that a similar model may be constructed for RNA, this has not yet been done. Probably the RNA helix is imperfect, defects occurring in the form of unpaired bases.[59]

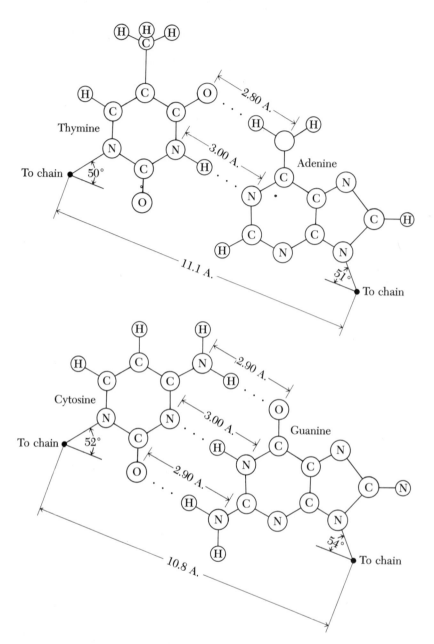

Fig. 3.15. The pairing and adenine and thymine (top) and cytosine and guanine (bottom) by means of hydrogen bonding. (From Anfinsen, 1958: The Molecular Basis of Evolution. Wiley, N. Y., p. 51.)

The presence of unpaired bases is reflected in the somewhat unequal proportions of adenine to uracil, and guanine to cytosine, found in RNA (Table 3.9).

The DNA helix is not a unique conception for structure of fibers, since helical models of proteins have a wide acceptance.[55] It is possible that the helix is

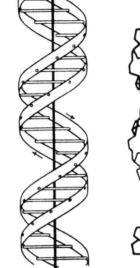
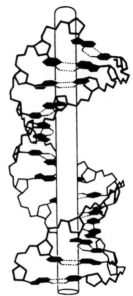

Fig. 3.16. *Left*—diagrammatic representation of the DNA molecule as proposed by Watson and Crick.[53] The two phosphate-sugar chains are represented by ribbons and the pairs of bases holding the chains together are shown as horizontal rods. *Right*— Drawing of a model of the DNA helix. The dotted lines represent the hydrogen bonds binding the purine base of one chain to the pyrimidine base of the other. The rod in the center is a support in a model, not a real structure. (From Davidson, 1960. The Biochemistry of the Nucleic Acids, 4th. Ed., Methuen, London.)

TABLE 3.9. *Molar Proportions of Bases (as Moles per 100 Moles Nucleotide) in Nucleic Acids from Various Sources**

RNA IN ORGAN OR ORGANISM	ADENINE	GUANINE	CYTOSINE	URACIL	5-METHYL CYTOSINE	THYMINE
Ox liver	17.1	27.3	33.9	21.7		
Ox kidney	19.7	26.7	33.4	20.2		
Rat kidney	19.4	29.5	30.7	20.4		
Sea urchin embryo	22.6	29.4	27.2	20.8		
Yeast	25.4	24.6	22.6	27.4		
Serratia marcescens	20.3	31.2	24.3	24.1		
Escherichia coli	25.3	28.8	24.7	21.2		
DNA IN ORGAN OR ORGANISM						
Ox thymus	28.2	21.5	21.2		1.3	27.8
Ox spleen	27.9	22.7	20.8		1.3	27.3
Ox sperm	28.7	22.2	20.7		1.3	27.2
Rat bone marrow	28.6	21.4	20.4		1.1	28.4
Herring testes	27.9	19.5	21.5		2.8	28.2
Sea urchin	32.8	17.7	17.3		1.1	32.1
Wheat germ	27.3	22.7	16.8		6.0	27.1
Yeast	31.3	18.7	17.1		—	32.9
Escherichia coli	26.0	24.9	25.2		—	23.9
Mycobacterium tuberculosis	15.1	34.9	35.4		—	14.6

* From Davidson, 1960: The Biochemistry of the Nucleic Acids, pp. 39 and 40. Methuen, London. For the structure of purine and pyrimidine bases, see Fig. 3.10.

the type of template upon which are formed all proteins (see Chapter 25).

Helical structure of DNA does pose some problems, however. For example, how does the new set of helices separate from the parent set when duplication occurs in the nucleus during mitosis? How does a protein helix separate from its nucleic acid enzyme? Consideration of these problems must be left to the original accounts in the literature.

Vitamins and Growth Factors

Vitamins, organic molecules of diverse chemistry, are required in minute amounts for the growth and normal functioning of cells. Sometimes the term "growth factors" is used to denote such substances required by plant cells and microbes, while "vitamins" is restricted to use as a term in animal physiology. The distinction is not valid and is not followed here.

Vitamins play an important part in cellular metabolism, acting chiefly as parts of enzymes or other biological catalysts. A table of vitamins is included (see Table 3.10) here, largely to complete the survey of biologically important compounds. Of the vitamins listed, only A, D and E are oil soluble; the others are water soluble. The functions of some of these vitamins, particularly the water-soluble groups, as

parts of cellular enzymes are considered in Chapters 17 and 18.

Chemical Composition of Cell Organelles[28-31]

Membranes of cells are made up primarily of protein and phospholipids, as well as some cholesterol. A more complete discussion of the cell membrane is given in Chapter 14, and additional information on cytoplasmic cell organelles and on the nucleus is given in Chapters 5 and 6, respectively.

The nucleus is made up, mainly, of protein and nucleic acid. On the chromosome thread of protein are found alternating disks of ordinary protein and nucleoprotein, the latter being present in the darkly staining disks. The nucleolus contains nucleic acid and the nuclear sap contains protein. The chemistry of the nucleus is of sufficient importance to be dealt with separately (see Chapter 6).

The ground substance of the cytoplasm of cells is made up mostly of proteins. The ribosomes present in the cytoplasm however, consist primarily of ribonucleic acid along with some proteins. A range of microsomes of different sizes and of different composition may exist. The microsomes may be fragments of the endoplasmic reticulum of the ground substance.[22]

TABLE 3.10. *Vitamins*

CLASS	CHEMICAL NATURE	EFFECT OF LACK ON VERTEBRATES	CELLULAR FUNCTION
A	Carotenoid	Growth interference, night blindness	Part of visual purple in retina; growth
D	Sterol	Bone defects	Not known; mobilizes salts in gut
E	Tocopherol	In rat, defective implantation and testis development	Unknown
B_1	Thiamine	Beriberi	Coenzyme for pyruvate metabolism

TABLE 3.10. *Vitamins (Cont.)*

CLASS	CHEMICAL NATURE	EFFECT OF LACK ON VERTEBRATES	CELLULAR FUNCTION
B_2	Riboflavin	Cataract	Prosthetic group of flavoprotein enzyme
Niacin	Nicotinic acid amide	Pellagra	Part of dehydrogenase coenzyme
Pantothen	Pantothenic acid	Dermatitis and spectacle eye	Part of coenzyme A
B_6	Pyridoxine	Need not demonstrated	Coenzyme for amino acid conversions
H	Biotin	Need not demonstrated	Coenzyme in CO_2 fixation in C_4 acids
Inositol	Cyclic Compound	Need not demonstrated	Unknown
Folic acid	Pteroylglutamic acid	Anemia	Coenzyme functioning in "one" carbon metabolism
B_{12}	Cyanocobalamin (tetrapyrrole with cobalt in center)	Anemia	Coenzyme of an enzyme involved in methyl transfer and nucleic acid metabolism[49]
Protogen	Thioctic acid	Need not demonstrated	Coenzyme in pyruvate oxidation
C	Ascorbic acid	Scurvy	Maintain optimal oxidation reduction potential?
K	1,4-naphthoquinone acetate	Hemorrhage	Prothrombin formation in blood
P	A mixture of substances*	Capillary fragility	Maintains cement of capillary walls
Essential amino acids	Essential amino acids†	Failure in growth or normal function Wasting of tissue	Structure of cells, etc.
Essential fatty acids	Linoleic, linolenic and arachidonic	Failure in growth or functioning	Structure of cells, etc.
Methyl compounds	Choline, methionine	Failure in growth, etc.	Structure of cells, etc.
Sulfhydryl-containing compounds	Cysteine, glutathione	Failure in growth, etc.	Structure of cells, etc.

* Eriodictin, hesperidin, rutin.

† Tryptophan, phenylalanine, lysine, histidine, leucine, isoleucine, threonine, methionine, valine and arginine are required by the rat. The requirement is not always the same for all types of animals.

They consist chiefly of proteins and phospholipids.[27]

The *mitochondria* are made up of protein, fats (glycerides), phospholipids and some ribonucleic acid. Analyses of mitochondria separated from other cell constituents and concentrated by centrifugation indicate that more than half of the solids present are proteins. Glycerides, phospholipids and cholesterol are the main lipids, glycerides being present in largest quantity. The main enzyme systems required in aerobic metabolism are found in the mitochondria.[23] The main enzyme systems required for anaerobic metabolism occur in the continuum of the cytoplasm between the organelles as well as in the nucleus.[24]

The *Golgi apparatus* like the mitochondria is made up of lipoproteins, phospholipids and proteins. Less is known of the Golgi apparatus since, it has only recently been possible to separate it fractionally from other constituents of the cell.[35]

Differences in the chemical nature of nucleus and cytoplasm are also indicated by their different staining reactions to the same aniline dyes at the same pH. To illustrate, in the mildly acid range of pH, negatively charged (acid) aniline dyes stain the cytoplasm, not the nucleus. In a more acid solution even the nucleus (i.e., the chromatin of the diffuse stage of the chromosomes or the condensed chromosomal material) is stained. On the other hand, positively charged (basic) dyes in mildly acid solution may stain the nucleus, not the cytoplasm, but in alkaline solutions they also stain the cytoplasm. By finding the pH at which staining ceases with both positively and negatively charged dyes, it is possible to determine the approximate isoelectric pH for the cytoplasm or the chromosomes. As determined by this method, the isoelectric pH for cytoplasm appears to be in the range of 4.7 to 5.0, whereas for chromosomes it appears to be about 3.3 to 3.6.[27]

The pH of the cytoplasm, estimated by injection of indicator solutions into the cell,[25] is found to be about 6.7 to 6.8. The pH of nuclei has been found to be about 7.5 to 7.8. While these values are controversial[33] because of various possible errors, measurements for both cytoplasm and nucleus are on the alkaline side of the isoelectric pH of the proteins and nucleoproteins found in the structures.[26] It appears that in the living cell both proteins and nucleoproteins are negatively charged. On the other hand, the nuclear membrane, with an isoelectric pH estimated to be between pH 10.5 and 11.5, has a positive charge.[27] The outer surface of the cell is usually positively charged, owing to a layer of positive ions outside the cell.

Localization of Chemicals in Cell Organelles: Cytochemistry

The aims of the cytochemist are (1) to determine the localization of various chemicals present in cells, that is, to find out in which part of the organelle they are present; (2) to measure the quantity in each locus; and (3) to establish the function of the various chemical constituents of the organelles. To accomplish these objectives he must be able to identify the chemicals by specific microchemical reactions and to make quantitative determination of the chemicals so identified. This is an ambitious and inclusive program.[28] Since the field is changing rapidly and new techniques continue to be developed and tested,[29, 30, 31] it is possible here to give only a few methods as samples of the kind of attack made and of the nature of the information obtained. Other examples are given elsewhere (for nucleic acids in Chapter 6, and for the cell membrane in Chapter 14).

In one of the newer methods of choice, tissues are frozen and freed of water by evaporation in vacuum at low temperatures, a method which minimizes shrinkage as well as a change in the state of aggregation of the colloidal particles. The proteins and other cell constituents are precipitated (fixed) *in situ*. A specimen dried in this manner may be directly embedded in paraffin for sectioning, and the sections may be stained or subjected to chemical treatment for identification of cellular constituents.

If the section of tissue so prepared is to be stained or treated with reagents in aqueous solution, the proteins must be rendered insoluble to prevent their solution in the reagents applied. For this purpose extensive testing may be necessary. A variety of fixing agents have been developed suitable for particular needs.

The histochemist is interested in staining specifically the chemicals in cell organelles. For example, the identification and cellular distribution of enzymes may be determined by color reactions. For phosphatase, this is done in the following way. The cell or section of the tissue is incubated with calcium and glycerophosphate. Calcium phosphate is deposited wherever the enzyme is present.

The calcium may then be identified by subsequent treatment of the tissue with a cobaltous salt and ammonium sulfide, upon addition of which a black precipitate is formed. By this method phosphatase has been demonstrated to be on or in the Golgi apparatus, outlining its structure. Various color reactions have been developed for other enzymes and for nucleic acids, proteins, lipids and carbohydrates.

Nucleic acids can also be identified by ultraviolet spectrophotometry. In a sense this extends a "color" reaction into the invisible span of the spectrum. This is based on the differential absorption of short wavelength ultraviolet light by nucleic acids and proteins. Nucleic acids absorb maximally at 2600 Å while proteins absorb maximally at about 2800 Å, as shown in Figure 3.17. The selective absorption of nucleic acids is accounted for by the purines and pyrimidines; that of the proteins is accounted for by the aromatic and heterocyclic amino acids.

In the radioautographic method, sec-

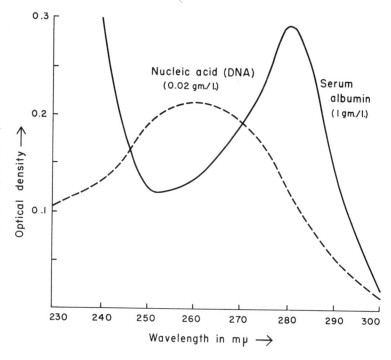

Fig. 3.17. Absorption spectra of nucleic acid and serum albumin. The optical density is highest where the absorption is greatest; therefore, the peaks in the figure indicate the regions of greatest absorption. Note that the albumin has a peak at 280 mμ while nucleic acid has a peak of 260 mμ. Also of interest is the relative absorption of ultraviolet light by the two compounds; for instance, a solution of only 0.02 gm./liter of nucleic acid absorbs at its region of maximum absorption almost as much of the radiation as does a solution of 1 gm./liter of albumin at its maximum.

Nucleic acid (DNA) (0.02 gm./l.)

Serum albumin (1 gm./l.)

Optical density →

Wavelength in mμ →

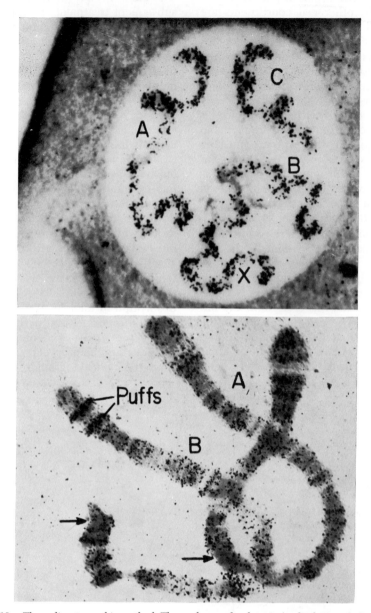

Fig. 3.18. The radioautographic method. The nucleus and polytenic (multiple-stranded) chromosomes of the larvae of the fly *Rhynchosciara angelae* injected 24 hours earlier with tritiated thymidine. (Tritium emits electrons of 10,000 electron volts.) In the upper part are shown the four chromosomes of a cell. In the stained chromosomes below it can be seen that the localization of the thymidine H[3] is in the bands of the chromosomes, indicating that incorporation occurs only here. P[32] may also be used as a marker. (Courtesy of A. Ficq and C. Pavan.)

tions of tissues of organisms fed nutrients containing radioactive markers (e.g., P^{32}) are applied directly to a photographic emulsion. After a period of exposure the film is developed, fixed and examined microscopically. The density of the developed film measures the relative concentrations of the radioactive material in various cell organelles (Fig. 3.18).

Sometimes enzymes are used to remove one protoplasmic constituent, making possible the identification of remaining constituents. Thus pepsin and trypsin remove the protein from a *Drosophila* chromosome but leave nucleic acids fixed with lanthanum salts (see also Chapter 6).

Still another type of cytochemical technique, used for determining the localization of salts in the cell, is *microincineration*, in which entire cells or slices of tissues are placed in an electric furnace at a sufficiently high temperature to oxidize all the organic materials. Only the

ash content of cells is then left. From the ash *in situ* it is possible to identify the tissue and make out some cellular detail (see Fig. 3.19). Calcium is seen to be concentrated around the chromosomes, and more iron is present in the nucleus than in the cytoplasm. Iron can be recognized by the red color of its oxide. The detection of some elements is difficult. Calcium often appears in the form of crystals of calcium sulfate. Magnesium cannot be detected in the presence of calcium. Silicon can be identified because it is doubly refractile. By using the microincinerated preparation as a source of electrons in an electron microscope it has been possible to identify the distribution of some of these elements, because the electrons are given off at different temperatures by different elements.[11] Not all the elements are retained in the ash, however; for example, sodium and potassium disappear because they volatilize at

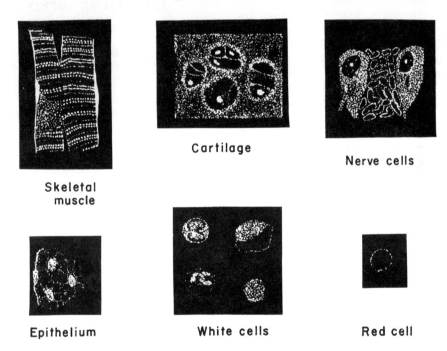

Cartilage

Nerve cells

Skeletal muscle

Epithelium

White cells

Red cell

Fig. 3.19. Microincinerated cells. Muscle from rectus abdominis of cat, cartilage from femur of cat embryo, nerve cells from cat brain, epithelium of corpus luteum of cat, blood cells from human. (Adapted from Scott: Am. J. Anat., 53:243, 1933.)

red heat. Distribution of potassium and sodium must be studied by first converting them into sulfates which do not volatilize at the temperatures used for incinerating the section. Some materials may be identified by the use of x-rays.[36]

It may be desirable not only to identify a constituent of protoplasm but also to determine how much of it is present. This is difficult, but by determining how much light is transmitted through a section of an organelle stained with a specific dye and comparing it with the light transmitted by a like thickness of a standard solution, color tests may be made quantitative or semiquantitative. Ultraviolet spectrophotometry of nucleic acid has also been made quantitative by comparing transmissions of ultraviolet light through tissues and the same thickness of a solution of a known nucleic acid concentration. It is even possible by a similar calibration to make estimates of concentrations from radioautographs.

Cytochemistry, like many other approaches to biological problems, has its pitfalls.[32] Purity of reagents is often of paramount importance here, since most of the work is done with minute quantities and at the cell level. Yet some biological reagents, e.g., enzyme preparations, are difficult to control. Then there is the problem of diffusion of a water-soluble constituent of a cell during the application of the very agent used for its identification. Also, the dynamic state of the cell, the continuous relocation of material in it, just prior to its fixation, must also be kept in mind.

Nonetheless, cytochemistry has added a wealth of material to our knowledge of cellular constituents and structure.

GENERAL REFERENCES

Advances in Carbohydrate Chemistry, 1961: Volume 16.

Advances in Protein Chemistry, 1961: Volume 16.

Anfinsen, C. B., 1959: The Molecular Basis of Evolution. Wiley, New York.

Bloch, K. (ed.) 1960: Lipide Metabolism, Wiley, New York.

Cantarow, A., and Schepartz, B., 1962: Biochemistry. 3rd Ed. Saunders, Philadelphia.

Davidson, J. N., 1960: The Biochemistry of the Nucleic Acids, 4th Ed. Wiley, New York.

Dawson, R. M. C., 1957: The Animal Phospholipids. Biol. Rev. 32:188–229.

De Robertis, E. D. P., Nowinski, W. W., and Saez, F. A., 1960: General Cytology. 3rd Ed. Saunders, Philadelphia.

Fieser, L. F., and Fieser, M. (eds.), 1959: Steroids, Reinhold, New York.

Fox, S. W., and Foster, J. R., 1957: Introduction to Protein Chemistry. Wiley, New York.

Lovern, J. A., 1957: Lipids of Biochemical Significance. 2nd Ed. Methuen, London.

Noller, C. R., 1957: Chemistry of Organic Compounds. 2nd Ed. Saunders, Philadelphia.

Physical Techniques in Biological Research. Vol. 1, 1955.

Vitamins and Hormones, 1961: Volume 19.

LITERATURE CITED

1. Verworn, M., 1903: Die Biogenhypothese. Jena, Germany.
2. Burrell, R. C., 1947: Organic Chemistry for Students of Biological Sciences. Burgess Publishing Co., Minneapolis.
3. Ephrussi, B.; 1933: Arch. de Biol. 44:1.
4. Vernon, M. H., 1895: J. Physiol. 19:18.
5. Lowry, O. H., 1943: Biol. Symp., 10:233.
6. Mommaerts, W. F. H. M., 1950: Muscular Contraction. Interscience, New York.
7. Sponsler, O. L., and Bath, J. D., 1942: in Structure of Protoplasm. (Seifriz, W., ed.) Iowa State College Press, Ames, Iowa.
8. Bull, H. B., 1951: Physical Biochemistry. 2nd Ed. Wiley, New York.
9. MacCallum, A. R., 1926: Physiol. Rev. 6:316.
10. Sverdrup, H. W., Johnson, M. W., and Fleming, R. H., 1942: The Oceans. Prentice-Hall, New York.
11. Horning, E. S., 1951: in Cytology and Cell Physiology (Bourne, ed.). Oxford Univ. Press. London.
12. Lovern, J. A., 1957: The Chemistry of Lipids of Biochemical Significance. 2nd Ed. Methuen, London.
13. Sanger, F., 1949: Biochem. J. 45:563.
14. Sanger, F., and Tuppy, H., 1951: Biochem. J. 49:463.
15. Prosser, C. L., and Brown, F. A., Jr., 1961: Comparative Animal Physiology. 2nd Ed. Saunders, Philadelphia.

16. Leise, J. M., and James, L. H., 1946: Arch. Dermat. and Syph. *53*:481.
17. Fraenkel-Conrat, H. L., and Cooper, M., 1944: J. Biol. Chem. *154*:239.
18. Loeb, J., 1923: Proteins and the Theory of Colloidal Behavior. McGraw-Hill, New York.
19. Springall, H. D., 1954: The Structural Chemistry of Proteins. Academic Press, New York.
20. McBain, J. W., 1950: Colloid Science. Heath, Boston.
21. Johnson, F. H., Eyring, H., and Polissar, M., 1954: The Kinetic Basis of Molecular Biology. Wiley, New York.
22. Palade, G. 1955: J. Bioph. Bioch. Cyt. *1*:567.
23. Lindberg O., and Ernster, L., 1954: Protoplasmatologia III; A, 4, Springer-Verlag, Vienna.
24. Claude, A., 1949: Adv. Protein Chem. *5*:423.
25. Chambers, R., 1949: Biol. Rev. *24*:246.
26. See discussion in Heilbrunn, L. V., 1952: An Outline of General Physiology. 2nd Ed. Saunders, Philadelphia, p. 59, ff.
27. De Robertis, E. D. P., Nowinski, W. W., and Saez, F. A., 1960: General Cytology. 3rd Ed. Saunders, Philadelphia.
28. Danielli, J. F., 1953: Cytochemistry: A Critical Approach. Wiley, New York.
29. Glick, D., 1962: Techniques of Histochemistry and Cytochemistry. 2nd Ed. Interscience, New York.
30. Moog, F., 1952: Histochemistry. Survey of Biological Progress 2:197.
31. Pearse, A. S., 1960: Histochemistry, 2nd Ed. Little, Brown, Boston.
32. Gomori, G., 1950: Ann. N. Y. Acad. Sci. *50*:968.
33. Caldwell, P., 1956: Internat. Rev. Cyt. *5*:229.
34. Von Euler, H., and Hahn, L., 1948: Arch. Biochem. *17*:285.
35. Kuff, C. L., and Dalton, A. J., 1959: *in* Subcellular Particles, Ch. 7 (Hayashi, T., ed.) Am. Physiol. Soc., Washington.
36. Coslett, V. E., Engstrom, A., and Pattee, H. H., Jr., 1957: X-ray Microscopy and Microradiography. Academic Press, New York.
37. Nord, F. F., and Schubert, W. J., Oct. 1958: Sci. Am. *199*:104.
38. Stein, W. H., and Moore, S., Feb. 1961: Sci. Am. *204*:81.
39. Vinogradov, A. P., 1953: The Elementary Chemical Composition of Marine Organisms. Sears Foundation for Marine Research #2, Yale University, New Haven.
40. Anfinsen, C. B., 1959: The Molecular Basis of Evolution, Ch. 5. Wiley, New York.
41. Kauzmann, W., 1959: Adv. Protein Chem. *14*:1.
42. Sanger, F., 1959: Science, *129*:1340 (Nobel Lecture).
43. Guyton, A. C., 1961: Textbook of Medical Physiology. 2nd Ed. Saunders, Philadelphia.
44. Canterow, A., and Schepartz, B., 1962: Biochemistry. 3rd Ed., Saunders, Philadelphia.
45. Preston, R. D., Sept. 1957: Sci. Am. *197*:157.
46. Doty, P., Sept. 1957: Sci. Am. *197*:173.
47. Schmitt, F. O., Sept. 1957: Sci. Am. *197*:205.
48. Fieser, L. F., Jan. 1955: Sci. Am. *192*:52.
49. Smith, E. L., 1960: Vitamin B_{12}. Methuen, London.
50. Miescher, F., 1897: Die Histochemischen und Physiologischen Arbeiten, Leipzig.
51. Dounce, A. L., 1954: Internat. Rev. Cyt. *3*:199.
52. Davidson, J. N., 1960: The Biochemistry of the Nucleic Acids. 4th Ed. Wiley, New York.
53. Watson, J. W., and Crick, F. H. C., 1953: Nature *171*:737.
54. Crick, F. H. C., Oct. 1954: Sci. Am. *194*:54.
55. Pauling, L., Corey, R., and Branson, H. R., 1951: Proc. Nat. Acad. Sci. U. S. *37*:205.
56. Allfrey, V. G., Meudt, R., Hopkins, J. W., and Mirsky, A. E., 1961: Proc. Nat. Acad. Sci. U. S. *47*:907.
57. Spencer, C. P., 1957: J. Gen. Microbiol. *16*:282.
58. Hurwitz, J., and Furth, J. J., Feb. 1962: Sci. Am. *206*:41.
59. Doty, P., 1961: Harvey Lectures. *55*:103.
60. Kendrew, J. C., Dec. 1961: Sci. Am. *205*:96.

COLLOIDAL PROPERTIES
OF CELLS

The various constituents and organelles of the cell, as we have seen, have been studied inside the cell as well as separately in suspensions; their chemistry has been subjected to careful study, and many of the enzymes of the cell have been purified and tested; but as everyone knows, when the various enzymes and other chemicals are put together in the proportions in which they occur in the cell, the resulting mixture does not come alive. It is not just the chemicals but rather the way in which they are put together which presumably gives the spark of life. While the specific features of organization which make cells alive have not been determined, the general principles underlying many of their properties have been shown to be those which govern the behavior of colloids. The theory of colloidal chemistry and the way in which it helps us understand the organization of cells and explains some of their activities are presented in this chapter.

Homogeneous and Heterogeneous Systems

A *homogeneous system* is identical throughout and consists of one *phase;* for example, a solution of glucose in water, in which the sugar molecules are equally distributed among the water molecules in all parts of the solution. In a *heterogeneous system* two or more phases are present, each distinct from the other. For example, when oil is shaken with water the oil forms one phase, the water another, and each phase is distinct. A *phase* of a heterogeneous system is a component which is homogeneous throughout itself, bounded by an interface, and mechanically separable from other phases of the system. The particles of oil in water are spoken of as the *disperse phase;* the water in which they are dispersed is called the *continuous phase* or dispersing medium.[1, 2]

Heterogeneous systems (see Table 4.1) may consist of liquid in liquid, solid in liquid, liquid in solid, solid in gas, gas in solid, gas in liquid, liquid in gas and solid in solid. It might be added, parenthetically, that from the molecular standpoint even a homogeneous solution—for example, glucose—has heterogeneity, because a glucose molecule in its microspace differs from the water molecules which surround it. The man-made definition of a heterogeneous system is arbitrary but

TABLE 4.1. *Types of Heterogeneous States of Matter*

DISPERSE PHASE	DISPERSION MEDIUM		
	GAS	LIQUID	SOLID
Gas	—	foam (soap bubbles)	some minerals (pumice), floating soap
Liquid	fog, mist, smog	emulsions (mayonnaise)	some minerals (opal, pearl), jellies
Solid	smoke	suspensions, colloidal solutions	metals in glass (colloidal gold in ruby glass)

of practical use in differentiating the two types of systems which in reality grade one into the other. Size of particles, we shall see, is of paramount importance for entry into the cell, however.

Surfaces, Interfaces and Interfacial Tension in Heterogeneous Systems

An interface always separates any two phases in a heterogeneous system. If the cohesive forces between the molecules (or atoms) in the aggregates of the dispersed particles are greater than the forces of attraction of the dispersion medium for these molecules, the aggregates of molecules will remain separate from the dispersion medium. The molecules at the surface of the aggregate are subjected to unequal forces and are pulled in toward the center of the aggregate, resulting in a tendency to contract the surface (interface) of the particle (see Fig. 4.1). An *interfacial tension* is developed as a consequence.

At liquid-gas and liquid-liquid interfaces the interfacial tension manifests itself as a *surface tension* (for details see Appendix, 4.1). The surface tension, usually designated by σ, is measured in units of force per unit of length, e.g., dynes per centimeter. The *surface energy* available per unit area of interface is given by the force acting through a given distance. For example, if in Figure 4.2 a force (σ in dynes/cm. $\times$ length of AB in centi-

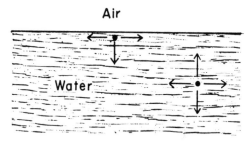

Fig. 4.1. Surface tension and forces in a liquid. The particle at the surface is pulled downward because of unbalanced forces. A particle deeper in the fluid is attracted by forces from all coordinates.

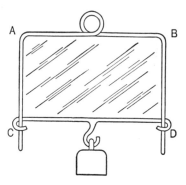

Fig. 4.2. Diagram illustrating the relation between surface area and free energy of the surface. When the force on AB (surface tension times the length of AB) acts through the distance AC, the surface free energy equals the area ABDC times the surface tension. (Reprinted with permission from Lloyd and Scarth: An Elementary Course in General Physiology. New York, John Wiley & Sons, Inc., 1930, p. 21.)

meters) acts through the distance AC, the surface free energy is:

$$\sigma \times AB \times AC = \sigma \times area \qquad (4.1)$$

In other words, increasing the surface area increases the surface free energy, this amount of energy being necessary to expand the film to this area.

According to the second law of thermodynamics, the free energy in a system tends to decrease; therefore, the surface free energy also tends to decrease and the dispersed particles in a heterogeneous system assume a shape with minimal surface area. Consequently, a drop of liquid freely suspended in another liquid or in a gas always assumes a spherical shape, since a sphere has a smaller area than any differently shaped object of the same volume. Because a single large globule has less surface area than many small ones, small ones coalesce unless they are stabilized, that is, unless they are coated with some substance which prevents their coalescence.

Adsorption occurs wherever there is a surface e.g., an interface, because of the unbalanced valency forces. Such accumulations cause a net decrease in free energy. At interfaces of systems other than liquid-gas or liquid-liquid, the interfacial tension manifests itself mainly by the ready adsorption of substances to the interface. For example, wood charcoal, which has the extensive surface areas of the charred remains of cell walls, is used to remove colored impurities from liquors and sugar solutions by adsorbing them. As a result of adsorption, materials present in solution in great dilution may be concentrated to a considerable extent at the interface of an adsorbent.

The magnitude of interfacial forces involved in adsorption may be very large. For example, water adsorbed to charcoal may be held so firmly that its volume is measurably decreased. This force will be appreciated when it is realized that water subjected to 100 atmospheres of pressure is compressed by only 0.0051. When molecules are adsorbed at an interface they lose their kinetic energy, which then appears as the *heat of adsorption*. The heat of adsorption may be very large, perhaps many thousands of calories per mole. Consequently, to free a surface of adsorbed materials, an input of energy (heat) is required, for sufficient kinetic energy must be given the molecules to enable them to escape from the forces attracting them to the adsorbing surface.[1]

The attractive forces at an interface may be general, e.g., those that bind gases to a surface, or quite selective. Many substances acting at interfaces in heterogeneous systems are endowed with great and specific catalytic activity. (In homogeneous systems catalysts act by virtue of other properties.) Attraction of a molecule to the surface of a catalyst lowers its energy of activation for a given reaction so that less energy is required than would otherwise be the case (see Fig. 16.1). Since a catalyst is chosen specifically to attract the reactants, the reaction products are attracted to the catalyst to a lesser degree and leave its surface, freeing it for further activity.

A wide variety of catalysts (e.g., spongy platinum) have been used to selectively catalyze different chemical reactions. In biological systems, similarly, many precisely selective biocatalysts (enzymes) are known and new ones are being found continually. A substance firmly bound to the active areas on a catalyst surface, but not participating in a reaction, acts as a catalyst poison because it prevents the adsorption of the reactants for the desired chemical reaction. When the poison is desorbed—for example, by heat—the catalyst regains its activity.

Emulsions and Suspensions

Since all cellular activities take place in solution, the heterogeneous systems that are most important to the study of cells are emulsions, suspensions and colloids. In a suspension a solid is tem-

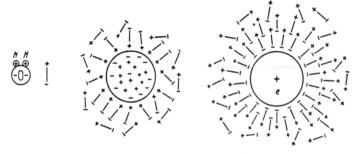

Fig. 4.3. Hydration and stabilization. *Left*, model and dipole diagram of a water molecule. *Middle*, diagram of the hydration of a colloidal particle at the isoelectric point. *Right*, hydration of a positively charged colloidal particle. (After Frey-Wyssling according to Pallmann, 1931.)

porarily suspended in a liquid, e.g., fine sand in water. When the particles are too large to remain in suspension, the solid phase soon separates from the liquid phase. In an emulsion one liquid is suspended in another, e.g., oil in water. An oil in water emulsion is very unstable because the globules coalesce to form larger ones until two layers are formed—oil and water.

If a protein is shaken up with an oil in water emulsion, the emulsion is stabilized. A film of protein forms about each particle of oil and prevents coalescence of the oil particles. This is made possible because the oil-soluble radicals (e.g., methyl and phenyl) of the protein dissolve in oil, while the water-soluble radicals (e.g., carboxyl, amino and hydroxyl) dissolve in water; thus, the oil phase is linked to the water phase. The water-soluble radicals of the protein film ionize; therefore, the particles of the emulsion repel one another, making coalescence impossible. Hydration of the ionized water-soluble part of the protein adds to the stability of the coated particles (see Fig. 4.3). As expected, when the protein stabilizer is destroyed by heat, or cold or chemical action, the emulsion is broken and the phases separate.

Soaps, also, may be used as stabilizers of emulsions. Sodium and potassium soaps shaken with oil and water form oil in water emulsions (see Fig. 4.4A),

whereas calcium soaps form water in oil emulsions (see Fig. 4.4B). The difference in the type of emulsion formed is thought to result from the difference in relative sizes of water-soluble and oil-soluble groups in the soaps. Thus, in a divalent soap the oil-soluble "wedge" is larger

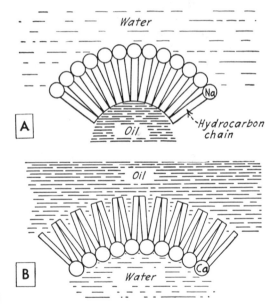

Fig. 4.4. A, Oil in water emulsion. Sodium stearate (soap) molecules at the interface of oil globules in an oil in water emulsion. B, Water in oil emulsion. Calcium stearate (soap) molecules forming the stabilization membranes of a water in oil emulsion. (By permission, from Seifriz: Protoplasm. Copyright, 1936, New York, McGraw-Hill Book Company, Inc., p. 130.)

than the water-soluble ionic portion, as is diagrammatically represented in Figure 4.4. Addition of a calcium salt to an emulsion stabilized by a sodium or potassium soap changes the emulsion from an oil in water type to a water in oil type when the calcium concentration reaches a critical level. This *reversal of phase* is readily observed in the laboratory.

Colloids

It is difficult to define colloid with precision. Some have defined a colloid as a state of matter in which the chemistry and physics of surfaces are dominant. The importance of the surface in the colloidal state becomes apparent if we consider a 1-cm. cube subdivided into cubes of a colloidal dimension, for example, 1 mμ. The surface area of the 1-cm. cube is 6 square cm. while the total area of all the 1-mμ cubes is 6×10^7 square cm. or nearly 1.5 acres. Sometimes the colloidal state is defined as a noncrystalline state of matter in which the particles are aggregates of atoms or molecules in the range between 1 and 500 mμ. This range is obviously arbitrary since of two substances within the above size range one may be colloidal, the other not. Nor are all colloids aggregates of molecules. It must be recognized, then, that defining colloid on the basis of size alone is rather arbitrary, especially since particles in nature grade imperceptibly from coarse to molecular (Table 4.2). A definition of the colloidal state should include consideration of some other properties of the colloidal state.

Colloids can be distinguished from crystalloids, such as glucose or sodium chloride, by the following four characteristics: (1) Crystalloids in solution pass through pores in a natural membrane, while colloidal particles do not. The membrane acts as a sieve, holding the larger colloidal particles back but permitting the crystalloidal molecules to come through. (2) Scattering of light by crystalloids is slight, while scattering of light by dispersed particles of colloids is quite marked. This is best seen when viewed at right angles to the incident beam. The murky cone of scattered light is called the *Tyndall cone*. The larger the difference between the refractive indices of the dispersing medium and the colloidal particle, the greater is the scattering of light. (3) Surface active interfaces exist between colloidal particles and the dispersing medium. As a result of these surface forces, colloids often show high resistance to flow or they may develop

TABLE 4.2. *Size Ranges for Different States of Matter*

SIZE IN CM.	CORRESPONDING UNITS	DIVISION OF MATTER	STATE OF MATTER	VISIBLE UNDER:
10^{-8}	Å	atoms	crystalloidal	invisible
10^{-7}	1 mμ	molecules		
10^{-6}			colloidal	electron microscope
10^{-5}				
10^{-4}	1 μ	aggregates of molecules (particles)	coarse suspensions and emulsions	ultraviolet microscope visible microscope
10^{-3}				
10^{-2}				
10^{-1}	1 mm			naked eye

TABLE 4.3. *Hydrophobic and Hydrophilic Radicals of Proteins*

HYDROPHILIC (LIPOPHOBIC)		HYDROPHOBIC (LIPOPHILIC)	
Carboxyl	—COOH	Methyl	—CH_3
Hydroxyl	—OH	Methylene	—CH_2—or=CH_2
Aldehyde	—CHO	Ethyl	—C_2H_5
Carbonyl	—CO	Propyl	—C_3H_7
Amino	—NH_2	Alkyl	—C_nH_{2n+1}
Imino	=NH	Isoprene	—C_5H_8—
Amido	—$CONH_2$	Phenyl	—C_6H_5
Imido	—CORNH		
Sulfhydryl	—SH		

After Frey-Wyssling, 1948: Submicroscopic Morphology of Protoplasm and Its Derivatives. The solubility of the hydrophilic groups in water decreases progressively from top to bottom, while the solubility of the hydrophobic groups in lipids increases from top to bottom.

structure and fail to flow, that is, they may gel. Because of the surface forces colloids are capable of adsorbing some substances from solution. (4) Colloidal particles, being large, diffuse slowly compared with crystalloids. If for comparative purposes sodium chloride is assigned a relative diffusion rate of 1, sucrose diffuses ⅓ as fast, caramel ¹⁄₄₂ as fast, and albumin ¹⁄₂₀,₀₀₀ as fast.[1]

Colloids in which no attraction exists between the solvent and the colloidally dispersed particles are not stable and are spoken of as *lyophobic* colloids (literally, solvent-hating). Some examples of lyophobic colloids are a gold sol (one prepared by reducing gold chloride in water), rubber dispersed in water and sodium chloride dispersed in alcohol. Colloids in which the solvent and dispersed particles mutually attract each other are quite stable and are designated *lyophilic* (solvent-loving) colloids. Examples are proteins in water and rubber in benzene. Lyophilic colloids are of most interest to the study of cells (see Table 4.3).

Colloidal Properties of Proteins

Proteins show all the characteristics of the colloidal state, even though they may be molecularly dispersed in water.[1, 3, 4] Thus, proteins do not pass through natural membranes. Solutions of proteins can therefore be freed of crystalloids (dialyzed) by being placed in cellophane sausage tubing immersed in distilled water or a buffer solution. Crystalloids from the solution in the bag pass into the distilled water or buffer, but the proteins do not.

Proteins in water show a typical Tyndall cone, although the opalescence is less marked than in a metallic colloid (such as gold sol) because the refractive index of protein is only slightly greater than that of water.

The interplay of surface active forces at the molecular interfaces in a protein solution is manifested by the high viscosity which such a solution quite often shows. The viscosity is a measure of the resistance of the protein molecules to flow past one another when force is applied to the solution in a confined space. This resistance may result from the attraction of the molecules for one another as well as from asymmetry in their structure.

A protein molecule will both attract and repel another molecule of the same kind, depending upon the distance separating them. Repulsion occurs because the over-all charge (positive or negative) is similar. But if the molecules approach one another so that at the point of closest approach local residual valency forces can act, the two molecules may be attracted to each other to form a hydrogen bond between electronegative elements or radicals in each. These bonds are in the dynamic state; they are made and broken continuously. Evidence of the presence of such bonds is shown by the resistance of the protein molecules to begin flowing when a force is first applied to a solution in a tube. The pressure which must be applied to start the flow is called the *yield value* and represents the force required to break these weak, temporary bonds. Even after the flow starts it may not be directly proportional to the pressure applied, but it gradually increases as more bonds are broken, as shown in Figure 4.5. Such a pattern of flow is called thixotropic. More generally, flow is proportional to the force applied, showing a constant increment with each increment of force, as in newtonian flow (e.g., in ordinary fluids) where it begins as soon as force is applied, or in plastic flow (e.g., in butter), past the yield value.

Some proteins (and some other colloids) exist in either of two states—sol or gel—depending upon the conditions. The sol is fluid because the particles are not able to form more than temporary bonds with one another. Gelation of proteins probably results from the formation of numerous strong linkages between protein molecules. Electron microscope study of a gel reveals a structure resembling a brush heap meshwork of intertwining fibers (see Fig. 4.6), verifying Nägeli's early hypothesis concerning the structure of gels.[6]

Proteins are stable colloids; i.e., they require no stabilizing agents. No stabilization is required because, first, protein ions in solution repel one another; second, each protein ion attracts and orients the water molecules surrounding it, thereby binding itself to the solvent. Each water molecule acts as a dipole with positive and negative ends (see Fig. 4.3).

The hydration of proteins deserves further notice because it is mainly upon this property that *imbibition* depends. Dry proteins adsorb (imbibe) water with great avidity—even against the osmotic pressure of saturated lithium chloride (about 1000 atmospheres). When gelatin has taken up four times its weight in water, it will no longer take up water from any solutions with a high osmotic

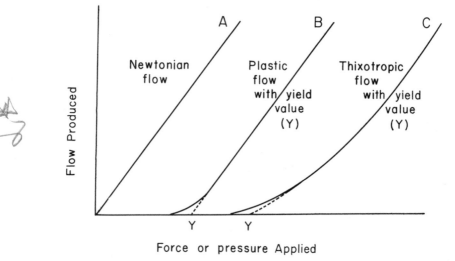

Fig. 4.5. Flow-force diagrams. The behavior in A is shown by gases and liquid solvents, in B by butter and clay, in C by proteins. (McBain, 1950: Colloid Science. D. C. Heath & Company, Boston.)

FUNCTIONAL ORGANIZATION OF THE CELL

pressure, but it will still take up water if the solution surrounding it has an osmotic pressure of only 0.2 atmosphere or less (see Fig. 4.7). Seeds also take up water against an osmotic pressure of more than 1000 atmospheres because of the dehydrated state of their proteins, but the force of uptake falls very rapidly as the proteins become hydrated. As previously pointed out (Chapter 3) water uptake is least at the isoelectric pH of proteins, increasing on either side.

Ions affect the uptake of water by proteins in characteristic ways. The sequence of their actions is spoken of as the *lyotropic*, or *Hofmeister, series*.[5] The monovalent cations of a series of chlorides, acting on a gelatin gel, for example, increase water uptake in the following order: Li > Na > K > Rb > Cs. In other words, Li increases the uptake of water more than Na, Na more than K, and so on. This effect may be explained on the basis of hydration of the ions and their adsorption to the oppositely charged protein. For example, Li^+ has a much greater sphere of water about it than Na^+, since the lithium ion is smaller and the electric

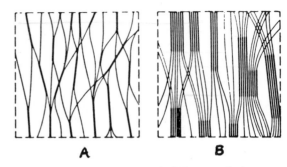

Fig. 4.6. Brushheap structure of gel. Diagram of gels of long polymeric particles (A) with some parallel orientation of the particles, and (B) with sites of crystalline structure. (Reproduced from Frey-Wyssling: Submicroscopic Morphology of Protoplasm. 2nd Ed. Elsevier Publishing Company, Amsterdam, 1953.)

charge is more concentrated. Therefore, when Li^+ combines with a protein which is negatively charged, it adds its layer of water to the protein. The sodium ion, being larger, adds less water; the potassium ion adds still less; and so on down the series. Although adsorption of the cations to the protein weakens the attraction of water to the protein, the water of hydration added by the ions more than compensates for the loss.

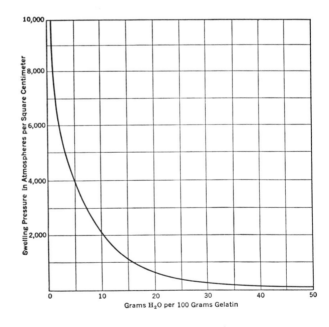

Fig. 4.7. Swelling pressure of isoelectric gelatin at 25° C. in atmospheres as calculated from aqueous vapor-pressure studies. (Reprinted with permission from Bull: Physical Biochemistry. New York, John Wiley & Sons, Inc., 1943, p. 334.)

(Figure axes: Swelling Pressure in Atmospheres per Square Centimeter, from 0 to 10,000; Grams H_2O per 100 Grams Gelatin, from 0 to 50.)

The calcium ion, being more strongly hydrated than the potassium ion, causes gelatin to swell to an even greater extent than the K^+ does and may even liquefy it.

An anionic Hofmeister series is often observed also. Trivalent citrate is a weaker swelling agent than bivalent tartrate and sulfate, and these, in turn, are weaker than the monovalent anions:[5]

SCN > I > NO$_3$,

BR > Cl > acetate,

SO$_4$ > tartrate > citrate

As might be expected, the ionic effects on the hydration (uptake of water) of proteins depend upon the pH (hydrogen ion concentration) of the medium in which the protein is dissolved, since the pH determines the sign and strength of the charge on the protein molecule (as seen in Chapter 3). For example, on the acid side of its isoelectric pH gelatin becomes positively charged and it then adsorbs anions which affect swelling in proportion to their degree of hydration.

When the charges on a protein molecule are neutralized by addition of salts, proteins may be precipitated or *salted out* (e.g., by ammonium sulfate). Salting out is often used in purification since each protein is precipitated by a specific concentration of salt and can be separated in this manner from other proteins.

The salting out of protein sols by cations or anions occurs according to a lyotropic series. Here, however, the order of effectiveness of the ions is the reverse of that given above for swelling of gels.

(For example, here citrate is the most effective anion.)

Lyotropic series are observed in studies of: the solubility of substances in solutions of electrolytes; the catalysis of hydrolytic reactions by ions; the effect of electrolytes on surface tension; the coagulation of sols; and the permeability of artificial membranes. The order of the ions is not invariably the same, and it changes with concentration, even during an experiment, indicating that under some conditions factors other than those discussed enter into determination of ionic order. The lyotropic series appears chiefly when concentrated solutions of salts are used. Since in biological systems the salt concentration is generally rather low, it is unlikely that many of the biological salt effects are interpretable on the basis of the lyotropic series.

Coacervates and Tactoids

Proteins and similar colloids are stabilized by electric charge and hydration. Discharge or dehydration of the dispersed particles precipitates the colloid. When partial discharge or dehydration occurs, the less fully hydrated particles of the colloid may then combine to form larger units with less solvent bound to them than the sum of what they had before. Such a system is called a *coacervate*,[19] and such a process is called *coacervation*. For example, addition of dehydrating agents, as alcohol or acetone, leads to coacervation. Partial discharge of colloids by addition of salts, or by mix-

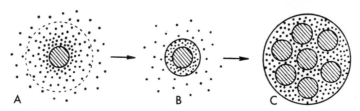

Fig. 4.8. Diagram of the process of coacervation. A, colloidal particle with diffuse hydration layer; B, hydration layer reduced and delimited; C, beginning of the coacervation phenomenon. (From Bungenberg de Jong: Protoplasma, *15* : 110, 1932.)

FUNCTIONAL ORGANIZATION OF THE CELL

ing two hydrophilic colloids of opposite charge, also results in coacervation. Coacervates (see Fig. 4.8) resemble some cellular inclusions and organelles, and it is possible that such structures may result from coacervation in protoplasm.

Tactoids are coacervates of fibrous proteins (see Fig. 4.9). Tactoids are spindle shaped, and studies with polarized light indicate that they are made up of elongate molecules linearly arranged.[5] Possibly the spindles and asters seen in the dividing cell are the result of tactoid formation by proteins in the protoplasm.

The Cell as a Polyphasic Colloidal System

Throughout the years many theories have been proposed to explain the structure of the living material within the cell, such as the reticular theory which conceived of the material as fibrillar, the granular theory which thought of it as a system of granules and the alveolar theory which accounted for the emulsion-like appearance of some cells (see Fig. 4.10 and Chapter 27). In 1925 E. B. Wilson proposed the colloidal theory of organization of the cell substance, a theory which has been and continues to be developed by others since that time because it best explains the properties of the cell. Experimental evidence in support of the colloidal theory of cellular structure is presented in the following paragraphs.

Any theory of the physical-chemical structure of the cell proposed must explain: (1) its appearance and rhythmic changes; (2) the variations in its viscosity from a fluidity approaching that of water to a gel approaching that of an elastic solid; and (3) the simultaneous occurrence of many different chemical reactions in a single living cell, none interfering with the others. Furthermore, such a theory must explain why some of the biochemical reactions occurring in the cell may be individually duplicated *in vitro*

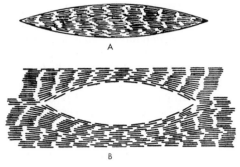

Fig. 4.9. Tactoids. A, Positive tactoid. B, Negative tactoid. A *positive tactoid* is formed when a fibrous colloid in solution is partially dehydrated or partially discharged. Under these circumstances the less fully hydrated particles of the colloid combine to form larger units containing less solvent than they did before. In the unit the individual fibrous protein molecules are oriented to form a spindle-shaped particle. A *negative tactoid* is formed when the fibrous particles enclose nonfibrous ones. (Adapted from Bernal and Fankuchen: J. Gen. Physiol., 25:128, 1941.)

only at high temperatures or high pressures or both, while in the cell they occur at comparatively low temperatures and seemingly at atmospheric pressure.

Even a casual microscopical examination indicates that the cell is heterogeneous, not homogeneous. It was previously noted that the endoplasmic reticulum ramifies throughout the ground sub-

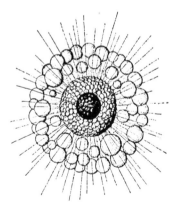

Fig. 4.10. A radiolarian (*Thalassicolla nucleata*, Huth) showing the frothy or alveolar appearance of the protoplasm. The rays are part of the skeleton. (From Kudo: Protozoology. 3rd Ed. Springfield, Ill., Charles C Thomas, 1946, p. 422.)

stance of the cytoplasm including the ectoplasm.[13] It is probable that the structure of the reticulum is dynamic and that it gives way in the path of large particles moving through it under the influence of a strong centrifugal force, imposed during centrifugation. Presumably the links which are broken are reformed again. The redistribution of the mitochondria, granules and particles, once the centrifugal force is withdrawn, indicates that the normal random distribution of these bodies in the cell is the result of the action of the kinetic energy forces acting upon them and leading to an equilibrium. This would suggest that at least part of the organization of the endoplasmic reticulum must be dependent upon the making and breaking of bonds of lesser strength than primary valency bonds (see Fig. 2.3). Most cells contain granules and many have oil droplets dispersed in a continuous aqueous phase. However, on centrifugation such granules and oil droplets are separated from the fundamental structure of the *ground substance* or clear zone through which the particles move, indicating that they are merely suspended there (see Fig. 2.3).

The persistence of organization in the ground substance of the cell is indicated by experiments testing the effect of centrifugation on the polarity of an egg. Polarity of an egg is shown by the difference between the two ends of the egg; the end at which the polar bodies are given off designates the anterior, or head end, of the individual developing from the egg. Polarity is therefore an indication of a fundamental architectural plan of the cell. In experiments with the egg of the roundworm *Ascaris*, it was shown that regardless of the angles at which the various granules and oil droplets are layered with respect to the polar axis, the original polarity of the egg is maintained, provided the packed materials do not interefere with the position of the first cleavage spindle. Similar results were obtained with eggs of a number of other

organisms as well.[16] In some cases, however, experiments indicate that polarity may be influenced by stratification of cell inclusions during centrifugation (e.g., the brown alga, *Fucus*).[17] It would seem that polarity probably depends upon the maintenance of some structure which resists deformation during centrifugation. This could be either the endoplasmic reticulum or the material between, called the *hyaloplasm* (Chapter 5). It would be of interest to compare these structures before and after centrifugation in the two classes of eggs, those that show changes in polarity after centrifugation and those that do not.

By means of appropriate staining reactions it is possible to demonstrate that the ground substance is composed of protein in aqueous solution. Like a protein solution, the ground substance shows the properties of the colloidal state.[7-10] It appears opalescent, because light passing through it under dark field is scattered as in the Tyndall cone of a colloid. The relative viscosity of the ground substance (see Appendix 4.2) varies from a value as low as that for water to a very high value in gelating cytoplasm such as the pseudopodium of an ameba.[7, 8] Chemical analyses indicate that several kinds of proteins are present in the ground substance, some fibrous, some globular. In addition, ribosomes, containing ribonucleic acid, may be present, adhering to the sacs and canals of the endoplasmic reticulum or free in the hyaloplasm. These are also in the colloidal state. Since all the particles in the disperse phase are not alike, cytoplasm is said to be a *polyphasic* colloid.

Experiments indicate that the ground substance of the cytoplasm has some of the properties of a solid. When the displacement of naturally occurring particles in the ground substance is photographed during the process of centrifugation, the particles are seen to move in a series of zigzag jumps, even in the more fluid endoplasm, as if they were tearing through a meshwork. If the ground substance were a simple viscous liquid, the movement of the particles should be smooth. Presumably the jumps are due primarily to the structure of the endoplasmic reticulum, although to what extent bonding between the reticulum and the proteins of the hyaloplasm helps account for these properties is unknown.[5]

Another indication of structure in protoplasm is provided by experiments with changes in its viscosity when sucked up into a tubule.[5, 11, 12] The viscosity decreases rapidly with increased pressure, much like the thixotropic flow of protein solutions illustrated in Figure 4.5. Cytoplasm occasionally shows an unusual behavior known as *dilatancy*, namely an increase in viscosity with increase in applied force. (This occurs in some physical systems also, e.g., a dense suspension of quartz particles in water.) Dilatancy of protoplasm is most marked when it is densely packed with particles.[18]

Further evidence of structure in the ground substance is the manner in which some plant cells plasmolyze. Long strands which attach the protoplast to the cell wall are often seen in such plasmolyzed cells[5] (see Fig. 4.11). The reticulum demonstrated in the endoplasm as well as in the ectoplasm of all kinds of cells (see Chapter 5) by electron microscopy may account for these structural properties.[13]

The fluidity of the cytoplasm under some conditions and its rigidity under others indicate that the endoplasmic reticulum should not be considered a rigid and fixed cytoskeleton, but rather a shifting and changeable structure sensitive to the environment and in a state of dynamic change.

Heilbrunn[18] has pointed out that cytoplasm flows out of the cut end of a cell as if it were liquid in consistency and has suggested the possibility that the more rigid structure which appears in the cytoplasm may be the result of a coagulation process catalyzed by a specific enzyme,

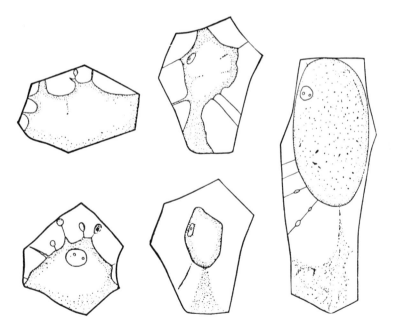

Fig. 4.11. Plasmolyzed plant cells showing strands of cytoplasm. (From Kuster: Pathologie der Pflanzenzelle I. Protoplasma Monographien III, Berlin, Borntraeger, 1929, p. 95.)

different degrees of coagulation accounting for different degrees of structural rigidity.

Nature of Structural Bonds in the Cytoplasm

Any structure, whether it be that of the endoplasmic reticulum or the hyaloplasm, must be accounted for in terms of chemical bonds. The variation of the structural strength of cytoplasm when subjected to stress indicates that these bonds are of varying degrees of strength, but according to recent studies, on final analysis all are presumably electromagnetic in nature.[20]

Frey-Wyssling, in his monograph on the subject,[5] postulates four main types of bonds between protein molecules in the ground substance: (1) Homopolar cohesive bonds (London-van der Waals forces) of the type which hold a paraffin crystal together. In proteins this type of bond is formed by the interlaced methyl groups or other hydrophobic groups of adjacent molecules (see Table 4.3). Such bonds in proteins are easily broken by heat, as they are in paraffin. (2) Heteropolar cohesive bonds, such as dipole to dipole attraction and hydrogen bonds, which result from attraction of neighboring proteins by residual valencies. These bonds are broken by mild heat, the bond strength being 5000 calories per mole or less. (3) Heteropolar valency bonds (Coulomb forces), such as those which form a salt or ester linkage. These bonds are much stronger than the first two kinds and are not likely to be broken by heat. (4) Homopolar valency bonds which involve formation of a bridge (as exemplified in the elimination of hydrogen between two sulfhydryl radicals). These are also relatively strong bonds. All these types of bonds are illustrated in Figure 4.12, but their postulation represents an attempt to formulate a working hypo-

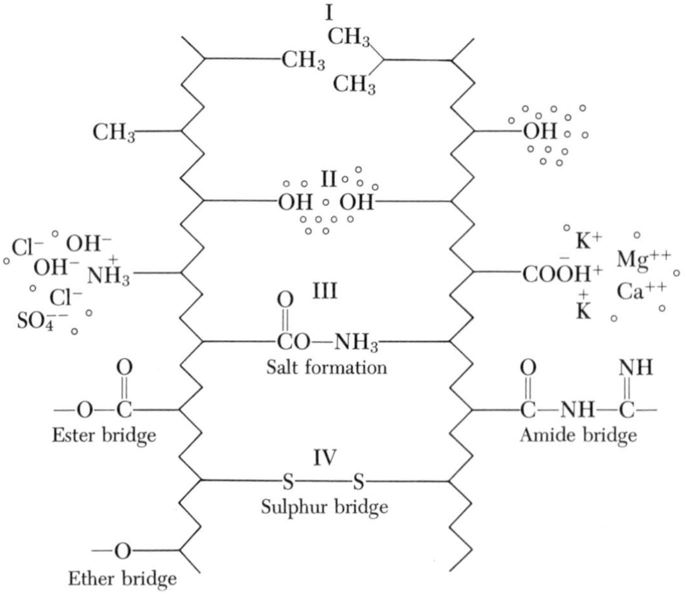

Fig. 4.12. Schematic representation of types of bonds possible between neighboring polypeptide chains of protein molecules in the cytoplasm. The small circles represent water molecules. (Reproduced from Frey-Wyssling: Submicroscopic Morphology of Protoplasm. 2nd Ed. Elsevier Publishing Company, Amsterdam, 1953.)

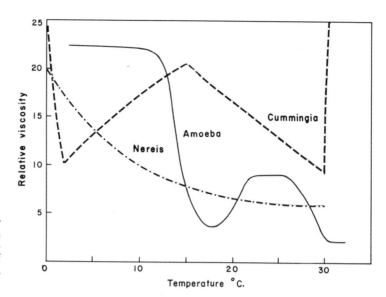

Fig. 4.13. Changes in viscosity of various cells with changes in temperature. (Data from Heilbrunn, 1958: The Viscosity of Protoplasm, Protoplasmatologia, II, C 1, Springer, Vienna.)

thesis for further research rather than a finite answer to the problem of cytoplasmic structure.

Booij and Bungenberg de Jong point out that the bonds between phosphatides (heteropolar valency bonds) should be added to the list since they are likely to play a role of importance in explaining some phenomena such as the structure maintained in highly swollen cytoplasm where protein bonds of the first three classes are likely to have been broken.[19] It should also be realized that such ions as magnesium and calcium may help in linking carboxyl groups. Water plays an important part in hydrophilic bonding as well, becoming part of the cellular structure.

As an inference from this conception, if the molecules in the cytoplasm are held together by bonds such as described above, its viscosity might be expected to fall when some of these bonds are broken, and to rise when additional bonds are formed. Since these bonds are susceptible to environmental conditions such as heat, pH, oxidation reduction agents, etc., variation in such conditions should affect the viscosity of cytoplasm. An interpretation of the manner in which the viscosity of

cytoplasm is affected by the action of environmental or internal changes is considered in several examples below.

The viscosity of an ameba varies greatly with temperature.[18] It is high at low temperatures (see Fig. 4.13) but falls to a relatively low value with a rise in temperature from about 12.5° to 19° C. As the temperature rises further the viscosity increases, a plateau existing between 21° and 26° C. With a still further rise in temperature the viscosity again falls, with a low value at 30° C. When the temperature rises beyond this point, the viscosity rises abruptly as the cell is injured by heat. These changes in viscosity are interpreted by Frey-Wyssling's hypothesis[5] as follows: Slight heat probably disrupts the homopolar cohesive bonds, lowering the viscosity. At temperatures beyond 20° C. another process sets in, namely, the dehydration of the molecular framework at those spots where hydrophilic chains come together, resulting in some sort of solidification. At the same time, however, the rupture of homopolar junctures continues, and at 25° C. it becomes of greater importance than the tendency toward solidification brought about by the simultaneous dehydration of the molecules due to heat. Further rise in temperature may again raise the viscosity as a result of the predominance of the dehydration of cytoplasmic proteins. Within the physiological range of temperatures, it is doubtful that heat would affect heteropolar cohesive bonds or main valency bonds. However, it is interesting to note how differently temperature affects the viscosity of the cytoplasm of the three types of cells, *Amoeba*, *Nereis* eggs and *Cummingia* eggs. It would be rather difficult to explain all of these on the same grounds.

Experiments have shown that anaerobiosis generally causes a decrease in viscosity of protoplasm.[5] In the absence of oxygen as a hydrogen acceptor, metabolic hydrogen may reduce the disulfide linkage in protein to sulfhydryl, thus breaking the disulfide bonds and thereby decreasing the viscosity. A lack of oxygen may also lead to the formation of organic acids from anaerobic metabolism, and the hydrogen ions thus produced may then catalyze the breakage of linkages between amino and carboxyl groups of side chains in proteins, thereby also decreasing the viscosity.

Hypertonic solutions are found to increase the viscosity of cytoplasm. This could be caused by diminished distance between the colloidal particles following withdrawal of water, an action that would strengthen the binding between the particles. Conversely, hypotonic solutions cause the opposite effect because the particles are separated by more water.

While the viscosity of cytoplasm varies greatly under different physiological and environmental conditions, presumably in the living state some structure always remains, even in a state of low viscosity. If all the bonds were broken, the structure which characterizes life would disappear and death would result.[5]

Summary

Such physical properties of protoplasm as its opalescence and its granular appearance are explainable on the basis of its being a colloid. As in all colloids, light is scattered at each interface because of the difference in refractive indices of the dispersing medium and the suspended particle.

The viscosity of cytoplasm and the variability of the viscosity with changed conditions are best interpreted on the basis of the surface active forces of a heterogeneous system and on the basis of the formation of temporary bonds between adjacent particles. Cytoplasmic flow and the resistance to flow upon application of force are interpretable in similar ways. The paradox of cytoplasm behaving like a liquid while displaying the structural properties suggestive of a solid scaffolding is also best explainable on the basis of colloidal theory.

It is not difficult to comprehend the occurrence of many simultaneous but different chemical reactions in a cell. The presence of selectively permeable membranes surrounding certain discrete structures such as the mitochondria, the Golgi apparatus and the endoplasmic reticulum probably plays an important role in separating the major reactive systems of the cell from one another. Thus the mitochondria are known to be the center of aerobic reactions liberating and storing energy; the hyaloplasm is the center of anaerobic energy-liberating reactions; the lysosomes, for hydrolytic reactions; the Golgi apparatus and the endoplasmic reticulum, for the manufacture or the assembly of lipids and perhaps other materials; and the ribosomes, for the manufacture of proteins. However, each of these is also a polyphasic colloid. Because the phases are chemically different, one phase of a polyphasic colloid may attract one set of reactants, while another phase may attract others. Therefore, biochemical reactions of entirely different character might occur simultaneously at the interfaces of nearby but chemically different phases in each of the cell organelles.

It is also conceivable how a chemical

present in relatively low average concentration in the entire cell might reach a very high concentration at an interface to which it is attracted and adsorbed selectively. Chemicals, coming through the cell membrane or synthesized inside, could thus be sorted out and concentrated by the different phases present in cytoplasm.

The surface forces of a colloid (e.g., enzyme) may serve as a substitute for the high temperature and pressure required to duplicate cellular reactions *in vitro*. The reactants adsorbed to an interface in the cell are subjected to the distorting force of adsorption. Catalysis of chemical reactions in heterogeneous systems, whether inanimate or biological, is a result of distorting forces acting on the molecules adsorbed at interfaces. Such distorting forces lower the energy of activation required for the reactions (Chapter 15). In cells the molecules are probably adsorbed to the surfaces of enzymes (see Chapter 16). Consequently, the kinetic energy available at ordinary temperatures is sufficient to activate the molecules and to provide for continuation of the reaction. Duplication of the same reactions *in vitro* in homogeneous systems, however, may require high temperatures or high pressures, or both, because all the energy of activation and of reaction must then be supplied to the reacting molecules by the heat they obtain from the environment.

APPENDIX

4.1 Surface Tension

The molecules in the interior of a homogeneous liquid are free to move and are attracted by surrounding molecules equally in all directions. At the surface of the liquid, where it touches air or some other liquid, however, they are attracted downward and sideways, or inward, more than upward; consequently, they are sub-

jected to unequal stress and are held together to form a membrane. The force with which the molecules are bound is called the surface tension of the liquid. It depends upon cohesion of the molecules, or their attraction for one another. A needle placed carefully on the surface of water will float because of the interfacial tension between the air under the needle and the water. Smaller particles, for example, powdered sulfur or talc, float readily on the surface of water.

Surface tension is measured in force per unit of length, generally in dynes per centimeter. Various methods are used for this purpose. A convenient one, attributed to Du Noüy, measures the weight required to just lift away a ring in contact with the solution to be tested (see Fig. 4.14). The stronger the surface tension, the larger the weight required. The sur-

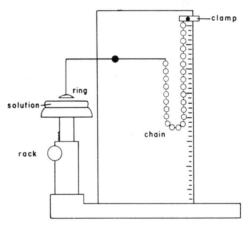

Fig. 4.14. Ring method of determining surface tension. A length of chain is measured on the scale on the right of the stand. Enough is measured to balance a given weight placed on the ring (100 mg., 200 mg., and 500 mg. in successive trials). The points are then connected by a line. When this is done the ring is allowed to come in contact with the test solution which is then racked up until the arm from which the ring is suspended is horizontal. The clamp is then released and moved down until the ring breaks from the surface of the solution. From the extra weight required to break the contact, the surface tension can be determined. (After Lloyd and Scarth: An Elementary Course in General Physiology. New York, John Wiley and Sons, 1930, p. 199.)

face tension σ in dynes/cm. is given by the following equation:[15]

$$\sigma = \frac{\text{wt. in grams} \times 980}{2\,(2\,\pi\,r)} \qquad (4.2)$$

In this equation r is the radius of the ring.

The surface tension of liquids which wet glass, may be measured by the capillary height method. The solution rises in a capillary because it tends to contract to reduce the surface, thereby pulling the liquid upward. The surface tension is given by the following equation:[2]

$$\sigma = \tfrac{1}{2}\,hdgr \qquad (4.3)$$

In this equation h is the height in centimeters, d is the density of the liquid, g is the acceleration due to gravity (980) and r is the radius in centimeters.

By the use of appropriate equations the surface tension may also be determined from the size of drops formed at the end of a tube. The droplet is essentially spherical when small but becomes oval in shape and constricts at the end until it falls.[1, 2] The surface tension of various solutions is given in Table 4.4.

4.2 Viscosity

Viscosity is a measure of the friction between molecules as they slide by one another. The unit of viscosity, the *poise*, is a viscosity such that unit force per unit area is required to cause two parallel liquid surfaces of unit area and unit distance apart to slide past one another with unit velocity. The absolute viscosity of water at 25° C. is 0.008937 poises, or 0.8937 centipoises (see Table 4.5).

For biological purposes the viscosity of various substances is usually measured relative to water. The Ostwald viscosimeter is most commonly used for this purpose (see Fig. 4.15). It consists of a

TABLE 4.4. *Surface Tension of Various Substances*

SUBSTANCE	TEMPERATURE °C.	SURFACE TENSION DYNES/CM.	AGAINST
Tristearin	60	29.6	air
Oleic acid	20	32.5	air
Glycerol	20	63.4	air
Mercury	15	487	air
Ethyl alcohol (100%)	20	22.75	vapor
Ethyl alcohol (100%)	0	24.05	air
Water	18	73.05	air
Water	25	71.97	air
Benzene	20	40.04	air
Acetic acid (1%)	30	68.0	air
Acetic acid (100%)	30	26.6	air
Sucrose 10%	25	72.5	air
Sucrose 55%	25	75.7	air
CaCl$_2$ (1M)	25	3.2 + 71.97 (water)	air
NaCl (1M)	20	1.64 + 72.75 (water)	air
Oil	20	ca. 15	water
Oil with protein film	20	ca. 1	water
Arbacia cell membrane	20	.08 − .2	sea water
Amoeba dubia	20	1.3	fresh water
Physarum	20	.45	fresh water
Triturus egg	20	.1	fresh water

Data for first 15 items from Handbook of Chemistry and Physics, 35th Ed.; the remaining six items from Davson and Danielli, 1952: Permeability of Natural Membranes.

TABLE 4.5. *Viscosity of Various Substances*

SUBSTANCE	TEMPERATURE °C.	VISCOSITY IN CENTIPOISES
Water	25	.8937
Benzene	10	.758
	60	.392
Glycerin	20	1490.0
	30	629.0
Castor oil	20	986.0
	30	451.0
Pitch	15	1.3×10^{12}
Sucrose solution (20%)	20	1.960
(60%)	20	56.5
(60%)	50	14.01
Alcohol-water (50%)	25	2.40
Nerve fiber	20	5.5
Cummingia egg (shed)	20	4.3
Cummingia egg (during maturation)	20	21 to 26
Amoeba dubia	18	2
Amoeba dubia	varied	2 to 14
Slime molds	20	9 to 18
Chara	20	10
Arbacia egg	20	7
Paramecium	20	50

Data for first seven items from Handbook of Chemistry and Physics, 35th Ed.; values on proto-plasm from Heilbrunn, 1952: An Outline of General Physiology. 3rd Ed.

U-shaped pipette with a capillary leg that is bent, widened to form a reservoir and continued up to the same level on the opposite side, making possible immersion of the whole in a thermostat.[1] The time required for water to flow from a mark above the upper reservoir to one just below it is measured. The time required for the flow of a second fluid is determined in the same way. The ratio of the viscosities of the two liquids, called the relative viscosity, is directly proportional to the lengths of time required to empty the reservoir.

Viscosity may also be measured in a number of other ways:[1] (1) The time required for a steel ball to fall a fixed distance through a solution is compared with the time required for it to fall the same distance through the solvent alone. (2) The rate of movement of an inner cylinder separated from an outer cylinder by a thin layer of the fluid whose viscosity is to be determined is also used to measure viscosity (Couette method). The outer cylinder is moved by suitable gearing, and the amount of movement induced in the inner cylinder is then determined.

For determining the viscosity within the cell it is necessary to employ methods quite different from those used to measure solutions. The rate of layering of various inclusions in an egg such as that of a sea urchin or an ameba during centrifugation has been used for this purpose.[7, 8] The rate at which the layered particles return to their original locations might also serve as a measure, although it is less precise than the first. The rate of fall of starch granules in plant cells under the influence of gravity is also a measure of viscosity.[11] In essence all these methods are akin to the falling ball method for measuring the viscosity of solutions.

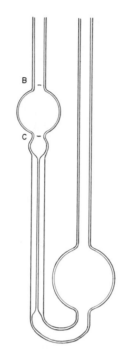

Fig. 4.15. Ostwald viscosimeter. To get the relative viscosity, the time required for the meniscus of a solution to move from B to C is compared with the time required for the meniscus of water to move the same distance. (After McBain: Colloid Science. Boston, D. C. Heath & Company, 1950, p. 143.)

GENERAL REFERENCES

Booij, H. L., and Bungenberg de Jong, H. G., 1956: Biocolloids and Their Interactions. Protoplasmatologia I, 2, (Heilbrunn, L. V., and Weber, F., eds.). Springer-Verlag, Vienna.

De Robertis, E. D. P., Nowinski, W. W., and Saez, F. A., 1960: General Cytology. 3rd Ed. Saunders, Philadelphia.

Derjaguin, B. V., July, 1960: The Force between Molecules. Sci. Am. *203*:47–53.

Frey-Wyssling, A., 1953: Submicroscopic Morphology of Protoplasm. 2nd Ed. Elsevier, Amsterdam.

Frey-Wyssling, A., 1955: Die Submikroskopische Structur des Cytoplasmas. Protoplasmatologia II, A, 2.

Heilbrunn, L. V., 1956: The Dynamics of Living Protoplasm. Academic Press, N. Y.

Heilbrunn, L. V., 1958: The Viscosity of Protoplasm. Protoplasmatologia II, C, 1.

McBain, J. W., 1950: Colloid Science. Heath, Boston.

Mysels, K. J., 1959: Introduction to Colloid Chemistry. Interscience, New York.

Springall, H. D., 1954: The Structural Chemistry of Proteins. Academic Press, New York.

LITERATURE CITED

1. McBain, J. W., 1950: Colloid Science. Heath, Boston.
2. West, E. S., 1942: Physical Chemistry for Students of Biochemistry and Medicine. MacMillan, New York.
3. Loeb, J., 1922: Proteins and the Colloidal Theory of Behavior. McGraw-Hill, New York.
4. Springall, H. O., 1954: Structural Chemistry of Proteins. Academic Press, New York.
5. Frey-Wyssling, A., 1953: Submicroscopic Morphology of Protoplasm. 2nd Ed. Elsevier, Amsterdam.
6. Seifriz, W., 1936: Protoplasm. McGraw-Hill, New York.
7. Heilbrunn, L. V., 1928: Colloid Chemistry of Protoplasm. Protoplasma Monographien *1*. Borntraeger, Berlin.
8. Heilbrunn, L. V., 1956: The Dynamics of Living Protoplasm. Academic Press, New York.
9. Seifriz, W., (ed.), 1942: A Symposium on the Structure of Protoplasm. Iowa State Coll. Press, Ames, Iowa.
10. Bourne, G. H., (ed.), 1951: Cytology and Cell Physiology. Oxford Univ. Press, London. Especially Chapter 2.
11. Frey-Wyssling, A., 1955: Protoplasmatologia (Heilbrunn, L. V., and Weber, F., eds.). *2*:2A, Springer, Vienna.
12. Frey-Wyssling, A., 1952: Deformation and Flow in Biological Systems. N. Holland Publishing Co., Amsterdam.
13. Palade, G. E., and Porter, K. R., 1954: J. Exp. Med. *100*:641.
14. Johnson, F. H., Eyring, H., and Polissar, M., 1954: The Kinetic Basis of Molecular Biology. Wiley, New York.
15. Lloyd, F. F., and Scarth, G. W., 1930: An Elementary Course in General Physiology. Wiley, New York, Chapter 3.
16. Child, C. M., 1941: Patterns and Problems of Development. Univ. of Chicago Press, Chicago, p. 584.
17. Whitaker, D. M., 1940: J. Cell. Comp. Physiol. *15*:173.
18. Heilbrunn, L. V., 1958: The Viscosity of Protoplasm. Protoplasmatologia II, C, 1. (Heilbrunn, L. V., and Weber, F., eds.) Springer-Verlag, Vienna.
19. Booij, H. L., and Bungenberg de Jong, H. G., 1956: Biocolloids and their Interactions. Protoplasmatologia I, 2. Springer-Verlag, Vienna.
20. Derjaguin, B. V., July, 1960: Sci. Am. *203*:47.

THE STRUCTURE AND
FUNCTIONS OF THE
CELL ORGANELLES

Perhaps the greatest contribution to our knowledge of the structure of the cell organelles came from the discovery of electron microscopy on the eve of World War II. This, coupled to the development of the method of fractional centrifugation for separation of the cell organelles and electron microscopic and chemical studies of the organelles so isolated, led to a much greater understanding of their functions, which shall be discussed in this chapter. The nucleus, because of its importance in cell syntheses and heredity, is treated separately in Chapter 6. The cell membrane is also considered separately, in Chapter 14, because its structure is best examined after discussion of the permeation of materials into and out of the cytoplasm.

The Endoplasmic Reticulum

As we have already seen, the cytoplasm of plant and animal cells is organized into a network or endoplasmic reticulum. Electron micrographic studies of ultra-thin sections of a wide variety of cells cut with glass and diamond knives[2] indicate that this network is made of thin membrane-bound cavities which vary considerably in size and shape under different physiological conditions. In some cells the network appears to consist of fine tubules of 50 to 100 mμ in diameter; in others it may be vesicular and of larger diameter (Fig. 5.1, 5.3, 5.4). In some places the enlargements form flattened sacs and vesicles called *cisternae*. Because in the initial studies the network seemed to be confined to the endoplasm of the cell, it was called the *endoplasmic reticulum*. Since that time, in thin sections of cells, the reticulum has been found to extend into the peripheral part of the cell (the ectoplasm), even connecting with the cell membrane. Study of serial sections of cells, which permits reconstruction of structure in three dimensions, has shown the endoplasmic reticulum to have connections also to the Golgi apparatus and the nuclear membrane.

The endoplasmic reticulum is less well developed in some cells than in others;

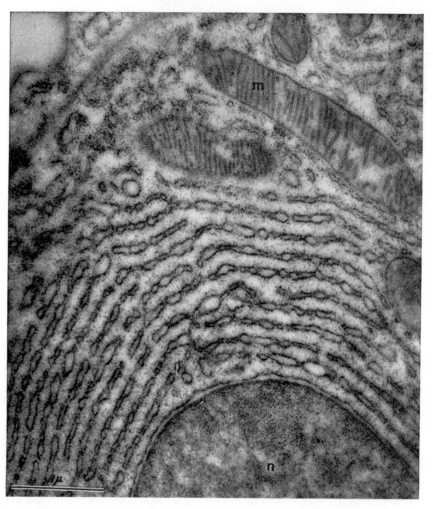

Fig. 5.1. The endoplasmic reticulum as shown in an electron micrograph of a section through an acinar cell of a guinea pig pancreas. Near the nucleus (n) are paired cytoplasmic membranes of the endoplasmic reticulum to which are attached the ribosomes, the electron-dense granules on the surfaces. The mitochondria (m) show much finer lamellae. At the top of the micrograph unattached ribosomes are free in the hyaloplasm. (Courtesy of G. E. Palade from Maximow and Bloom, 1957: Textbook of Histology. W. B. Saunders Company, Philadelphia.)

for example, in spermatocytes few vacuoles are present. In adipose tissue cells, brown fat cells and cells of the adrenal cortex, the endoplasmic reticulum is also simple. In cells engaged in protein synthesis a high degree of development is found. Cells with a basophilic (i.e., staining with basic dyes) cytoplasm generally have a well-developed endoplasmic reticulum. The reticulum is entirely absent from erythrocytes and bacteria.[1]

The membranes of the endoplasmic reticulum divide the ground substance of the cytoplasm into two phases, the (1) *lumen* of the canals and vesicles (matrix) and (2) the *hyaloplasm* outside. The tubules and vesicles have surfaces which may well play a role in enzymic reactions.

FUNCTIONAL ORGANIZATION OF THE CELL

The membranes of the endoplasmic reticulum have been shown to possess osmotic properties, restricting entry or exit of materials into the internal matrix. It is possible that materials are assembled inside the membrane either for synthesis or storage, and that the canalicular sys-tem allows intercommunication between the outside and the inside of the cell, especially if the membranes of the endo-plasmic reticulum are truly continuous at some points with those of the cell mem-brane, as claimed by some workers.[3]

In muscle, it has been suggested that

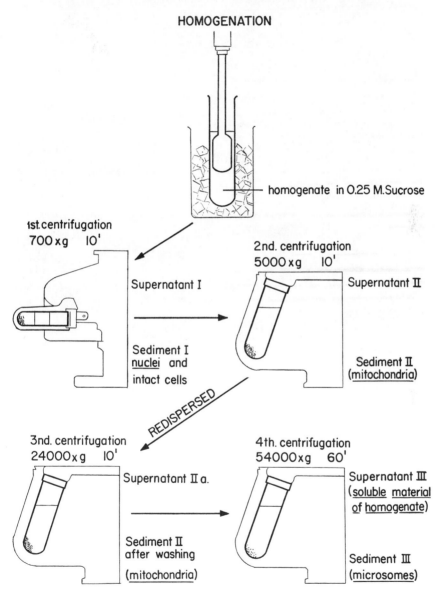

HOMOGENATION

homogenate in 0.25 M.Sucrose

1st.centrifugation
700 xg   10'

Supernatant I

2nd. centrifugation
5000 xg   10'

Supernatant II

Sediment I
nuclei and
intact cells

Sediment II
(mitochondria)

REDISPERSED

3nd. centrifugation
24000xg   10'

Supernatant II a.

4th. centrifugation
54000xg   60'

Supernatant III
(soluble material
of homogenate)

Sediment II
after washing
(mitochondria)

Sediment III
(microsomes)

Fig. 5.2.   Diagram of cell fractionation. (From DeRobertis *et al.*, 1960: General Cytology, 3rd Ed. W. B. Saunders Company, Philadelphia.)

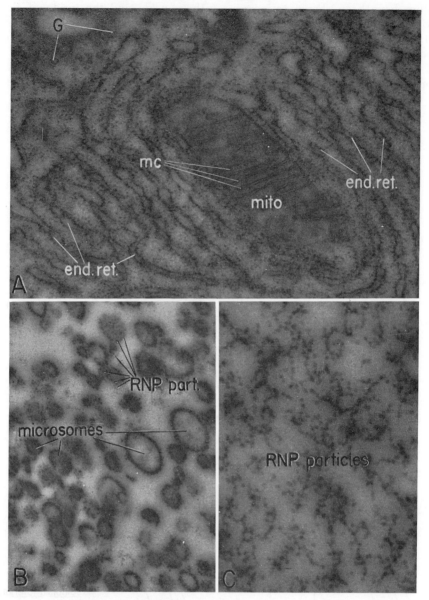

Fig. 5.3. A. Electron micrograph of the basal portion of a pancreatic cell showing the endoplasmic reticulum (end. ret.) with vacuolar enlargements, the largest of which are called cisternae. Mitochondria (mito) show cristae (mc); at G are shown Golgi vacuoles. (× 47,000.)

B. Microsomic fraction isolated from homogenized pancreatic cells. The microsomes are the membranous vesicles to which are attached the ribonucleoprotein granules (RNP part). (× 47,000.)

C. Centrifugate of B after treatment with desoxycholate to solubilize the membranes. (× 8,000.) (Courtesy of G. E. Palade, *in* DeRobertis, Nowinski and Saez, 1960: General Cytology. 3rd Ed. Saunders, Philadelphia.)

FUNCTIONAL ORGANIZATION OF THE CELL

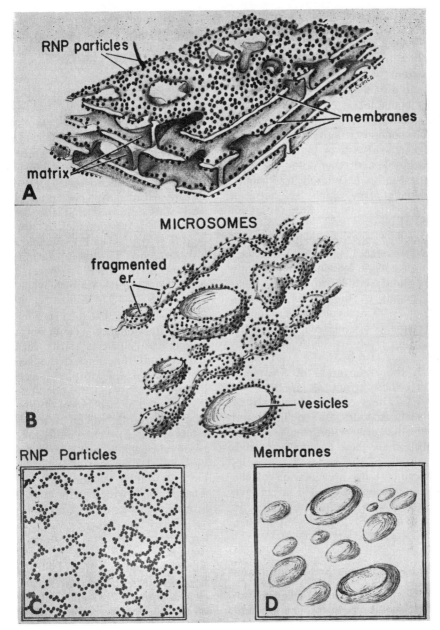

Fig. 5.4. Diagram of the endoplasmic reticulum of a cell and its fragmentation during disruption of the cell by homogenization.

A shows the probable nature of the canicular system of the endoplasmic reticulum, bejewelled with the ribonucleoprotein particles (RNP), and the matrix within.

B, a homogenized cell with fragments of the endoplasmic reticulum forming microsomes.

C, ribonucleoprotein particles (RNP) removed from the membranes of the endoplasmic reticulum by action of desoxycholate.

D, appearance of the membranes without the RNP particles.

(From DeRobertis *et al.*, 1960: General Cytology, 3rd Ed. W. B. Saunders Company, Philadelphia.)

the endoplasmic reticulum is a means for conduction of the excitation from the surface of the cell to the fibrils deep inside. The morphology of the muscle cell is consistent with such a possibility although no direct evidence for this hypothesis is available.

The membranes of the endoplasmic reticulum contain enzymes which may be involved in synthesis of cholesterol and triglycerides[7] and therefore probably play a part in lipid metabolism.

The *hyaloplasm* which lies between the canals of the endoplasmic reticulum appears structureless under the electron microscope except for the presence of scattered ribosomes (see below), although a few workers cite evidence for very fine fibers.[3] Some soluble ribonucleic acid (RNA) occurs in the hyaloplasm (see Chapter 25). The hyaloplasm contains the enzymes concerned with anaerobic metabolism.[3] The hydrolytic (digestive) enzymes may also be in the hyaloplasm, although the discoverers of *lysosomes* think that these structures are the specialized portions of the cytoplasm in which such enzymes are confined, and postulate that only when the lysosomes are ruptured are these enzymes released.

The origin of the endoplasmic reticulum is uncertain. Invagination of the plasma membrane of the cell might give rise to a canicular system, but there is no fully convincing evidence that such a process occurs on a large scale.[3]

Microsomes, Ribosomes and Ergastoplasm

Palade, in 1953, focused attention on the particulate units in the ground substance. These are electron-dense particles of macromolecular (100 to 150 Å) dimensions usually attached to the outer surfaces of the endoplasmic reticulum and its vesicles. In some cells, however, e.g., those in active growth, such particles may also be free within the hyaloplasmic matrix (Fig. 5.1 top). The number of

such particles free and attached varies, being especially large in cells carrying on active syntheses and small in less active cells or in cells which have been starved for a time. Cells from cancerous tissue may show a large number of particles.[4]

It has long been known that basophilic granules existed in the cytoplasm and such names as the *ergastoplasm*[5] of glandular cells or *Nissl bodies* of nerve cells had been given to the basophilic material. These granules also have high electron density. Studies by Caspersson, Brachet and others showed that the basophilic material in the granules is ribonucleic acid (RNA).[6, 7] [The nucleic acid is probably attached to protein, forming ribonucleoprotein (RNP).] These granules containing the RNA are therefore called *ribosomes*.

From another line of experimentation —cell fractionation—came information which has helped to clarify further the nature and function of the basophilic granules. For this purpose a suspension of cells or a tissue is homogenized, that is, subjected to mechanical disintegration, in a sucrose medium or in nonpolar solvents (Fig. 5.2). When centrifuged after removal of the largest bodies, the particles will sediment at different levels according to their size and specific gravity. The particles which settle out after prolonged centrifugation at high speeds are submicroscopic, varying in dimensions from 100 to 1500 Å. Therefore, many of the particles are larger than ribosomes. The pellet obtained by such centrifugation has 50 to 60 per cent of the ribonucleic acid of the cell and constitutes 15 to 20 per cent of the cell mass. Because of their small size the particles making up the pellet have been called *microsomes*. Electron microscope studies of ultra-thin sections of the centrifugal pellet[8] of a homogenized liver cell show that many microsomes are fragments of the vacuolar system of the endoplasmic reticulum, appearing as isolated vesicles, tubules and cisternae with attached ribosomal granules, while homogenized pancreas cells show round vesicles with numerous attached ribosomal granules.[8] The range in size of microsomes obtained by centrifugation is probably the result of different degrees of fragmentation of the endoplasmic reticulum. Some microsomes therefore consist of ribosomal granules alone; others are various-sized chunks of the reticulum or vesicles with attached ribosomal granules.

It is clear from what has been said above that the ribosomes are quite different in chemical constitution from the membranes of the endoplasmic reticulum. The ribosomes appear to be engaged in protein synthesis.[9-12] For example, when C^{14} leucine is provided it is incorporated into protein by the granular component (RNA) of the microsomes. When RNAase is used to remove the RNA, the ribosomes disappear and synthesis of protein is reduced or ceases, depending on how long the RNAase had been permitted to act.[1, 6, 7] The ribosomes are probably not all alike. Five different kinds of RNA have been identified from ribosomes by analysis of purine and pyrimidine bases. At least three varieties of RNA have been identified on the basis of its synthetic activity.[13]

Whether the synthesis occurs in ribosomes at the outer surface of the endoplasmic reticulum to which they are attached, or inside the canals, is not known. Palade has described granules of protein about 250 to 350 mμ in diameter inside the canals. It is not yet possible to say that proteins are synthesized inside the canals and are then extruded and form the larger secretion granules seen outside the reticulum, as for example, in cells of the pancreas which manufacture the enzymic proteins.[14]

Mitochondria

Mitochondria* have been known for many years and, as already stated (Chapter 2), were once defined as the organelles which stain specifically with Janus green B. Many other names[3] have been given to them but in the body of literature which has grown up recently the name *mitochondrion* is rather generally applied to a single unit of these organelles and *mitochondria* for several or for the mass of units, regardless of size or shape. This terminology will be followed here.

Mitochondria (Fig. 5.1, 5.5, 5.6) are usually 0.5 to 1.0 μ in diameter and vary in length up to a maximum of 7 μ. They may be filamentous or granular and may change from one form to another depending upon the physiological conditions of the cells. They may also attach to one another and then dissociate at a later time.[15]

Mitochondria may show active movement, especially in cells undergoing division or in tissue culture cells moving about. In some cells, however, they appear to be stationary.[16] They may aggregate in very characteristic ways about some cell structures, e.g., as rings in the bands of muscle cells. In neurons mitochondria accumulate at the internodes where the passage of the nervous impulse is supposed to occur. In secretory cells they may accumulate basally and in the retina at one end of the rod cells.

The number of mitochondria may be very large. In a liver cell as many as 2500 may be present. The mitochondria account for 30 to 35 per cent of the nitrogen content of the liver cells.

Because the specific gravity of mitochondria is greater than that of the hyaloplasm (the larger fragments having first been removed), ultracentrifugation of

*In an attempt to clarify the terminology some workers have called the whole mass of organoids of this type the *chondriome*, the granular bodies, the *mitochondria* and the long rods, *chondrioconts*— a single body of either type being designated a *chondriosome*.[3]

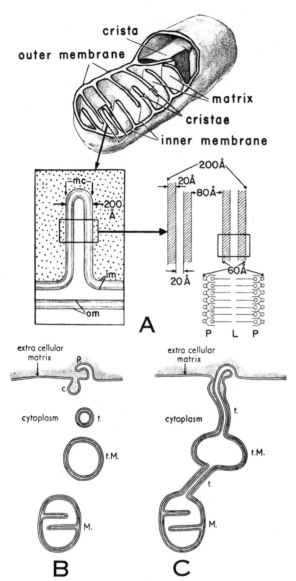

Fig. 5.5. *A*, diagram of the ultrastructure of a mitochondrion. *Above*, tridimensional diagram showing outer and inner membranes and the cristae, which project into the body of the mitochondrion containing the matrix. *Below, left*, at higher magnification the structure of a single crista (mc). *Below, right* (at much higher magnification), molecular structure of a unit membrane of a crista. The outer membrane (om) and inner membrane (im) of the mitochondrion are similar. (P) refers to protein; (L) to lipid. (From DeRobertis *et al.*, 1960: General Cytology, 3rd Ed. W. B. Saunders Company, Philadelphia.)

B and *C*, a way in which mitochondria might originate from cell surfaces. *B* illustrates a segment through a muscle fiber, showing structures observed. In *C*, these structures are related speculatively. The protuberance (p) in *B*, passing into the invagination (c) to form a double-membrane lined tubule which enlarges into a vesicle (t.M.). Ingrowth of the inner membrane of such a vesicle to form cristae could give rise to a mitochondrion (M). (From Robertson, 1959: Biochem. Soc. Symp. 16, p. 38. Cambridge Univ. Press, London.)

mechanically disintegrated cells at 200,000 to 400,000 times gravity will deposit the mitochondria at the bottom of a centrifuge tube. The mitochondria so separated, carefully washed free of other particles, consist of 65 to 70 per cent protein, 25 to 30 per cent lipids and 0.5 per cent RNA. The sulfur content is also relatively high because of consider-

able —SH present as part of the active groups of some of the enzymes.[3]

The mitochondria have a complex organization. The over-all structure is a double-walled rod with rounded ends.[17] The inner wall or membrane of the mitochondrion is 60 to 80 Å thick and in most mitochondria is extended as a sheet called the *crista* (or crest) into the inside almost across the internal cavity. Many such cristae may be present (Fig. 5.5). The cristae greatly extend the laminar surface exposed to the inside cavity of the mitochondrion. The cristae usually run at right angles to the long axis of the rod-shaped mitochondrion. The space in which these infoldings lie is filled with a relatively dense fluid *matrix* in which no structure is seen with the electron microscope, although fibrils have been observed in some cases.[3] The outer membrane of the mitochondrion is about 60 Å thick and is separated from the inner membrane by a clear space.

However, many variations on the fundamental structure are found in different types of cells. In protozoans, in insect flight muscle cells and in adrenal cells the infolding may take the form of tubules rather than lamellar infoldings (Fig. 5.6). Sometimes in mitochondria of different cells of the same species both types of infoldings are found, e.g., in insects tubules occur in flight muscle cells while lamellar cristae occur in the leg muscle cells.[18] In *Chaos chaos*, the multinucleate ameba, the tubules have an interesting zigzag pattern and appear different from those seen in cells of other species.[19] In cells of some species the mitochondria seem to branch.[18]

Under the electron microscope each outer and inner unit membrane of the mitochondrion appears in turn to be made up of three layers, a middle layer (the lighter layer)—less dense to electrons —being sandwiched between two electron-dense (darker) layers. Robertson[20] suggests that the lighter inner layer as seen in section is made up of two rows of lipid molecules with their nonpolar groups in the center, the two denser outer layers consisting of protein molecules as shown diagrammatically in Figure 5.5.

The membrane of the mitochondrion, like the cell membrane, is selectively permeable and the "rules" governing the relative rates of entry of various nonpolar and polar materials into the mitochondria seem to resemble those observed for the cell membrane (see Chapters 11 and 12). The mitochondria, as do entire cells, swell when placed in solutions containing a concentration of solute lower than (hypotonic to) that characteristic of the cell. Isolated mitochondria, placed in hypotonic solutions, may swell to five times their normal volume yet remain intact. The membrane is therefore a sturdy structure. On the basis of rate of entry of some water-soluble materials into mitochondria, it is postulated that there is unfolding of a corrugated lipid layer, although such foldings have not been seen under the electron microscope.[21]

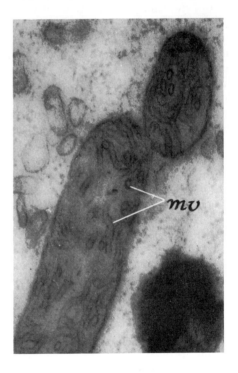

Fig. 5.6. Electron micrograph of a mitochondrion of a ciliate protozoan, *Paramecium multimicronucleatum*, showing the microvilli (mv) which are present here in place of cristae. [From Sedar and Rudzinska, 1956. J. Biophys. and Biochem. Cytology, 2:335 (Plate 109).]

Mitochondria have been fragmented by the use of the surface-active substance deoxycholate (a mild detergent), and many enzymes have been isolated from them. Some of these enzymes are firmly bound to the membranes and have resisted purification. However, it is clear that all of the enzymes which have to do with the complete breakdown (aerobic) of nutrients to CO_2 and water in the cell occur in the mitochondria. Also, the enzymes which enable the cell to transfer the released energy used to form stable high energy compounds (high energy phosphates, such as adenosine triphosphate; see Chapter 17) occur in the mitochondria. Consequently, the mitochondria have been called the "powerhouses of the cell."[22] Here is released most of the energy on the basis of which the work (osmotic, electrical, mechanical, etc.) of the cell is performed, a small amount (about 5 per cent) occurring outside the mitochondria.[23] Therefore, their condition and activity are likely to influence practically all the functions of the cell. The involvement of mitochondria in such functions is more effectively discussed when each of these functions is considered in turn in later chapters.

When some enzyme-catalyzed reactions occur in the test tube, as contrasted to their action in the cell, many co-factors (e.g., salts, vitamin B components, etc.) must be added to get optimal conditions for the reactions, the required concentration of these co-factors being larger than when the enzymes are inside the cell. This and the difficulty of removing some of the enzymes in an active form from the membranes make it appear that the enzymes are probably arranged in some specific steric spatial relationship which facilitates their activity inside the cell.[24] The lamellar structure of the mitochondria is ideally suited for this purpose, providing a large surface area to accommodate the enzymes and a three-dimensional matrix for juxtapositioning enzymes involved in sequences of reactions. The details of these sequences are considered in Chapter 17.

It has already been pointed out that mitochondria make intimate contact with some portions of a cell involved in active work, being present, for example, among the fibrils in muscle cells and at internodes of nerve cells. They have also been described in contact with the ribosomes on the endoplasmic reticulum and it has been suggested that they might serve to supply energy for protein synthesis.[25] If this were true, all dividing cells and secretory cells, which produce proteins, should show more frequent contacts than they actually do.

Mitochondria appear to be partitioned between cells during cell division[26] and in the aftermath of the mitotic division they multiply. Whether this results from fragmentation or splitting,[27] or whether they arise from submicroscopic bodies is not determined. It is known, however, that mitochondria seem to arise from invisible submicroscopic bodies under some circumstances, much as do chloroplasts (see Fig. 5.12). For example, mitochondria may be concentrated at one end of an *Arbacia* egg by centrifugation, and the centrifugal and centripetal halves of the egg may be pulled apart by further centrifugation, leaving one half of the egg free of mitochondria visible with the light microscope.[28] However, minute bodies which may be precursors of mitochondria are seen with the electron microscope. When mitochondria are destroyed by treatment of cells with chemicals and other unfavorable conditions, they also arise from invisible structures. Since microsomes appear in various sizes, it has been suggested that the mitochondria arise from them.[29] However, the difference in chemical composition between the mitochondria and most microsomes suggests that mitochondria may have a different origin. No direct evidence is yet available.[3]

Golgi Apparatus

The Golgi apparatus (Fig. 5.7, 5.8), like the endoplasmic reticulum, is a canalicular system with sacs, but its selective staining by osmium tetroxide and silver salt indicates its uniqueness. It was by these staining reactions (Fig. 2.2) that Golgi first recognized the apparatus, long before any evidence was available for an endoplasmic reticulum.[3] Electron micrographs of thin sections of cells indicate that the canals of the Golgi apparatus are of different shape, usually consisting of

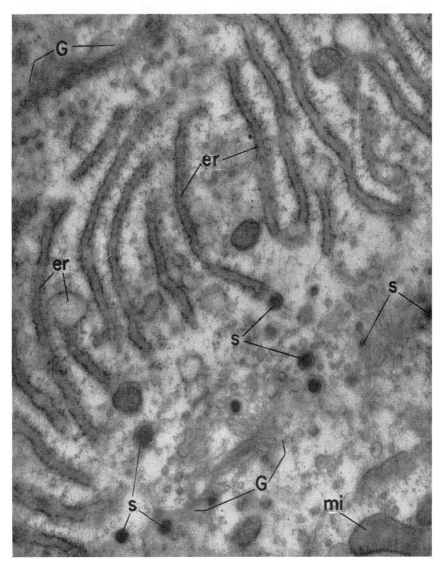

Fig. 5.7. The Golgi complex as shown in an electronmicrograph of a cell of the hypophysis of a toad. The Golgi complex consisting of membranes and vacuoles is indicated as (G), the endoplasmic reticulum as (er), secretory granules as (S) and the mitochondrion as (mi). (From Gerschenfeld and DeRobertis in DeRobertis, *et al.*, 1960: General Cytology. 3rd Ed. W. B. Saunders, Philadelphia.)

THE STRUCTURE AND FUNCTIONS OF THE CELL ORGANELLES　　　　　93

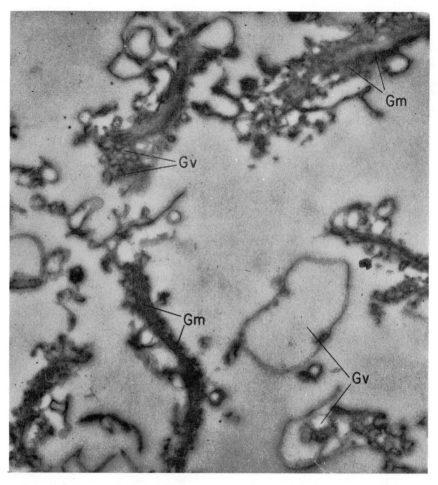

Fig. 5.8. Fragments of the Golgi apparatus after homogenization of cells of the epididymis. Golgi membranes (Gm); Golgi vacuoles (Gv). (Courtesy of A. J. Dalton.)

flattened sacs associated with small vesicles and vacuoles of various sizes. The surface of the canal and sacs is always smooth, in contrast to the frequently encountered rough granule-encrusted outer surfaces of the endoplasmic reticulum.[30]

The Golgi apparatus is organized in basically different ways in different types of cells, but its organization for any one kind of cell is usually the same. Thus it is small in muscle fibers and many other types of cells, but it is large and well developed in secretory cells and in nerves, where it is clearly a reticulate

structure. It occupies different positions in different kinds of cells—being polar and between the nucleus and the periphery in cells of ectodermal origin, circumnuclear in nerve cells and scattered in other parts of the cell in other cases.[31]

The surface of the Golgi apparatus is covered by a double membrane. The two faces, each 20 to 30 Å thick, lie on either side of a space 140 to 160 Å wide, the entire double membrane being about 200 Å across. The two faces of the membrane have different staining properties, only the outer part reacting with silver

FUNCTIONAL ORGANIZATION OF THE CELL

salts and osmic acid. This indicates a difference in chemical composition of the two faces.[30]

The inside of the Golgi apparatus appears to be rather fluid in consistency, judging from experiments with microdissection. Needles inserted into the canals are moved with apparent ease, there being no indication of resistance, although this might be the result of injury. Nevertheless, in centrifugation experiments the entire apparatus moves as a unit, being displaced toward the centripetal pole. This indicates a specific gravity of the Golgi apparatus less than that of the surrounding cytoplasm.

It has been possible to isolate for chemical study the membranes of the Golgi apparatus by fragmenting the cells and fractionally centrifuging them in a sucrose density gradient.[31] The Golgi membranes (Fig. 5.8) are found in the interface between the fluids having a specific gravity of 1.09 and 1.13. The membranes appear to contain much lipid and lipoproteins and a number of enzymes. The membranes are very low in nucleic acid content, at least when they are carefully washed free of contaminating granules (ribosomes). The low enzymatic content of the membranes is somewhat startling compared to the large number of enzymes found in the mitochondria. As a consequence, it is postulated that, perhaps, the Golgi apparatus acts to concentrate and channel various materials rather than to actively synthesize them. Lipid globules and protein granules have been found in the Golgi channels as, for example, in cells of the hypophysis and pancreas.[33]

Attention has been called to the similarities in the many membranes of the cell—on its surface and bounding the endoplasmic reticulum, Golgi apparatus, mitochondria and nuclear surface as shown in Figure 5.9. Although the membranes differ from one another to some extent, as already pointed out in description of the various organelles, their general similarity to the plasma membrane, and the similarity of the connections of the channels of the endoplasmic reticulum to the surface of the cell seen in electron micrographs, point to the plasma membrane as the possible source of all the membranes. Evidence is still scanty and circumstantial.

Lysosomes

This class of particles has centrifugal properties between those of the mitochondria and the ribosomes and has been studied in only a restricted number of cell types.[32] The particles range in size from 0.25 to 0.8 μ. Morphologically, lysosomes are still not adequately characterized. Under the electron microscope they appear dense and finely granular, individual granules having a diameter of about 55 to 80 Å. They are distinguished from other types of particles in the cytoplasm mostly on the basis of their biochemical properties, namely, their content of enzymes which are primarily hydrolytic in function. The lysosomes are covered by a membrane which retains the enzymes. The enzymes may be released from the particles by the action of a wide variety of lytic agents such as action of a blender, freezing and thawing, and detergents, all of which disrupt the membranes.

While these enzymes have also been found in the general supernatant of all disrupted cells tested, this does not argue against the generality of lysosomes. It is quite possible that the lysosomes, normally present in cells, are ruptured by the treatment used to fragment cells, and their enzymes might be liberated in this manner.

Lysosomes of injured or dying cells probably rupture spontaneously, in this way lysing the decrepit cells of an organism. They also enable a developing organism to remove useless structures; for

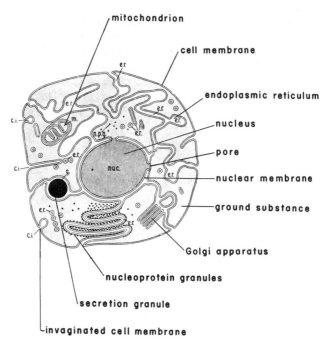

mitochondrion

cell membrane

endoplasmic reticulum

nucleus

pore

nuclear membrane

ground substance

Golgi apparatus

nucleoprotein granules

secretion granule

invaginated cell membrane

Fig. 5.9. Diagram of a section of a hypothetical cell illustrating possible relationships of the cell membrane to various cell organelles. The cell membrane is shown as a pair of dense lines separated by a light interzone. The invaginations of the cell surface (c.i.) are indicated in several areas. Some of these extend for a considerable distance into the cell and they may connect with the endoplasmic reticulum (e.r.). The nuclear membrane is composed of flattened sacs of the endoplasmic reticulum, and by means of the nuclear pores, nucleoplasm (nuc.) is in continuity with cytoplasm. The Golgi apparatus is here shown as a modified component of the endoplasmic reticulum. Secretion granules are shown as dense aggregates contained within membranes of the endoplasmic reticulum. Nucleo-protein granules are shown scattered through the cytoplasm and in some regions attached to the cytoplasmic surfaces of membranes of the endoplasmic reticulum. In some regions the endoplasmic reticulum is shown as tubules, either in longitudinal section or cross-section. It is not clear on present evidence how many of these round membranes are transected tubules and how many, if any, represent isolated vesicles. One mitochondrion is shown with its cristae formed by invagination of its inner membrane. (From Robertson, J. D., 1959: Biochem. Soc. Symp. 16, p. 33. Cambridge University Press, London.)

example, the tail of a metamorphosing tadpole.

Chloroplasts and Other Plastids

Plastids are microscopic organelles found in plant cells such as leucoplasts in which starch granules develop, chloroplasts which contain the chlorophyll (green pigment) of plants, and chromoplasts which contain other pigments (e.g., the red carotenoid in the tomato). Best known are the chloroplasts, since they have been of interest in the extensive studies on photosynthesis.

Chloroplasts are of various shapes—spherical, discoidal or ovoidal and sometimes even disk shaped. The discoidal ones frequently have a colorless center containing a starch granule. Chloroplasts of shade plants are larger than those of sun plants, but the commonest ones are 4 to 6 μ in diameter in higher plants. The number of chloroplasts in a cell ranges from one—as in some algal cells—to a very large number in cells of higher plants.[3] The single chloroplast in an algal cell may form a network, a spiral band, a stellar plate, or a large massive structure occupying much of the cell.

Chloroplasts, isolated by centrifugation of mechanically disrupted spinach leaf cells, contain about 56 per cent protein, 32 per cent lipids and 8 per cent chlorophyll. Among the lipids are carotenoids and xanthophylls, as well as triglycerides, steroids, phospholipids and waxes. The chlorophyll probably exists in combination with some of the protein.[35]

When chloroplasts are microsectioned they appear to be lamellar. The lamellae, being on the border of resolution under the ordinary microscope, can be seen quite plainly with the electron microscope (Fig. 5.10). Some chloroplasts show, in addition to the general lamellation, denser green bodies called *grana* (Fig. 5.10). In grana the lamellae are more numerous and more closely packed than in the remainder of the chloroplast. Therefore, the grana appear to be distinct bodies suspended in the matrix of the chloroplast which has less dense lamellations. The grana are formed by the localized bifurcation of the lamellae containing the chlorophyll, thus doubling the chlorophyll content and increasing the optical opacity (Fig. 5.11). In a given species grana may be present in chloroplasts in some locations and absent from those in others; for example, in maize the mesophyll chloroplasts have grana while sheath parenchyma chloroplasts do not.[33]

When chloroplasts, containing grana, are fragmented by mechanical means or by detergents, the grana may be separated from the rest of the lamellae as individual bodies made up of stacked lamellae. Grana vary in size from 0.3 to 1.7 μ in various species; in spinach chloroplasts they are about 0.6 μ in diameter.

The structure of lamellae and grana has been determined from studies with polarizing and electron microscopes. The latter show that the various layers making up a single membrane of a granum differ in electron density. Chemical analysis of isolated grana indicates that, per unit weight, they contain more lipids of various types and more chlorophyll than the entire chloroplast. Using inferences from all available data, the structure of lamellae and grana has been reconstructed[33] as shown in Figure 5.11.

The importance of this highly organized structure to photosynthesis is discussed in Chapter 20. It need only be mentioned here that when a culture of *Euglena* is kept in the dark the lamellae of the chloroplast and the chlorophyll disappear. Replacing the cells in the light is followed by the simultaneous recovery of chlorophyll content and lamellation.[34]

Chloroplasts swell in hypotonic solutions and shrink in hypertonic solutions, resembling entire cells. The properties of the limiting membrane of the chloroplast appear to be similar to those of the external cell membrane.[35]

Chloroplasts originate from minute submicroscopic ameboid proplastids. When the proplastid reaches a diameter of 1 μ, its inner membrane invaginates to form lamellae which, in light, continue developing and differentiating to the mature condition found in the chloroplast (Fig. 5.12). Because the lamellae develop in the same way as they do in the bodies which give rise to mitochondria, some workers believe the two structures (which are also the major loci of cellular energy conversions) to be closely related.[44]

Vacuoles

A vacuolar system of very small dimensions is found in the endoplasmic reticulum of all cells and in the Golgi apparatus of the cells that possess this organelle. However, both plant and animal cells may have much larger vacuoles. For example, many plant cells have large central sap vacuoles, which contain various salts and organic molecules and which

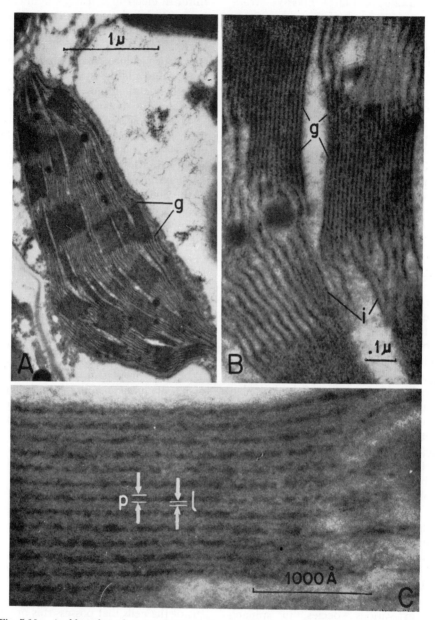

Fig. 5.10. *A*, chloroplast of a mesophyll cell of maize showing numerous grana (g). (× 30,000.) *B*, higher magnification of a portion of a chloroplast showing two grana (g); lamellae (i) between grana. (× 105,000.)

C, higher magnification of a portion of one granum; protein lamellae (p); lipid (l). (× 370,000.) (Courtesy of A. J. Hodge.)

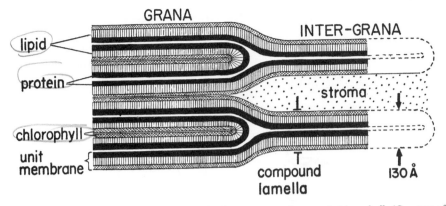

GRANA

INTER-GRANA

lipid

protein

stroma

chlorophyll

unit
membrane

compound
lamella

130 Å

Fig. 5.11. Diagram of probable macromolecular structure of grana of chlorophyll. (Courtesy of A. J. Hodge.)

maintain the turgor or rigidity of the plant cell upon uptake of water. In animal cells (e.g., in protozoans and in cells of lower multicellular invertebrates), various types of vacuoles may occur. Sometimes such cells form minute vacuoles following degenerative changes or by "cell drinking"—the engulfment of some of the surrounding fluid forming *pinosomes* (see pinocytosis, Chapter 13). Food vacuoles (*phagosomes*) are formed by evagination of the cell membrane surrounding food particles and enclosing some of the fluid or by the invaginated membrane of the mouth. Contractile vacuoles may be formed in either of two ways—by coalescence of many spherical vacuoles or by filling with fluid from channels in the cytoplasm.[37] Contractile vacuoles are of special interest because of their dynamic nature and cyclic appearance and disappearance. Minute vacuoles appear as a result of cell drinking in some cells of vertebrates as well.

Little is known of the structure of the membranes surrounding the kinds of vacuoles described above. In general they appear to be similar to the cell membrane (see Chapter 14), but their permeability properties may be quite different.[36, 37]

Cilia, Flagella, etc.

Cilia (and flagella) are not universal cell organelles but are found in many animal and plant cells. Cilia are short motile organelles, generally present in large numbers, covering the surface of ciliated cells. Flagella are similar but larger and less numerous, as well as more complex in their movements. The physiology of ciliary and flagellar motion is dealt with in Chapter 23.

Little structure is visible in cilia and flagella under a light microscope or under a polarizing microscope, unless the cilium is frayed by chemical treatment. However, the detailed structure of cilia and flagella is clearly resolved by the electron microscope. Nine sets of paired peripheral fibers surround two larger centrally placed fibers,[3] as seen in cross section in Fig. 5.13. This pattern, with slight variations, recurs in the tails of various spermatozoa, in cilia from ciliated epithelia, in ciliate and flagellate protozoans and in the cilia of plant cells (e.g., zoospores of algae).

Spermatozoan tails have an additional element, a helical fibril around the periphery of the cilium. Fin-like structures have also been found projecting in the

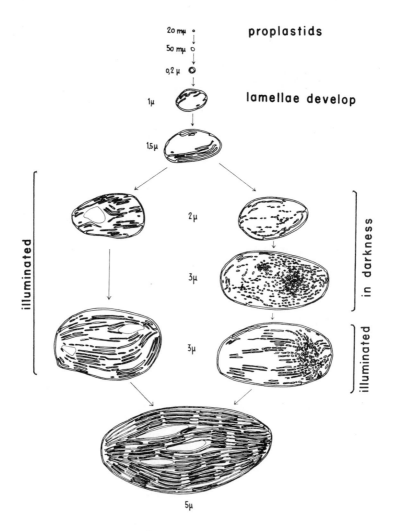

proplastids

20 mμ

50 mμ

0,2 μ

lamellae develop

1μ

1,5μ

illuminated

in darkness

illuminated

2μ

3μ

3μ

5μ

mature chloroplast

Fig. 5.12. The development of a chloroplast from a submicroscopic proplastid. When the illuminated proplastid is 1 μ in diameter, its inner surface membrane begins to invaginate to form lamellae. The proplastids grow and, in light, progressively develop lamellae to form the mature chloroplast (left). In darkness, however, the lamellae break up into vesicles (right), but on reillumination the vesicles unite to reform the lamellae. (From Mühlethaler and Frey-Wyssling, 1959: J. Biophys. Biochem. Cytol., 6:509.)

direction of the central fibers in spermatozoan tails of some species.[38]

The surface of a cilium (or flagellum) is an extension of the cell membrane, the origin of the cilium being below the surface of the cell in a *basal granule* connected to the cilium by the ciliary root. Electron micrographs reveal a basic structural resemblance between cilium, ciliary root and basal granule. Studies on the development of a cilium indicate that it takes origin from the basal granule,[40] the cilium being essentially an extension of the basal granule. The importance of the basal granules to the ciliature has been the subject of extensive studies in the protozoa.[41, 42]

The flagella of bacteria are somewhat different in plan of organization, consisting of single fibers. These fibers are made up of long chains of molecules of a fibrous protein belonging to the keratin-myosin-elastin-fibrinogen group. However, some claims have been made for the presence of three or more spiraling fibers of this type in a few cases.[39]

The Centriole

The centriole is a structure about 0.2 μ in diameter present in all cells but not always visible, except possibly during cell division. At that time it divides, forming the two poles for the division spindle. When asters are present as part of the division figure they radiate from the cen-

triole. The centriole consists of a central body (the centrosome) and a surrounding centrosphere.

Electron micrographs show that the centriole is a short cylinder which has a structural plan essentially like that of the basal granule and the cilium (Fig. 5.14). Centrioles are generally paired, the two cylinders always being oriented at right angles to one another. Each centriole shows nine peripheral paired filaments in a circle, as in cilia.

In spermatozoa the tail filaments are directly in contact with the tubule of one centriole, the other centriole remaining separate. It is suggested that the basal granules of cilia take origin in the centriole.[3]

Retinal Rod Cells

The receptor cells of dim vision in the eye are called *rods*. These cells consist of three parts, an outer segment containing

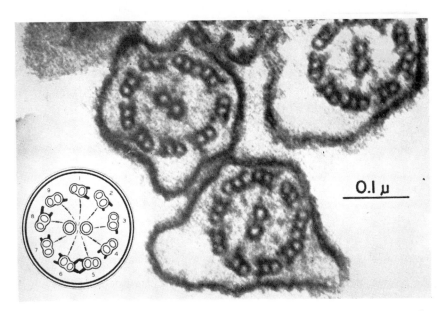

Fig. 5.13. Electron micrograph of a cross section through the tails of three spermatozoans with an arrangement of the filaments similar to that indicated in the inset. The inset shows the radial projections and the arms that each pair of spermatozoan filaments possesses. (Courtesy of B. Afzelius.)

the visual pigment, a thin middle connecting segment and an inner segment containing the nucleus of the cell, mitochondria, etc. (see Chapter 9). Studies on the embryological development and differentiation of a rod from an embryonic cell indicate similarities between the outer segment of the rod and a cilium. Electron micrographs of the middle segment of the rod reveal the unmistakable

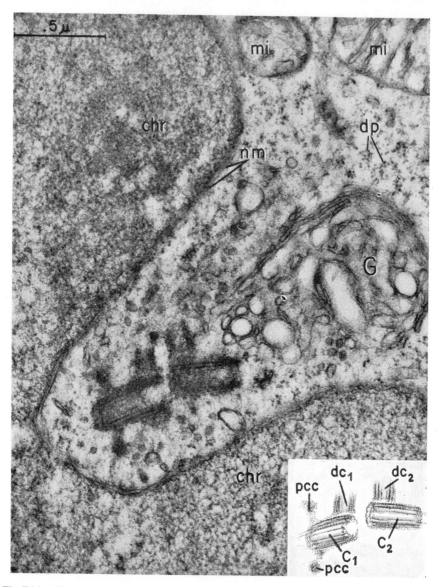

Fig. 5.14. Electronmicrograph of two centrioles of an embryonic cell in chicken spleen. The two centrioles (C_1) and (C_2) are in the invaginated portion of the nuclear membrane near the Golgi complex (G); chromatin with filamentous structure (chr); pericentriolar bodies (pcc); (dc_1) and (dc_2) are daughter centrioles of (C_1) and (C_2), respectively; mitochondria (mi); dense particles (dp). × 60,000. (Courtesy of E. DeHarven and W. Bernhard.)

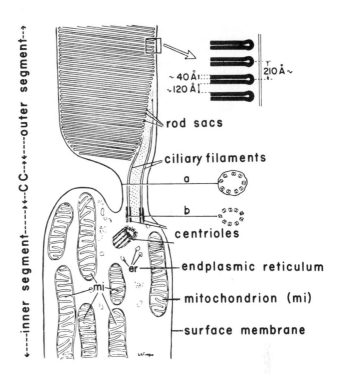

Fig. 5.15. Diagram of a retinal rod cell in the rabbit. The upper portion with the rod sacs is the outer segment, connected to the inner segment (lower portion) by a connecting cilium (CC), in which can be seen the ciliary filaments, lengthwise (vertical) as well as in cross-section at (a). The two centrioles are shown in typical position, approximately at right angles to one another and in cross-section at (b), in which the origin of the ciliary filaments is observed. The inner segment has the organelles of a typical cell—endoplasmic reticulum, mitochondria, etc. (nucleus not shown). (From DeRobertis, Nowinski, and Saez, 1960: General Cytology, 3rd Ed. W. B. Saunders Company, Philadelphia.)

pattern of a cilium—nine paired filaments forming a circle, as shown in Figure 5.15. During histogenesis a cilium-like bulge appears on the embryonic cell. This projection enlarges and becomes filled with vesicles. These vesicles, initially displaced to one side, gradually flatten, enlarge and reorient, coming to occupy the major part of the terminal segment. These form the discs found in the external segment rod of the mature retinal cell. Only the narrow connecting segment then retains the structural pattern of a cilium.[43]

Summary

Knowledge of the organization and activity of the cell organelles is ever widening. It is to be noted, of course, that structural analysis of these organelles is limited by the resolving power of the various microscopes now available, while the study of their functions is beset with technical difficulties. Clearly, further progress depends upon the development of new and ingenious methods for a coordinated study of both structure and functions of the cell organelles.

GENERAL REFERENCES

Albertson, O., 1961: Partition of Cell Particles and Macromolecules. Wiley, New York.

Brachet, J., and Mirsky, A. E., (eds.) 1959–1961: The Cell. Academic Press, New York, 5 vols.

DeRobertis, E. D. P., Nowinski, W. W., and Saez, F. A., 1960: General Cytology. 3rd Ed. Saunders, Philadelphia.

Engstrom, A., and Finean, J. B., 1958: Biological Ultrastructure. Academic Press, New York.

Goodwin, T. W., and Lindberg, O. (eds.), 1961: Biological Structure and Function. Academic Press, New York.

Hayashi, T. (ed.), 1959: Subcellular Particles, Ronald Press, New York.

Heilbrunn, L. V., and Weber, F. (eds.): Protoplasmatologia, Handbuch der Protoplasmaforschung, Springer-Verlag, Vienna.

International Review of Cytology

Journal of Cell Biology, formerly Journal of Biophysical and Biochemical Cytology.

Journal of Ultrastructure Research

Onclay, J. L. (ed.), 1959: Biophysical Science: A Study Program. Wiley, New York.

Picken, L., 1960: The Organization of Cells, Clarendon, Oxford.

Szent Gyorgyi, A., 1960: An Introduction to a Submolecular Biology. Academic Press, New York.

Waddington, C. (ed.), 1959: Biological Organization, Cellular and Subcellular. Symposium Edinburgh Univ., Pergamon Press, New York.

LITERATURE CITED

1. Porter, K. R., Claude, A., and Fullman, E. F., 1945: J. Exp. Med. 81:233.
2. Fernández-Morán, H., 1956: J. Biophys. Biochem. Cyt. suppl. 2:28.
3. DeRobertis, E. D. P., Nowinski, W. W., and Saez, F. A., 1960: General Cytology. 3rd Ed. Saunders, Philadelphia.
4. Palade, G. E., 1955: J. Biophys. Biochem. Cyt. 1:567.
5. Haguenau, F., 1958: Internat. Rev. Cyt. 7:425.
6. Caspersson, T. O., 1950: Cell Growth and Cell Function, Norton, New York.
7. Brachet, J., 1957: Biochemical Cytology. Academic Press, New York.
8. Slautterback, D. B., 1953: Exp. Cell Res. 5:173.
9. Littlefield, J. W., and Keller, E. B., 1957: J. Biol. Chem. 224:13.
10. Zamecnik, P. C., Stephenson, M. C., and Hecht, L. T., 1958: Proc. Nat. Acad. Sci. U. S. 44:73.
11. Zamecnik, P. C., March 1958: Sci. Am. 198:118.
12. The Biophysical Society: First Symposium, Cambridge, Mass. Feb. 5–8, 1958: Pergamon Press, New York.
13. Siekevitz, P., and Palade, G. E., 1959: J. Biophys. Biochem. Cyt. 5:1.
14. Palade, G. E., 1956: J. Biophys. Biochem. Cyt. 2:417.
15. Bennett, H. S., 1956: J. Biophys. Biochem. Cyt., suppl. 2:99.
16. Tobioka, M., and Biesele, J. J., 1956: J. Biophys. Biochem. Cyt. suppl. 2:319.
17. Palade, G. E., 1952: Anat. Rec. 114:427.
18. Roullier, C., 1960: Internat. Rev. Cyt. 9:227.
19. Pappas, G. D., and Brandt, P. W., 1959: J. Biophys. Biochem. Cyt. 6:85.
20. Robertson, J. D., 1959: Biochem. Soc. Symp. 16:3.
21. Tadeschi, H., 1959: J. Biophys. Biochem. Cyt. 6:241.
22. Siekevitz, P., July 1957: Sci. Am. 197:131.
23. Watson, M. L., and Siekevitz, P., 1956: J. Biophys. Biochem. Cyt. 2:653.
24. Green, D. E., and Hatef, Y., 1961: Science 133:13.
25. Copeland, D. E., and Dalton, A. J., 1959: J. Biophys. Biochem. Cyt. 5:393.
26. Reverberi, G., 1958: Acta Embryol. Exp. 2:78.
27. Oberling, C., 1959: Internat. Rev. Cyt. 8:1.
28. Harvey, E. B., 1951: Ann. New York Acad. Sci. 51:1336.
29. Lindberg, O., and Ernster, L., 1954: Chemistry and Physiology of Mitochondria and Microsomes, Photoplasmatologia (Heilbrunn, L. V., and Weber, F., eds.). Springer-Verlag, Vienna.
30. Pollister, A. W., and Pollister, P. F., 1957: Internat. Rev. Cyt. 6:85.
31. Kuff, E. L., and Dalton, A. L., 1959: Subcellular Particles (Hayashi, T., ed.). Ronald Press, New York, p. 114.
32. deDuve, C., 1959: Subcellular Particles (Hayashi, T., ed.). Ronald Press, New York, p. 128.
33. Hodge, A. J., McLean, J. D., and Mercer, F. V., 1955: J. Biophys. Biochem. Cyt. 1:605.
34. Wolken, J. J., and Palade, G. E., 1953: Ann. New York Acad. Sci. 56:873.
35. Mercer, F. V., Hodge, A. J., Hope, A. N., and McLean, J. D., 1955: Austral. J. Biol. Sci. 8:1.
36. Blinks, L. R., 1955: in: Electrochemistry in Biology and Medicine (Shedlovsky, T., ed.), Wiley, New York, p. 187.
37. Kitching, J. A., 1956: Contractile Vacuoles, D3a, Food Vacuoles, D3b. Protoplasmatologia, Springer-Verlag, Vienna.
38. Fawcett, D. W., and Porter, K. R., 1954: J. Morph. 94:221.
39. Mudd, S., 1954: Ann. Rev. Microbiol. 8:1.
40. Porter, K. R., 1957: Harvey Lectures 51:175.
41. Lwoff, A., 1950: Problems of Morphogenesis in the Ciliates. Wiley, New York.
42. Weisz, P., 1954: Quart. Rev. Biol. 29:207.
43. DeRobertis, R., 1956: J. Biophys. Biochem. Cyt. suppl. 2:209.
44. Muhlenthaler, K., and Frey-Wyssling, A., 1959: J. Biophys. Biochem. Cyt. 6:509.

CHAPTER

6

THE CHEMICAL ORGANIZATION
AND FUNCTION OF
THE CELL NUCLEUS

Ever since its discovery by Robert Brown in 1835, the nucleus has been recognized as the most important organelle of the cell. Today it is understood to be the major seat of heredity and of the control over all synthetic reactions in the cell. Investigators from various disciplines—cytology, genetics, virology, physical chemistry and biochemistry—have converged in attacking problems of the cell nucleus, and a large volume of literature has been amassed. While it is impossible to cover here all studies on the nucleus, some of the most basic features of this research are considered in this chapter.

Relation between Nucleus and Cytoplasm

There exists a well-knit and delicately balanced relationship between the nucleus and the cytoplasm of a cell. This can be seen best if we study the cell after the nucleus is removed. A cell may be enucleated in any one of a number of ways—for example, by removing the nucleus from a cell with a hooked needle or a micropipette, or by centrifuging a cell until it breaks into two pieces, one with and one without a nucleus. An even simpler operation for this purpose, which may be done free hand with a glass needle, is to cut an *Amoeba proteus* into two portions, one with and one without the nucleus (see Fig. 6.1). The enucleate half continues moving for a while but soon rounds up

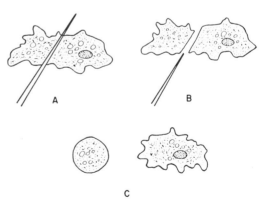

Fig. 6.1. Fate of nucleate and enucleate pieces of an ameba.

and becomes inactive and unresponsive to its environment, although chemical activity continues. Thus it will digest food previously ingested but will not take in any more, and it will continue to absorb and bind radioactive phosphorus when tested,[25] but at a lesser and continually decreasing rate, until the cell dies. The nuclear portion, in contrast, reacts normally, eats, grows and in time divides.[1]

When the nucleus of an ameba is removed, the ameba behaves as in the experiment above. However, its activities are restored to normal when it is renucleated. Since the nucleus deteriorates even if kept briefly outside the cytoplasm, renucleation is usually done by placing donor and recipient amebas of the same species close together and with the hooked needle quickly pulling the nucleus out of one and inserting it into the other. In this manner an ameba may be renucleated successfully even several days after its enucleation.

These experiments indicate that the cytoplasm of a cell cannot survive alone and that its activities are in some manner initiated and regulated by the nucleus.[1]

Enucleation and renucleation of amphibian eggs have also been successfully accomplished in a similar manner. In fact, a nucleus taken from one of the cells of the blastula or gastrula stage gives rise to a normal embryo if it is inserted into an enucleated and unfertilized egg of the same species. It is interesting to note here that a nucleus from an older gastrula, however, in some species is no longer effective, indicating that the nucleus has lost its totipotency between early and late gastrula stages.[2] However, in some species as in the larva of the toad, *Xenopus*, differentiation does not become irreversible until the cell, from which the nucleus is taken, is about to become an organ.[42]

If the nucleus of one species of ameba is introduced into an enucleated specimen of a different, but closely related species, the nucleus and cytoplasm are generally not quite compatible, and while the newly restored ameba may continue to move about, eat and divide, its progeny usually die. However, if the new strain continues to multiply for a while, its descendants take on a character intermediate between the two strains from which they sprang,[1] which indicates that the nucleus seems to influence cytoplasmic characteristics.

Similar nuclear transfers have been made between species of *Acetabularia*, a sizable single-celled alga which has a foot, a stalk and a cap (see Fig. 6.2). The cap has a characteristic shape for each species, and if removed it is easily regenerated. When a nucleus from an individual of one species of *Acetabularia* is transferred to an enucleate individual of a different species, from which the cap has also been removed, the cap when regenerated is intermediate in form between the two species. If more than one nucleus is introduced from the donor species, the cap which regenerates has more resemblance to that of the donor than to that of the recipient species. The nucleus therefore exerts quantitative morphogenetic influence.[3]

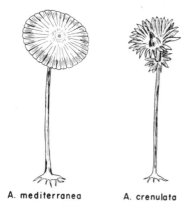

A. mediterranea   A. crenulata

Fig. 6.2. Two species of *Acetabularia* used in experiments. The caps are about a centimeter in diameter, and the stalks are usually 2 to 6 centimeters in length. (After Hammerling: Internat. Rev. Cyt., 2:475, 1953.)

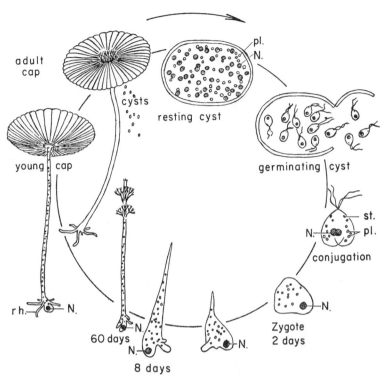

Fig. 6.3. Life cycle of *Acetabularia mediterranea*. (N) refers to nucleus, (rh) to rhizoid, (st.) to stigma on the isogametes and (pl) to the plastids. (From Brachet, 1957: Biochemical Cytology, Academic Press, N. Y.)

The nucleus of *Acetabularia* does not divide until just before gamete formation, at the end of its life cycle (Fig. 6.3). Division of a nucleus from a "young" cell can be induced, however, much before its time, if the nucleus of such a cell is introduced into an enucleated "old" cell, of the same species, which is about to form gametes. Apparently, in the chain of reactions the cytoplasm gradually develops substances which induce nuclear division. A two-way influence seems to exist—nucleus upon cytoplasm and cytoplasm upon nucleus.[3]

An unfertilized sea urchin egg, enucleated by being cut or centrifuged, may be stimulated to divide, without fertilization, by brief immersion in hypertonic solutions. In the total absence of a nucleus it undergoes divisions to form a multicellular embryonic form which later degenerates (see Fig. 6.4). Apparently, division of cytoplasm, for a limited time, can continue without the presence of a nucleus,[4] but a nucleus is necessary for continued and normal functioning and differentiation of the cytoplasm of a cell.

On the other hand, a nucleus without its cytoplasm is helpless. If it is removed from the cytoplasm of an ameba and kept in physiological balanced salt solution it dies within a few hours. Even the thin layer of cytoplasm covering the nucleus of a sperm enables the sperm to live, to take up and use nutrients from its medium.[5] Sperm of choice stock animals are thus kept alive at low temperatures for long periods and used for artificial insemination. Nucleus and cytoplasm of the living cell, therefore, constitute a

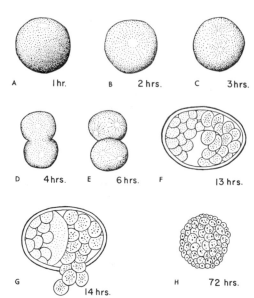

A I hr. B 2 hrs. C 3hrs.

D 4 hrs. E 6 hrs. F 13 hrs.

G 14 hrs. H 72 hrs.

Fig. 6.4. Development of an enucleated *Arbacia* egg, artificially stimulated to divide. Note aster formation in figures B and C, division in D and E, and the many cells which developed later. No further division occurred after the stage shown in figure H, although the cells vacuolated and lived for a month. (After Harvey: Biol. Bull., 71:101, 1936.)

reciprocal system in which each requires the other.

It is often stated that bacteria and blue-green algae have no nuclei. It is noted, however, that during division in bacteria and blue-green algae, chromosome-like bodies are partitioned equally between the daughter cells. Genetic evidence also indicates that chromosomes and genes of bacteria behave like those in true cells, even to the extent of mutation and exchange of genes during sexual reproduction.[6, 7] The main difference, therefore, is the absence of a nuclear membrane in resting bacteria and the presence of such a membrane in the resting nuclei of cells of higher organisms.

The cytology of the nucleus and the sequence of events which almost miraculously takes place, step by step, in the nucleus during cell division, have been the subject of thorough study. The series

of events by which haploid gametes form a diploid zygote which divides by mitosis to form the cells of the adult, and during reproduction divides by meiosis once again to form the haploid gametes, and the correlations between chromosomal behavior and the distribution of genes are familiar to everyone. Since the nuclear cycle is outlined in most elementary textbooks of biology, further consideration of it is omitted here. Textbooks of cytology should be consulted for details of these important studies.[8]

Chemical Composition of the Nucleus—Histochemistry

Under the microscope, the resting nucleus of a cell usually shows a nucleolus and the chromosomal chromatin, sometimes in threads, suspended in the nuclear sap, the entire mass being surrounded by a double nuclear membrane. The inner nuclear membrane (about 90 Å thick) is closely applied to the nuclear material while the outer membrane (about 90 Å thick) appears to be a membrane of the endoplasmic reticulum applied to the nucleus, a space of about 140 Å separating the two structures. The nuclear membrane is seen in the electron micrograph of Figure 6.5 and its permeability properties are discussed in Chapter 14.

The electron micrograph of an intermitotic nucleus shown in Figure 6.6 shows a rather irregular accumulation of granular material, probably representing DNA and protein. Some workers have reported minute fibrils, presumably in the chromosomes, but upon this there is no general agreement.

The chemistry of nuclei can be studied readily because, like other cell organelles, the nucleus can now be separated from other cell constituents by fractional centrifugation. The cells are first disrupted, by means of various methods such as laking (for red cells) or freezing and thawing, or applying lytic agents such as

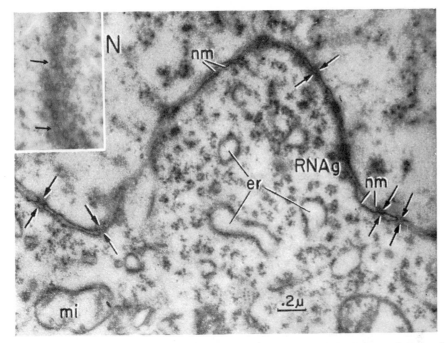

Fig. 6.5. Electron micrograph of a neuroblast nuclear membrane (nm) (and between the pairs of opposed arrows where several pores show up); (er) endoplasmic reticulum; (RNAg) granules of RNA; (N) nucleus; (mi) mitochondria. × 48,000. *Upper left,* Tangential view of the nuclear membrane of a nerve cell showing the pores (arrows). (From DeRobertis, *et al.,* 1960. General Cytology, 3rd Ed.)

saponin. The fragmented cells are placed in solutions of sucrose and $CaCl_2$ or a weak acid, such as citric acid, and differentially centrifuged and washed with the solution.[9] Unfortunately, the procedures cause a loss of some of the material from the nucleus, but addition of appropriate salts and adjustment of concentration, salts and pH of the medium minimize such losses. Isolated nuclei in buffered sucrose are found to retain some metabolic ability and can incorporate radioactive precursors into their nucleic acids and proteins.[12]

Nuclei have also been isolated from frozen, dried tissues in nonaqueous solvents of graded density. Such nuclei retain all their water and acid-soluble constituents and nuclear proteins (see Reference 9). With carefully designed procedures this is also possible with aqueous solvents, e.g., buffered sucrose.[14] The two types of analysis thus complement each other.

Nuclear mass varies from one cell type to another and from one species to another. For example, the nucleus of a mammalian liver cell constitutes 10 to 18 per cent of the cell mass, whereas that of a thymus cell of the same individual may represent 60 per cent of the cell mass.

Certain chemical constituents are almost always present in nuclei of all cells, such as: DNA (deoxyribonucleic acid), RNA (ribonucleic acid), lipids, a basic protein (either histone or protamine), more complex proteins including enzymes, other phosphorus-containing organic compounds and various inorganic compounds, mostly salts.[10]

The chemistry of the nucleus is also studied by histochemical techniques. The

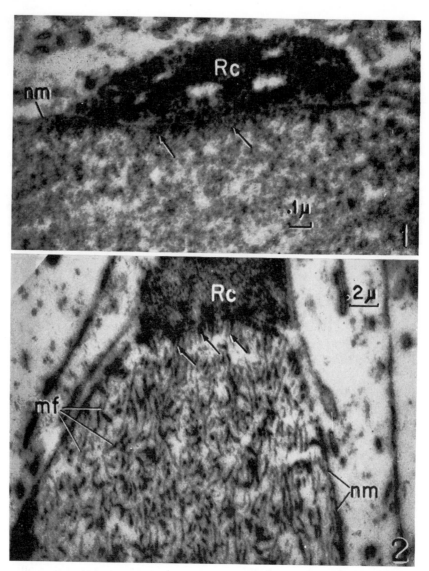

Fig. 6.6. *1*, electron micrograph of one region in the nucleus of a young locust spermatid. Region near the ring centriole (Rc); nuclear membrane (nm). The nucleus has a fine, fibrillar, dispersed appearance. The microfibrils, indicated by the arrows, are oriented in the vicinity of the centriole. (× 60,000.) *2*, later stage in the development of the spermatid. The microfibrils (mf) are now thicker and generally oriented in the axis of the spermatid head. (× 40,000.) (From DeRobertis, 1955.)

aim of cytochemistry is to determine not only the kinds of various materials present in the cell, but also their distribution in the differentiated structures of the cell and the amount present in each structure. To some extent differential centrifugation

of the cell particulates and their chemical analysis permits some localization of chemicals. However, cytochemical methods not only serve to check these but also to give additional information, especially as to detailed localization of the materials in a structure, providing the procedures do not destroy the materials or cause them to diffuse to new locations. The two methods—cytochemical and biochemical—are especially effective when used in conjunction with one another.

The location of some chemical constituents of the nucleus, e.g., the nucleic acids, can also be determined by ultraviolet photomicrography which permits the amount of nucleic acid to be estimated as well.[15] This method is based on the fact that no other protoplasmic constituents absorb ultraviolet light significantly at the absorption peak of nucleic acid at 2600 Å (see Chapter 3, Fig. 3.17); therefore, the density of photomicrographs at this wavelength measures the relative content of nucleic acid in the cell. The measurements of nucleic acid in cells may be rendered quantitative by comparison with the optical density of a known sample of nucleic acid in solution. The measuring equipment is illustrated in Figure 6.7. A graph showing the absorption spectra for nucleus and cytoplasm appears in Figure 6.8. Because the method involves inherent approximations

and errors, the measurements cannot be expected to give precision as to absolute amounts of nucleic acids present.

Some staining reactions may also be used as chemical analyses. For example, by the Feulgen reaction, sections of material, fixed in the usual manner, are hydrolyzed by HCl to liberate the aldehyde group of the pentose sugar of DNA and are then treated with leucofuchsin (basic fuchsin in sulfurous acid). The reaction between leucofuchsin and the aldehyde in deoxyribose results in the appearance of a purplish-blue color. The depth of color can be measured under a microscope spectrophotometrically and used for quantitative determinations. DNA is Feulgen positive and RNA is Feulgen negative.[10, 17] Polymerized DNA may also be stained specifically with methyl green, which does not stain the RNA in cells.[10, 13] However, methyl green will not stain depolymerized DNA even though it is still present in its original location in the cell. Acridine orange differentially stains single-stranded DNA (present in some viruses), double-stranded DNA and RNA.[53]

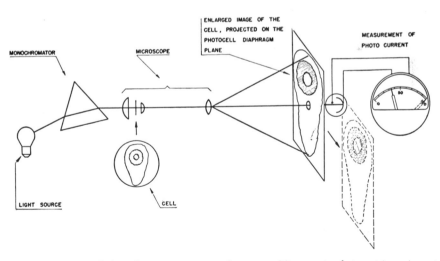

Fig. 6.7. Principle of photoelectric microspectrophotometry. Microspectrophotometric equipment of Caspersson (diagrammatic). (From Caspersson: Cell Growth and Cell Function. New York, W. W. Norton & Company, 1950, p. 21.)

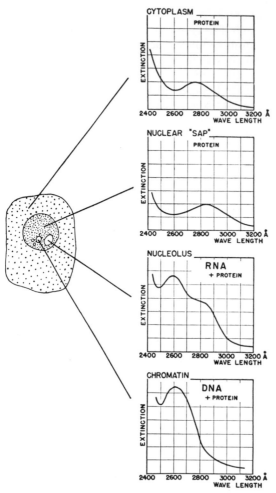

Fig. 6.8. Absorption spectra of constituents of nucleus and cytoplasm measured on a section of a cell. (Adapted from Caspersson: Cell Growth and Cell Function. New York, W. W. Norton & Company, 1950, p. 79.)

Studies of nuclear sap, removed by microdissection from amphibian oocytes, showed it to contain proteins and salts in solution and no detectable nucleic acid.[10]

Studies of the nucleolus[59] under the electron microscope show no outer limiting membrane and some fine coiled material in an amorphous background.[45] The nucleolus contains most of the RNA of a resting nucleus. Thus, the nucleolus stains deeply with basic dyes, but after

action of ribonuclease this reaction is lost in the central part of the nucleolus. The outer envelope of the nucleolus, not affected by ribonuclease, has been shown to contain a small amount of DNA. Isolated nucleoli, which may have lost some of their constituents during the procedure, have been found to have 3 to 5 per cent RNA. Some of the proteins of the nucleolus are of the complex type, for example, enzymes.[8, 10] Relatively few enzymes have been identified in the nucleolus, e.g., enzymes having to do with RNA synthesis and the manufacture of a coenzyme (diphosphopyridine nucleotide, see Chapter 17). As shown by radioautography, tagged molecules are incorporated readily into protein and RNA in the nucleolus, suggesting that the nucleolus plays a role in the synthesis or accumulation of these compounds.[8, 10] The nucleolus becomes enlarged during periods of synthetic activity in cells and is less well developed in quiescent stages.

The nuclear enzymes have been studied but controversial findings have been reported, some workers claiming a large number of different types of enzymes to be present in their nuclear preparations, others claiming far fewer. These differences in findings probably result from differences in technique. If cytoplasmic granules are not carefully removed from the surface of the nucleus, enzymes of the granules will be added to those of the nucleus. On the other hand, very careful washing without proper precautions may remove nuclear enzymes normally present. There now seems to be general agreement that the nucleus lacks some of the enzymes for aerobic metabolism, such as are found in the mitochondria (see Chapter 5), but that it contains enzymes for anaerobic metabolism and those enzymes which are involved in the formation of high-energy phosphates, transferring the energy liberated, for example, during anaerobic metabolism. It also contains enzymes for protein synthesis, as well as coenzyme synthesis (diphosphopyridine nucleotide, see Chapter 17). The latter two syntheses require the presence of oxygen.

The nucleus contains some lipids such as might be expected in any cellular materials and in a membrane. The lipids of the nucleus do not seem to have been the subject of any extensive and pointed study, nor do there seem to be any lipids unique to the nucleus.

The most characteristic constituents of the nucleus are the nucleic acids, DNA and RNA. The amount of DNA in salmon sperm heads (being mostly nucleus) may constitute 48.5 per cent of the dry, fat-free material. Generally, DNA constitutes considerably less than that percentage of the dry weight of the nucleus. The absolute amount of this nucleic acid varies from species to species, but for a given species it is constant for a haploid set of chromosomes.[10] When diploid, tetraploid and octaploid cells are present as in the liver, the absolute amount of DNA per cell varies accordingly. DNA, as we have seen, is Feulgen positive, and its concentration can also be measured by the depth of color thus obtained. While the total amount of DNA in a cell varies by as much as 15 per cent as determined by quantitative analysis, the larger variations reported by cytologists on the basis of staining reactions are probably erroneous. DNA is attached to residual proteins which vary extensively, especially with nutritional conditions, falling markedly on starvation. Since staining often depends upon the DNA-protein complex, an error in estimation by this means could easily be introduced.[13]

In still another test for DNA, enzymes specific for the hydrolysis of DNA or RNA have been used. For example, treatment of cells with deoxyribonuclease removes the DNA, and a Feulgen test on the residue is negative.[10, 16] Ribonuclease, on the other hand, removes the RNA and does not affect Feulgen-positive material.

The two treatments thus complement each other.

Ribonucleic acid may be selectively stained with pyronin.[17] The amount of RNA may then be estimated from the depth of color by spectrophotometric methods in the same way as DNA. Treatment of a section of tissue with ribonuclease before staining removes the pyronin-reacting material (RNA) from a cell and the test is then negative.

Since DNA and RNA can be selectively stained by the above method in a fixed cell or tissue, their distribution in the cell can be ascertained. DNA is apparently present chiefly in bands on the metaphase chromosome, most clearly seen in the multiple (polytene) chromosomes of the salivary gland cells of flies (Fig. 6.9). In interphase nuclei the DNA is visible primarily in the granules of the nucleolus, which gives a positive reaction with the Feulgen reagents.

RNA is present in large amounts in the nucleolus. It is also found around the chromosomes. However, it will be recalled (see Chapter 5) that the major part of the RNA of the cell occurs in the ribosomes, both those free and those attached to the endoplasmic reticulum. RNA is also present in a diffuse form (in solution) in the hyaloplasm and a small amount is found in the mitochondria.[14]

By cytochemical methods all the RNA molecules appear to be alike. Chemical methods, however, detect differences. The primary difference that is stressed in most reports is a difference in base ratios. It will be recalled (Chapter 3) that RNA contains the nucleotides of the purines, adenine and guanine, and of the pyrimidines, cytosine and uracil (Table 3.9). In a given RNA the ratios of these bases is always constant. However, the RNAs from the ribosomes, the nucleolus, the chromosomes and the soluble RNA separated from one another by fractional centrifugation all show different base ratios from one another, indicating a different

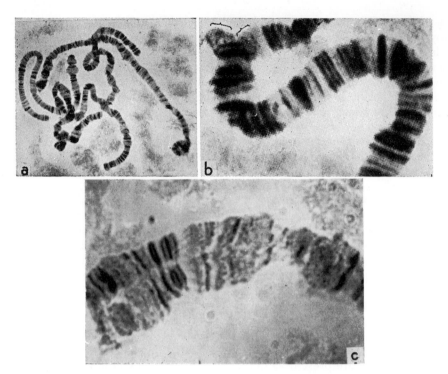

Fig. 6.9. Polytene chromosomes of *Drosophila melanogaster. a.* View of the chromosomes of one nucleus, showing the dark bands and the clear interbands. Preparation by crushing in acetocarmine. *b.* Part of the sex chromosome X, as it is observed with ultraviolet light; photograph taken at 2750 Å (after Schultz, 1941). *c.* Absence of pairing in chromosome III of a female hybrid of *Drosophila pananaensis* X. (From DeRobertis *et al.,* 1960. General Cytology, Saunders, Philadelphia, p. 272. Courtesy of Dr. Rosina de Barros.)

chemical composition. There are, presumably, other differences in properties less readily detectable at the present time, such as molecular weight and affinities for other molecules.[18, 19]

The chemistry of the chromosomes has also been extensively studied. Chromosome-like threads can be separated from nuclei fragmented in a Waring Blendor and their chemical composition can be determined. By this means "isolated chromosomes" from lymphocytes, from fish and fowl erythrocytes and from thymus cells and liver cells have been studied. Lymphocyte chromosomes in neutral, molar sodium chloride disperse to form a viscous suspension which, after centrifugation at 18,000 to 19,000 rpm for 1 to 2 hours, separates into a highly viscous, somewhat opalescent supernatant and a tightly packed sediment. The fluid consists of practically all of the DNA and of nucleohistone which constitutes 90 to 92 per cent of the mass of the chromosome. Pouring the fluid into water yields a fibrous precipitate containing 45 per cent DNA and 55 per cent histone.[10, 13, 14]

The sediment, which does not dissolve in sodium chloride, consists of a mass of coiled threads resembling chromosomes but somewhat smaller. They have been called residual chromosomes and account for about 8 to 10 per cent of the mass of the original chromosomes and show longitudinal differentiations and variations in diameter corresponding to similar regions on the original chromosomes. The nucleic acid content of the residual chromosomes is about 4 per cent of the total originally in the chromosome and is chiefly RNA, there being only a small amount of DNA left. Removal of the nucleic acid with hot trichloracetic acid leaves a residual protein, of complex nature, containing aromatic amino acids and different from histone and protamine.[14]

The chromosome thus appears to be made up of residual protein and DNA, to which is attached the histone (in all somatic cells) or the protamine (in sperms). The histone or protamine can be removed from isolated metaphase chromosomes without altering the morphology of the latter. Only when the DNA is removed from the residual protein, or the protein removed from the DNA, is the chromosome structure destroyed. Neither the combination nor the configuration can be restored by mixing the two once they have been separated. Residual protein, therefore, shares in some way with DNA the architectural framework of the chromosomes.[13]

The relative proportions of these constituents varies in chromosomes from cells of different tissues and for cells from the same tissue in different species. For example, only 45 per cent of the mammalian liver cell chromosome consists of nucleohistone, 12 per cent of the nucleic acid is RNA and 39 per cent consists of residual protein.[14]

The Molecular Structure of the Chromosome

In the huge chromosomes of the salivary gland cells of *Drosophila* larvae, in which the hereditary units have multiplied without accompanying division of the chromosome, the gene-containing regions are large, and it is possible to show, by staining reactions, that they are marked by bands of deoxyribonucleic acid.[15] These bands may be removed by action of the enzyme deoxyribonuclease,

yet a matrix remains, a matrix shown by color tests to be composed of protein. The protein matrix may also be removed selectively from these chromosomes by the action of pepsin and trypsin. If the nucleic acid is first rendered insoluble by the action of lanthanum salts and then the protein of the chromosomes is digested by such proteolytic enzymes as pepsin or trypsin, the DNA remains as a series of disks.[15] In the chromosome, therefore, nucleic acid is seemingly applied to a core, or matrix, of protein (see Fig. 6.9). Similar experiments have also been performed with chromosomes from other animals, and similar results have been obtained.[15]

The organization of the chromosome has been conceived to be either (1) a sort of protein backbone to which disks or masses of DNA or deoxyribonucleoprotein are applied;[15] (2) a string of protein and nucleoprotein masses such as were described above. While the integrity of chromosomes as indicated by their resistance to various physical and chemical procedures appears to support the first of the above possibilities, treatment of chromosomes with chelating agents (which bind calcium and magnesium and so remove these ions from the chromosome), making possible easy fragmentation of the chromosomes,[50] supports the second. It would seem that calcium and magnesium may normally bind these units together in the chromosomes. The union between these large units is therefore not easily broken by various chemical procedures applied during separation of chromosomes from other materials, during all of which the chromosomes maintain their indentity.

To ascertain the fine structure of the chromosomes electron micrographs have been made (Fig. 6.10). In such studies the chromosomes usually are visible as accumulations of dense granules, each chromosomal mass being without a visible limiting membrane. Only in a few

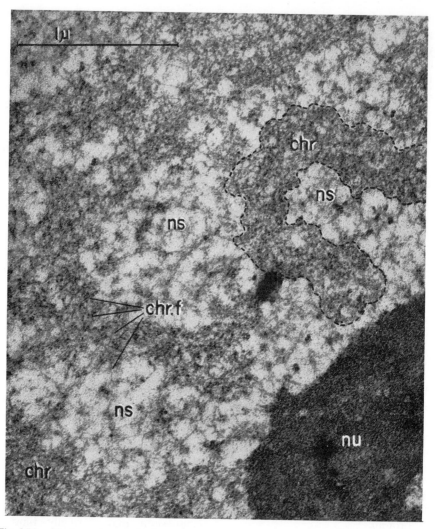

Fig. 6.10. Electron micrograph of a group of chromosomes (chr) in the nucleoplasm (ns) of an onion root tip nucleus. Microfibrils (chrf) constitute the ultrastructure of the chromosome. The chromosome on the right has been outlined to make its identity clearer. The compact nucleolus (nu) has a characteristic macromolecular structure. (Courtesy of Peraz del Cerro and Solari.)

specialized cells are more details of structure evident. For example, in some sperm cells dense striations running the length of the nucleus have been seen. In some spermatocytes thread-like elements with delicate side chains the size of nucleic acid helices, extending laterally, are reported.[20]

The electron microscope also reveals the more primitive hereditary material, analogous to the genes, in bacteria and viruses to be thread-like in organization (see Fig. 6.11). The DNA thread of phages is about 20 Å thick, and in the nucleoids of the bacteria filaments of like macromolecular dimensions are seen. Larger helices are reported in *Amoeba*. (It should be mentioned that the helices, seen by the cytologist viewing stained chromosomes under the light microscope,

116

are of a larger order of magnitude and are not to be confused with the macromolecular helices seen in these instances under the electron microscope.)

On the whole, the electron micrographs of chromosomes have not been as successful in revealing the details of the macromolecular structure of chromosomes as they have been for the structures of the cytoplasm. Consequently, the concepts of molecular structure of the chromosome must be based largely on speculation founded on what is known of the electron microscopic appearance of genic material in phages and bacteria and the little detail which shows up in electron micrographs of such favorable materials as the spermatocytes mentioned above. Two models have been suggested, one, that the structure of the chromosome consists of helices of DNA linked end to end and applied to a protein core and, a second, that a chromosome consists of a central core of protein representing the long axis of the chromosome with paired helices of DNA extending from it at right angles on each side (Fig. 6.12).

The second model of chromosome molecular organization has more appeal because it is easier to see how it might explain the partition of the hereditary materials between daughter chromosomes during cell division. In a cell about to undergo division the core splits lengthwise and separates into two units, each of which carries one of the members of each of the pairs of DNA molecules; each helix may then re-form its complementary helix as required by the Watson-Crick model of DNA. The structure of chromosomes in spermatocytes cited above suggests that such a structure might very well be possible.

This (latter) model for the molecular structure of the chromosome is also in keeping with the division of chromosomes as revealed in experiments with labeled preparations (see Fig. 3.18). For example, seedlings of the broad bean

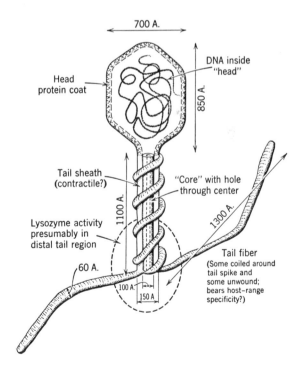

Fig. 6.11. A schematic reconstruction of the morphology of a bacteriophage particle. The dimensions shown are approximate and are averaged from several sources. (From Anfinsen, 1959: The Molecular Basis of Evolution. Wiley, N. Y.)

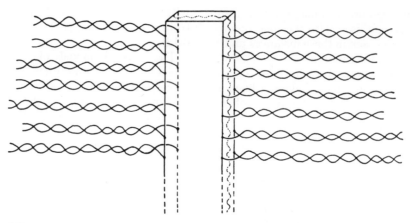

Fig. 6.12. A schematic diagram showing how the chromosome might be organized to account for data obtained from a labelled chromosome in which only one of the daughter cells gets the label. The chromosome is depicted as consisting of a central core divided into two halves. Each half is attached to one strand of a large number of DNA double helices. (Redrawn from J. H. Taylor, Am. Naturalist. *91*:209, 1957.)

(*Vicia faba*) were incubated in a medium containing tritiated (H^3) thymidine as a marker (tritium emitting a low-energy beta particle gives a sharp photographic image). Most of the twelve chromosomes present in cells became labeled, as evidenced by the correspondence between the location of silver grains in the photographic emulsion and the microscopically visible chromosomes in the control root cells. The roots were then transferred to solutions with nonradioactive thymidine containing colchicine and incubated for various times. Colchicine causes the chromosomes to contract to the metaphase condition in which sister chromatids (the two strands in a chromosome duplex) are spread and are more readily observed than in controls, but it prevents anaphase. Since colchicine does not prevent the cells from growing or the chromosomes from dividing—although it prevents the cell from dividing—a count of the number of chromosomes in each cell is a measure of the number of rounds of chromosome replication. When 24 chromosomes are present each chromosome has divided once; when 48 are present each has divided twice.[21, 22]

The results indicate clearly the presence in each chromosome of two morphological halves held together at the centrosome and containing two equivalent strands. During the initial labeling period each chromatid becomes radioactive and metaphase figures in cells with 12 chromosomes show them all to be equally effective in blackening the test photographic emulsion. On division, however, only one of the two strands of each chromosome pair is labeled, indicating that the new one, presumably complementary to it, is assembled from nonradioactive material. When there were 48 chromosomes, only one of each four strands of each type of chromosome was marked. Occasionally, a "second generation" chromosome was labeled over part of its length; in that case its partner was labeled over the remainder of the length, indicating a crossover.[21, 23] These experiments suggest that DNA is synthesized as a unit extending the length of the chromosome, the units remaining intact throughout subsequent replications.[21, 23]

A series of somewhat similar experiments was carried out on the colon bacillus, *Escherichia coli*. The bacteria were

118   FUNCTIONAL ORGANIZATION OF THE CELL

grown on a medium containing labeled nitrogen (N^{15}) which appeared in the DNA. They were then grown on a medium with ordinary nitrogen and samples of the bacteria were withdrawn each generation thereafter. The DNA was isolated and it was shown that after one generation on unlabeled nitrogen, only one-half the DNA was labeled; after two generations, only one-fourth. This shows that the original DNA remains intact, the new DNA being synthesized from the unlabeled material.[24]

Deoxyribonucleic Acid Content of Nuclei

Regardless of whether the nucleus of a liver cell, an erythrocyte or a nerve cell of a given species is tested, the same amount of DNA is found per haploid set of chromosomes of a resting cell nucleus. Cells such as the gametes, with only one set of chromosomes, possess only half the DNA of a diploid cell of the organism tested. Polyploid nuclei have the haploid quantity of DNA times the degree of the polyploidy.[26]

Although the quantity of nuclear DNA per set of chromosomes is constant, that of cytoplasmic DNA may vary. Usually so little is present in the cytoplasm (mostly in mitochondria and in nucleoplasm) that it is difficult to detect. However, the nurse cells of the ovaries of animals or of the ovules of many plants inject DNA into the cytoplasm of the egg cell, where it accumulates. In egg cells of some echinoderms the quantity of DNA may be many times that for a haploid set of chromosomes for the species. This is believed to provide a ready supply of DNA for the rapid series of divisions which occurs after fertilization.[14] Cytoplasmic DNA may not stain noticeably with Feulgen because of its dispersed condition, yet it can be extracted by standard biochemical methods.[14]

Each species of organism has a characteristic amount of DNA per haploid set of chromosomes. It should be noted that the amount of DNA per cell of a species does not necessarily indicate its evolutionary position: Even though in invertebrates DNA content per cell progressively increases with increasing degree of complexity, in vertebrates, little relation is found between DNA content and phylogenetic position.[26]

The amount of DNA in a dividing cell is duplicated in the later interphase (or in very early prophase in some cases) long before the cell is ready to divide. The DNA therefore varies in discrete amounts, the unit being the amount per haploid set of chromosomes.

It is interesting that the DNA of a set of chromosomes does not decrease when the cells are starved or exposed to other unfavorable physiological conditions, although the RNA and protein decrease markedly. It would thus appear that the genes, necessary for instituting growth when favorable conditions again appear, are protected in some manner.[56] This may be an evolutionary adaptation even though it seems to result primarily from the general metabolic inertness of the DNA. Studies with P^{32} indicate that the phosphorus of the DNA is not readily exchanged or incorporated, except when DNA is being duplicated before a cell division and when P^{32}, and C^{14}, used to label compounds serving as purine precursors, are incorporated into the new DNA.[26] However, some of the other markers are exchanged to some extent, even in the DNA of nondividing cells,[27] although not as rapidly as in RNA.

Ribonucleic Acid Content of Nuclei

Cyclic variations in the content of RNA in nucleus (and cytoplasm) occur with activity cycles of the cell. In a cell about to divide the RNA of the nucleolus gradually passes into the cytoplasm of the cell as the chromosomes re-form during prophase, and the nucleolus as a separate structure disappears. The nucleolus is re-formed at the telophase of mitosis and meiosis. The nucleolus appears to be formed from a section of a chromosome (nucleolus organizer), and some of the chromatin of this chromosome remains directly associated with the nucleolus during the interphase.[8] If the nucleolar organizer is damaged, e.g., by radiation, multiple small nucleoli may form. The nucleolar cycle is shown in Figure 6.13. The RNA of the cytoplasm increases in amount during the growth of the cell preceding mitosis and is partitioned equally during cell division. Some workers believe that the ribosomes also divide and are partitioned equally between the daughter cells (see Chapter 5).[8]

Wherever high metabolic activity or active growth occurs RNA also accumulates in both nucleus (especially in the nucleolus) and cytoplasm. For example, embryonic eggs contain accumulations of RNA, and similar stores occur in regenerating nerve cells, active neurons, gland cells, cells infected with virus and cells of tumors. Actively metabolizing yeast cells contain a large amount of RNA, but those in a starved culture possess little.[15] Starved cells in general show a depletion of RNA. RNA also varies with other physiological conditions such as lack of oxygen and presence of metabolic poisons.

Since RNA varies so markedly with the conditions and metabolic state of cells one might expect it to be quite labile, that is, to be degraded and rebuilt readily. This is indeed indicated by the quick incorporation of radioactive markers such as P^{32} in phosphate and C^{14} in precursors of the purine and pyrimidine bases into RNA. It is interesting that the RNA is labile, not just in dividing cells but also in cells which are not dividing. Consequently, the RNA turnover must accompany various cell activities. Nuclear RNA (chiefly nucleolar) appears to be more readily turned over than cytoplasmic, but this may be an artifact of the methods (see Reference 10 for discussion).

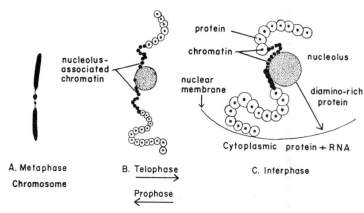

protein

chromatin

nucleolus

nucleolus-associated chromatin

nuclear membrane

diamino-rich protein

Cytoplasmic protein + RNA

A. Metaphase Chromosome

B. Telophase

C. Interphase

Prophase

Fig. 6.13. Nucleolus-associated chromatin in the nucleus, and formation of the nucleolus, A, Chromosome with a centromere in the center, as it would appear in metaphase. B, Chromosome as it would appear in prophase or telophase. C, Chromosome as it would appear in the interphase. As protein forms about the chromatin in telophase and interphase, the chromatin loses its characteristic staining properties except for the small amount called the nucleolus-associated chromatin, which remains about the nucleolus. The nucleolus, in which RNA accumulates, serves as a center of production of diamino-rich protein, while at the border of the nuclear membrane, RNA and cytoplasmic proteins, rich in aromatic amino acids, are formed. Usually only one nucleolus is present per nucleus, although in some species several may be present. (After Caspersson: Cell Growth and Cell Function. New York, W. W. Norton & Company, 1950, p. 95; and after Darlington: Nature, 149:66, 1942.)

Chemical Nature of the Gene

At one time it was thought that DNA was too simple to code the information transmitted in heredity. The present consensus, however, is that the helical structure, proposed for DNA by Watson and Crick, allows for considerable specificity.[28] It is believed that a code made up only of the four main nucleotides could give sufficiently complex information to the cytoplasm to account for inheritance.[10, 22, 28] Evidence which has accumulated to support this postulate is summarized below.

No cell can long exist without nuclear DNA after enucleation. As we have already seen, a cell can continue limited activities, but synthesis of enzymes and other needed substances is not continued and the cell deteriorates, some types of cells dying much sooner than others. It is considered that DNA directly or indirectly influences the most vital syntheses of the cell, such as the synthesis of enzymes and other proteins. Presumably, these are synthesized by the ribosomes, but the information as to what kind of protein is to be synthesized comes from the nucleus. The constant quantity of DNA among all the other varying materials in the cell bespeaks of its importance as well.

More direct information is gained from experiments using radioactive markers for study of the syntheses induced by phages. About 45 per cent of the dry weight of a given phage (T_2 of *Escherichia coli*) consists of DNA. Shortly after adsorption of an active phage particle to the surface of a bacterium, the DNA portion of the phage enters into the cell and replicates (Fig. 6.14), ultimately forming many phage particles, even if the phage protein portion originally adhering to the surface of the bacteria is washed off, leaving not more than 1 per cent of the S^{35}-labeled phage protein with the bacterium. On the other hand, phage "ghosts," prepared by subjecting active phage particles to osmotic shock, during which the DNA portion is lost, still retain their ability to adsorb to the host and to modify the surface of the host in certain ways, but they have lost the power of reproduction.[29, 30] Since phage genetic material shows a variety of characters apparently arranged in linear order, as in a chromosome, it is clear that the genetic information is here carried by DNA alone. Somewhat similar experiments have been done with plant viruses in which, apparently, RNA replaces DNA as the hereditary material. In these experiments the virus protein and the virus RNA were separated from one another in each of two strains of virus. When the protein from a mutant form was mixed with the wild-type virus RNA, a new "hybrid" virus was formed. Such a virus would infect plants and reproduce, but when the protein formed under the influence of the hybrid virus was isolated, it proved to be like that formed by the wild-type RNA. The protein which had come in with the virus evidently had had no genetic effect.[48]

Equally direct evidence for the importance of DNA in heredity is the transformation (Fig. 6.15B) of *Pneumococcus* from one type to another.[31, 34] Such studies were possible since the smooth and rough colony types of this bacterium are quite distinct. Addition of extract of the smooth colony transforms a rough strain into a smooth (virulent) strain. The provocative constituent in the extract is the DNA of the smooth strain, since incubation with deoxyribonuclease prevents the transformation because the enzyme destroys the DNA. It would appear that the added DNA of the extract of the smooth strain replaces the DNA of the rough strain and induces manufacture of more material like itself, since the change is hereditary. (In this instance the DNA of the rough strain does not transform the smooth strain.) Similar changes have

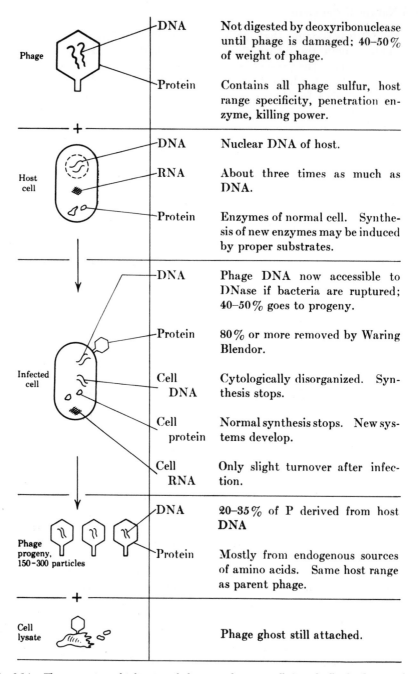

	DNA	Not digested by deoxyribonuclease until phage is damaged; 40–50% of weight of phage.
Phage	Protein	Contains all phage sulfur, host range specificity, penetration enzyme, killing power.
+		
	DNA	Nuclear DNA of host.
Host cell	RNA	About three times as much as DNA.
	Protein	Enzymes of normal cell. Synthesis of new enzymes may be induced by proper substrates.
	DNA	Phage DNA now accessible to DNase if bacteria are ruptured; 40–50% goes to progeny.
	Protein	80% or more removed by Waring Blendor.
Infected cell	Cell DNA	Cytologically disorganized. Synthesis stops.
	Cell protein	Normal synthesis stops. New systems develop.
	Cell RNA	Only slight turnover after infection.
Phage progeny, 150–300 particles	DNA	20–35% of P derived from host DNA
	Protein	Mostly from endogenous sources of amino acids. Same host range as parent phage.
+		
Cell lysate		Phage ghost still attached.

Fig. 6.14. The events in multiplication of phage in a bacteria cell. Specifically the diagram shows what happens in the course of infection of the colon bacillus with bacteriophages of the T series. (Redrawn after Hotchkiss, R. D., 1954: The Nucleic Acids. Vol. 2, Academic Press, New York.)

A. Conjugation (E. coli)

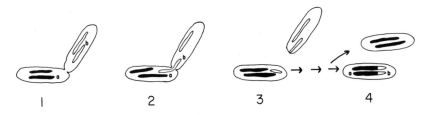

1   2   3   4

B. Transformation

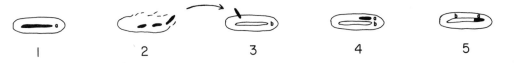

1   2   3   4   5

C. Transduction

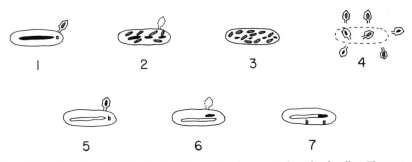

1   2   3   4

5   6   7

Fig. 6.15. *A*, conjugation in bacteria, with special reference to the colon bacillus. The conjugating strains shown (a and b) are multinucleate. The conjugants remain linked together for an hour or two by a bridge of cytoplasm during which the male cell contributes some genetic material to the female (passive) cell. By labeling, it is shown that passage of material is in one direction only. Fertilization is progressive and can be stopped by shearing the bacteria apart, for example, with a Waring blendor. *B*, Transformation in bacteria. Resistance to drugs and biochemical variations can be transmitted by nucleic acid from one strain (a) to another (b). While pieces of the chromosome are shown to be transmitted in the diagram, this has been accomplished experimentally for specific characters by solutions of the nucleic acid of a given strain applied to the other (see text). *C*, Transduction in bacteria. Infection by a phage may bring in genetic material picked up by the phage from another strain of bacteria; such introduced genetic material may become incorporated into the genome of the bacterium. Note that in each of the three cases, *A*, *B*, and *C*, a piece of the new chromosomal material from another bacterium is at first loosely added but later may become incorporated into the genome of the bacterium, probably as part of its chromosome. The resultant products of each of the processes have some of the characters of each of the two strains of bacteria.

been induced as well in other microorganisms,[32-35] including a protozoan.[36] In some cases biochemical traits such as specific nutritional requirements have been transmitted from one strain of bacteria to another. Evidence has accumulated that such transformations consist of incorporation of the new DNA into the chromosomes of the recipient bacterium, which, being haploid, breeds true to the new DNA (Fig. 6.15B). The transforming principle in one case has been "mutated" by HNO_2 outside the cell and the bacterium transformed by the mutated DNA was altered in its hereditary characteristics by the process.[49]

Lysogeny, already considered briefly in Chapter 2, is another instance in which genetic material—in this case the DNA of the phage—has been attached to the chromosome of a bacterium (Fig. 6.16) which, accepting the phage DNA, is thereby changed in one of several ways, the most noticeable being its increased resistance to the infection by the lytic variety of the phage.[22]

Akin to lysogeny is transduction in bacteria, in which genetic material from one strain of bacteria is transferred to another strain of the same species by phages.[6, 37, 40] For example, each of two strains of *Salmonella typhimurium* lacked the ability to synthesize one of the amino acids, but each one had a deficiency for a different amino acid. Had the bacteria mated, a certain percentage would have transferred genes, enabling the offspring of the recipient to synthesize all the amino acids. However, even when mating was prevented by interposing between suspensions of the two strains a membrane through which they could not move, new strains of bacteria appeared which were able to produce the respective amino acids for which the two original strains were deficient. Similar results were obtained when lysed filtrates of bacteria of one strain were mixed with the bacteria of the other strain. The only possible carrier of the hereditary material which could pass the membrane is a phage. It has now been shown that the phage, which transmits the information from one strain of bacterium to another,

Lysogeny

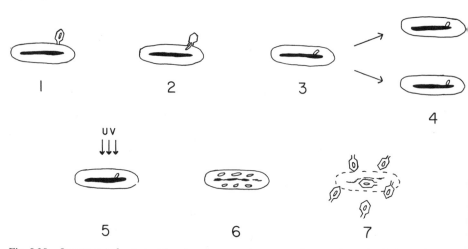

Fig. 6.16. Lysogeny in bacteria. The phage genome does not replicate independently but, added to the bacterial genome, replicates when the latter divides. Injury of the bacterium by ultraviolet radiation or other harmful agents, however, activates the phage, which then multiplies rapidly like a lytic phage and lyses the bacterium.

FUNCTIONAL ORGANIZATION OF THE CELL

s incapable of multiplication and cannot yse the infected bacteria (Fig. 6.15C). Presumably the genetic material of the phage has become defective and can no longer replicate, perhaps because by a mistake during its replication in the preceding bacterium, a part of its chromosome has been replaced by a gene block of the bacterium. The phage's very effectiveness in transduction might thus prevent its further effectiveness as a phage.

Since the transduced bacteria breed true, it must be assumed that the apparent place on the chromosome occupied by genic material, which previously produced the deficiency in amino acid manufacture, has now been replaced by material brought in by the phage, making it competent in this respect. Experiments in which radioactive markers were used show that only DNA has been transferred by the phage. Transduction is thus another evidence that DNA is the genetic material.

Functions of the Nucleic Acids

The functions of the nucleic acids have always been of great interest, because the prominence of DNA in the chromosomes and of RNA in the nucleolus and ribosomes suggests that the nucleic acids are closely connected with cell activities.[10, 38, 39] It is also likely that DNA is involved in cell differentiation during development, but less is known about its function in this regard.[56]

The synthesis of DNA *in vitro* by Kornberg, who received the Nobel prize for these studies in 1959, indicates the probable mechanism by which this synthesis occurs in the cell.[41] The requirements for this purpose are certain enzymes (in Kornberg's studies extracted from the colon bacillus, *Escherichia coli*), the nucleotides usually found in DNA in the form of triphosphates (to provide the material necessary and the energy required for the synthesis) and a DNA primer, or template, which serves as a model for the synthesis of the new DNA. It will be recalled from Chapter 3 (Fig. 3.16) that the Watson and Crick DNA model consists of two strands in a helix, bonded from purine to pyrimidine residues, so that thymine (T) attracts adenine (A) and cytosine (C) attracts guanine (G); hence the linkages across the two strands are T-A, C-G, A-T and G-C. In the presence of the enzyme the triphosphates of the nucleotides become linked, in accordance with the above attractions of bases, and in the processes of the formation of bonds between the nucleotides two phosphates (as pyrophosphate) are split out of each triphosphate. In this way a strand of DNA which is complementary to the template in its placement of bases is formed. Since each strand forms its own complement, the net effect of the synthesis is the formation of a new complete unit of DNA similar to the template (Fig. 6.17). In the synthesis of DNA the specificity is determined solely by the template DNA presented. The same enzyme when presented with the same four nucleotide triphosphates was found capable of duplicating a variety of DNA models. The identity of the DNA produced was determined by comparing its base ratios with those of the DNA used as a primer.

In the cell DNA duplication occurs during late interphase or early prophase.[8, 10, 14] Presumably, DNA synthesis occurs only in the chromosomes, the little DNA present in the cytoplasm probably coming there from the nucleus.[10] It is apparent that DNA duplication, by the method described above, ensures that duplication of DNA present in a cell will continue from cell generation to cell generation, unless a "mistake" in copying (mutation) is made.

It is well known that DNA is in some manner in control of protein synthesis, since removal of the nucleus or the removal of DNA by deoxyribonuclease stops protein syntheses in the cell (as indi-

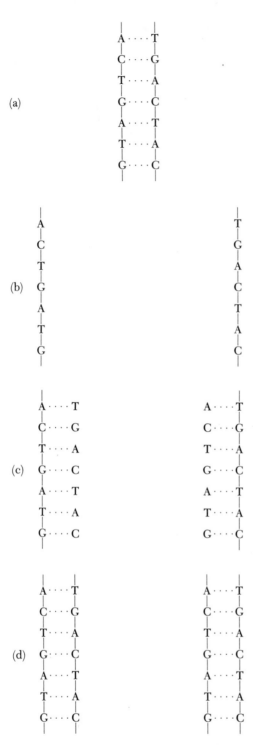

cated by failure in incorporation of labeled amino acids precursors of proteins). Cytoplasmic changes accompanying DNA removal include the gradual loss of basophilia, indicating the loss of RNA in ribosomes which are the centers of protein synthesis in the cytoplasm.

While there is a possibility that some protein may be synthesized directly under the influence of DNA, this is not proved since RNA always is present, in one form or another, when protein synthesis occurs. This is true even in phage which has DNA but no RNA. The DNA of phage, however, induces in its bacterial host the production of a new RNA, under the influence of which is synthesized the protein which the phage needs for coating its new DNA molecules. In general, protein synthesis in cells is accompanied by a large turnover of RNA as is shown in experiments with incorporation of labeled precursors. Apparently, RNA is first formed in the nucleus since in radioautographs the label appears over the nucleus (chromosomes) in 5 minutes, the nucleolar count being low until after 10 minutes have passed. The label appears in the cytoplasm much later.[46] Although it seems most likely that protein production depends upon RNA directly, the RNA involved in protein synthesis is produced by DNA or under its influence. DNA production is, therefore, the master reaction and DNA is the ultimate agent indirectly controlling protein synthesis.

Protein is synthesized in several locations in the cell. In the nucleus it is synthesized around the chromatin, thus

Fig. 6.17. Replication of DNA. If the short helix of DNA is uncoiled and the two strands separated as in (b), then in the presence of the appropriate enzymes and nucleotide triphosphates, the complementary bases of the nucleotides are attracted as shown in (c) and after reacting, these are linked to form the complementary strands of nucleic acid as shown in (d). (From Davidson, 1960: The Biochemistry of the Nucleic Acids. Methuen, London, p. 213.)

pushing the DNA staining material farther apart during telophase.[15] However, it is to be remembered that some RNA is also present on the chromosomes. In the nucleolus protein is also produced and the nucleolus in some cases has a very high density because of its high protein concentration. But in the nucleolus, also, there is present a high concentration of RNA, presumably produced under the influence of the nucleolus-associated chromatin.[15] There is thus ample RNA to account for protein synthesis in the nucleus. However, the main protein production takes place in the cytoplasm and more specifically in the ribosomes which contain 80 per cent of the RNA of the cell. In gland cells with a well-developed endoplasmic reticulum, protein globules may be readily identified within the canals.[38]

The RNA, like DNA, consists of four nucleotides, except that uracil has replaced thymine, and the sugar molecules have hydroxy groups (which are absent in the deoxy sugars of DNA). Ideas concerning replication of RNA on DNA templates are largely speculative, although some proof is accumulating. Presumably, as in the case of DNA duplication, the ribonucleotide triphosphates are attracted in the same manner to the template DNA, guanine to cytosine, adenine to thymine, cytosine to guanine and uracil to adenine, in accordance with the pattern on the template. In this manner would be formed the RNA-messenger molecule, which leaves the nucleus and goes to the cytoplasm, carrying the information as to what protein is to be made. There it attaches itself to a ribosome, presumably by complementarism of bases.[38, 43, 51] The ribosomal RNA is presumably made directly or under the influence of DNA since it disappears if the DNA is removed by DNAase or the cell is enucleated.

The clearest evidence for a messenger RNA is perhaps that from work on T-2 and T-4 phages. Soon after infection of the colon bacillus a new RNA is produced in which the adenine-uracil/guanine-cytosine ratio duplicates the phage DNA adenine-thymine/guanine-cytosine ratio. The RNA is rapidly formed after infection and just as rapidly destroyed.[51] The purpose of the RNA messenger is to inform the bacterial cell ribosomes as to what kind of protein to produce as a coating for the phage DNA.

In the hyaloplasm of the cytoplasm occurs another form of RNA, presumably also made under the influence of DNA, but having free terminal groups by which it can attach amino acids. This RNA, originally thought to be a part of a ribosome which had been solubilized by treatment, is different in chemical properties from the ribosomal RNA. The hyaloplasmic RNA, called *soluble* or *transfer* RNA, consists of relatively small molecules (low molecular weight) which combine with amino acids before the latter can be united to form a protein.* For this purpose the amino acids must be in a phosphorylated (high-energy) form. Such compounds of RNA with amino acids have been isolated from the cell; there are some 20 of them and they are being purified. Presumably, by attaching to a transfer RNA the amino acids obtain an identity which the RNA templates in the ribosome can recognize. The amino acid–RNA complexes are, therefore, attached to the appropriate places on the template, fitting by the method of complementarism already described above for DNA. Once the RNA–amino acid complexes are affixed to the surface of the ribosome the respective amino acids, which are in an activated or energetic form, combine to form peptide bonds with one another, at the same time detaching from the RNA nucleotide, which detaches from the ribo-

---

* See Chapter 25 for further discussion and diagrams of protein synthesis.

some and presumably goes on for another round of transfers.[38, 43]

That existing ribosomes of the bacterial cell are used in the synthesis of phage proteins is shown by growing bacteria on nutrients labeled with heavy C and N until these bacteria are infected with phage. At this time the bacteria are returned to unlabeled N and C sources, but are briefly supplied with P^{32} to label newly-formed RNA (messenger RNA). Density gradient separation of the light and heavy ribosomes shows all the new RNA (marked with P^{32}) associated with the old (heavy) ribosomes.[51]

It was also demonstrated in parallel experiments, in which S^{35} was supplied in protein precursors, that the new proteins (S^{35}-labeled) were associated with the old ribosomes before they appeared elsewhere in the cell.[55]

The enzymes which catalyze union of RNA-carriers and amino acids are probably produced in the same way as other enzymes, i.e., on an RNA template, but are probably always present in "starter" proportions at the beginning of any protein synthesis in the cell (see Chapter 25).

Amino acid activation, attachment of amino acids to transfer RNA, and the final building of protein in ribosomes are facts supported by good data. Evidence is also good that RNA originates in the nucleus and is under the control of the DNA of the chromosomes. However, some of the hypothetical steps outlined here require further documentation.[47, 57]

The Genetic Code and DNA

Since only four purine and pyrimidine bases (sometimes a fifth, and even a sixth) are present in RNA and DNA, it would, at first glance, seem difficult to make a code from just four units sufficient to locate 20 amino acids on a ribosome as is done in the synthesis of proteins. However, it has been possible to develop codes which are specific to each one of the 20 amino acids by using only four nucleotides. Only one code is given below since they are all hypothetical.[38] Thus, designating the nucleotides 1, 2, 3 and 4 for purposes of argument, one can make the following sequences of three each, each to designate one and only one amino acid: 112, 212, 131, 132, 133, 231, 232, 233, 141, 142, 143, 144, 241, 242, 243, 244, 341, 342, 343 and 344.* If transfer RNA nucleotides with one of these sequences were to pick up one amino acid each, and unite with the complementary spaces on the messenger RNA, it would be possible to line up the amino acids to build any protein, even with this relatively simple code.[28, 38]

Experimental support for DNA coding of protein synthesis is provided by the production of protein-like molecules in response to artificial RNA-like polyribonucleotides of known composition [for example, a polyuridine made up only of uridine (U)]. When an RNA-like polyribonucleotide composed of three repeating units of uridine [the U-U-U sequence of the polyuridine being complementary to the adenine (A) sequence, A-A-A, of the DNA] is supplied, the synthesized protein-like polypeptide molecule consists of repeating phenylalanine residues (polyphenylalanine). When other synthetic RNA-like compounds are used [e.g., polyribonucleotides made up of uridine (U), cytosine (C), guanine (G) and adenine (A), in each case consisting of units of three—UUA, UGG, UUC, UCA, UGA, etc.], the protein-like polypeptides synthesized are characteristic for each type of RNA-like polyribonucleotide supplied. Experimental data suggesting the RNA code (and so also the complementary DNA code) for all of the amino acids have now been gathered.[52, 54, 60]

The kind of protein produced from the same pool of amino acids would then de-

* Perhaps 111, 222, 333, and 444 might figure in this series as well.

pend upon the template presented. The template would depend upon what DNA unit (gene?) had produced it, since presumably many types of DNA molecules are present on the chromosomes of a cell, each capable of producing a corresponding RNA messenger. On this basis, a cell can have only as many types of proteins as it has types of DNA molecules.[38, 43, 44]

GENERAL REFERENCES

Allen, J. M. (ed.), 1962: The Molecular Control of Cellular Activity. McGraw-Hill, New York. Especially chapters 2, 3, and 5–8.

Allfrey, V. G., Mirsky, A. E., and Stern, H., 1955: The Chemistry of the Cell Nucleus. Adv. Enzymol. 16:411–500.

Anfinsen, C. B., 1959: The Chemical Basis of Evolution. Wiley, New York.

Benzer, S., Jan. 1962: The Fine Structure of the Gene. Sci. Am. 206:70.

Brachet, J., 1957: Biochemical Cytology. Academic Press, New York.

Brachet, J., 1960: Ribonucleic acids and the Synthesis of Cellular Proteins. Nature 186:194–199.

Caspersson, T. O., 1950: Cell Growth and Cell Function. Norton, New York.

Chantrenne, H., 1958: Syntheses of Protein and Nucleic Acid in Enucleate Cytoplasm. Proc. Roy. Soc. London B 148:332–339.

Davidson, J. N., 1960: The Biochemistry of the Nucleic Acids. 4th ed. Methuen, London.

DeRobertis, E. D. P., Nowinski, W. W., and Saez, F. A., 1960: General Cytology, 3rd ed. Saunders, Philadelphia.

Fraenkel-Conrat, H., 1957–58: Structure and Infectivity of Tobacco Mosaic Virus. Harvey Lect. 53:56–68.

Gale, E. F., 1955–56: Nucleic Acids and Protein Synthesis. Harvey Lect. 51:25–63.

Glick, D., 1953: A Critical Survey of Current Approaches in Quantitative Histo- and Cytochemistry. Internat. Rev. Cyt. 2:447.

Hershey, A. D., 1955–56: Bacteriophage T$_2$: Parasite or Organelle? Harvey Lect. 51:229–239.

Lederberg, J., 1957–58: Bacterial Reproduction. Harvey Lect. 53:69–82.

McElroy, W., and Glass, B. (eds.), 1957: A Symposium on the Chemical Basis of Heredity. Johns Hopkins Press, Baltimore.

Mitchell, J. S. (ed.), 1960: The Cell Nucleus (Symposium). Academic Press, New York.

Strauss, B. S., 1960: An Outline of Chemical Genetics. Saunders, Philadelphia.

LITERATURE CITED

1. Danielli, J. F., 1959: Ann. New York Acad. Sci. 78:675.
2. Briggs, R., and King, T. J., 1956: Cold Spring Harbor Symp. 21:271.
3. Hammerling, J. 1953: Internat. Rev. Cyt. 2:475.
4. Harvey, E. B., 1936. Biol. Bull. 71:101.
5. Tyler, A., and Rothschild, L., 1951: Proc. Soc. Exp. Biol. Med. 76:52; 1953: Biol. Bull. 104:224.
6. Adelberg, E., 1960: Papers on Bacterial Genetics. Little, Brown, Boston.
7. The Biological Replication of Macromolecules. Symp. Soc. Exp. Biol. 12. Cambridge Univ. Press, 1958.
8. DeRobertis, E. D. P., Nowinski, W. W., and Saez, F. A., 1960: General Cytology. 3rd Ed. Saunders, Philadelphia.
9. Siebert, G., and Smellie, R. M. S., 1957: Internat. Rev. Cyt. 6:383.
10. Davidson, J. N., 1960: The Biochemistry of the Nucleic Acids. 4th Ed. Methuen, London.
11. Allfrey, V. G., Osawa, S., and Mirsky, A. E., 1957: J. Gen. Physiol. 40:451, 491.
12. Siebert, G., and Smellie, R. M. S., 1957: Internat. Rev. Cyt. 6:383.
13. Allfrey, V. G., Mirsky, A. E., and Stern, H., 1955: Adv. Enzymol. 16:411.
14. Allfrey, V. G., and Mirsky, A. E., 1959: in: Subcellular Particles (Hayashi, T., ed.), Ronald Press, New York, p. 186.
15. Caspersson, T. O., 1950: Cell Growth and Cell Function. Norton, New York. 1955: Experimentia 11:45; 1962: in The Molecular Control of Cellular Activity (Allen, J. M., ed.). McGraw-Hill, New York, p. 127.
16. Kurnick, N. K., 1950: J. Gen. Physiol. 33:243.
17. Kurnick, N. B., and Mirsky, A. E., 1950: J. Gen. Physiol. 33:265.
18. Edstrom, J. E., 1960: J. Biochem. Biophys. Cyt. 8:39, 47.
19. Edstrom, J. E., 1958: Microchem. J. 2:71.
20. Bennett, H. S., 1959: Biophysical Science, A Study Program (Onclay, J. L., ed.). Wiley, New York.
21. Taylor, J. H., 1957: Am. Natural. 91:209.
22. Anfinsen, C. O., 1959: The Chemical Basis of Evolution. Wiley, New York.
23. Taylor, J. H., Woods, P. S., and Hughes, W. L., 1957: Proc. Nat. Acad. Sci. 43:122.
24. Meselson, M., and Stahl, F. W., 1958: Proc. Nat. Acad. Sci. U. S. 66:71.
25. Mazia, D., and Hirshfield, H., 1950: Science 112:297.
26. Mirsky, A. E., 1950–51: Harvey Lectures 46:98.
27. Brachet, J., 1957: Biochemical Cytology. Academic Press, New York.
28. Watson, J. W., and Crick, F. H. C., 1953: Nature 171:737. 1962: Sci. Am. 207 (4):66.

29. Taylor, A. R., 1946: J. Biol. Chem. *165*:271.
30. Hershey, A. D., and Chase, M., 1952: J. Gen. Physiol. *36*:39.
31. Avery, O. T., MacLeod, C. M., and McCarty, M., 1944: J. Exp. Med. *79*:137.
32. Braun, W., and Whallom, J., 1954: Proc. Nat. Acad. Sci. *40*:112.
33. Hotchkiss, R. D., 1955: Harvey Lect. *49*:124. J. Cell. Comp. Physiol. *45* (suppl. 2):1.
34. Zinder, N. D., 1955: J. Cell. Comp. Physiol. *45* (suppl. 2):23.
35. Hotchkiss, R. D., and Weiss, E., Nov. 1956: Sci. Am. *195*:48.
36. Honigman, B. M., and Read, C. P., 1960: Science *131*:352.
37. Zinder, N. D., Nov. 1958: Sci. Am. *199*:38.
38. Hoagland, M. R., Dec. 1959: Sci. Am. *201*:55.
39. Gay, H. J., Jan. 1960: Sci. Am. *202*:126.
40. Wollman, E. L., and Jacob, F., July 1956: Sci. Am. *196*:109.
41. Kornberg, A., 1960: Science *131*:1503; 1962: *in* The Molecular Control of Cellular Activity (Allen, J. M., ed.). McGraw-Hill, New York, p. 245.
42. Moore, J. A., 1960: *in* New Approaches in Cell Biology (Walker, P. M. B., ed.). Academic Press, New York, p. 1. See also Fishberg, M., Gordon, J. B., and Elsdale, T. R., 1958: Exp. Cell. Res. suppl. *6*:161.
43. Crick, F. H. C., 1958: Symp. Soc. Exp. Biol. *12*:138.
44. Loftfield, R. B., 1957: Progr. Biophysics & Biophys. Chem. *8*:348.
45. Vincent, W. S., 1955: Internat. Rev. Cyt. *4*:269.
46. Goldstein, L., and Micou, J., 1959: Anat. Rec. *134*:570 (abstr). 1958: Exp. Cell. Res. *15*:635.
47. Harris, R. T. C. (ed.), 1960: Protein Biosynthesis. Academic Press, New York.
48. Fraenkel-Conrat, H., 1959: Harvey Lect. *53*:56.
49. Gierer, A., and Mundry, K. W., 1958: Nature *182*:1457.
50. Mazia, D., 1954: Proc. Nat. Acad. Sci. U.S.A. *40*:521.
51. Hurwitz, J., and Furth, J. J., Feb. 1962: Sci. Am. *206*:41.
52. Ochoa, S., Burma, D. P., Krozer, H., and Weill, J. D., 1961: Proc. Nat. Acad. Sci. U.S.A. *47*:670.
53. Mayor, H. D., and Diwan, A. R., 1961: Virology *14*:74.
54. Lengyel, P., Speyer, J. F., Basilio, C., and Ochoa, S., 1962: Proc. Nat. Acad. Sci. U.S.A. *48*:282.
55. Brenner, S., Jacob, F., and Meselson, M., 1961: Nature *190*:576.
56. Swift, H., 1962: *in* The Molecular Control of Cellular Activity (Allen, J. M., ed.). McGraw-Hill, New York, p. 73.
57. Hogness, D. S., 1962: *in* The Molecular Control of Cellular Activity (Allen, J. M., ed.). McGraw-Hill, New York, p. 189.
58. Martin, R. G., Matthei, J. H., Jones, O. W., and Nirenberg, M. W., 1962: Biochem. Biophys. Res. Commun. *6*:410.
59. Sirlin, J. L., 1961: Endeavour, *20*:146.
60. Henning, U. and Yanofsky, C., 1962: Proc. Nat. Acad. Sci. U.S. (in press).

SECTION
II

THE CELL
ENVIRONMENT

Microorganisms and single-celled animals and plants are subjected directly to all the changes in the external environment: changes in concentration of oxygen, carbon dioxide, salts, hydrogen ions and changes in temperature and in the quality and intensity of light. Cells of higher animals and plants are also subjected to such changes, but their cells are protected to various degrees by the development of an internal environment in the form of sap, body fluid or blood, in which a considerable degree of constancy of conditions is maintained. The greatest control of the internal environment is reached in the warm-blooded animals, in which the oxygen, hydrogen ion concentration, salts, foods, proteins and temperature of the blood which bathes the cells of the animal are maintained within narrow limits. Such control has been called *homeostasis*.[1]

It will be interesting to consider the degree of variation in the factors of the natural environments and the degree to which these variations are tolerated by various forms of life, because from this inquiry certain fundamental characteristics of life will become apparent. Furthermore, it will be of interest to see to what extent an organism which controls its internal environment has been able to invade and occupy successfully an environment inaccessible to an organism without such control.[13, 19] Only the major environmental factors will be considered here; e.g., water, carbon dioxide, oxygen, salts, pressure, hydrogen ion concentration, radiations (light, ultraviolet rays and ionizing radiations) and temperature.

7

WATER, GASES AND PRESSURE IN THE CELL ENVIRONMENT

Water as a Factor in the Cell Environment

A cell must always possess direct or indirect water frontage, inasmuch as all cell reactions occur in aqueous solutions. In simpler forms of life this is achieved by direct contact with environmental water. The more complex plant or animal may become covered with a coating impervious to water, but its cells have contact with the aqueous environment of the internal medium (the *milieu interieur* of Claude Bernard).[1, 2] For instance, cells of vascular plants are in contact with cell sap, while cells of most multicellular animals are bathed by body fluid or blood.

Water makes up 80 per cent of the cell. When the cell loses water, life is suspended or extinguished. Activity reappears in desiccated, dormant cells only when water again becomes available. The cells of some dried mosses, lichens, rotifers, tardigrades and nematodes resist unfavorable conditions for years, only to resume activity quickly when moistened, provided other conditions are favorable. Many protozoa encyst and some bacteria

sporulate when deprived of water. Such dried resistant stages are characteristic of fresh water and terrestrial organisms which are subjected to seasonal drying.

Many properties of water make it suitable not only as the main constituent of the cell, but also as the main factor in the environment, as Henderson emphasized in 1927.

Water as a Temperature Stabilizer. Among the most important properties of water are its temperature-stabilizing properties, especially its high specific heat, its high heat of vaporization and its high heat of fusion.[5]

The *specific heat* of a substance is defined as the number of calories required to raise the temperature of 1 gram of that substance 1 degree centigrade. The specific heat of water is 1.0, a value exceeded only by that of liquid ammonia. Most liquids have a lower specific heat.

The *latent heat of vaporization* is the number of calories required to change 1 gram of liquid to vapor. For water at 100° C. this is 539 calories, one of the highest values known. Close to the heat of vaporization of water is that of hydrofluoric acid (360 calories); that of ammonia is less.

The *heat of fusion* is the number of calories required to convert 1 gram of solid at the freezing point to 1 gram of liquid at the same temperature. For water it is 80 calories and for ammonia, 108 calories per gram. While the heat of fusion of water is less than that of ammonia, it is greater than that of most other organic or inorganic materials tested.[15]

How do these properties of water provide a better control of temperature on the surface of the earth as well as in the external and internal environment of the cell? This can be illustrated best by a number of examples. Radiant energy of the order of 10^{15} calories per square kilometer per year falls on the surface of the earth at the equator. This is equivalent to the energy liberated by the fission of 100 kilograms of uranium 235 or by the burning of 700,000 tons of coal. If a dry land mass made up of rock and soil with a low specific heat were to absorb this much radiant energy, it would rise to a lethal temperature by day and fall below the freezing point of water by night, as it apparently does on the moon. However, the water vapor in the atmosphere of the earth absorbs some of the incoming infrared radiation in sunlight, preventing overheating in daylight. The sunlight which gets through this atmospheric water vapor "blanket" is absorbed and heats the land masses (Fig. 7.1). As the heat is reradiated from the land by night, the atmospheric water vapor absorbs the outgoing infrared rays of longer wavelength, preventing the earth from cooling at night as rapidly as it otherwise would. This so-called greenhouse effect of the atmospheric water vapor is therefore of special importance in moderating the temperature of the land masses.[3, 16]

Because of the high specific heat of water, the great bodies of water covering the earth's crust are heated much less than the land. A body of water can absorb or lose a considerable amount of heat without much change in temperature; that is, its heat capacity is high. The *heat capacity* of a body may be defined as the number of calories required to raise the temperature of the entire body 1 degree centigrade. The larger a body is and the higher its specific heat, the greater is its heat capacity. The vastness of the oceans makes them of especial importance as thermostats resisting temperature change. Consequently, the climate of the shores of land masses and even of inland areas is tempered by nearby water.

The oceans moderate the temperature in yet another way. Because of the high heat of vaporization of water, a tremendous amount of the sun's heat is absorbed during evaporation from the vast surface of the oceans. The vapor holds the heat until the warm, water-laden air is chilled in a cooler part of the earth. Then the vapor condenses and liberates the heat, thereby counteracting the coolness of the region in which precipitation occurs. The water-laden air may move far from its original source before it condenses and gives off its heat; therefore, the heat absorbed at the surface of the ocean may moderate conditions far away. For example, heat absorbed in the tropics may be carried to the northern polar regions.[22]

The high heat of fusion of water is another factor serving to reduce radical changes in temperature, since ice is formed from water only after a considerable loss of heat, and it melts only when this amount of heat is replaced. The system:

$$[water]_{0°C.} \underset{+\ heat}{\overset{-\ heat}{\rightleftharpoons}} [ice]_{0°C.} \qquad (7.1)$$

remains at 0° C during the withdrawal of heat, accompanied by ice formation, or the addition of heat, melting the ice.

An additional thermostabilizing property of water is its high specific gravity at

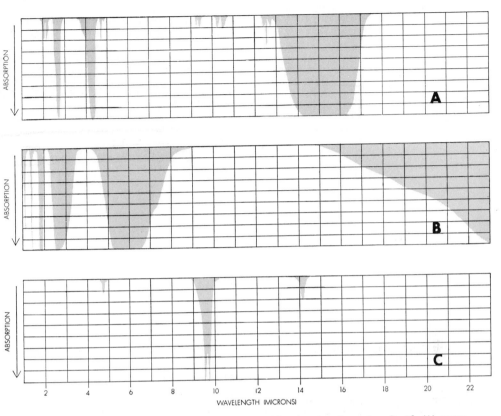

Fig. 7.1. Absorption of infrared radiations in the earth's atmosphere by carbon dioxide (A), water vapor (B) and ozone (C). (From Plass, July 1959: Sci. Am. *201*:42.)

4° C. Because of this, pure water cooled below 4° C. rises and freezes only at the surface. If it were not for this, bodies of water such as lakes might freeze solid and become uninhabitable.[3]

Finally, water is a very much better heat conductor than any other common liquid. Consequently the heat it absorbs is readily distributed. This tends to equalize the temperature, not only in the external and internal environment but also in cells inside the bodies of animals and plants.

Water as a Solvent. Besides serving as a thermostabilizer, *water is the best solvent known*—more substances dissolve in it than in any other solvent.[4, 5] Electrolytes dissolved in water readily ionize because water molecules, by virtue of their own charged nature (see Fig. 7.2), act as small dipoles attracting the ions of the solute, thereby weakening the attraction between them. In more technical terms it may be said that water is a polar solvent of high dielectric constant. Such a constant can be measured by placing the vapor or solution of a substance between the plates of a condenser and comparing the attraction between the plates with that which occurs in a vacuum. For example, water has a dielectric constant of 78.5, ethyl alcohol 24.3 and benzene 2.28. Ionization and ionic reactions are of great importance to life, as will be shown in later chapters. For all its importance as a solvent, water is remarkably inert and innocuous and most substances are unchanged by being dissolved in it.

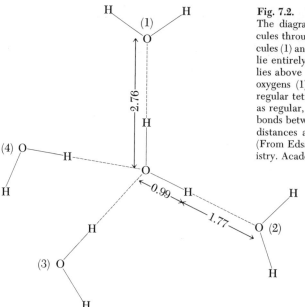

Fig. 7.2. The dipolar nature of the water molecule. The diagram shows the orientation of water molecules through tetrahedral coordination in ice. Molecules (1) and (2), as well as the central water molecule, lie entirely in the plane of the paper; molecule (3) lies above this plane; molecule (4) below it, so that oxygens (1), (2), (3) and (4) lie at the corners of a regular tetrahedron. In water the orientation is not as regular, but multiples occur bound by hydrogen bonds between the molecules (shown in dashes). The distances are given in Angstrom units (10^{-8} cm.). (From Edsall and Wyman, 1958: Biophysical Chemistry. Academic Press, New York, p. 31.)

Therefore, they may remain in solution in the cell, unaltered until such time as they may be utilized.

Water is also necessary for *hydrolyses* and for biological *oxidations*, the two chemical reactions most fundamental to the cell.

Special Properties of Water. Water has several other properties which make it particularly fit as part of the external and internal environment. It is *transparent to light*, enabling the specialized photosynthetic organelles, the chloroplasts, inside the plant cells to absorb the sunlight—a process upon which depends all life on earth. The transparency of the ocean also enables floating plants and plants attached to rocks to grow below the surface. This property is of considerable importance since marine plants are the ultimate source of food for most marine animals. The *high surface tension* of water is also an important property since it enables the water to move closer to the surface of the soil than would otherwise be possible, making it available to life.

Structure of Water. Some of the re-markable properties of water are now interpretable on the basis of its structure. The shape of a water molecule is that of an isosceles triangle; the intermolecular O—H distance is nearly 0.99 Å, and the H—O—H angle is not far from 105°. The powerful attraction of the oxygen nucleus tends to draw electrons away from the protons (H-nuclei), leaving the region around them with a net positive charge. Since only two pairs of electrons around the oxygen atom are shared with the protons, the two other pairs in the 8-electron shell point outward from the O—H bond, attracted to the net positive charge of other water molecules with a force of about 4500 calories per mole.[5] A group of water molecules therefore describes a tetrahedron around the oxygen atom, the positively charged region of one water molecule tending to orient itself toward a negatively charged region of one of its neighbors. This is shown in Figure 7.2. Each water molecule therefore tends to have four near neighbors and each oxygen atom is the center of a tetrahedron of other oxygens, the O—O distance as determined by x-ray diffraction studies being 2.76 Å.[5]

The highly regular arrangements found in ice break in about 15 per cent of the places when ice melts. Even at higher temperatures, however, some of the structure remains and the high heat of vaporization of water indicates some quasi-crystalline structure even at 100° C.

The type of linkage indicated in Figure 7.2 by a dotted line between the proton and the neighboring oxygen atoms is called a *hydrogen bond*. As already pointed out in Chapter 3, hydrogen bonds are of great importance in aqueous systems and occur in solutions of proteins and other relatively polar substances. Formation and breakage of hydrogen bonds (about 4500 calories per mole) give water most of its peculiar properties.[15] For example, the heat of vaporization of water is high because all the hydrogen bonds between a water molecule and its neighbors must be broken before it can escape from the surface of the liquid. The high heat of fusion results from similar attraction.[3]

Carbon Dioxide in the Cell Environment

Carbon dioxide is present in the crust of the earth, in the air and in all natural waters. It is difficult to displace carbon dioxide from water; for example, even after water is boiled, it is rapidly acidified by the reentry of carbon dioxide. The great solubility of carbon dioxide in water is evident when it is compared with that of other gases. For example, 1.715 liters of carbon dioxide are absorbed at zero degrees centigrade by 1 liter of distilled water when the pressure of the carbon dioxide is 1 atmosphere, as compared with 0.049 liters for oxygen and 0.024 liters for nitrogen (see Table 7.1). Increases in temperature decrease the solubility of carbon dioxide in water as shown in Table 3.1. Increases in salt content of the water, as measured by the chlorinity,

TABLE 7.1. *Solubility or Absorption Coefficients of Some Gases*

TEMPERATURE °C.	SOLUBILITY COEFFICIENTS		
	CO_2	O_2	N_2
0	1.713	0.0489	0.0235
5	1.424	0.0428	0.0209
10	1.194	0.0380	0.0186
15	1.019	0.0341	0.0168
20	0.878	0.0310	0.0154
25	0.759	0.0283	0.0143

The solubility or absorption coefficient of a gas is the volume of gas reduced to 0°C. and 760 mm. Hg dissolved per volume of distilled water when the partial pressure of the gas is 1 atmosphere. To obtain ml. of gas per ml. water in equilibrium with air, multiply by the partial pressure of the gas in air: 0.03 per cent for CO_2, 20.99 per cent for O_2 and 78.03 per cent for N_2. (Data from Handbook of Chemistry and Physics, 35th Ed.)

have a like effect (see Table 7.2). Since CO_2 enters water so readily, an equilibrium always exists between the carbon dioxide in water and in air; water can never completely remove it from air, nor can air remove it from the water. At room temperature the amount of carbon dioxide dissolved in water is about equal to that in the air with which the water is in contact.

TABLE 7.2. *Solubility Coefficients of Carbon Dioxide, Showing Variation with Temperature and Chlorinity*

TEMPERATURE °C.	CHLORINITY IN GM./KGM.		
	0	16	20
	SOLUBILITY COEFFICIENTS OF CO_2		
0	1.715	1.489	1.438
12	1.118	0.980	0.947
24	0.782	0.695	0.677

Chlorinity is the halide content of sea water in grams per kilogram. Salinity = 0.03 + 1.805 × chlorinity. For other terms see Table 7.1. For conversion of data to ml. of carbon dioxide in equilibrium with air multiply by the partial pressure of carbon dioxide in air, 0.03 per cent. (Data from Sverdrup, Johnson and Fleming.[12])

Forming an acid as it dissolves in water, carbon dioxide increases the solvent powers of water for many substances. As a weak acid, it forms one of the primary buffers of the internal fluids of organisms and of terrestrial water, a role which will be discussed later (Chapter 8).

The importance of carbon dioxide as a raw material for photosynthesis in plants and as one of the wastes from the respiratory processes of plants and animals will also be discussed later (Chapters 19 and 20). Its fitness for these roles depends upon some of its properties already enumerated.

Carbon dioxide in the air absorbs some of the sunlight entering the atmosphere at wavelengths between 2 and 5 μ, and in this manner tempers the heating of the surface of the earth's crust. It also absorbs strongly the radiations between 13 and 17 μ, near the wavelengths at which the infrared radiations reradiated from the earth's crust are most intense (Fig. 7.1), thereby delaying the cooling of the surface of the earth with nightfall much as in the "greenhouse effect" described for water vapor.

A current theory ascribes an important role to carbon dioxide in regulating the over-all climate of the earth.[16] If the theory is valid the increase in carbon dioxide content of the atmosphere (11 per cent since 1870), from burning of fossil fuels, may have had and continues to have important consequences. Records indicate a rising temperature at the surface of the earth for the last 90 years. If the carbon dioxide concentration in the earth's atmosphere should double, the average temperature increase of the earth's surface would be 3.6° C. If the concentration of carbon dioxide should decrease to one half of its present value, the temperature would fall by 3.6° C, enough to cause great ice sheets to form again, as in the great glacial epochs of the earth's history. However, some workers postulate that variations in the output of the sun may also account for the great changes in climate.[21]

Oxygen in the Cell Environment

Because most organisms are aerobic, requiring oxygen to carry on life activities, oxygen is an important factor of the cellular environment. Oxygen is present in the air and constitutes 20.99 per cent of the atmosphere of the earth. The oxygen in the atmosphere becomes available to living cells as it is dissolved in the liquid medium outside and inside the cell. The oxygen of the atmosphere is continually being replenished as it is liberated in photosynthesis of green cells.

Oxygen is much less soluble in water than is carbon dioxide and diffuses slowly in water. If oxygen were to be distributed by diffusion alone, the oxygen content of a body of water would fall off rapidly below the surface because of the slowness of the diffusion process. However, turbulence caused by currents or welling up mixes a body of water and thereby carries oxygen down from the surface waters, greatly facilitating its distribution. The photosynthetic process of plant cells is also a major source of oxygen in natural waters. Water may even become saturated or supersaturated with oxygen in the neighborhood of photosynthetically active plants. On the other hand, if photosynthetic plants are absent and organic material is available, water may become devoid of oxygen as a consequence of the respiration of microorganisms of decay. In muds containing much organic matter, as for example those under brine pools, oxygen is absent within less than a millimeter of the surface. Wet, mucky soil is usually more or less lacking in oxygen, but loose soil contains air pockets with oxygen equal in concentration to that of air.

The solubility of oxygen in water falls with increase in temperature (see Table

7.1). The deleterious effect of high temperature on animals confined in an aquarium is often the result of lack of oxygen in the water, and care must be exercised to provide an adequate supply.

The solubility of oxygen in water also decreases with increase in salinity[12] (see Table 7.3). The oxygen content of sea water is therefore slightly less than that of fresh water at the same temperature. The oxygen content of brine, which may contain ten times as much salt as sea water, is very much less than that of sea water.

The gaseous content of liquids is presented in a variety of ways. In Tables 7.1 and 7.3 it is given in terms of the absorption (or solubility) coefficient, which is the volume of gas dissolved per volume of liquid when the partial pressure of the gas in question is 1 atmosphere. It is of greater biological interest to know how much of a particular gas is dissolved in a given volume of liquid in equilibrium with air at 1 atmosphere pressure rather than with the pure gas. According to Dalton's law, the total pressure of a mixture of gases is equal to the sum of the partial pressures of the gases constituting the mixture. If a liquid is exposed to a mixture of gases, each gas dissolves in proportion to its own *partial pressure* and independently of the other gases present. The volume of a gas dissolved per unit volume of water may therefore be determined by multiplying the absorption coefficient of the gas by the ratio of its partial pressure to the total gas pressure (e.g., at 1 atmosphere). To obtain the volume of a gas dissolved in any volume of water, the volume of gas dissolved per unit volume of water need only be multiplied by the volume of the water. For example, to determine the oxygen content of 100 ml. of water in equilibrium with air at 20° C. and 1 atmosphere pressure, multiply the absorption coefficient, 0.031 (see Table 7.1), by 0.2099, since air contains 20.99 per cent oxygen, and multiply the product by 100. This gives a value of 0.65 ml. oxygen per 100 ml. distilled water. In physiological literature the volume of the dissolved gas per 100 volumes of liquid is often spoken of as "volumes per cent."[18] However, the concentration of dissolved oxygen, from a physical-chemical standpoint, is better expressed in terms of the partial pressure of oxygen with which the liquid would be in equilibrium, a value which some physiologists call the *oxygen tension*[7, 18] of the liquid. The partial pressure of the oxygen is readily determined, if the solubility coefficient of the oxygen and the volume dissolved in the liquid under the particular experimental conditions are known, by the use of the equation:

$$\text{volume} = \text{partial pressure} \times \text{solubility coefficient} \quad (7.2)$$

where the volume of dissolved oxygen is given as volumes of gas per unit volume of liquid, the partial pressure in atmospheres (converted to mm. Hg by multiplying the fraction found by 760 mm.) and the solubility coefficient in volumes

TABLE 7.3. *Solubility Coefficients of Oxygen, Showing Variation with Temperature and Chlorinity*

TEMPER-ATURE °C.	CHLORINITY IN GM./KGM.			
	0	15	17	20
	SOLUBILITY COEFFICIENTS OF O_2			
0	.0489	.0406	.0395	.0378
5	.0429	.0359	.0350	.0336
10	.0380	.0321	.0313	.0301
15	.0342	.0292	.0284	.0274
20	.0310	.0267	.0262	.0253
25	.0283	.0246	.0240	.0231

For definition of terms see Tables 7.1 and 7.2. For conversion of data to ml. of oxygen in equilibrium with air multiply by the partial pressure of oxygen in air, 20.99 per cent. (Data from Sverdrup, Johnson and Fleming,[12] and Handbook of Chemistry and Physics. 35th Ed.)

of oxygen per volume of liquid under the conditions of the experiment.[7]

The problem of an adequate oxygen supply for the cells inside the body of a large animal is one which in the course of evolution has been solved by the development of oxygen-transporting pigments such as the hemoglobin in our blood. When these are lacking, as they are in the majority of echinoderms, the body fluid contains only as much oxygen as an equal volume of water under the same conditions of temperature and pressure. However, when an oxygen-transporting pigment is present, as in the blood of some mollusks, the amount of oxygen rises to 1 or 2 volumes per cent. In cephalopod mollusks, chironomid larvae (larvae of midges in pond mud) and annelid worms, it is about 2 to 10 volumes per cent. In the blood of fishes, amphibians and reptiles it is 5 to 15 volumes per cent and in birds and mammals 15 to 20 volumes per cent. The blood of some diving mammals has an oxygen capacity of 40 volumes per cent; that is,

almost twice as much oxygen is combined with the hemoglobin of the blood as is present in an equal volume of air.[18]

The oxygen loosely combined with the oxygen-transporting (or the respiratory) pigment is carried to all the cells where the oxygen is continually depleted during metabolism. A quantity of oxygen is then readily liberated in proportion to the difference between the higher oxygen tension in the blood and the lower one in the cells, in accordance with the relationship shown in Figure 7.3. Some respiratory pigments take up oxygen readily and almost saturate at relatively low oxygen tensions (e.g., the blood of the worm, *Arenicola*, and the eel), whereas others saturate only at much higher oxygen tensions (e.g., man and the pigeon).[6, 19] The advantage of the blood pigment such as that of *Arenicola* is the ready uptake of oxygen even when the oxygen tension of the environment is relatively low. However, such a pigment will not release the bound oxygen until the oxygen tension of the tissue cells is

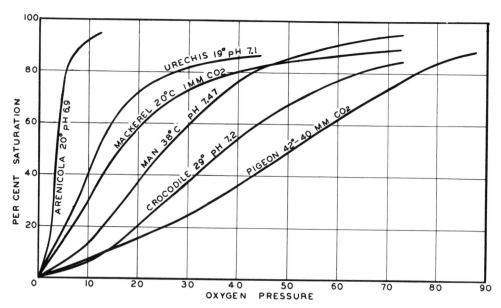

Fig. 7.3. Oxygen dissociation curves in per cent saturation of hemoglobin as a function of oxygen pressure (in mm. Hg) in a variety of animals. (Data assembled by Redfield, A. C., Biol. Rev., Vol. 9.)

THE CELL ENVIRONMENT

less than that of the blood, which in this case would have to be below 10 mm. Hg. In the pigeon an oxygen tension a little below 80 mm. Hg is sufficient to withdraw oxygen from the blood.

In the cells of green plants, the oxygen is supplied from the photosynthetic cells during the day. At night the cells must draw upon the oxygen reaching them by diffusion through neighboring cells or fluids in vessels which they may border. If utilization of oxygen is faster than can be supplied by diffusion, the plant cells are capable of anaerobic metabolism which can tide them over until oxygen becomes available (see Chapter 17).

Pressure as an Environmental Factor

Because dredgings from deep waters of the Mediterranean Sea disclosed no animal or plant life, it was once thought that no life existed in the depths of the ocean. Early in the last century, however, several peculiar animals were brought up on cables laid in the deep waters of the Atlantic, and later some peculiar fishes were caught where water wells up from the depths of the ocean near Madeira off the northwest coast of Africa. Since that time, towing, dredging and trawling have disclosed life at various levels of the ocean, including the greatest depths such as the Marianas Trench near the Philippines.[8] Life is not only present in deep waters but it is diverse, bacteria and representatives of all the animal phyla being found. Plants are largely confined to the upper 100 meters of the ocean but some microscopical forms occur in the unlighted deep waters where they presumably live on nutrients released by the decomposition of dying organisms. The failure to find animals in the Mediterranean Sea has been attributed to lack of oxygen in the particular regions initially tested; however, they do occur in other parts of the Sea floor sampled.

The cells of organisms in deep waters are under great hydrostatic pressures. For every 10 meters down (slightly over 5 fathoms or 33.4 feet) the pressure increases by about 1 atmosphere (0.987 atmosphere). At the bottom of the Marianas Trench, which is over 10,000 meters deep, the pressure is over 1000 atmospheres. Organisms of the depths therefore live in a unique environment quite different in several respects from that of surface forms.

Since hydrostatic pressure is distributed equally over the surface of organisms, it has been argued that deep water organisms need no special adaptations except, perhaps, receptors which enable active animals to perceive each other in the dark. Sensitive, large, stalked or tubular eyes, luminous organs and other receptors are common in deep water fishes and squids.[8] Deep sea fishes also lack swim bladders.[8] However, when coastal animals (mussels, clams, snails, worms and crustaceans) are subjected to pressures gradually increasing to 600 atmospheres, they are first stimulated to greater activity, then depressed and inactivated.[10] Of all the invertebrates tested, starfish and coelenterates tolerated the highest pressures and were inactivated only by exposure for 1 hour to 1000 atmospheres, which is equivalent to the pressures of the deepest oceans. At this pressure they swelled, but several hours after their return to atmospheric pressure, they recovered. Frogs and fishes were more sensitive than the invertebrates, and were killed by 300 to 400 atmospheres of pressure.[10] It would seem that organisms of the deep seas have developed some special adaptations enabling them to withstand the great pressures at these depths and still carry on their activities.

The nature of the pressure tolerance adaptations at the cell level have been investigated to only a limited extent and primarily with marine eggs and microorganisms. Sea urchin eggs (*Arbacia punctulata*), beginning to cleave, revert back to the one-celled stage under pressures of more than 400 atmospheres. The contraction and gelation required for cleavage are suppressed. If released within a short time, cleavage is resumed. About the same amount of pressure suppresses formation of pseudopodia in *Amoeba proteus;* the plasmagel appears to solate and the viscosity of the cytoplasm falls to a value so low that the food vacuoles and the nucleus sink to the bottom of the cell.[17] It is thus apparent that pressure has a striking effect on sol-gel relationships of the cell. One might expect that chemical reactions would also be affected by pressure, and investigations have demonstrated suppression of bacterial luminescence under certain conditions. Presumably, growth also is suppressed by pressure because cultures of such bacteria as *Bacillus subtilis* and *Pseudomonas fluorescens* fail to grow at pressures

of 300 atmospheres or more.[20] Replication of phage in *Escherichia coli* is prevented by 300 atmospheres of pressure, but as soon as the pressure is released, growth is resumed. Yet there exist marine bacteria, such as *Bacillus submarinus,* isolated from the ocean depths where pressure approximates 500 atmospheres, which grow readily at a pressure of even 600 atmospheres.[11]

Since most of the reactions of the cell are catalyzed by enzymes, it is thought that the suppression of cell activities by pressure is a result of action of pressure upon cell enzymes which are proteinaceous in nature. Some evidence has already been presented (Chapter 3) that pressure reverses the denaturing effect of temperature on proteins. It will be recalled that an increase in temperature influences the equilibrium between native and denatured protein in the direction of

TABLE 7.4. *Effect of Temperature and Hydrostatic Pressure on Bacterial Growth*

CULTURE	300 ATM (4410 PSI)			400 ATM (5880 PSI)			500 ATM (7350 PSI)			600 ATM (8820 PSI)		
	20°	30°	40°	20°	30°	40°	20°	30°	40°	20°	30°	40°
Terrestrial:												
Clostridium												
sporogenes	—	4+	4+	—	2+	3+	—	—	—	—	—	—
Bacillus subtilis	—	3+	4+	—	2+	4+	—	—	3+	—	—	2+
Pseudomonas												
fluorescens	2+	3+	4+	—	2+	4+	—	—	3+	—	—	—
Marine:												
Achromobacter												
thalassius	—	4+	2+	—	—	3+	—	—	—	—	—	—
Bacillus submarinus	2+	4+	4+	1+	4+	4+	—	4+	4+	—	4+	4+
Pseudomonas												
xanthocrus	4+	4+	—	4+	3+	1+	2+	2+	2+	1+	1+	—

All cultures, except *P. xanthocrus,* showed 4+ growth at all three temperatures at atmospheric pressure; this culture grew at 20° and 30°, but not at 40°. ATM signifies atmospheres; PSI, pounds per square inch.

After Zobell and Johnson;[20] from Oginsky and Umbreit, 1954: Introduction to Bacterial Physiology. W. H. Freeman & Co., San Francisco.

the denatured form. Denaturation in most proteins is accompanied by an increase in volume as shown by dilatometric measurements. Since pressure and temperature act in opposition to one another, one would therefore expect pressure to reverse thermal denaturation by suppressing volume increase in accordance with the principle of Le Chatelier.[11] This is indeed found to be the case. Enzymes which are necessary for life activities are catalytic in only a particular configuration, neither fully unfolded nor folded.[11]

Thus, surface bacteria which cannot tolerate the pressures of deep waters at low temperatures are shown to tolerate them and grow if the temperature is increased, as seen in the data of Table 7.4. Perhaps the truly barophilic (literally, pressure-loving) bacteria and other organisms are those in which the enzymes have the proper configuration even under great pressures and at relatively low temperatures.[20]

GENERAL REFERENCES

Blum, H. F., 1955: Time's Arrow and Evolution. 2nd Ed. Princeton Univ. Press, Princeton, N. J. In Chapter 6, Dr. Blum brings up to date Henderson's arguments on the fitness of the environment, and he adds newer experimental data.

Cattell, J. M., 1936: The Physiological Effect of Pressure. Biol. Rev. 11:441–476.

Edsall, J. T., and Wyman, J., 1958: Biophysical Chemistry. Academic Press, New York, I: 27–46 (water) and 550–590 (carbon dioxide).

Henderson, L. J., 1927: Fitness of the Environment. Macmillan, New York.

Hess, S. L., 1958: Atmospheres of Other Planets. Science 128:809–814.

Johnson, F. H., Eyring, H., and Polissar, M., 1954: The Kinetic Basis of Molecular Biology. Wiley, New York.

Johnson, F. S., 1961: Satellite Environment Handbook. Stanford Univ. Press, Stanford, Calif.

Marshall, N. B., 1954: Aspects of Deep Sea Biology. Philosophical Library, New York.

Sverdrup, H. U., Johnson, M. W., and Fleming, R. H., 1942: The Oceans. Prentice-Hall, New York.

LITERATURE CITED

1. Cannon, W. B., 1932: The Wisdom of the Body. Norton, New York. See also Richards, 1954: Sci. Month. 77:289, for criticism of homeostasis.
2. Bernard, C., 1879: Leçons sur les Phénomènes de la Vie aux Animaux et aux Végétaux, 2 vols. Paris.
3. Blum, H. F., 1955: Time's Arrow and Evolution. Princeton Univ. Press, Princeton, N. J., Chapter 6.
4. Höber, R. (ed.), 1945: Physical Chemistry of Cells and Tissues. Blakiston, Philadelphia, Chapter 2.
5. Edsall, J. T., and Wyman, J., 1958: Biophysical Chemistry I: 27–41, Academic Press, New York.
6. Manwell, C., 1960: Ann. Rev. Physiol. 22:191.
7. Guyton, A. C., 1961: Textbook of Medical Physiology. Ed. 2. Saunders, p. 450.
8. Marshall, N. B., 1954: Aspects of Deep Sea Biology. Philosophical Library, New York.
9. Zobell, C. E., 1952: Science 115:507.
10. Cattell, J. M., 1936: Biol. Rev. 11:441.
11. Johnson, F. H., Eyring, H., and Polissar, M., 1954: Kinetic Basis of Molecular Biology. Wiley, New York.
12. Sverdrup, H. U., Johnson, M. W., and Fleming, R. H., 1942: The Oceans: Their Physics, Chemistry and General Biology. Prentice-Hall, New York.
13. Lederberg, J., 1960: Science 132:393.
14. Benson, O. O., Jr., and Stughold, H., 1960: Physics and Medicine of the Atmosphere and Space. Wiley, New York.
15. Buswell, A. M., and Rodebush, April. 1956: Sci. Am. 194:77.
16. Plass, G. N., July 1959: Sci. Am. 201:41. 1958: Am. Scient. 44:302.
17. Marsland, D., Oct. 1958: Sci. Am. 199:36–43.
18. Krogh, A., 1941: The Comparative Physiology of Respiratory Mechanisms. Univ. Pennsylvania Press, Philadelphia.
19. Prosser, C. L., and Brown. F. A., Jr., 1961. Comparative Animal Physiology. 2nd Ed. Saunders, Philadelphia.
20. Zobell, C. E., and Johnson, F. H., 1949. J. Bact. 57:179.
21. Öpik, E. J., June 1958: Sci. Am. 198:85.
22. Davis, K. S., and Day, J. A., 1961: Water, the Mirror of Science. Doubleday, New York.

ELECTROLYTES IN THE CELL ENVIRONMENT

Electrolytes in the external cell environment and in the inside of the cell play a role in all cell activities. Many ions affect the consistency of protoplasm, the selectivity of the cell membrane and the activity of enzymes in cells. Contractility of muscular cells requires the presence of magnesium, potassium and other ions. Irritability of cells depends upon the concentrations and proportions of various monovalent and divalent cations. The hydrogen ion concentration determines not only the degree of dissociation of a protein but also its charge. Since, next to water, protein is the most prevalent substance in protoplasm, the hydrogen ion concentration exerts a profound effect, not only on the structural relations of protein molecules in protoplasm but also on the activity of proteins as enzymes.

Acids, Bases and Hydrogen Ions

An *acid* may be defined as a substance which forms hydrogen ions in solution and from which hydrogen may be displaced by a metal when a salt is formed. A hydrogen ion is a positively charged hydrogen atom or proton. A *base* may be

defined as a substance which yields hydroxyl ions in solution and reacts with an acid to form a salt and water. A *salt* may be defined as a compound formed when the hydrogen of an acid has been replaced by a metal. (For more general definitions, see Appendix 8.1).

Acids and bases are present in natural waters and in the internal media of plant and animal cells. The total acid or base content of a given quantity of medium can be determined by titration (see Table 8.1), but we are much more interested in the concentration of the hydrogen ions present than in the titratable acid or base, since the hydrogen ion is such an important catalyst in biological reactions.

Dissociation of Weak Acids, Weak Bases and Water

Strong acids and strong bases are completely ionized and dissociated in water, but weak acids and weak bases are only partially dissociated in water, the degree of dissociation depending upon the strength of the acid or base. The degree of dissociation of weak electrolytes may be determined by the conductivity of solutions, as well as by other methods.

When a weak acid, HA, is dissolved in water, it dissociates, and if the velocity of the reaction in the direction of dissociation is given by V_1, and the velocity of association of the ions to re-form molecules of acid is given by V_2, at equilibrium we have the following relationship:

$$HA \underset{V_2}{\overset{V_1}{\rightleftharpoons}} H^+ + A^- \qquad (8.1)$$

The value of V_1 increases as the acid dissociates more completely, and the equilibrium is then said to lie to the far right. Under a given set of conditions the velocity of the reaction to the right depends primarily on the concentration of HA:

$$V_1 = k_1 [HA] \qquad (8.2)$$

where k_1 represents a constant.

The velocity of the reaction to the left depends upon the concentration of H^+ and A^-.

$$V_2 = k_2 [H^+] [A^-] \qquad (8.3)$$

k_2 represents another constant.

When equilibrium is reached the quantity of acid dissociating is equal to that reassociating; therefore, V_1 equals V_2, and

$$k_2 [H^+] [A^-] = k_1 [HA]. \qquad (8.4)$$

By dividing each side by k_2 and by [HA], expression of the law of mass action is obtained:

$$\frac{[H^+] [A^-]}{[HA]} = \frac{k_1}{k_2} = K_a \qquad (8.5)$$

where K_a is the dissociation constant of the weak acid or the ratio of dissociation to association. At room temperature for acetic acid, K_a is 1.85×10^{-5} (or 43 molecules in 10,000); for formic acid, it is 2.4×10^{-4}; and for boric acid, 6.4×10^{-10}. It should be apparent that the smaller the dissociation constant the weaker the acid. A parallel formulation might be developed for dissociation of weak bases.[2]

Water also dissociates, though very slightly, and at all times is present in the two states, dissociated and undissociated. Water is unique in that, on dissociation, it gives rise to both hydrogen ions (like an acid) and hydroxyl ions (like a base). For the dissociation of water the following equations may be written:

$$H_2O \rightleftharpoons H^+ + OH^- \qquad (8.6)$$

$$\frac{[H^+] [OH^-]}{[H_2O]} = K \qquad (8.7)$$

where K is the dissociation constant of water.

Then,

$$[H^+] [OH^-] = K [H_2O] \qquad (8.8)$$

Since the degree of dissociation is so slight, $[H_2O]$ may be considered as approximately constant. Therefore it may be combined with K, giving K_w:

$$[H^+] [OH^-] = K_w \qquad (8.9)$$

The experimentally determined electrical conductivity of pure water at room temperature indicates that the concentration of hydrogen (or hydroxyl) ions is approximately 10^{-7}N.

Therefore,

$$K_w = 10^{-7} \times 10^{-7} = 10^{-14} \qquad (8.10)$$

The dissociation of water, as is true of dissociation in general, depends upon the temperature. At lower temperatures it is somewhat less than the value given for room temperature, and at higher temperatures somewhat greater. For example, K_w is 0.115×10^{-14} at $0°C$. and 9.614×10^{-14} at $60°C$. Since the hydrogen ion is one of the important biological catalysts, the increase in hydrogen ion concentration with rise in temperature may explain in part the increased activity of reactions in organisms when the temperature is raised,[1] although effects of temperature on the dissociation constants of buffer systems are probably of greater importance.

TABLE 8.1. *Difference Between Normality and pH of Acetic and Hydrochloric Acids*

N of solution	pH of HAc	pH of HCl
.20	2.69	0.81
.10	2.85	1.09
.04	3.08	1.46
.02	3.24	1.77
.01	3.39	2.06

The pH Scale

Although the hydrogen ion concentration can be expressed in terms of normality (see Tables 8.1 and 8.2), this is inconvenient because either exponents or small decimals must be employed. To avoid these difficulties Sørensen chose to express the concentration of hydrogen ions by negative logarithms of the hydrogen ion concentration. This function he called the pH:

$$pH = -\log_{10} [H^+] \qquad (8.11)$$

The relation between pH and hydrogen ion concentration is given in Table 8.2. The pH scale ranges from 0 to 14 or from 1N $[H^+]$ to 1N $[OH^-]$. A greater range of acidity and alkalinity is possible but is not likely to be encountered in biological systems or in the normal environment. Even the present scale is beyond the limits normally encountered in nature.

Because, in water, the concentration of hydrogen ions equals the concentration of hydroxyl ions, water is considered neutral. Since the hydrogen ion concentration of water is 10^{-7}, at room temperature the pH of water is 7.0. Therefore a pH lower than 7.0 indicates a concentration of hydrogen ions greater than that found in water and the solution is considered acid. The acidity increases as the pH falls (see Table 8.2). When the pH is greater than 7.0, the hydrogen ion concentration is less than that in water and the solution is considered alkaline or basic. The higher the pH, the more alkaline the solution. The product of the concentrations of the hydrogen and the hydroxyl ions is always 10^{-14}N at 20° C.

The effects of pH upon cells and biological reactions have been extensively explored and references to these effects will be encountered in succeeding chapters as various biological functions are considered.

While biologists were the first to emphasize the importance of pH, chemists also soon became aware of the need to control the hydrogen ion concentration, especially in industrial operations.

Measurement of the Strength of a Weak Acid by the pKa

By applying the law of mass action to dissociation of a weak acid, HA, the following expressions may be written:

$$HA \rightleftharpoons H^+ + A^- \qquad (8.1)$$

TABLE 8.2. *The Relation Between Normality and pH*

[H$^+$]		[OH$^-$]	LOG [H$^+$]	$-$LOG [H$^+$] = pH
1N	10^0N	10^{-14}N	0	0
0.1N	10^{-1}N	10^{-13}N	-1	1
0.001N	10^{-3}N	10^{-11}N	-3	3
0.000,01N	10^{-5}N	10^{-9}N	-5	5
0.000,000,1N	10^{-7}N	10^{-7}N	-7	7
0.000,000,001N	10^{-9}N	10^{-5}N	-9	9
0.000,000,000,01N	10^{-11}N	10^{-3}N	-11	11
0.000,000,000,000,01N	10^{-14}N	10^{-0}N	-14	14

$$\frac{[H^+][A^-]}{[HA]} = K_a, \text{ the acid dissociation} \quad (8.5)$$
$$\text{constant.}$$

Solving for $[H^+]$:

$$[H^+] = \frac{K_a[HA]}{[A^-]} \quad (8.12)$$

Taking the negative logarithm of each side,

$$-\log_{10}[H^+] = -\log_{10}K_a - \log_{10}\frac{[HA]}{[A^-]}. \quad (8.13)$$

By definition, $-\log_{10}[H^+] = pH$, and $-\log_{10}K_a = pK_a$; and since

$$-\log_{10}\frac{[HA]}{[A^-]} = +\log_{10}\frac{[A^-]}{[HA]},$$

substitution of these values in equation 8.13 gives:

$$pH = pK_a + \log_{10}\frac{[A^-]}{[HA]} \quad (8.14)$$

When the salt of a weak acid is added to a solution of that acid, the dissociation of the acid is suppressed by the common ion effect (law of mass action). Consequently, most of the acid is present in the undissociated form and the concentration of anion in solution becomes approximately equal to the concentration of dissolved salt. By applying equation 8.14 to this case it will be seen that the term for anion concentration may be replaced by a term for salt concentration, and the acid concentration may be considered approximately equal to the total acid. The equation may now be written:

$$pH = pK_a + \log_{10}\frac{[salt]}{[acid]} \quad (8.15)$$

This equation is known as the Henderson-Hasselbalch equation for buffer action.

When the concentrations of salt and acid are equal, the second term drops out of the Henderson-Hasselbalch equation, since the $\log_{10}$ of 1 is zero. The pH then equals the pK_a. By this method it is relatively easy to determine the pK_a values for acids.

It should be noted that a large pK_a indicates a weak acid, a small pK_a a strong acid. Multivalent acids possess several dissociation constants, for each of which a pK_a may be determined.[2]

Once the pK_a of an acid is known, the ratio of acid to salt required to attain a desired pH may be readily calculated. Conversely, if the concentrations of salt and acid are known, the pH of the mixture may be readily calculated. However, it must be remembered that the Henderson-Hasselbalch equation is an approximation only. It holds best near the midportion of the curve where salt and acid are in nearly equal concentration. It is most in error when applied to widely divergent ratios of acid and salt. As the pK_a is also a function of the total salt concentration, an experimentally determined pK_a may differ significantly from a handbook value which is cited for the weak acid and its salt at a given concentration in the absence of extraneous salts.

Effects of Buffers on pH

The commonest buffer is a mixture of a weak acid and its salt. When acid is added to a buffer the pH changes slowly since, according to the Henderson-Hasselbalch equation, the pH depends upon the ratio of the salt to the undissociated acid and this ratio changes slowly when acid is added, because the salt suppresses the dissociation of the acid by the common ion effect.

The pK_a of the acid used in a buffer represents the midpoint of the effective buffer range because at this point acid and salt are present in equal concentrations. If acid is added the pH slowly falls; if base is added the pH slowly rises. The range at which a buffer is most useful lies between one pH unit on either side of the pK_a. The change in pH with addition of acid or base is shown in Figures 8.1, 8.2 and 8.3. When the acid is completely

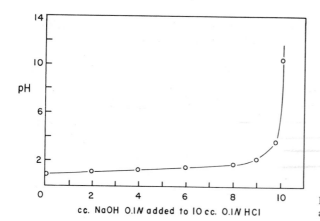

Fig. 8.1. Change in pH when a strong acid is titrated with a base.

neutralized the pH will sweep to the alkaline range.

Often weak acids with several dissociation constants are used as buffers. Each pK_a of a multivalent acid represents the midpoint of one of the buffer ranges. The effective buffer ranges of such a system are about one pH unit to either side of each of these pK_a values. When the dissociation constants are close together, as in citric acid, a wide pH range may be covered by buffers made from the acid. Citric acid, in fact, is one of the favorite acids used in buffers (see McIlvaine buffer series, Table 8.3), although like phosphate it removes calcium ions, a factor which

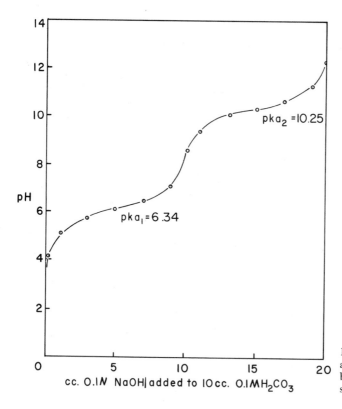

Fig. 8.2. Change in pH when a weak acid, carbonic acid, is titrated with a base. Note the two dissociation constants of carbonic acid (25° C.).

must be taken into account in making up physiological media.

When a strong acid and one of its salts are used to make a buffer system the buffering action is restricted to the low pH range, because no matter how much salt is present the acid remains completely dissociated and the pH low. The pK_a of a strong acid cannot be determined because in absence of the common ion effect suppressing ionization of the acid, the Henderson-Hasselbalch equation does not apply. A buffer made from a strong acid and its salt also resists pH change on addition of base, changing no more than one pH unit until about 80 per cent of the acid is neutralized (see Fig. 8.1).

All that has been said of acids and their salts as buffering systems may also be said of bases and their salts. Since nothing would be gained by repeating the entire formulation for bases and their salts as buffering systems, discussion of them is omitted here but may be found in references cited[2] (see Appendix 8.2).

Buffer Capacity. A buffer's capacity is measured by the degree of change of pH following addition of a given amount of acid or base. A buffer of a given concentration has greatest buffer capacity at a pH near the pK_a of the buffer acid. The concentration of the buffer determines its capacity to absorb base or acid at any pH. Dilution of a buffer usually changes the pH slightly. Dilution also proportionally decreases the buffer capacity, and if very close control of pH is desired this must be taken into account. Some characteristics of buffers are given in Table 8.3.

Buffering Systems in the Cell Environment

Environmental waters free of decomposing organic matter are generally alkaline or neutral, as may be seen from the

TABLE 8.3. *Standard Buffer Mixtures*[1]

NAME OF BUFFER	CONSTITUENTS	pH RANGE	
Clark and Lubs	Phthalate-HCl	2.2 – 3.8	(20° C.)
Clark and Lubs	Phthalate-NaOH	4.0 – 6.2	(20° C.)
Clark and Lubs	KH_2PO_4-NaOH	5.8 – 8.0	(20° C.)
Clark and Lubs	Boric acid, KCl-NaOH	7.8 –10.0	(20° C.)
Clark and Lubs	HCl-KCl	1.0 – 2.2	(20° C.)
Sørensen	Glycine-NaCl-NaOH	8.58–12.97	(18° C.)
Sørensen	Borate-NaOH	9.24–12.38	(18° C.)
Sørensen	Borate-HCl	7.61– 9.23	(20° C.)
Sørensen	Citrate-HCl	1.04– 4.96	(18° C.)
Sørensen	Glycine-HCl	1.04– 3.68	(18° C.)
Sørensen	Na_2HPO_4-KH_2PO_4	5.29– 8.04	(18° C.)
Sørensen	Citrate-NaOH	4.96– 6.69	(20° C.)
Palitzsch	Borax-borate	8.69– 6.77	(18° C.)
McIlvaine	Citric-NaH_2PO_4	2.2 – 8.0	
Tris(hydroxymethyl) aminomethane[2]	Tris + HCl	7.0 – 9.0	(20° C.)
Kolthoff and Vleeschhouwer	Na_2CO_3-borax	9.2 –11.0	(18° C.)
Kolthoff and Vleeschhouwer	Na_2HPO_4-NaOH	11.0 –12.0	(18° C.)

[1] Data from Clark.[5]
[2] Whitehead, 1959: J. Chem. Educ. *36*:297; and Bulletin 106, Sigma Chemical Co., St. Louis.

data in Table 8.4. For example, the pH of ocean water is generally 7.8 to 8.2. Fresh water is more variable, and if any decomposing material is present, the pH falls because of the organic acids produced by organisms growing in the water.

In the ocean, rivers and lakes the primary buffering is accomplished by the carbonate-bicarbonate system (see Fig. 8.2). Because of the ubiquity of carbon dioxide in natural waters this buffer system is unavoidable in nature; in the presence of such ions as sodium, potassium, calcium and magnesium, carbon dioxide forms bicarbonates, thereby keeping natural waters on the slightly alkaline side of neutrality. Whenever living organisms are present in natural waters they constantly contribute some carbon dioxide, but unless many are crowded in a small space this is not likely to have much effect upon the pH, unless at the same time organic acids are being produced, as occurs in bogs covered by mosses.

Since carbon dioxide is one of the main wastes of cell metabolism and is constantly being formed in the organism, it is always available in the internal environment. Therefore, the carbonate-bicarbonate buffer system is also the main buffer of plasma and body fluids of organisms. The pK_{a1} of carbonic acid is 6.34, the pK_{a2} is 10.25 at 25° C.[3, 4]

Another buffer system of considerable importance to the cells of the organism is the phosphate buffer system.[2, 3, 4] At 25° C. phosphoric acid of very low concentration has a pK_{a1} value of 2.12, a pK_{a2} value of 7.12 and a pK_{a3} value of 12.66 (see Fig. 8.3). The values differ with change of temperature and with change in concentration, as has already been pointed out, and these factors

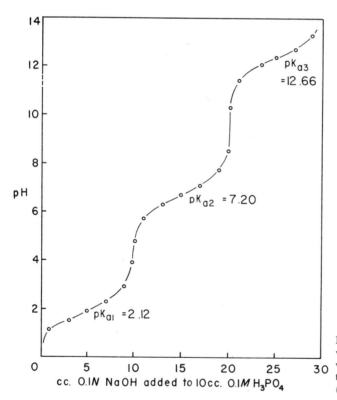

Fig. 8.3. Change in pH when a weak acid, phosphoric acid, is titrated with a base. Note the three dissociation constants of phosphoric acid (25° C.).

THE CELL ENVIRONMENT

TABLE 8.4. *pH Values of Environmental Media and Some Organisms Found Therein*

TYPE OF HABITAT	pH RANGE	MEDIUM	CHARACTERISTIC ORGANISMS
Very acid	0.0	Sulfur and salts	*Thiobacillus thiooxidans.*
	1.0– 3.0	Organic	The fungus, *Merulius lacrymans.*
	2.0	Organic	Acetate flagellates after adaptation.
	3.2– 4.6	Peat bogs	Mosses: *Sphagnum* and *Drepanocladus.*
	3.4	Vinegar	Vinegar eels (nematodes), vinegar bacteria.
	3.2	Soil water	High moor vegetation.
	3.3– 3.7	Organic	The flagellate, *Astasia*, in tryptone (lower limit).
Somewhat acid	5.2	Sour milk	Lactic acid bacteria.
	5.7– 5.8	Distilled water Fresh rain	
Somewhat acid to alkaline	5.2– 9.0	Soil water	Peat pit mosses.
	6.2– 9.2	Neutro-alkaline lakes	Mosses at edge.
	4.5– 8.5	Soil water in most soils	Various forest and field plants.
Nearly neutral	6.8– 7.0	Freshly boiled (cooled) distilled water	
	6.5– 8.0	Drinking water	
	6.8– 8.6	River water	River plants and animals.
	6.2– 8.2	Springs	Algae around springs.
	7.8– 8.6	Sea water	Marine plants and animals.
Alkaline	7.5– 9.1	Soil water	Greasewood, rabbit bush, salt grass and brome grass growing on alkaline flats.
	9.0– 9.6	Organic medium	*Astasia*, extreme alkaline range.
	10.0	Alkaline desert pool	Cyprinid fishes (Denio, Nevada).
	10.5	Organic medium	Dermatophytes.
	10.5	Inorganic	Larvae of *Aedes matronius.*
	9.3–11.1	Organic medium	Several species of *Penicillium*, one of which tolerates pH 11.1; also some species of *Aspergillus.*

Data for *Thiobacillus* from Stanier, Doudoroff and Adelberg, 1957: The Microbial World; for fungi from Wolf, 1947: The Fungi, II, and Leise and James, 1946: Arch. Dermat. & Syph. *53;* for mosses from Sørensen, 1948: Dansk Botanisk Arkiv., *12:*5, and Richards and Verdoorn, 1932: Manual of Bryology; for Salt Lake from Flowers, 1933: The Bryologist, 34; for acetate flagellates, Hutner and Provasoli, 1951, in Lwoff: Biochem. & Physiol. of the Protozoa, I; for *Astasia* from Schoenborn, 1949: J. Exp. Zool., *111;* for desert pool near Denio, personal communication from Eminger Stewart; for *Aedes* from Beadle, 1932: J. Linn. Soc. London, Zool 38; others from the Handbook of Chemistry and Physics, 35th Ed., and various other sources.

Note: More examples are given for the extremes because endurance of these conditions is so unusual. Most organisms occur in an environment slightly to the acid or alkaline side of neutrality.

should be taken into account when buffers are used in experiments. The middle pK_a value lies in the pH range which is of importance in biological systems and helps maintain the pH of blood and body fluids. In this range the buffer salts present are usually NaH_2PO_4 and Na_2HPO_4.

Proteins, amino acids, fatty acids and various organic acids may also serve as buffers in organisms. Some of the organic acids like citric acid are especially suitable. However, the role of such buffers is decidedly secondary to carbonic acid.

Inside the living cell phosphate is an important buffer (see Fig. 3.1) being present in relatively large amounts, together with the carbonate and protein buffers. The pH readings inside cells depend upon the part of the cell tested and the species. For example, animal tissue cells and *Amoeba* varied between pH 6.5 and pH 7.5, while yeast and plant cells were below pH 6.0. However, none of the methods of measurement appears satisfactory because they require piercing the cell, a procedure likely to be injurious.[16]

Ampholytes or Zwitterions

Ampholytes are inorganic and organic substances which can act as acids or as bases; that is, they can either give off or take up hydrogen ions, depending upon the conditions under which they are placed. If an acid is added to an ampholyte, the latter will dissociate as a base. If a base is added, the ampholyte will dissociate as an acid. Perhaps the concept may be illustrated best with amino acids (and proteins), which are of special importance to the cell.

An amino acid probably exists as a zwitterion, i.e., charged both positively and negatively, at the electrically neutral point, which is called the *isoelectric point*. At this *isoelectric* pH there is no net accumulation of amino acid at either anode or cathode of an electric field, and the ions are therefore considered to be equally charged negatively and positively. Several lines of evidence indicate that amino acids exist as zwitterions rather than as uncharged molecules. For instance, they have a high solubility in water; they have a highly polar nature, shown by their behavior in an electromagnetic field; and they have relatively high boiling points—properties which cannot be explained if uncharged molecules are assumed. The isoelectric pH is different for different amino acids (6.1 for glycine, 5.7 for serine, 3.0 for aspartic acid), and it depends upon the number and relative strength of acid and basic groups in the amino acid, i.e., their tendency to ionize. On the acid side of the isoelectric pH an amino acid is positively charged, and on the alkaline side, negatively charged:

$$\overset{+}{H_3N}-R-COO^- + H^+ \rightleftharpoons$$
$$\overset{+}{H_3N}-R-COOH \quad (8.16)$$

zwitterion

$$HO^- + \overset{+}{H_3N}-R-COO^- \rightleftharpoons$$
zwitterion
$$H_2N-R-COO^- + H_2O \quad (8.17)$$

It must not be construed that proteins dissociate as if they were a multitude of amino acids. The peptide backbone of the protein binds most of the amino and carboxyl groups of the constituent amino acids. Only the end groups of the peptide chains and the extra amino and carboxyl groups of the polyamino and polycarboxy amino acids and special groups such as the hydroxy group of tyrosine are free to dissociate as the pH of the solution containing the protein is changed.

Resistance of Cells to pH Changes

An ameba tolerates an environmental pH range of 4.2 to 8.2, and yeast tolerates a range of about 4.5 to 8.5. Since each pH unit is equal to a tenfold change in hydrogen ion concentration, this range represents a ten-thousandfold change. As seen from the data in Table 8.4, cells of organisms, such as vinegar bacteria, vinegar eels (nematodes), certain mosses and some fungi, tolerate much more acid conditions; others, such as the dermatophyte fungi and plants of the alkali regions, tolerate more alkaline conditions, while most organisms exist in a range of pH 6.0 to 8.0. The hydrogen ion does not penetrate into cells rapidly, but under certain conditions hydrogen ions may drive a weak acid into cells. For example, carbonic acid at a low pH is largely in the molecular form, which enters cells readily. Inside the cell is dissociates, acidifying the cell. Conversely, under alkaline conditions carbonic acid may be withdrawn from the cell, combining with the alkali to form bicarbonate. The pH may therefore influence entry into and exit from cells of various weak acids. (For the converse effects obtained with a weak base such as ammonia, see Chapter 12).

While the pH of environmental waters and soil water containing decomposing material is highly variable, the pH of body fluids and bloods, particularly of higher animals, is found to be held within narrow limits as seen in Table 8.5. For example, the blood of man is very closely regulated at a pH of 7.4 and if the pH of blood falls to 7.0, acidotic coma and death ensue, while at a pH of 7.8 life terminates in tetany. The body fluids of a number of invertebrates lie in the same pH range as those of the vertebrates. However, a few are neutral—for example, the body fluid of ascidians—and others are as alkaline as pH 7.8. In fact, the fluid inside a coelenterate may have the same pH as sea water, approximately 8.2. On the other hand, the body fluid of some insects undergoing metamorphosis may be as acid as pH 6.8. Acidity in such cases may result from the accumulation of metabolic carbon dioxide and organic acids which are incompletely voided

when the excretory system is not functioning.

Some plant saps and fruit juices are highly acid (see Table 8.5), but it must be remembered that most of the organic acids are stored in the vacuoles of the cells, not in the protoplasm. The pH of sap obtained by squeezing fruits is probably the pH of the vacuolar contents, not necessarily that of the protoplasm of the cell.

The pH of cells is variable but is usually in a narrow zone on either side of neutrality.[7, 8]

Methods of Measuring pH

Because of its simplicity and inexpensiveness, the most readily available method for measuring pH is the *colorimetric method*. Dyes, usually weak acids and bases which are either differently or more intensely colored in their ionic form than in their undissociated form, are used for this purpose. Standard solutions are made up in carefully prepared buffers against which unknown solutions, containing the same amount of dye as the standard, may be matched.

TABLE 8.5. *pH Values of Body Fluids, Blood and Plant Fluids*

pH RANGE	FLUIDS
7.3–7.5	Blood of man
7.3–7.5	Spinal fluid of man
6.9–7.2	Whole blood, dog
6.7–7.9	Body fluids or blood of various invertebrates
6.6–7.6	Milk, human
6.9–7.5	Saliva, human
1.0–3.0	Gastric contents, man
4.8–8.2	Duodenal contents, man
2.9–3.3	Apple juice freshly extracted
2.2–2.4	Lemon juice
1.8–2.0	Lime juice
5.0–5.2	Expressed juice of *Sedum* leaf

Data from Handbook of Chemistry and Physics, 35th Ed., and from Prosser and Brown.[17]

The pKa value of the dye acid (or base) gives the point of half dissociation. The approximate range over which the dye may be used effectively is roughly one pH unit to either side of the pKa value. Various dyes used for this purpose are described by Clark.[5] Some data for dyes frequently used in the biological range are given in Table 8.6.

One disadvantage of the dye method is that it depends upon the hue sensitivity of the human eye, a variable trait. Another disadvantage is the effect of some opaque or light-scattering material which obscures color matching. Furthermore, when a solution to be tested has a deep color, e.g., blood, colorimetric methods are useless. In the presence of proteins, or in the presence of salt, additional errors arise. The colorimetric method is therefore largely limited to colorless materials containing little or no salt or protein. With the exercise of proper precautions the colorimetric method can be accurate to about 0.1 pH unit for solutions not subject to the above errors, but under crude conditions it is probably accurate to only one pH unit. Nonetheless, it is effective for field studies where a pH meter is not available.

For routine determination of pH the simpler and more accurate electrometric method is now used much more commonly than the colorimetric method.[9] In the commercial pH meter two electrodes, a glass electrode and a calomel electrode, are dipped into the unknown solution, as shown in Figure 8.4. The glass electrode consists of a bubble of glass containing a solution of known concentration of hydrochloric acid, usually 0.1 normal with respect to hydrogen ions, into which extends a silver-silver chloride wire.[6] The calomel electrode contains calomel (Hg_2Cl_2) in contact on one side with saturated potassium chloride and on the other with mercury from which a platinum wire connects to the potentiometer. A potential arises because of a difference in concentration between the hydrogen ions inside the glass electrode and in the unknown solution, the two being sepa-

TABLE 8.6. *Characteristics of Indicators for Measuring pH*

CONCENTRATION OF INDICATOR IN SOLUTION, %	pH RANGE COVERED	NAME AND ABBREVIATION	pKa	COLOR CHANGE
0.04	1.2–2.8	Thymol blue (TB)	1.5	Red–yellow
0.04	3 –4.6	Brom phenol blue (BPB)	3.98	Yellow–blue
0.01	3.2–5	Congo red (CoR)	—	Blue–violet–scarlet
0.016	3.8–5.4	Brom cresol green (BCG)	4.67	Yellow–blue
0.02 in 60% alc.	4 –6	Methyl red (MR)	5.1	Red–yellow
0.010	4.8–6.4	Chlor phenol red (CPR)	5.98	Yellow–red
0.04	5.2–6.8	Brom cresol purple (BCP)	6.3	Yellow–purple
0.04	6.0–7.6	Brom thymol blue (BTB)	7.0	Yellow–blue
0.01 in 50% alc.	7 –8	Neutral red (NR)	—	Yellow–red
0.02	6.8–8.4	Phenol red (PR)	7.9	Yellow–red
0.02	7.2–8.8	Cresol red (CR)	8.3	Yellow–red
0.04	8.0–9.6	Thymol blue (TB)	8.9	Yellow–blue
0.05 in 50% alc.	8 –10	Phenolphthalein (P)	9.7	Colorless–red

Data mostly from Clark.[5] Aqueous solutions are used except as indicated. Congo red is considered undesirable because of large salt errors. Details for making up solutions may be found on pp. 91 to 94 of Clark's treatise. Most of the aqueous indicators are made up in 0.01N NaOH, appropriately diluted. Salts of the dyes, however, are soluble in water. Many of them are now available in this form.

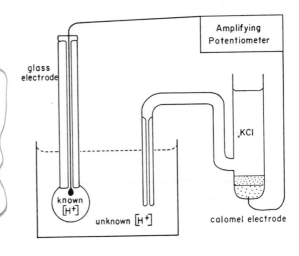

Fig. 8.4. A simplified diagram of the electrometric determination of pH with a glass electrode. The sample whose pH is to be determined is placed in the vessel marked "unknown [H⁺]" into which dip the glass electrode (containing 0.1N H⁺) and the calomel electrode. A potential is developed between the solution in the vessel and the glass electrode because of the difference in hydrogen ion concentrations between the two. This potential is amplified and measured by a potentiometer. The dial on the instrument is generally read directly in pH units. For details of the calomel electrode see Fig. 18.1.

rated by the glass membrane through which only the hydrogen ions can pass. The potential developed is proportional to the difference in concentration between the two solutions. While hydrogen ions, in sufficient numbers to set up a potential, pass from the solution in which they are more concentrated through the glass electrode* toward the other solution, actual leakage of acid does not occur, because anions cannot accompany the hydrogen ions. In a potentiometer the potential developed between the two solutions inside and outside the glass electrode is balanced by that from a battery, the point of balance being indicated by a null point on the dial of the galvanometer. The calomel electrode is used in the pH meter because potentials are relative values and can be determined only between two electrodes, one of which is the reference electrode. In the pH meter the calomel electrode is used for reference against which the potential between the two solutions inside and outside the glass electrode is measured (see Chapter 18). In practice, the potential is amplified, and the dial of the potentiometer slide wire, which then measures the potential, is calibrated to read directly in pH units.

For measurement of the pH inside the living cell, special micromethods (injec-

tion of indicator dyes and microelectrodes) have been devised.[7, 8, 16]

Salts

Most plant and animal cells can live only in a medium which contains some salts. As a rule, they do not tolerate pure distilled water, although some fresh water forms are remarkably resistant to melted snow. Freshly fallen rainwater is sometimes devoid of salt and seldom contains more than 0.003 per cent salt. Hard water contains about 0.1 per cent salt. At the present time sea water contains about 3 per cent salt (30 grams per liter) and salt lakes in which salt is beginning to crystallize, about 30 per cent. The principal salts in sea water are the chlorides, sulfates and carbonates of sodium, potassium, calcium and magnesium. Sodium is the predominant cation, and chloride the predominant anion (see Table 8.7). In hard fresh water, calcium is the predominant cation and carbonate the predominant anion.

The salt content of natural waters is determined by a variety of methods, e.g., the total salt content by evaporation

---

* A glass electrode useful in determining sodium and potassium ions has been described by Friedman, et al., 1959: Science 130:1252.

TABLE 8.7. *Composition of Some Typical Natural Waters in Grams per Liter*

WATER	Na	K	Ca	Mg	Cl	SO$_4$	CO$_3$
Sea water	10.7	0.39	0.42	1.34	19.3	2.69	0.073
Hard fresh water	0.021	0.016	0.065	0.014	0.041	0.025	0.119
Soft fresh water	0.016	—	0.010	0.00053	0.019	0.007	0.012

Data from Baldwin, 1948: An Introduction to Comparative Biochemistry.

under vacuum, and individual salt ions by quantitative analytical methods.[10]

Because chloride is the commonest ion in salt waters, the chlorinity, as determined by silver nitrate titration, is often used to indicate the relative salinity of a salt water. The chlorinity is related to the salinity of sea water as follows: Salinity = 0.03 + 1.805 × chlorinity, when both are expressed in grams per kilogram of sea water.[12]

Every cell contains salts (see Chapter 2), and salt is always present in the blood and body fluid of organisms, constituting the internal environment of the cells. In most marine invertebrates, the salt concentration of the blood is equal to that of sea water (3 per cent). In all other animals the concentration of salt in blood is less than that of sea water. For example, vertebrates, whether fresh water, marine or terrestrial, have less than 1 per cent in their blood plasma (0.68 to 0.9 per cent), while fresh water and terrestrial invertebrates have even less (0.3 to 0.7 per cent).

Life can exist only in the presence of certain salts, and it is interesting to note that the relative proportions of the various ions most favorable for biological functions are approximately those of the ions characteristic of sea water (see Table 8.8). Perhaps this can be understood best from an example. The heart of a frog stops beating when placed in pure sodium chloride solution equal in concentration to the total salt content in blood. If a soluble calcium salt is added, the heart may resume beating, but the beat becomes normal only when potassium is also added

and only when the three salts are present in the relative proportions characteristic of blood. The cations are said to act antagonistically to one another (see Chapter 12). It must be emphasized, therefore, that not only the total concentration of salt (osmotic factor) but also the concentration of each ion relative to that of the others (antagonism) is important in making a *balanced medium* such as blood or sea water.

Although neither the relative nor the absolute concentrations of salts are exactly the same in blood as in sea water, a fundamental relation between sea water and the blood of animals is suggested by the striking similarity in the relative concentrations of the ions found in each. Paleontologic evidence indicates that life originated in the sea, and at the stage in evolution when animals first developed an internal environment, the blood may have simulated the medium in which life arose. With this general concept most everyone seems to agree.[17]

The question, however, arises: If blood resembles sea water because of its ultimate derivation from a marine environment, why is the blood of the vertebrate so dilute compared with present-day sea water? (Fig. 8.5) Also, why is it that potassium, for example, is often present in slightly larger proportions, and magnesium in considerably smaller proportions in blood than in sea water? This has been explained by MacCallum as a relic of the ancient and more dilute seas in which potassium was relatively more concentrated and magnesium less so than in

TABLE 8.8. *Relative Ionic Composition of Sea Water as Compared with the Relative Ionic Composition of the Blood or Body Fluid of Various Animals*

(The Na ion in all cases is taken as 100.)

A

LOCATION OF SEA WATER	ION					
	Na	K	Ca	Mg	Cl	SO₄
Woods Hole	100	2.74	2.79	13.94	136.8	7.10
Japan	100	2.14	2.28	11.95	119.0	5.95

B

ANIMAL	CLASSIFICATION	Na	K	Ca	Mg	Cl	SO₄
Aurelia	Coelenterate	100	2.90	2.15	10.18	113.05	5.15
Strongylocentrotus	Echinoderm	100	2.30	2.28	11.21	116.1	5.71
Phascolosoma	Sipunculid	100	10.07	2.78	—	114.06	—
Venus	Mollusk	100	1.66	2.17	5.70	117.3	5.84
Carcinus	Crustacean	100	2.32	2.51	3.70	105.2	3.90
Cambarus	Crustacean	100	3.09	2.60	6.70	30.9	—
Hydrophilus	Insect	100	11.1	0.92	16.8	33.6	0.12
Lophius	Fish	100	2.85	1.01	1.61	71.9	—
Frog	Amphibian	100	2.40	1.92	1.15	71.4	—
Man	Mammal	100	3.99	1.78	0.66	83.97	1.73

Calculated from Data in Prosser and Brown.[17]

present-day sea water.[14] While this theory has a great appeal, newer evidence indicates that the primeval sea was probably at least twice as concentrated as present-day vertebrate blood at the time it first evolved in the Ordovician period.[11]

On the other hand, Pantin suggests that in the course of evolution the presence of some ions in blood in proportions different from those in sea water has been found to be more effective for biological functions.[15] For example, it is advantageous for an active species to eliminate a substance with narcotic action like the magnesium ion. Such differences in the proportions of ions in blood and sea water could be maintained by marine animals only as kidneys developed, because the differences are the result of a balance between the input

and outgo of salts as determined by kidney function. A steady state is achieved, characteristic of the blood of each animal species.

It is to be noticed in Figure 8.5 that animals (e.g., echinoderms) whose body fluids are almost identical to sea water in absolute concentration and in the relative concentration of the various ions have no kidneys or nephric organs, while those with good nephric organs (e.g., mollusks, crustaceans and vertebrates) have blood and body fluid most unlike sea water, either in relative concentration of the various ions or absolute concentration or both.

In hard fresh water the concentration of calcium relative to sodium and other cations is higher than in sea water. This is important to life in fresh waters since

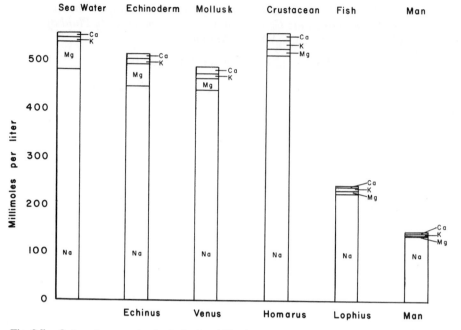

Fig. 8.5. Cations in sea water, body fluid and blood. Note the decreased amount of magnesium in the three forms on the right and the relative increase of potassium. The much lower concentration of total salt in the vertebrate is also readily noticeable.

calcium retards the transfer of materials across the plasma membrane of the cell, protecting the cells of the organism from the loss of useful salts to the dilute external medium (see Chapter 12).

Relation between Concentration and Activity of Electrolytes

X-ray diffraction studies show that salts are completely ionized even in the dry, crystalline state. On solution in water the ions of the salt become freely movable because of the high dielectric constant of water (see Chapter 7).

Salts, then, are completely dissociated, but the effective concentration of the salt ions, as measured by some property which depends upon the number of active particles (e.g., the depression of the freezing point of a solution), is less than the value given by the concentration (in molality) of the salt ions (see Chapter 11). The ap-

parent decrease in concentration results mainly from attractions between salt ions of opposite sign, but attractions between solvent and solute molecules and even attractions between solvent molecules themselves may effectively reduce the activity of the ions.

The same principles apply to hydrogen ions as well. The pH of a weak acid is less than would be expected on the basis of the normality of the acid, obviously because dissociation in incomplete. However, the concentration of hydrogen ions of even a strong acid like hydrochloric, which is considered to be completely dissociated, is also somewhat less than would be expected on the basis of its normality. This is because the electrostatic attraction between oppositely charged ions in concentrated solutions prevents free activity of the ions. Some hydrogen ions are therefore not free to act at any given moment. If strong acid is sufficiently diluted, how-

THE CELL ENVIRONMENT

ever, the concentration of hydrogen ions as measured by pH approaches the normality of the acid, because as interionic distance increases, ionic interference decreases to the vanishing point. This is strictly true only at infinite dilution.

Since in solutions of electrolytes, ionic interference reduces the effectiveness of ions so that their concentration seems lower than it is, the concept of activity has been introduced. *Activity* is the effective concentration of an ion. The activity is equal to the activity coefficient times the true concentration (molality). The *activity coefficient* is defined as the ratio of the activity, as measured by some property such as the depression of the freezing point of a solution, to the true concentration (molality):

$$\text{activity coefficient } (\gamma) = \frac{\text{activity}}{\text{concentration}} \quad (8.18)$$

The activity coefficient, which is usually less than one, increases as the solution becomes more dilute, reaching unity at infinite dilution at which the attractive forces between oppositely charged ions become negligible.

Since pH measures the hydrogen ions free to act, it is a measure of the hydrogen ion activity, and pH should therefore be more strictly defined as:

$$\text{pH} = -\log_{10} [\text{hydrogen ion activity}], \quad (8.19)$$

or pH is the negative logarithm of the effective hydrogen ion concentration. When this is done the pK_a obtained for a weak acid is designated $pK_a{}'$. While this added precision may not affect the general discussion of the pH relationships or the Henderson-Hasselbalch equation, it must be borne in mind should it become necessary to calculate with this degree of accuracy.

In a like manner the activity of bases is restricted by electrostatic attraction between oppositely charged ions. The pOH is therefore the negative logarithm of the hydroxyl ion activity rather than the negative logarithm of the hydroxyl ion concentration.

APPENDIX

8.1   Hydronium and Hydrogen Ions

According to Brönsted,[13] an *acid* is a substance capable of giving off a proton (hydrogen ion), and a *base* is a substance capable of combining with a proton. By this definition the chloride ion is a base because it is capable of combining with a hydrogen ion. Since water combines with hydrogen ions to form hydronium ions, H_3O^+, it is a base, but since H_3O^+ may yield a proton, the hydronium ion is an acid. Since NH_3 combines with a proton to form $NH_4{}^+$, it is a base, whereas $NH_4{}^+$ is an acid since it is capable of yielding a proton. This method of defining acids and bases has special use for non-aqueous systems.

The *hydronium ion* is always formed by combination of a proton with water whenever free protons are dissociated from acids; it is not probable that free hydrogen ions exist. Proof of the presence of H_3O^+ is obtained from x-ray diffraction study of the crystalline hydrate of perchloric acid. The distances between the ions identified indicate H_3O^+ and $ClO_4{}^-$. The hydronium rather than the hydrogen ion is also demonstrated by electrolysis of hydrogen bromide and water dissolved in liquid sulfur dioxide. Neither hydrogen bromide nor water alone conducts electricity in sulfur dioxide. Yet in the mixture of hydrogen bromide and water in liquid sulfur dioxide, water and hydrogen are obtained at the negative pole, not hydrogen alone, as would be the case if hydrogen ions were migrating as such. The presence of hydronium ions rather than hydrogen ions has been assumed throughout the discussion here and in subsequent chapters, but following custom, all formulations (since they apply equally well to hydronium or hydrogen ions) are given in terms of hydrogen ions.

8.2 Buffer mixtures using a weak base and its salt.

For making buffers it is possible to calculate the ratio of the salt of a weak base to the base (BOH) in much the same way as is done for a weak acid. From the relationship,

$$BOH \rightleftharpoons B^+ + OH^- \qquad (8.20)$$

the Henderson-Hasselbalch equation is derived

$$pOH = pK_b + \log_{10} \frac{[salt]}{[base]} \qquad (8.21)$$

Since $\quad [H^+] \cdot [OH^-] = 10^{-14} \qquad (8.22)$

and $\quad\quad pH + pOH = 14 \qquad (8.23)$

or $\quad\quad pOH = 14 - pH \quad (8.24)$

Then, substitution of equation 8.24 for pOH in equation 8.21 gives:

$$14 - pH = pK_b + \log_{10} \frac{[salt]}{[base]} \qquad (8.25)$$

or $\quad -pH = -14 + pK_b + \log_{10} \frac{[salt]}{[base]} \qquad (8.26)$

or $\quad pH = 14 - pK_b - \log_{10} \frac{[salt]}{[base]} \qquad (8.27).$

GENERAL REFERENCES

Bates, R. G., 1954: Electrometric pH Determination. Wiley, New York.

Bull, H. B., 1951: Physical Biochemistry. 2nd Ed. Wiley, New York, Chapter 7.

Caldwell, P. C., 1956: Intracellular pH. Internat. Rev. Cyt. 5:229–277.

Clark, W. M., 1928: The Determination of Hydrogen Ions, 3rd Ed. Williams & Wilkins, Baltimore.

Clark, W. M., 1952: Topics in Physical Chemistry, 2nd Ed. Williams & Wilkins, Baltimore, Chapters 14–16.

Davenport, H. W., 1958: The ABC of Acid-Base Chemistry. 4th Ed. Univ. of Chicago Press, Chicago.

Edsall, J. T., and Wyman, J., 1958: Biophysical Chemistry. Academic Press, New York, Chapters 8 and 9.

Gold, V., 1956: pH Measurements. Wiley, New York.

Joseph, N. R., 1958: A pH Calculator Based on Linear Transformations of the Henderson-Hasselbalch Equation. Science 128:1207.

Small, J., 1954: Modern Aspects of pH with Special Reference to Plants and Soils. van Nostrand, New York.

West, E. S., 1942: Physical Chemistry for Students of Biochemistry and Medicine. Macmillan, New York, Chapters 5, 6, and 7.

LITERATURE CITED

1. Harned, H. S., and Hamer, W. J., 1933: J. Am. Chem. Soc. 55:2194.
2. West, E. S., 1942: Physical Chemistry for Students of Biochemistry and Medicine. Macmillan, New York.
3. MacInnes, D. A., and Belcher, D., 1933: J. Am. Chem. Soc. 55:2630.
4. MacInnes, D. A., and Belcher, D., 1935: J. Am. Chem. Soc. 57:1683.
5. Clark, W. M.: 1928: The Determination of Hydrogen Ions. 3rd Ed. Williams & Wilkins, Baltimore.
6. Dole, M., 1941: The Glass Electrode. Wiley, New York.
7. Small, J., 1955: The pH of Plant Cells: Protoplasmatologia II, B, 2. Springer-Verlag, Vienna.
8. Wiercinski, F., 1955: The pH of Animal Cells, Protoplasmatologia II, B, 2c. Springer-Verlag, Vienna.
9. McInnes, D. A., Jan. 1951: Sci. Am. 184:40.
10. Kolthoff, I. M., and Belcher, R., 1957: Voltametric Analysis, Interscience, New York.
11. Edsall, J. T., and Wyman, J., 1958: Biophysical Chemistry I. Academic Press, New York.
12. Sverdrup, H. O., Johnson, M. W., and Fleming, R. H., 1942: The Oceans, Prentice-Hall, Inc. New York.
13. Brönsted, J. N., 1928: Chem. Rev. 5:231.
14. Macallum, A. B., 1926: Physiol. Rev. 6:316.
15. Pantin, C. F. A., 1931: Biol. Rev. 6:459.
16. Caldwell, P. C., 1956: Internat. Rev. Cyt. 5:229.
17. Prosser, C. L., and Brown, F. A., Jr., 1961: Comparative Animal Physiology. 2nd Ed. Saunders, Philadelphia.

RADIATIONS IN THE CELL ENVIRONMENT

Life is profoundly affected by radiation, and the effects are not limited to visible radiations alone. Everyone knows that all life is ultimately dependent on energy stored by photosynthetic plant cells during the action of sunlight,* but in addition to this primary role of light in the living economy, a persistent environment of various radiations produces a host of other effects, reactions and adaptations, which may influence strikingly the life activities of the organisms living within this environment.

Natural Radiations

In addition to the radiation of the sun's spectrum, natural radiations include radio waves from the sun and the stars, ionizing radiations from the breakdown of the radioactive elements in the earth's crust, and the cosmic rays coming from the sun and from the depths of space. While natural ionizing radiations are usually of a minor consequence on the earth's surface, protons of solar flares and the van Allen belts of ionizing radiation around the earth (as shown in Fig. 9.1) and prob-

ably other planets become hazards in space travel.[54, 83]

Radiations of Sunlight. Sunlight is the major source of radiations on earth. Its spectrum (see Fig. 9.2) includes ultraviolet radiation, visible light, infrared rays and radio waves, the latter only recently discovered as a part of the sun's spectrum.[2] Solar flares are a source of x-rays which on absorption produce ionization 60 miles high in the earth's atmosphere.[39] While the visible wavelengths are the most noticeable, about 60 per cent of the energy of sunlight is in the infrared span, the limit of which is indefinite in sunlight.[2] The sun is the major source of the earth's heat without which life as we know it would be impossible on earth. The emission from the sun in the visible and infrared parts of the spectrum suggests a body with a surface temperature of 6000° absolute.

At the surface of the earth little ultraviolet radiation of wavelengths shorter

---

*Photosynthesis is treated in Chapter 20. It is given separate treatment because of its importance in the economy of nature.

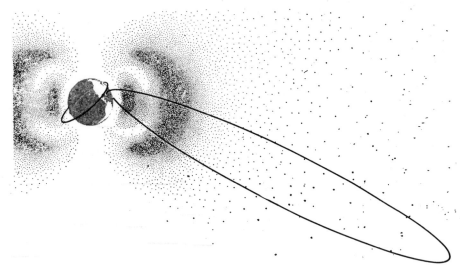

Fig. 9.1. Van Allen belts of ionizing radiation around the earth. The satellites Explorer IV and Pioneer III gave the first detailed information of the radiation belts. Explorer IV (short ellipse) monitored radiation levels for nearly two months at altitudes up to 1,300 miles. Pioneer III, a lunar probe (long ellipse) provided data out to 65,000 miles. [From Van Allen, 1959: Sci. Am. *200*(3):39.]

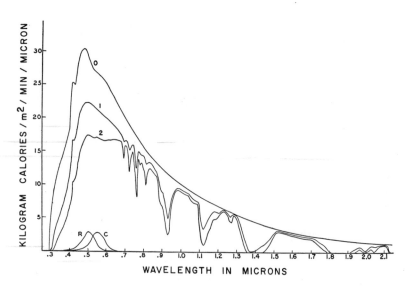

Fig. 9.2. Spectral distribution of sunlight: 0, outside the atmosphere; 1, with the sun at zenith; 2, with the sun at 60° from zenith. Curves 1 and 2 are for 20 mm. H_2O, 2.8 mm. ozone, and 300 dust particles per cc. Curves R and C indicate, respectively, the spectral sensitivity of the human rods, and cones; the ordinate units are arbitrary. (From Blum: J. Clin. Invest. *24*:713, 1945.)

than 2900 Å is measured, the shortest wavelength recorded on a clear day with the sun at the zenith being 2870 Å. Such a source as the sun theoretically should emit ultraviolet radiations shorter than 2870 Å. To determine whether it does, spectrographs were first placed on V-2 rockets soon after World War II and sent over 50 miles up into the atmosphere of the earth.[2] Records from these rockets showed the presence of ultraviolet light of wavelengths as short as 2200 Å. Recent records from double spectrographs in Aerobee-High rockets have demonstrated the presence of radiation of ultraviolet wavelengths so short as to overlap with the x-ray region[83] (see Table 9.1). Apparently sunlight radiations of wavelengths shorter than 2870 Å are absorbed in the earth's atmosphere before these radiations reach the surface of the earth. The nature of the substances in the earth's atmosphere which absorb the short ultraviolet radiations has been the subject of many investigations. It has been demonstrated that high in the atmosphere oxygen absorbs ultraviolet radiation, forming a layer of ozone. The ozone in turn absorbs somewhat longer ultraviolet rays, re-forming oxygen. The ozone umbrella, as this layer has sometimes been called, exists about 25 to 30 miles high in the atmosphere and is apparently the agent which removes the ultraviolet radiations of very short wavelengths.[39]

Radioactive emanations consist of three components: (1) gamma rays, which are penetrating radiations of very short wavelength but otherwise like x-rays; (2) alpha particles, positively charged helium nuclei; and (3) beta particles, rapidly moving electrons. Besides the naturally occurring radioactive elements such as radium and polonium, many elements have been made radioactive by bombardment with high energy particles such as helium nuclei.[35] These are known as artificial radioactive elements.

Cosmic Rays. Cosmic rays were once thought to be produced by the creation and annihilation of matter in the depths of space. It is now thought that they may obtain their energy by passing through enormous magnetic fields (galactic accelerators) that drift among the stars in the Milky Way galaxy.[35] On entering the earth's atmosphere cosmic rays consist of charged particles, mainly protons (positively charged hydrogen nuclei), and in addition some particles heavier than protons. After collisions of these particles with atmospheric gases, cosmic rays include also uncharged particles (neutrons), gamma rays and charged particles other than protons, such as mesons (positively or negatively charged particles intermediate in mass between protons and electrons) and positive and negative electrons.[52, 53]

Several cosmic rays strike the human body every second. Even organisms which escape the effect of visible and ultraviolet radiation are reached by cosmic radiations, some components of which are able to penetrate many centimeters of lead. Because of the difficulty of screening them out, the effects of cosmic rays on life have not yet been fully ascertained.

Measurement of Radiation. The intensity of all radiations, other than ionizing radiations, is measured in terms of amounts of energy per unit time per unit area. It may be given in terms of any energy unit, for example, the calorie or the erg (the work done by a force of 1 dyne acting through a distance of 1 centimeter). One calorie equals 4.186×10^7 ergs.

When radiations are measured in terms of their heating power, it is only necessary to absorb all the incident radiation on a black surface and convert the radiation to heat. If much heat is formed it may be taken up in water and measured by a thermometer (as in a heliometer

TABLE 9.1. *Wavelengths of Radiations*

TYPE OF RADIATION	SUBDIVISION	WAVELENGTH IN Å*
Gamma		0.001–1.4
X-rays		0.005–200
	hard	0.005–1
	soft	1–200
Ultraviolet		150–3900
	very short	150–2000
	short (far)	2000–3000
	long (near)	3000–3900
Visible		3900–7800
	violet	3900–4300
	blue	4300–4700
	blue green	4700–5000
	green	5000–5300
	yellow green	5300–5600
	yellow	5600–5900
	orange	5900–6200
	red	6200–7800
Infrared		$7800 – 4 \times 10^6$
	near	$7800 – 2 \times 10^4$
	far	$2 \times 10^4 – 4 \times 10^6$
Hertzian waves		$10^6 – 3 \times 10^{14}$
	space heating	$10^6 – 10^7$
	radio	$10^7 – 10^{13}$
	radar	$10^7 – 10^{10}$
	television	$10^{10} – 10^{12}$
Power A.C.		10^{16}

*Å = Ångstrom unit = 10^{-8} cm., a unit of wavelength; 1 mµ = 10Å.

used to measure sunlight). If a smaller amount of radiation is to be measured, thermocouples are placed in the water or on the black receiving surface. A thermocouple consists of a junction of two metals between which a thermoelectric current is induced by a change in temperature. This current is measured by a galvanometer (see Fig. 11.5). If minute amounts of radiation are to be measured, a thermopile, which consists of a series of thermocouples, is the instrument of choice because the current passing from the thermopile to the high-sensitivity galvanometer is the sum of the currents induced in each of the thermocouples.

Because measurements of radiations by a thermopile usually require a high-sensitivity galvanometer, itself a delicate instrument, photoelectric cells are more frequently used for measuring light. However, unlike the thermopile, which absorbs all wavelengths of light equally, photoelectric cells absorb some wavelengths of light more than others. Therefore, to be useful for measuring the intensity of radiation at different wavelengths, photoelectric cells must be calibrated wavelength for wavelength, generally with a thermopile or a bolometer.[3]

While it is also possible to measure the intensity of ionizing radiations by converting them to heat, the amount of heat produced by a strong dose of x-rays is rather small and difficult to measure with accuracy. Therefore, the ionizing power of these radiations is usually measured instead. One unit of ionizing radiations is the *roentgen*. The roentgen, abbreviated "r," is defined as the quantity of x- or γ-radiation which will produce, as a consequence of ionization, one electrostatic unit of electricity, either positive or negative, in 1 cc. of dry air as measured at 0° C. and standard atmospheric pressure. "It corresponds to the liberation of 2.082×10^9 ion pairs per cc. of air at 0° C. and 760 mm. pressure, and involves an energy dissipation of 0.1083 ergs/cc. of air . . ."[4]

Exposure of tissue or water to 1 roentgen of radiation results in the uptake of about 100 ergs of energy per gram of tissue or water irradiated (84 ergs per gram of air). This is a small amount of energy when one considers that 42 million ergs are required to raise the temperature of 1 gram of water 1° C.[50] Another unit which has come into widespread usage recently is the *rad*. The rad is the quantity of ionizing radiations that results in an energy absorption of 100 ergs per gram of the irradiated material.[51]

Nature of Radiations. All radiations, from radio waves to the shortest gamma rays produced by cosmic ray bombardment of the atmosphere, are electromagnetic in nature and travel at the same speed (3×10^{10} cm./sec.); they differ only in wavelength. The wavelength distribution in the radiation spectrum is shown in Table 9.1. Alpha particles, electrons, protons and other particulate radiations travel at various speeds, depending upon the voltage gradient. However, they are accompanied by electromagnetic radiations which travel with the speed of light (see also Appendix 9.4).

While radiation travels as a wave and many of its properties are best explained by its behavior as a wave, radiation acts as if it were produced and delivered in discrete amounts of energy called quanta. The energy in a quantum is related to the wavelength of radiation, being greater the shorter the wavelength, as shown by the following law (Planck's law):

$$q(\text{quantum}) = h\nu = \frac{hc}{\lambda} \qquad (9.1)$$

where h is Planck's constant,
$\qquad$ 6.624×10^{-27} erg-seconds,
ν is the frequency of light in waves per second, equal to c/λ,
c is the velocity of light, 3×10^{10} cm./sec.,
λ is the wavelength expressed in cm.

As may be seen by dimensional analysis of the right-hand term, the energy in a quantum is expressed in ergs.

According to the quantum theory, quanta of light are absorbed at random. The absorption of 1 quantum of light by a molecule (or atom) produces only one activated molecule. This is known as the Einstein-Starck law of photochemical equivalence. Absorption of light constitutes the *primary reaction,* which is independent of temperature since the addition of kinetic energy does not increase the probability that a molecule will absorb light. The primary reaction is followed by any one of a number of *secondary reactions.* For example, the energy absorbed may be reradiated at the same wavelength (resonance) or at longer wavelengths (fluorescence), or degraded to heat. On the other hand, the energy absorbed may render the activated molecule capable of reacting with other molecules.[5] These secondary reactions are affected by temperature (see Chapter 10).

Photodynamic Sensitization of Cells

In 1898 Raab found that protozoans were killed when exposed to strong light in the presence of dilute solutions of some fluorescent dyes, but that they were unaffected in the dark in the same solutions. On the other hand, light, even

$\qquad$

intense light, had no effect in the absence of the dyes.[6, 7]

Protozoans, such as paramecia, which possess no pigment, are translucent and appear white because the particles in their cytoplasm pass or scatter all wavelengths of visible light. They are unaffected even by fairly intense visible light, because they do not absorb it. However, when a dye such as erythrosin is present, it becomes adsorbed to the surface of the paramecia, and the energy of the light is absorbed by the dye and transferred to the cytoplasm, resulting in injury or death. Such a dye is spoken of as a *photosensitizer* and its action is *photodynamic*. Dyes of similar concentration illuminated in the absence of paramecia are not injurious to paramecia subsequently immersed in them. This set of experiments is an illustration of the *Grotthus-Draper law*, which states that only absorbed light produces photochemical (or photobiological) reaction.

If the light intensity and the time of exposure are varied in such a way that the product of the two is always the same, the photochemical effect is the same. This principle is called the *Bunsen-Roscoe reciprocity law* and is well known in photography. The photodynamic effect obeys the reciprocity law but deviates from it if the intensity of the light is reduced to a very low level, in which case the effect diminishes, perhaps because the organism has a chance for some recovery simultaneously with injury.

Photodynamic action occasionally occurs in nature. The protozoan *Blepharisma* if grown in the dark produces a red pigment which accumulates in the outer part of the protoplasm. Deeply pigmented individuals are killed if exposed to intense light. The pigment extracted from the colored *Blepharisma* also sensitizes colorless cells to visible light.[8, 9]

Another case of natural photosensitization is that observed in the carotenoidless mutant strain of the bacterium, *Rhodo-* *pseudomonas spheroides*, which can carry on photosynthesis in absence of oxygen but is killed by light when oxygen is present. The action spectrum for photosensitization resembles the absorption spectrum of chlorophyll; therefore chlorophyll, in the absence of carotenoid (such as is present in the wild type parental form), photosensitizes the destructive photo-oxidation. When cultures of the carotenoidless strain are grown in the dark in the presence of oxygen, they become essentially chlorophyll-free and at the same time lose their photosensitivity. These experiments are of interest because they suggest that carotenoid has a protective role in photosynthesis, preventing oxidation of important cell materials by oxidants produced in the process.[56]

A photodynamic effect is occasionally found in the cells of higher animals. For instance, cells in the unpigmented skin of cattle eating certain weeds (St.-John's-wort, *Hypericum crispum*) are sensitized by a dyestuff which is present in the leaves. The dye is absorbed during digestion and is carried by the blood to the cells of the skin. Exposure of unpigmented skin to the sun then results in a rash, an edematous swelling or, in extreme cases, convulsions and death. This dye has been extracted from the leaves, purified and injected into animals with the same result. Similar effects have been demonstrated with dyes from various parts of other plants on white horses or sheep as well. In human beings a photodynamic effect is observed when abnormal metabolic reactions occasionally form products which sensitize the body to sunlight.[6]

Photodynamic action occurs only in the presence of oxygen. When oxygen is withdrawn no injury is observed, even when cells in dye solutions are exposed to bright visible light. These experiments, and the increased uptake of oxygen during illumination of the organisms in dye, indicate that during photodynamic action photo-oxidation occurs, and evidence is available that the proteins of the cell are selectively oxidized. The aromatic amino acid residues in the proteins seem to be most susceptible.[6] Some dyes, however, appear to combine selectively with nucleic acids.[26]

Response in Photoreceptor Cells—Vision

Most organisms respond to visible light. The entire cell of a unicellular animal, plant or microbe, for example, ameba, paramecium or zoospores of some algae, may be sensitive to light and the cell may move toward the light or away from it.[62] The streaming of plant cells is affected by light so that, even though the entire cell cannot move, the cytoplasm is sensitive to light. It is probable that the cytoplasm of cells is generally sensitive to light, but it is not possible to observe the reaction.

Some unicellular organisms have developed a receptor especially sensitive to light, that is, a region of the cell in which the threshold for light stimulation has been lowered. Flagellates, both photosynthetic, plant-like ones and the non-photosynthetic animal-like forms, usually display a stigma containing carotenoid pigments and a photoreceptor. Such a receptor enables an organism to make a response to smaller changes in intensity of light and sometimes to even determine the direction of the light.[62]

While some multicellular organisms have scattered photoreceptive cells in many parts of the body, such as the interesting isolated photoreceptive cells found in the nervous system of some invertebrates, most of them have photoreceptors, e.g., eyespots and eyes of different degrees of complexity. (These are considered in textbooks of comparative animal physiology.) Multicellular plants have also developed photoreceptors which usually consist of cells near the growing tip that contain a pigment enabling them to absorb light and a means of relaying the signal to the growing region.[61] Reception of light results in differential auxin transport and differential growth at a distance from the receptors. (Plant photoreceptors are covered in textbooks of plant physiology.)

The focus of interest here is analysis of the nature of the cellular responses to light. This has been done adequately only in the studies on vision. The visual process in its essential features is a cellular process and is much the same in eyes throughout the animal kingdom. The chemistry of visual reactions has been studied and analyzed most carefully in the photosensitive cells of eyes of vertebrates.[10]

The inside of the vertebrate eye is lined by the cells of the *retina*, which receives the light after it has passed through the cornea, aqueous humor, lens and vitreous humor. The cornea and the lens are the refracting parts of the eye; the humors are the bathing media; the retina is the seat of photochemical and excitatory processes. In the retina of many vertebrates there are two types of photoreceptive cells, the *rods* and the *cones*. The cones are cone shaped, the rods, narrow and spindle shaped (see Figure 9.3). Cones, exclusively, are present in the central fovea of man; both rods and cones are present in the rest of the retina. The cones are concerned with color vision and the fovea is the center of acuity or detailed form vision. While all cones appear alike histologically, physiological evidence (electric recording after stimulation by light) indicates the presence of several types of cones, each specialized for reception of light from a certain span of the spectrum. Although rods are incapable of distinguishing colors, they are sensitive to much lower intensities of light than the cones; therefore, they serve as photoreceptors in a much lower intensity range. At night a very dim light can be seen from the cor-

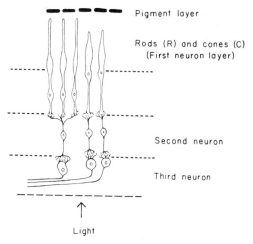

Pigment layer

Rods (R) and cones (C)
(First neuron layer)

Second neuron

Third neuron

↑
Light

Fig. 9.3. Diagram of rods (upper left) and cones (upper right) in a vertebrate retina.

ner of the eye because of its action on the rods, which are more concentrated at the periphery of the retina. If the head is turned so that the light falls directly on the fovea, the light seems to disappear because the cones are insensitive to such dim light. This difference in sensitivity is

best illustrated by the dark adaptation curves (see Fig. 9.4).

Though rods do not register a sense of color, both rods and cones are differentially sensitive to the various wavelengths in the visible spectrum. To determine the relative effectiveness of light at different wavelengths the dark-adapted individual in a dark chamber determines the lowest intensity of light of a given wavelength which he can see (Fig. 9.5). The visual efficiency of a wavelength of light is accordingly given as the reciprocal of the intensity required to stimulate the eye. In Figure 9.6 the relative efficiencies of different wavelengths for rod and cone vision are plotted. A diagram plotting the relative efficiencies of different wavelengths in producing a biological effect is spoken of as an *action spectrum*. It is apparent that the action spectrum has a maximum for rod vision at 5050 Å and for foveal cone vision at 5620 Å. This suggests that the rods and the cones each possess distinctive photosensitive pigments.

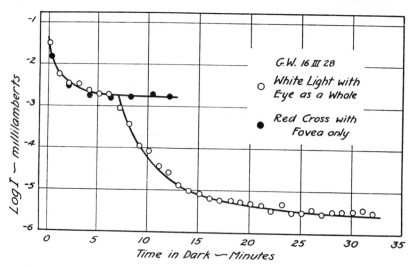

Fig. 9.4. The dark adaptation of the human eye. The points are single measurements of the just perceptible intensity at different times in the dark after high light adaptation. The white circles are for white light. The black circles are for the extreme red end of the spectrum which stimulates the cones alone. Dark adaptation is thus in two stages; first, cone adaptation; and second, rod adaptation. (From Hecht, 1929: J. Op. Soc. Am., *18*:269.)

THE CELL ENVIRONMENT

That the retina is bleached by light is shown by experiments obtaining an optogram formed when the dark-adapted eye of an animal is briefly exposed to a brilliantly illuminated window. If the eye is quickly removed and the retina separated and fixed in alum, it shows an image of the bright window.

The visual purple pigment, or *rhodopsin*, may be extracted in the dark by rupturing with a detergent the rods of a dark-adapted animal. Rhodopsin is a typical protein of large molecular weight with an absorption spectrum almost identical with the action spectrum for rod vision, as can be seen in Figure 9.7. It is readily bleached by light and regenerates to some extent in the dark.

The nature of the chemical reactions following absorption of light by rhodopsin in the rods of vertebrates has been investigated extensively in the last 20 years. The spectacular recovery from night blindness observed in individuals treated with vitamin A connected this vitamin with vision. Research showed dark-adapted retinas to possess little vitamin A, but light-adapted retinas had an abundant supply. When retinas from dark-adapted animals were treated with strong fat solvents, a carotenoid called *retinene* (retinaldehyde) appeared in place of vitamin A. As this carotenoid disappeared during light adaption, an equivalent amount of *trans*-vitamin A appeared in the excised retina. Experimentation has demonstrated that vitamin A is indeed a

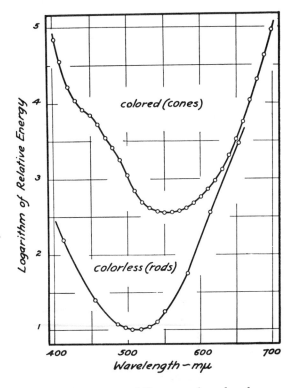

Fig. 9.5. Spectrum sensibility curves for rods and cone vision on a real energy basis. The position of the two curves on the ordinates corresponds to the fact that after complete dark adaptation, any region of the retina outside the fovea sees red light of 650 mμ as colorless at the threshold, and as colored only above the threshold. (From Hecht and Hsia, 1945: J. Op. Soc. Am., 35:262.)

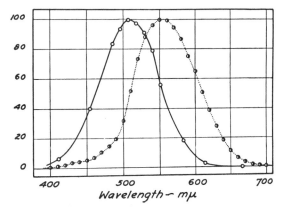

Fig. 9.6. Luminosity curves for scotopic (rod) vision and for photopic (cone) vision. Since the maxima are arbitrarily set at 100, these curves give no information about the relative sensitivity of rods and cones for red, or for any other part of the spectrum. (From Hecht and Hsia, 1945: J. Op. Soc. Am., 35:262.)

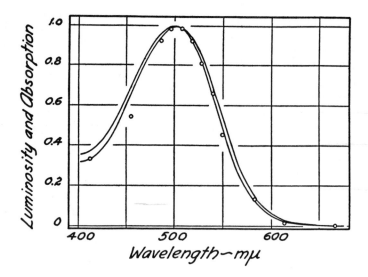

Fig. 9.7. Comparison of scotopic luminosity at the retina with visual purple absorption. The points are corrected for quantum effectiveness and ocular media transmission. The curves are the percentage absorption spectra of visual purple; the upper curve represents 20 per cent maximal absorption, and the lower one 5 per cent maximal absorption. All curves have been made equal to 1 at the maximum, 500 mμ, for ease in comparison. (From Hecht, 1942: J. Gen. Physiol., 25:831.)

reduced form of retinene. During light adaptation the rhodopsin decomposes to form *trans*-retinene and the protein *opsin* (see Fig. 9.8). The released *trans*-retinene then becomes reduced to *trans*-vitamin A.[11]

Retinene and opsin obtained experi-mentally by action of light on retinas or retinal extracts do not recombine to form rhodopsin, nor do vitamin A and opsin. In seeking the reason for this, optical isomers of retinene were tested and it was discovered that while the *cis*-isomer combines with opsin to form rhodopsin,

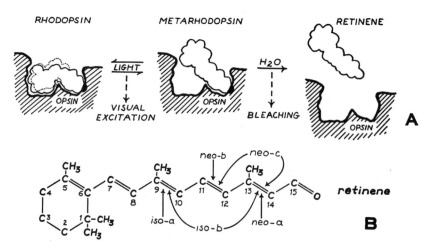

Fig. 9.8. A, hypothetical scheme showing the effect of light on vertebrate rhodopsins. In rhodopsin, the neo-b (11-*cis*) chromophore fits into the chromophoric site on opsin. Light isomerizes the *cis* chromophore to the all-*trans* configuration, thus decreasing the interaction between the chromophore and opsin. The result is all-*trans* metarhodopsin, which hydrolyzes readily to retinene and opsin. The isomerization of rhodopsin to metarhodopsin is probably responsible for visual excitation, but bleaching is due to the hydrolysis of metarhodopsin. B, structural formula of retinene, showing the system of numbering carbon atoms. The structure as shown has the all-*trans* configuration. Arrows indicate the double bonds which are in *cis* configuration in the various *cis* isomers. (From Kropf and Hubbard, 1958: Annals New York Acad. Sci. 74:266.)

THE CELL ENVIRONMENT

the *trans*-isomer does not. Evidence has been gathered which indicates that the isomerization from *trans*- to *cis*-vitamin A normally occurs under the influence of isomerizing enzymes acting only on vitamin A, not retinene; consequently, the reduction of retinene to vitamin A and its reoxidation to retinene subsequent to isomerization are necessary for completion of the cycle.[12] The cycle of transformations involved in the breakdown and resynthesis of rhodopsin is called the *visual cycle* (see Fig. 9.9). Recently methods have been developed to measure the bleaching of rhodopsin in the intact eye.[36] These studies indicate that only a very small proportion (0.1 per cent) of the rhodopsin is bleached even when the retina is fully light-adapted.

Just which of these chemical changes, if any, enables the rods to excite the neurons connected with them to carry messages to the central nervous system is not yet known. The amount of energy required to stimulate the dark-adapted eye of man is exceedingly small. Hecht and his co-workers[13] have shown that only 5 to 14 quanta need be delivered to the retina. Since each of these is probably absorbed by a different rod, a single rod probably absorbs only a single quantum. Therefore only a single light-activated molecule is probably produced in a

rod and it seems most likely that the rod is already set to discharge. The light-activated molecule probably acts only as a trigger which upsets a delicately balanced system.[11] Consideration of such irritability problems is reserved for Chapters 21 to 24.

The pigment *iodopsin*, in the cones of the eye, has never been extracted free of rhodopsin and has been studied only in mixtures with the latter. The absorption spectrum of iodopsin, determined by indirect means, corresponds to the action spectrum for cone vision. There is some evidence that vitamin A is also involved in visual responses of the cones.[11] In general, however, relatively little is known of the biochemistry of cone vision at present although the response of cones in intact eyes is being effectively studied at present.[60]

Carotenoids and a pigment resembling rhodopsin are also present in the cells of the eyes of various types of invertebrates, e.g., the squid, the blue crab and the king crab. However, visual processes in these organisms may be somewhat different from those which occur in vertebrates. For example, when the squid eye is exposed to light, vitamin A is not formed from retinene.[11] Even in flagellates with eyespots, e.g., *Euglena*, carotenoids are associated with responses to visible light,

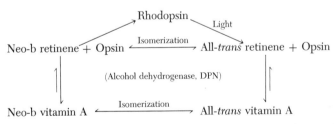

Fig. 9.9. The visual cycle. The *cis* form of retinene present, conjugated with opsin (protein) in rhodopsin, is transformed by light to the all-*trans* retinene. *Trans*-retinene is most readily isomerized back to the *cis* form by an indirect route (lower path), but direct isomerization may occur under the influence of blue light (upper path). The *trans*-retinene is first reduced to *trans*-vitamin A which is isomerized to the *cis*-form, neo-b vitamin A, in the presence of an isomerase. When the bond between opsin and retinene is broken the retina becomes yellow. Reduction of retinene to vitamin A results in loss of color (After Wald, 1961: Light and Life, McElroy and Glass, eds. Johns Hopkins Univ. Press, p. 731.)

and the light absorbed most effectively by these substances is most effective in phototaxic responses. The phototropism of plants is probably affected by different mechanisms, not as well analyzed as those in animals, since recently even the role of carotenoids in this process has been questioned.[14, 15]

Diurnal Rhythms

Much attention has recently been focused on the effect of light on diurnal rhythms which occur even in the activities of unicellular plants and animals.[71-75,80] It had long been supposed that the natural alternating periods of day and night impose the diurnal rhythm. But, if the rhythm is related to environmental periodicity in this simple causative way it should disappear when the plant or animal is placed in continuous darkness. Experiments show that the rhythm is usually found to persist in continuous darkness (or continuous dim light in some cases), indicating that it cannot be under direct environmental control. Significantly, the rhythm in continuous darkness is never exactly 24 hours, being slightly more or slightly less than this figure, suggesting an endogenous cycle close to, but not exactly, 24 hours. Such an endogenous rhythm within cells suggests some clock-like mechanism which times the rhythm, hence the name *biological clock.* It would be impossible to discuss or appraise the vast literature on the subject which includes considerable information on biochemical and cellular rhythms in man [75] (see references 71 to 75 and 80). Instead, only one example of an endogenous rhythm and its characteristics in a unicellular dinoflagellate, *Gonyaulax polyhedra,* is considered in detail here.[76-78]

Gonyaulax is a photosynthetic cell which emits a brief flash of light (90 milliseconds) when stimulated by agitation. Cultures grown in a daily cycle of day and night display rhythmically a greater luminescence upon agitation during the dark period than during the day, as shown in Figure 9.10A. When such cultures are transferred to a dark chamber, the rhythm continues, but its amplitude decreases progressively because of lack of nutrients, since photosynthesis ceases in the dark. Bright light permits photosynthesis but inhibits the rhythm, while dim light permits just enough photosynthesis to supply necessary nutrients to the cell but does not inhibit the rhythmic bioluminescent response which persists in dim light indefinitely without decrease in amplitude. Even cultures grown in bright light for a year, during which time the rhythm disappears, show the diurnal rhythm when again grown in dim light. The *innate period* of the rhythm, that is, the time from one peak to another, under constant dim illumination is somewhat less than 24 hours under some conditions (lower temperatures), somewhat more under others (higher temperatures), but always almost 24 hours. It should be noted that many nonphotosynthetic organisms show persistent endogenous rhythms of almost 24-hour periodicity when placed under conditions of continuous complete darkness.

The phase of the rhythm of luminescence in *Gonyaulax* can be shifted, as shown in Figure 9.10B and C. For example, if a culture of *Gonyaulax,* which has been grown under natural periods of night and day, is exposed to bright light during the night, and then placed in continuous dim light, it will once again show an endogenous rhythm but with a *phase shift* of several hours, the shift span depending especially upon the intensity of illumination and its duration. The rhythm will now operate from this new base line and without reference to the solar day, which the organisms do not see in continuous dim light. Clearly, the biological clock of *Gonyaulax* is set by bright light, but its innate period is set by endogenous factors, and so long as conditions are constant it will continue with its innate rhythm.

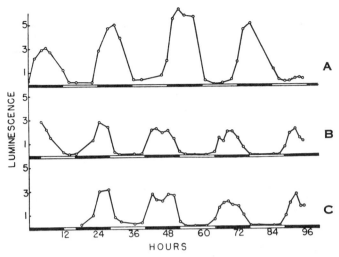

Fig. 9.10. Phase shift. This experiment illustrates the effect of changing the solar time at which the light and dark periods occur. Curve *A* shows the pattern of luminescence changes in the dinoflagellate, *Gonyaulax*, in an LD culture [one exposed to a diurnal rhythm of 12 hours light (L) and 12 hours of darkness (D)], which had been on the schedule indicated for some time. The black bars on the time axis indicate dark periods. The lower two graphs, *B* and *C*, illustrate the effect of imposing upon cultures (which were previously on the schedule shown in the top graph) an LD schedule in which the light and dark periods were at a different time of day. The new schedules were started at zero hours on the graph. Temperature, about 26°C. Light intensities used, about 250 foot-candles. (From Hastings and Sweeney, 1958: Biol. Bull. *115*:443.)

Gonyaulax taken from a rhythmic culture with an innate period of 24 hours and exposed to alternate periods of 7 hours of darkness and 7 hours of light for a while become *entrained* to a new rhythm (Fig. 9.11). However, as soon as they are again placed under continuous dim illumination they revert to the innate period of almost 24 hours. It appears that the light, as a timer, has a powerful effect but not a persistent one—the cells do not "remember" the entrained rhythm. Similar entraining periods of 6, 8 and 16 hours give like results.[78, 79] In other species of organisms it has usually been found possible to entrain periods only when they are very close to the natural periods of the organisms.[78, 79]

Besides the luminous rhythm, a rhythmic outburst of divisions was also observed in cultures of *Gonyaulax* on a diurnal natural period. These show some of the same features as the luminous rhythm, including a phase shift.[77]

It is important to know what factors other than light play a part in setting the biological clock. Experiments with suspensions of *Gonyaulax* have shown that there is apparently no relation between mechanical disturbance of any kind and the innate period.[78, 79] However, an increase in period occurs with a rise in temperature (Fig. 9.12). Thus at 16° C. the period was 22.8 hours, while at 26.7° C. it was 26.5 hours. At 11.5° C. and 32° C. rhythms practically ceased. Relative independence of temperature has generally been observed for endogenous rhythms, although some minor changes in period are almost always observed, as in the above instance.[79]

It is not possible at present to do more than make a consistent verbal framework for the description and interpretation of existing data on rhythms since specific cellular components have not yet been identified as parts of the mechanism of the clock. The biological clock is con-

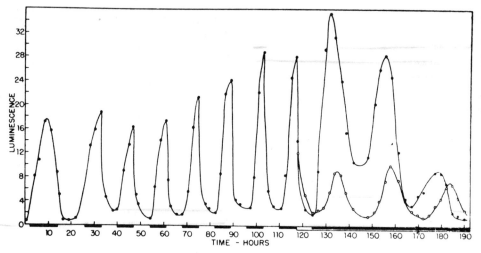

Fig. 9.11. This illustrates the entrainment of the luminescence rhythm in the dinoflagellate, *Gonyaulax* to a 14-hour cycle and the manifestation of an endogenous diurnal rhythm when the cells are placed in constant conditions subsequent to the treatment. Dark periods are indicated by black bars on the time axis. The cells were on an LD [12 hours light (L) 12 hours darkness (D)] schedule previous to the time when the 14-hour cycle was started (at 26 hours). Light intensity throughout the 14-hour cycling was 800 foot-candles. At 117 hours some aliquots were removed from the dark and placed in constant dim light at 230 foot-candles. The luminescence changes in these cultures are shown by the open circles. From 124 hours on, the other aliquots were left in the dark. Luminescence changes are plotted with solid dots. Note rapid decline of peak luminescence in darkness. Temperature, 21° C. (From Hastings and Sweeney, 1958: Biol. Bull. *115* : 444.)

sidered to be protected from the input of information coming to the cell from the environment in the form of pressure (including osmotic pressure), mechanical disturbance, ionizing radiations (e.g., cosmic rays) and to a considerable extent from temperature. Whereas the endogenous period depends upon a metabolic supply of energy, as already shown, it is unlikely that the period is determined by metabolic reactions in a simple manner. Most metabolic reactions are increased by temperature within the viable range (see Chapter 10), whereas temperature has little effect on the endogenous period; in fact, an increase in temperature may increase the period—the opposite of what might be expected of increased metabolism stimulated by temperature rise. Therefore it is postulated that two systems exist, coupled to one another, one of them light-sensitive and temperature-insensitive which serves as the pacemaker, and a second system temperature-sensitive but light-insensitive, phased by the first.

Shocks of ultraviolet light which affect the nucleic acids of the cell set the clock back (in *Paramecium*). However, visible light which affects the clock in all organisms does not affect nucleic acids. In *Gonyaulax*, the action spectrum for visible light-induced shifts in period implicates chlorophyll as the absorbing causative chemical, but obviously chlorophyll is absent from colorless cells (and organisms) whose rhythms are also set by visible light. Therefore some substance other than chlorophyll must absorb the light which sets the biological clocks in these instances. A wide variety of poisons which act upon diverse reactions fail to give clear-cut evidence of the nature of the pacemaker reaction.[70]

174

Photoperiodism

Photoperiodism is the growth response of cells in plants and animals to alternate periods of light and darkness. Thus, in plants, flowering is correlated with day length, some plants (long-night plants) blooming only when exposed to a number of short days, others (short-night plants) blooming only if exposed to a number of long days. Experiments have demonstrated that it is the cells in the young leaves of a plant that receive the stimulus from the light and that the cells produce a diffusible substance (hormone) that arouses the floral organs and results in growth. This material can pass by direct contact from induced plant cells to others not treated, but will not pass through agar or cellophane. Variations in the intensity of the light, above threshold, such as are caused by clouding of the skies, do not affect the response, which is regulated only by the number of hours of exposure.

The red end of the spectrum, particularly at wavelength 6600 Å, is the region of maximal stimulation for photoperiodic response in plant cells. Blue light is relatively ineffective. The period of darkness

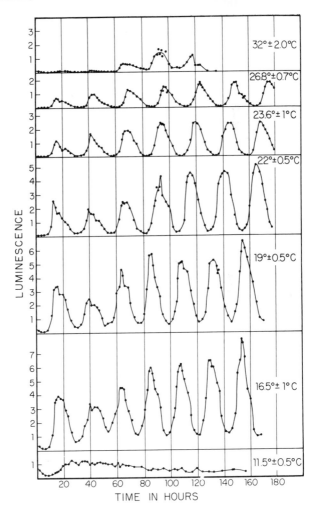

Fig. 9.12. Characteristics of the persistent rhythm of luminescence in the dinoflagellate, *Gonyaulax* at several different temperatures. The cells were kept at 22° C. in LD conditions prior to the beginning of the experiment shown on the graph. At that time the cells were transferred from the dark at 22° to the various temperatures, all in dim light, and left in these conditions throughout the experiment. The luminescence of the cells was determined approximately every 2 hours. At the dim light intensity used, there is little cell division, even at the optimal temperature for growth. The number of cells therefore remained essentially the same in all tubes at all temperatures. (From Hastings and Sweeney, 1957: Proc. Nat. Acad. Sci. U.S.A. 43:804.)

is also of primary importance and its interruption even with a brief flash of light alters the response. In other words, alternate periods of light and darkness are required. Many other growth responses, including germination of seeds, are regulated by the same part of the spectrum and the same rhythms of day and night.[37] In some cases, by manipulation of the light periods, several flowering cycles have been induced in one calendar year, during which normally only one cycle occurs.

The photoperiodic response induced by red light (6600 Å) can be reversed by illumination with far red (7300 Å), reactivated by another exposure to red (6600 Å) and again reversed by far red (7300 Å). Consequently, a pigment called *phytochrome* was postulated. The pigment was conceived to have two forms, one absorbing strongly in the red, another form in the far red (Fig. 9.13):

$$P_r \underset{7300 \text{ Å}}{\overset{6600 \text{ Å}}{\rightleftharpoons}} P_{fr} \qquad (9.2)$$

P_{fr} is considered the active form, which is perhaps an enzyme inducing the photoperiodic responses, probably by affecting some key enzymatic reaction. P_{fr} gradually and spontaneously reverses to form P_r, quickly in long-day plants and

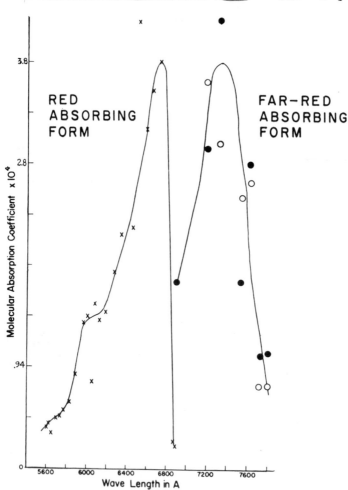

Fig. 9.13. Molecular absorption coefficients of the red and far-red absorbing forms of phytochrome. [After Hendricks, S. B., 1959: Photoperiodism and Related Phenomena in Plants and Animals, (R. Withrow, ed.). American Association for the Advancement of Science, Washington, p. 435.]

lowly in short-day plants. The dark conversion is somewhat affected by temperature.

Although phytochrome is present in exceedingly small amounts (1 part in 10 million), it has been extracted from the cells of the tips of young albino plants and appears to be a bluish compound consisting of a protein and another molecule attached to it. It has all the properties predicted for it from photoperiodic studies. It shows maximal absorption in one form at 6600 Å, being converted to the other form with maximal absorption at 7300 Å (Fig. 9.13). The latter wavelength reconverts it to the form with maximal absorption at 6600 Å. The conversions are entirely photochemical and occur at very low temperatures as readily as at high. Phytochrome is as widely distributed as chlorophyll and is to photoperiodism as chlorophyll is to photosynthesis.

Photoperiodic phenomena similar to those just discussed for plant life have been observed for animal life also. For example, many birds breed in the spring when days are getting longer, and precocious breeding can be induced in winter by artificially lengthening the days, even when the temperature is below freezing. The converse pattern is found in some mammals that breed in the fall when the days are short and produce their young in the spring. Here the stimulus of the light apparently acts upon cells in the hypophysis. When the hypophysis is activated it stimulates growth of gonadal cells. Some evidence exists that photoperiodic control regulates breeding in many lower forms of animal life as well. The photoperiod also controls fat deposition, migration and other behavior patterns.[43] In some cases (e.g., some insects) reproduction can be controlled practically at will by manipulation of the photoperiod, although nutrition and temperature play a role as modifiers.[42-45] The analysis of the cellular mechanisms involved in these responses is as yet rudimentary.[37, 42-44]

Effects of Ultraviolet Light on Cells

One effect of ultraviolet rays that everyone has experienced is *sunburn*. The ultraviolet radiations in sunlight injure cells in the epidermis (see Fig. 9.14). The injured cells (prickle cell layer) liberate chemicals which diffuse out and cause a relaxation of the walls of blood vessels in the derma, resulting in a reddening of the skin (erythema). If the injury is slight, the red or pink color soon disappears, and in most individuals a small amount of pigment develops (tanning). If the injury is more severe, the prickle cells may die, whereupon the layer is invaded by white cells and serum accumulates, causing a blister which later dries, and the skin "peels" off as new epidermis takes the place of the old.[17, 18]

Another injurious effect of the sun on man is eyeburn or snow blindness. Ultraviolet radiations directly striking the eye, reinforced by those reflected from snow (or water), may kill the superficial layers of cells covering the cornea. These cells become opaque, blinding the individual until the layer of dead cells is shed after a few days. For this reason exposure to a source of ultraviolet radiations of short wavelength is dangerous. While painful, the injury resulting from ultraviolet exposure is superficial and leaves no permanent damage.

Ultraviolet radiation does not penetrate deeply into large animals or plants and its effects are confined to the surface layers. However, prolonged exposure induces superficial skin cancer in experimental animals such as rats and mice.[20]

The effect of ultraviolet radiation of sunlight on unicellular organisms is much more drastic. Ever since Downes and Blunt, in 1877, discovered that ultraviolet radiation killed bacteria, all types of cells —microbes, protozoans, eggs of marine

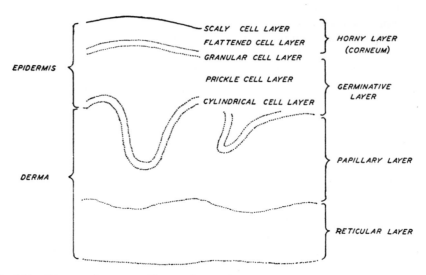

Fig. 9.14. Diagram of a section of human skin. Sunburn, or killing of cells, occurs in the prickle cell layer; erythema (reddening) occurs in the derma, especially the papillary layer, as a result of dilatation of blood vessels. Pigment develops chiefly in the cylindrical cell layer. (From Giese and Wells, 1946: Scient. Monthly, *62*:464.)

animals, algae and fungi, and cells in tissue culture—were shown to be killed by ultraviolet radiations of wavelengths shorter than 3100 Å. Dosages of ultraviolet radiation sufficient to prevent division of cells (that is, to produce reproductive death) induce mutations in surviving cells. Consequently, ultraviolet radiations have been extensively used by geneticists to produce mutations in microorganisms. Dosages of the radiations milder than necessary for reproductive death retard cell division, decrease respiration and affect most cellular functions, especially synthetic processes.

If different wavelengths of ultraviolet radiation are tested for their relative efficiency in producing a certain cellular effect (e.g., retarding cell division or mutation), a curve called the action spectrum (illustrated in Fig. 9.15) is obtained. Scrutiny of the figure shows that it resembles the absorption spectrum of nucleic acid (Fig. 3.17) more that the absorption spectrum of any other cellular constituent. This suggests that retardation of division, induction of mutations, killing of

bacteria and other effects of ultraviolet radiations with similar action spectra are caused by the effects of these radiations on nucleic acids in cells.[21] Furthermore, when nucleated and non-nucleated halves of sea urchin eggs are treated with ultraviolet radiations and both are fertilized with untreated sperm, the treated nucleated halves are strongly retarded in division, whereas the treated non-nucleated halves are not. This experiment supplies strong supporting evidence that the rate of division is affected by damage to the nucleic acid in the nucleus.[27]

Experiments have shown that inhibition of DNA synthesis by ultraviolet radiation stops cell division. Larger dosages progressively inhibit RNA synthesis and protein synthesis as well. Inhibition of synthetic processes probably underlies the various deleterious effects of ultraviolet radiations.

Ultraviolet radiation is more strongly and selectively absorbed by many organic chemicals than visible light. The absorption spectra are so characteristic that many compounds may be identified by

THE CELL ENVIRONMENT

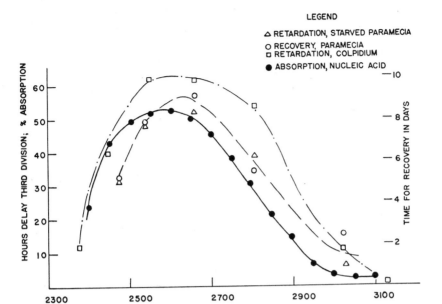

Fig. 9.15. Action spectra for retardation of division of paramecia and colpidia by ultraviolet radiation; and absorption spectrum of nucleic acid. (From Giese, 1953: Physiol. Zool., 26:12.)

their ultraviolet absorption spectrum.[16] The distinctive absorption spectra for nucleic acid and serum albumin were already given in Figure 3.17 and serve as examples of selective uptake of ultraviolet radiation. Thousands of compounds have been studied in a similar manner. Selective absorption underlies the effects of ultraviolet radiation upon cells (for laws of absorption see Appendix 9.1).

Much excitement was aroused when Kelner[23] found that visible light, either accompanying or immediately succeeding ultraviolet radiation, will, to a considerable extent, reverse the injurious effects of the latter (photoreversal or photoreactivation; see Figure 9.16). Fungus spores, bacteria, animal and plant cells and viruses inactivated by ultraviolet radiations are photoreactivated by treatment with visible light.[24, 25] Mutations and cytological changes induced by ultraviolet radiation are also reversed by treatment with visible light as is ultraviolet tumor induction.[38]

Photoreactivation is never complete, and cells act as if they had been given a smaller dosage of ultraviolet than that actually given, a finding called the dose-reduction principle. A residual damage from ultraviolet always remains after treatment with visible light, damage which increases with the dose and with the repetition of these two treatments (e.g., Fig. 9.17). Whether this damage occurs to the same systems which are being photoreactivated or to others which are not subject to photoreactivation (e.g., cytoplasmic effects) is not known with certainty.[65-67]

Only the blue end of the visible spectrum and the bordering long ultraviolet region are effective in photoreversal. Theoretically it should be possible to determine the substance absorbing the visible light from the action spectrum of photoreactivation. Unfortunately, determinations of the action spectrum are not in agreement, and also the action spectra are not detailed enough to identify the

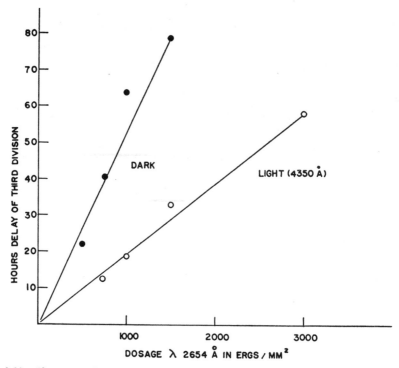

Fig. 9.16. Photoreversal recovery of *Colpidium colpoda* treated with various doses of λ 2654 Å followed by treatment with blue light of λ 4350 Å. (From Giese, 1953: Physiol. Zool., *26*:14.)

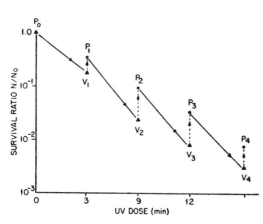

Fig. 9.17. Four cycles of ultraviolet inactivation and photoreactivation in a bacterium (*Escherichia coli*). The slopes of the ultraviolet curves do not differ significantly. (V_1), after first ultraviolet treatment; (P_1), after first photoreactivation, etc. (From Nishiwaki, Y., 1954: Yokohama Med. Bull. 5:21.)

absorbing material, although riboflavin and a porphyrin have been suggested.[46]

Photoreactivation appears to involve a photochemical reaction (absorption of visible and long ultraviolet light in the chromophore), followed by a thermochemical reaction, as indicated by a marked temperature effect (photoreversal even ceases entirely when the cells are placed on ice before illumination).[26]

Photoreactivation is coincident with the restitution of syntheses inhibited by ultraviolet radiation. The cell is thus able again to produce the materials necessary for growth and division. The process that is most sensitive to inhibition by ultraviolet radiation, as shown through experiments with the colon bacillus, is the production of some material required for cell division, which is arrested even though DNA, RNA and protein syntheses all continue. This process is also most

180

readily photoreversed. The causative process is not yet identified, but its action spectrum resembles nucleic acid absorption.[63] Sensitive to ultraviolet radiation and to photoreactivation, in a decreasing order, are DNA synthesis, RNA synthesis and protein synthesis.

Since DNA seems to be the main focus of action of ultraviolet radiations, attempts were made to determine whether DNA itself was injured by ultraviolet radiations and whether this injury could be reversed by visible light. For this purpose, a change in the transforming reaction (Fig. 9.15B) was used as a sensitive biological test of damage to DNA. It is known that in the bacterium *Hemophilus influenzae*, for example, some strains are streptomycin-resistant and others are not, and a streptomycin-sensitive strain can be rendered streptomycin-resistant by adding to it the pure DNA extracted from the streptomycin-resistant strain (Chapter 6). It was found that the DNA of the streptomycin-resistant strain is altered when subjected to ultraviolet treatment and apparently loses its capacity to transform the streptomycin-sensitive strain. Also, experiments show that if the ultraviolet-treated DNA from the resistant strain is illuminated with visible light before it is added to the sensitive strain, there is no photoreversing effect in the DNA-altering process (Fig. 9.18).

However, if a crude extract from yeast (or some other organism) that shows photoreactivation is added to the irradiated transforming DNA before illumination, then photoreactivation is obtained. It was found by fractionation that in yeast, for example, an enzyme is present that, combined with the ultraviolet-treated DNA from the streptomycin-resistant *Hemophilus*, will facilitate photoreactivation. It is therefore inferred that the enzyme of yeast which facilitates photoreversal combines only with the ultraviolet-treated DNA, and the DNA-enzyme complex absorbs light which in some way restores the function of the DNA. Irradiation, then, alters the DNA molecule in some way, making it possible for it to combine with the enzyme from yeast; unirradiated DNA (from *Hemophilus* or other sources) does not combine with the enzyme (see Fig. 9.18 and equations 9.3 to 9.6). Extraneous ultraviolet-treated DNA acts as a competitive poison in the system, uniting with the yeast enzyme and interfering with photoreactivation of the *Hemophilus* transforming DNA. This indicates that irradiation alters some bond, presumably in every DNA molecule, making it capable of uniting with the photoreversing enzyme in yeast:

$$DNA_H + E \rightarrow$$
$$DNA_H + E \quad \text{(no combination)} \quad (9.3)$$

$$DNA_H + UV \rightarrow \quad (DNA_H)_{uv} \quad \text{(alteration)} \quad (9.4)$$

$$(DNA_H)_{uv} + E \rightarrow$$
$$(DNA_H)_{uv} \cdot E \quad \text{(enzyme complex)} \quad (9.5)$$

$$(DNA_H)_{uv} \cdot E + \text{visible light} \rightarrow$$
$$DNA_H + E \quad (9.6)$$

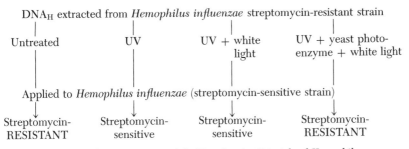

Fig. 9.18. Photoreactivation of the Transforming Principle of *Hemophilus*.

Whether this scheme is applicable to photoreactivation in all cells is not known. Since continued ultraviolet action involves a progressive effect on a variety of reactions in the cell (i.e., cleavage, DNA synthesis, RNA synthesis, protein synthesis, etc.), all of which seem to be subject to photoreactivation, it is probably not the complete story.

Some evidence has been presented that ultraviolet radiation causes formation of thymine dimers in DNA. In that case photoreactivation might consist of restoration of monomers. The study of alteration of DNA and of other molecules in cells by radiations is being actively studied.[81]

The ecological significance of photoreactivation should be self-evident. Ultraviolet radiations in sunlight injure small organisms or cells and induce mutations, but the accompanying visible light greatly reduces its injurious action.

Effects of Ionizing Radiations on Cells

Superficially, some of the effects of ionizing radiations resemble those of ultraviolet radiations. Thus, brief exposure of the cells of the skin leads to a reddening, or erythema, that is followed by slight tanning; such brief exposures are used in the treatment of various skin diseases. More prolonged exposure, however, leads to injuries to the skin which are quite different from those caused by ultraviolet light (see below).

Many ionizing radiations (e.g., hard x-rays) readily penetrate through a considerable thickness of living tissue and some of them will even go through a mass of concrete or lead (see also Appendix 9.4). In any case, the effect of ionizing radiations is not confined to the surface (except in the action of alpha rays or very soft x-rays); therefore, cells deep in the body may be injured. Certain kinds of cells are especially sensitive to ionizing radiations, e.g., lymphocytes, synthetically active cells and proliferating cells. Thus

the cells of the germinative layer in the skin (Fig. 9.14) are more readily destroyed than the surrounding connective tissue cells, so that injuries may be healed only by the deposit of scar tissue (keloids). Similarly, blood-forming cells are selectively killed; consequently there is a change in the number and the proportion of the various types of cells. Actively growing, undifferentiated cells such as are found in tumors are more readily affected than the normal, differentiated cells about them, so that ionizing radiations have been especially useful in retarding or inhibiting the growth of tumors. Gametogenic cells, even those deep in a gonad, are selectively affected by ionizing radiations. As a result, mutations are induced in gametes later formed; therefore these radiations are the choice for genetic experiments. Dosages greater than mutagenic inhibit gametogenesis completely, thereby sterilizing the organism.[27-29] Extensive tests on plant cells[8] make it appear likely that the above differential sensitivities of cells are correlated with the nuclear DNA content—the greater their DNA content the greater their sensitivity to ionizing radiations (Fig. 9.19).

The marked contrast in action between ionizing radiations, on the one hand, and visible light or ultraviolet radiations, on the other, is largely attributable to a difference in energy content of the quanta of these radiations (see Table 9.2). It is to be noted that quanta of short ultraviolet radiations are only about twice the magnitude of visible light quanta, but x-ray quanta are 2000 to 200,000 times greater. Differences in potency, penetration and in manner of action between ultraviolet and x-ray quanta are therefore not surprising.[4]

Ionizing radiations are absorbed in proportion to the density of the absorbing materials. Thus, metal is most opaque to x-rays, bone is next, cells in tissue are still less opaque, and air least. Of these,

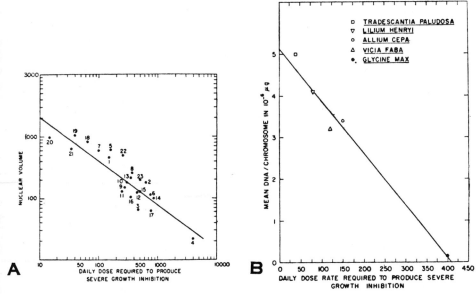

Fig. 9.19.   Relationship between DNA content and sensitivity to ionizing radiations. In *A* is shown the relationship between nuclear volume in cubic microns and radiosensitivity in 23 species of plants. 1, *Allium cepa.* 2, *Anethum graveolens.* 3, *Antirrhinum majus.* 4, *Arabidopsis thaliana.* 5, *Brodiaea bridgesii.* 6, *Graptopetalum bartramii.* 7, *Haworthia attenuata.* 8, *Helianthus annuus.* 9, *Impatiens sultanii.* 10, *Luzula purpurea.* 11, *Nicotiana glauca.* 12, *Oxalis stricta.* 13, *Pisum sativum.* 14, *Raphanus sativus.* 15, *Ricinus communis.* 16, *Saintpaulia ionantha.* 17, *Sedum oryzifolium.* 18, *Tradescantia ohiensis.* 19, *Tradescantia paludosa.* 20, *Trillium grandiflorum.* 21, *Tulbaghia violacea.* 22, *Vicia faba.* 23, *Zea mays.* B, relationship between mean DNA values per chromosome and radiosensitivity in five species of plants. (From Sparrow and Miksche, 1961: *Science 134*: 282.)

metal has the greatest density (the density of gold is 19.3); that of bone is slightly over 3 (apatite, the mineral present in bone, has an average density of 3.2); that of tissue or water is close to 1.0; and of air, 0.00125. Two solutions of the same density but chemically differing in solute will absorb ionizing radiations to the same extent. Therefore, x-rays cannot be used to obtain absorption spectra in the same manner as spectra are determined for various substances in the infrared, visible or ultraviolet parts of the spectrum, because absorption of x-rays is

TABLE 9.2.   *Comparison of Energy Content of Quanta of Various Wavelengths*

WAVELENGTH IN Å (10^{-8} CM)	QUANTUM* $q = \dfrac{hc}{\lambda}$	RATIO OF ENERGY IN ONE QUANTUM TO THAT IN ONE OF GREEN LIGHT
Green (5000 Å)	hc/5000 $\times\ 10^{-8}$	1
Far ultraviolet (2500 Å)	hc/2500 $\times\ 10^{-8}$	2
Soft x-ray (2.5 Å)	hc/2.5 $\quad\times\ 10^{-8}$	2000
Hard x-ray (0.025 Å)	hc/0.025 $\times\ 10^{-8}$	200,000

*Where h = 6.62 $\times$ 10^{-27} erg-sec.; c = 3 $\times$ 10^{10} cm./sec.; and λ, the wavelength, is given in cm.

determined more by the physical properties of a substance than by its chemical nature.[28] However, x-rays can be used for identification of some elements and compounds.[49]

When a molecule absorbs a quantum of moderately hard x-rays it ionizes with the ejection of an electron which carries most of the energy of the x-ray quantum. This fast moving photoelectron collides with other molecules, giving to each of them some of its energy, as a consequence of which each of them ionizes. For every 34 electron volts (the charge on an electron times the voltage; an energy unit) of energy in the original x-ray beam, a pair of ions is formed.[4] A 100,000 volt x-ray, therefore, produces about 3000 ion pairs. Such a shower of ions produced by absorption of x-rays can be made visible in the following manner. An x-ray is passed through a Wilson cloud chamber saturated with water vapor. The volume of the chamber is suddenly increased when the piston forming the floor of the chamber is pulled. Around each ion formed by the x-ray beam, water vapor then condenses, forming a cloud which can be photographed. Very hard x-rays, on the other hand, transmit their energy to molecules in other ways; their action is considered in the references cited.[4]

The length of the ionizing pathway produced by an x-ray is directly proportional to a power function of the velocity of the electron ejected by some molecule ionized by the x-ray, and inversely proportional to the density of the absorbing material. Consequently, its length will be short in a very dense material like gold, considerably longer in bone and tissue, and much longer in air. The shorter the wavelength of the x-ray (and the higher the energy content) the greater will be the velocity of the primary electron. Therefore, other things being equal, a hard x-ray (short wavelength) will have a proportionally longer pathway in tissue than a softer ray[28] (see Appendix 9.3).

Some of the effects of x-rays, γ-rays, radioactive emanations and other ionizing radiations are understandable on the basis of the facts already presented. The effects of x-rays on cells are largely independent of wavelength, in striking contrast to the effects of ultraviolet and visible radiations. Ionizing radiations produce effects primarily related to the amount of ionization they induce in cells. Sometimes the density of ionization is also of importance. For example, a pathway of very dense ionization is most effective in splitting chromosomes. For this purpose, radiations such as α particles, which produce dense clusters of ions,[28] are more effective than hard x-rays or other radiations which have a greater range but produce a lesser density of ions per unit volume through which they pass.

Because the number of mutations produced by ionizing radiations is proportional to the dose, and for a given dose this number is always a given fraction of the population present—and so is related to the probability of a structure being "hit"—a target or "direct action" theory or ionizing radiation was proposed.[50] However, when it was discovered that addition of a reducing compound, such as cysteine, protects the cells against radiation action while substances promoting oxidation—like oxygen itself—potentiate the effect of the radiations upon cells,* indirect action of the radiations had to be taken into account.[27, 31] Radiochemical studies with enzymes, for example, also indicate that the environment affects the radiochemical efficiency of ionizing radiations upon molecules, whereas if the action were direct, the effect of the environment should be neg-

* However, increasing the oxygen tension of the culture medium containing the cells above that of the surrounding air does not potentiate effects of ionizing radiations.

igible. However, if the organisms or enzyme solutions are dried completely, the effects of the environment are essentially eliminated.

Under such conditions it is found that the effects of radiations are in accordance with the direct action theory. Because a single hit usually inactivates or produces a change such as mutation or inactivation (reproductive death) and because the slope of the line relating the logarithm of the survival ratio to the dosage indicates the size of the target, it has been possible to use this biophysical method to define the approximate size of biological entities such as viruses, genes and molecules. However, when water is present, both direct and indirect effects occur and the relative proportion of the effect resulting from direct and indirect action may be assessed by varying the environment.

Since the cell is essentially an aqueous system containing a matrix of proteins, most of the ionizing radiations falling upon the cell are absorbed by water. Water is ionized and decomposed with the formation of oxidizing free radicals like the hydroxyl and perhydroxyl, and of oxidizing compounds like hydrogen peroxide or organic peroxides,[47, 48] as shown in Table 9.3.

A free radical is unstable inasmuch as it has an unpaired or odd electron. Thus the hydrogen radical H· must lose an electron to become a hydrogen ion and the hydroxyl radical OH· must add an electron to form the hydroxyl ion, or each must become associated with a molecule forming another free radical in the process, or combine with another free radical forming a normal paired electron configuration of a stable compound (Table 9.3). Free radicals react very readily with organic compounds. Because the unpaired electron of a free radical can make a transition to a higher energy state as a result of resonant absorption in an electromagnetic field of appropriate frequency, free radicals produced in bio-

logical systems by ionizing radiations or in other ways can be detected and measured (See Chapter 18).[47]

There is considerable evidence to indicate that these oxidizing substances are responsible for many of the effects of ionizing radiations upon cells. The strongest evidence is perhaps the following: (1) The formation of such oxidizing materials during irradiation is decreased when the oxygen tension is lowered, and it occurs at only a very low rate when oxygen is lacking; (2) in apparent correlation with this, biological effects, such as induction of mutations, fragmentation of chromosomes and lethal effects, are decreased correspondingly when the oxygen tension is reduced; (3) pretreatment of organisms, particularly microorganisms, with reducing substances also protects them to a considerable extent from ionizing radiation even in the presence of air.[31, 32, 33]

Recently, colonies originating from single cells of human tissue have been grown on a synthetic medium (containing serum) much as microorganisms. Such a culture consists of a relatively homo-

TABLE 9.3. *Formation of Free Radicals as a Result of Absorption of Ionizing Radiations**

H_2O + ionizing radiation $\rightarrow H_2O^+$ + e (electron)
H_2O + e $\rightarrow H_2O^-$
$H_2O^+ \rightarrow H^+ + OH\cdot$ (hydroxyl radical)
$H_2O^- \rightarrow OH^- + H\cdot$ (hydrogen radical)

. . . .

$H\cdot + OH\cdot \rightarrow H_2O$
$OH\cdot + OH\cdot \rightarrow H_2O_2 \rightarrow H_2O + \frac{1}{2}O_2$
$H\cdot + H\cdot \rightarrow H_2$
$OH\cdot + H_2 \rightarrow H_2O + H\cdot$
$H\cdot + H_2O_2 \rightarrow H_2O + OH\cdot$

. . . .

In presence of oxygen:
$H\cdot + O_2 \rightarrow HO_2\cdot$ (perhydroxyl radical)
$HO_2\cdot + H\cdot \rightarrow H_2O_2$

* The unpaired electron of the radical is shown as a dot. (From Alexander.[50])

geneous population of cells and serves as a much more effective object for testing radiation effects than a mixed tissue culture such as had been used in the past. The experiments show that cells from several different tissues have about the same degree of sensitivity to ionizing radiations, as measured by reproductive death. The differential action of ionizing radiations, indicating some cells to be more sensitive (as described above), is apparently the result of the different degrees of activity of various types of cells. When they are all growing and dividing (about every 18 hours) as they do in tissue culture, they have the same radio-resistance. The dose required to produce reproductive death is only about 50 roentgens. This is closely correlated with the dosages needed for the production of

a chromosome break, resulting in abnormal division.[57]

Radiosensitivity varies markedly for cells of different species—the same effect being produced in the mammal tissue cell by 50 roentgens as in the colon bacillus by 10,000 r, in yeast by 30,000 r, in ameba by 100,000 r and in paramecia by 300,000 r—all of the cells being in approximately the same physiological state at the time of treatment.[50] In plant cells injury is greater the higher their DNA content (Fig. 9.19). This relationship between nuclear volume and DNA content and sensitivity to ionizing radiations perhaps applies to animal cells as well.

The nucleus of the cell is more sensitive to ionizing radiations than the cytoplasm.[55] When wasp eggs, in which the nucleus is asymmetrically placed, are

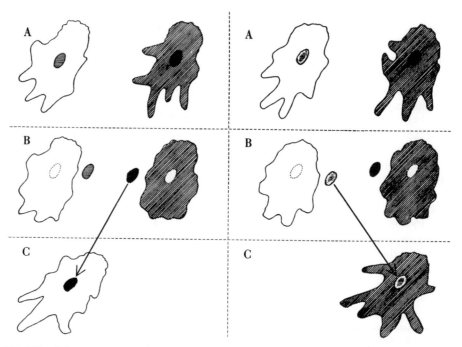

Fig. 9.20. Relative sensitivity of nucleus and cytoplasm to ionizing radiations. Transplantations of nuclei in the ameba by several workers has shown that the nucleus is more sensitive to these radiations than the cytoplasm. At left the nucleus of an irradiated ameba (colored) is transplanted to an unirradiated ameba; the latter survives about three days. At right, the nucleus of the unirradiated ameba is transplanted to an irradiated one; the latter survives some three weeks. (From Hollaender and Stapleton, Sept. 1959: Sci. Am. *201*:97.)

THE CELL ENVIRONMENT

rradiated, a single alpha particle delivered to the nucleus prevents division while a million particles are required in the cytoplasm to do the same. Also, when a nucleus is transferred from an irradiated *Amoeba proteus* to an unirradiated one, the effect is much greater than when a nucleus is transferred from an unirradiated ameba to an irradiated cytoplasm (Fig. 9.19).

The locus of action of ionizing radiations in the cell has not been identified with certainty. The over-all metabolism of the cell, as measured by oxygen consumption and carbon dioxide output, is not altered in a consistent way for all types of cells studied. Also, no evidence has been found for damage by ionizing radiations to specific metabolic enzymes in the cell. Some *in vitro* studies with enzymes which require a free SH group suggested their special vulnerability, but this has not been borne out in studies with SH-containing enzymes extracted from irradiated cells, these enzymes being no more sensitive when irradiated *in situ* in the cell than any of the others.

Doses which produce reproductive death do not necessarily stop DNA synthesis. The minimal dosages that are required for reproductive death of the cells, if applied before synthesis of DNA has begun, inhibit incorporation of P^{32} into DNA precursors. However, once the DNA synthesis has begun, much larger dosages are necessary to stop it. It has been suggested that the process most sensitive to ionizing radiation is the coupling of enzymes for energy transfer from the oxidative energy-liberating reactions of the nucleus to enzymes during phosphate bond formation. Nucleotides and nucleotide precursors of nucleic acid then accumulate, possibly because the DNA template has been damaged. A possible alternative explanation is that the Kornberg enzyme that bears the template has been damaged.

Synthesis of RNA and protein is not much affected by a dose that inhibits cell division (reproductive death). Cells in tissue culture given 10 to 100 times the reproductive death dose may grow up to a millimeter in diameter. The increase of protoplasm in such a giant cell indicates that many of the metabolic activities continue in a reproductively dead cell, including uptake of nutrients, liberation of energy and RNA and protein synthesis. Such an irradiated cell can be infected with a virus which grows and replicates in much the same manner as in the normal cell. From all such experiments it is apparent that the reproductive capacity of a cell is infinitely more sensitive to radiations than are its other functions.[57]

No photoreactivation by illumination with visible light has been demonstrated with tissues injured by x-ray. This probably indicates a fundamental difference between the actions of ionizing and ultraviolet radiations upon cells.

Biological Effects of the Atomic Bomb

An atomic bomb explosion lasts about 10^{-6} seconds and develops in its center a temperature of about $1,000,000°$ C. Its destructive effects are the result of its extreme heat, the ultraviolet flash, shock waves and ionizing radiations. The temperature of the surface of an object such as human skin at 400 yards from the bomb may be raised to about $50°$ C. The ultraviolet flash burn may be severe. Therefore, cells superficially exposed are readily damaged whether they are microorganisms or cells in the surface of the human skin. The shock waves rip the capillaries of the sense organs and lungs and cause hemorrhages throughout the entire digestive system. The ionizing radiations consist of about 15 per cent neutrons and about 15 per cent alpha and beta particles, and the remainder consists of short gamma rays. Cells, such as protozoans and bacteria as well as those in the body of an animal or plant, are injured in proportion to their sensitivity to these radiations.

A characteristic set of symptoms in a person injured by ionizing radiations is nausea accompanied by vomiting, prostration and, after a latent period, fever, bloody diarrhea, loss of hair and appearance of purple hemorrhagic spots in the skin. Should the individual survive, various skin lesions appear in areas where the germinative epithelium has been killed by the radiations. If infection is prevented and the wounds heal, great sausage-like growths of connective tissue known as keloids develop over severely burned areas of skin. The connective tissue of the keloids may contract enough to make it impossible for the victim to use hands, legs or other parts affected.[34] Delayed effects include mutations in the progeny of the affected organisms.

Some idea of the destructiveness of the bomb's radiations may be gathered from the fact that it takes only between 350 and 530 roentgens of ionizing radiations to kill a man. At 1250 meters from the center of the old type bomb, the calculated intensity is about 473 roentgens. Anyone caught in this range would receive a lethal dose unless hidden underground or behind thick concrete walls.[34, 35]

APPENDIX

9.1 Absorption of Light

Equal fractions of incident radiation are absorbed by successive layers of equal thickness of light-absorbing substance. The fraction of light transmitted (the total incident light minus that absorbed) by a solution is dependent upon the concentration of the absorbing substance, c (usually expressed in moles per liter), the thickness of the solution, 1 (expressed in centimeters), and the nature of the absorbing substance summarized

in ϵ (the molecular extinction coefficient). The relation between these factors is given in the Beer law:

$$T = 10^{-\epsilon c l} \qquad (9.7)$$

$$\text{or } \log_{10} T = -\epsilon c l \qquad (9.8)$$

$$\text{or } \log_{10} \frac{1}{T} = \epsilon c l \qquad (9.9)$$

Since by definition, D, the optical Density equals $\log_{10} 1/T$,

$$D = \epsilon c l \qquad (9.10)$$

$$\epsilon = \frac{D}{c l} \qquad (9.11)$$

Since the optical density of a solution is measured by a spectrophotometer, the extinction coefficient is readily determined.

Not all substances obey the Beer law. Association or dissociation of molecules may affect absorption. It is therefore desirable to study the absorption of a solution at different concentrations to test for obedience to the law.

The extinction coefficient, ϵ, is inversely proportional to the transmission. For purposes of illustration, various degrees of transmission are assumed when light is passed through 1 centimeter of an 0.1 M solution of a substance, S, and the values of ϵ are calculated as follows:

HYPOTHETICAL TRANSMISSION (0.1 MOLAR SOLUTION)	ϵ
90%	.46
75%	1.25
50%	3.02
25%	6.03
10%	10
1%	20
0.1%	30

9.2 Relation of X-ray Wavelength to Voltage

A quantum of x-rays is given by Planck's law: $q = h\nu$

$h\nu = Ve$ where V is the voltage through which the electron (e) falls in producing the x-ray, and e is the charge on the electron, 1.6×10^{-19} coulomb.

Since $h\nu = hc/\lambda = Ve$

$$\lambda = \frac{hc}{Ve} = \frac{hc/e}{V} = \frac{12.34}{V}, \qquad (9.12)$$

where V is given in kilovolts.

By this relation it is possible to calculate the minimal wavelength to be expected for a given voltage.

9.3 The Range of an Electron

The range, R, of an electron is related in the following way to its velocity and to the density of the material into which it enters:

$$R = \frac{V_0{}^4}{k \times P \times 10^{43}} \qquad (9.13)$$

Here R is the range in centimeters,
V_0 is the initial velocity of the photoelectron in cm./sec.,
k is the constant equal to 0.6 cm.^{6} sec.$^{-4}$ gm.$^{-1}$,
P is the density of the material.
The range is inversely proportional to the density and directly proportional to the initial velocity of the photoelectron. The initial velocity, V_0, may be determined from the relation,

$$Ve = \tfrac{1}{2} mv^2, \qquad (9.14)$$

where V is the voltage,
e is the charge on the electron $(1.6 \times 10^{-19}$ coulomb),
Ve is in volt coulombs or joules $(1$ joule $= 10^7$ ergs or dyne-cm.),
m is the mass of an electron $(9.1066 \times 10^{-28}$ gm.),
v is the velocity of the electron in cm./sec.,
and the dyne is a gram cm. sec.$^{-2}$.

The initial velocity of an electron produced by absorption of a maximum quantum of 100,000-volt x-ray is 1.87×10^{10} cm. per sec.; the range in air (density 0.00125 gm./cc.) is 16 cm., in tissue or water (density 1) about 0.02 cm., in bone about 0.007 cm. and in gold (density 19.3) about 0.00108 cm.

The density of ionization will be greater the shorter the range. Since soft x-rays produce primary photoelectrons of low velocity, the density of ionization is greater than for a hard x-ray in the same material, e.g., in tissue.

9.4 Characteristics of Different Kinds of Ionizing Radiations

Alpha particles are positively charged helium particles, produced by radioactive disintegration of natural or artificially radioactive elements. Polonium gives off only alpha particles and is therefore an ideal source of these radiations. Alpha particles produce intense ionization, especially at the end (tail) of the ionization trail, and are absorbed superficially. Alpha particles may have a velocity of about 3×10^9 cm. per second and energy corresponding to about 5 MeV (where M is 10^6 and e is the charge on an electron and V stands for volts). They are especially effective in causing chromosome breaks. Because they produce such a high density of ionization, reducing the oxygen tension does not reduce their effectiveness.

Beta particles are negatively charged particles. They vary in speed and energy, depending on the voltage by which they are accelerated. The ionization produced by beta particles is much sparser than that by alpha particles. As a consequence of their charge and resulting interaction with matter, beta particles are superficially absorbed in tissue. Usually they are polyenergetic, but monoenergetic particles can be produced. In tissue, less than 1 per cent of the beta particles are absorbed with the emission of an x-ray.

Fast neutrons are uncharged, highly energetic particles produced by bombarding low molecular weight substances with protons or deuterons. They may give rise to gamma rays on inelastic collision with some matter, but in tissue of organisms which consists of nuclei of atoms of low atomic weight, collisions give rise to protons. Protons are positively charged particles of about the same mass. Protons pass through tissue, forming a high density of ions. Because of the density of ionization, neutron effects are independent of oxygen. Since neutrons are absorbed in proportion to the number of atomic nuclei, light materials like paraffin or water are more effective absorbers of neutrons than sheets of lead because they have larger numbers of nuclei per unit mass. Most sources of neutrons are therefore kept in huge vats of water. Since neutrons are themselves uncharged they may penetrate deep into tissue of organisms before absorption brings about ionization.

Slow neutrons, also called thermal neutrons, are much less energetic (about 0.03 MeV), consequently they do not cause ionization or dislodge atomic nuclei but react with atomic nuclei to form a new isotope which may disintegrate to give rise to ionizing particles.

X-rays and γ-rays are photons. Gamma rays produced by radioactive disintegration of elements have energies of between 0.3 and 5 MeV, and x-rays have now been produced as energetic as gamma radiations. It is therefore best to speak of the properties of both, but with the understanding that the energy of both varies considerably with the voltage. Ordinary x-rays have much lower voltages than γ-rays. If the energy is less than 0.3 MeV the photoelectric effect is observed, the absorption of the quantum causing ionization of the atomic nucleus with the emission of an electron containing the energy of the quantum minus the binding energy of the electron. When more energy is available the photon and free or loose electrons collide (Compton effect), resulting in deflection of the electron and the photon, the latter now possessing a longer wavelength, having given up some of its energy. For quanta of energy of 5 MeV or more, absorption is usually followed by positron and electron formation.[35]

Gamma rays and x-rays penetrate deeply into material of low density, the depth depending upon the voltage. Consequently the density of ion pairs per unit path length varies, being quite sparse for hard or short wavelength radiations. These radiations penetrate deeper than the charged particles because they do not react at once with matter into which they penetrate. Once a photoelectron is ejected from a particle of absorbing material, its energy is quickly dissipated in formation of ion pairs, the density of which is greatest at the end (tail) of the ionization trail.

GENERAL REFERENCES

Advances in Biological and Medical Physics. Academic Press, New York.

Alexander, P., 1957: Atomic Radiations and Life. Pelican, London.

Allen, M. B. (ed.), 1960: Comparative Biochemistry of Photoreactive Systems. Academic Press, New York.

Bacq, Z. M., and Alexander; P., 1961: Fundamentals of Radiology, Pergamon, New York.

Blois, M. S., et al., 1961: Free Radicals in Biological Systems. Academic Press, New York.

Blum, H. F., 1959: Carcinogenesis by Ultraviolet Light. Princeton Univ. Press, Princeton, N. J.

Errera, M., 1957: Effects Biologiques des Radiations. Aspects Biologiques Protoplasmatologia *10*:3.

Hollaender, A. (ed.), 1954–1956: Radiation Biology, McGraw Hill, New York. The first volume (parts 1 and 2) deals with effects of ionizing radiations; the second volume deals with effects of ultraviolet radiations; and the third volume, with effects of visible light.

Hollaender, A. (ed.), 1960: Radiation Protection and Recovery. Pergamon, London.

Johnson, F. S., 1961: Satellite Environment Handbook. Stanford Univ. Press, Stanford, Calif.

Kiepenheuer, K., 1959: The Sun. Univ. of Michigan Press, Ann Arbor.

McElroy, W. D., and Glass, B. (eds.), 1961: Light and Life. Johns Hopkins Univ. Press, Baltimore.

Radiation Research: Current issues and supplements.

Rushton, W. A. H., 1959: Visual Pigments in Man and Animals and Their Relation to Seeing. Progr. Biophys. & Biophys. Chem. 9:240–283.

Thimann, K. V., and Curry, G. M., 1960: Phototropism and Phototaxis. Comp. Biochem. 1:243–309. Academic Press, New York.

Tousey, R., 1961: Solar Research from Rockets. Science 134:441–446.

Wald, 1960: The Distribution and Evolution of Visual Systems. Comp. Biochem. 1:311–345.

Withrow, R. B., 1959: Photoperiodism and Related Phenomena in Plants and Animals. A.A.A.S. Publ. 55, Washington.

LITERATURE CITED

1. Sanderson, J. A., and Hurlburt, E. O., 1955: in Radiation Biology, 2 (Hollaender, A., ed.). McGraw-Hill, New York, Chapter 3.

2. Menzel, D. H., 1959: Our Sun. Rev. Ed. Harvard Univ. Press, Cambridge.

3. Forsythe, W. E., 1937: Measurement of Radiant Energy. McGraw-Hill, New York.

4. Lea, D. E., 1955: Actions of Radiations on Living Cells. Macmillan, New York.

5. Livingston, R., 1955: in Radiation Biology 2 (Hollaender, A., ed.). Chapter 1. McGraw-Hill, New York.

6. Blum, H. F., 1941: Photodynamic Action and Diseases Caused by Light. Reinhold, New York.

7. Blum, H. F., and Kautzmann, E., 1954: J. Gen. Physiol., 37:301.

8. Giese, A. C., 1946: J. Cell. Comp. Physiol., 28:119.

9. Giese, A. C., 1949: J. Gen. Physiol., 32:529.

10. Davson, H., 1959: Textbook of General Physiology. 2nd Ed. Little, Brown, Boston.

11. Wald, G., 1954: Am. Sci., 42:73. References to an extensive literature are given here.

12. Hubbard, R., Gregerman, R. I., and Wald, G., 1953: J. Gen. Physiol., 36:415.

13. Hecht, S., Schlaer, S., and Pirenne, M. H., 1942: J. Gen. Physiol., 25:819.

14. Galston, A., 1950: Bot. Rev., 16:361.

15. Shrank, A. R., 1950: Ann. Rev. Plant Physiol., 1:59.

16. Sinsheimer, R. L., 1955: Radiation Biology, 2. Chapter 5.

17. Blum, H. F., 1955: Radiation Biology, 2. Chapter 13.

18. Giese, A. C., and Wells, P. H., 1946: Sci. Month., 62:458.

19. Giese, A. C., 1945: Physiol. Zool., 18:223.

20. Blum, H. F., 1955: Radiation Biology, 2. Chapter 14.

21. Giese, A. C., 1947: Quart. Rev. Biol., 22:253.

22. Blum, H. F., Robinson, J. C., and Loos, G. M., 1950: Proc. Nat. Acad. Sci. U. S., 36:623.

23. Kelner, A., 1949: Proc. Nat. Acad. Sci. U. S., 35:73.

24. Dulbecco, R., 1955: Radiation Biology, 2. Chapter 12.

25. Kimball, R. F., 1955: Radiation Biology, 2. Chapter 8.

26. Mayor, H. D., and Melnick, J. L., 1961: Virology 14:74.

27. Hollaender, A. (ed.), 1954: Radiation Biology, 1.

28. Fano, U., 1954: Radiation Biology, 1. Chapter 1.

29. Patt, H. M., and Brues, C. T., 1954: Radiation Biology, 1. Chapters 14 and 15.

30. Muller, H. J., 1954: Radiation Biology, 1. Chapters 7 and 8.

31. Hollaender, A., and Stapleton, G. E., 1953: Physiol. Rev., 33:77.

32. Patt, H. M., 1953: Physiol. Rev., 33:35.

33. Brues, C. T., and Patt, H. M., 1953: Physiol. Rev., 33:85.

34. Los Alamos Scientific Laboratory, 1950: The Effects of Atomic Weapons. U. S. Govt. Printing Office, Washington, D. C.

35. Glasstone, S., 1958: Sourcebook of Atomic Energy. 2nd Ed. Van Nostrand, New York.

36. Rushton, W. A. H., 1956: J. Physiol., 134:30.

37. Borthwick, H. A., Hendricks, S. B., and Parker, M. W., 1956: Radiation Biology, 3, Chapter 10.

38. Kelner, A., and Taft, E. B., 1956: Cancer Res., 16:860.

39. Kiepenheuer, K., 1959: The Sun. Univ. of Michigan Press, Ann Arbor.

40. Butler, W. L., and Downs, R. J., Dec. 1960: Sci. Am. 203:56.

41. Borthwick, H. A., and Hendricks, S. B., 1960: Science 132:1223.

42. Withrow, R. B. (ed.), 1959: Photoperiodism and Related Phenomena in Plants and Animals. A.A.A.S. Publ. 55, Washington.

43. Farner, D. S., 1961: Ann. Rev. Physiol. 23:71.

44. Beck, S. D., Feb. 1960: Sci. Am. 202:109.

45. Rupert, C. S., Goodgal, S. H., and Herriott, R. M., 1958: J. Gen. Physiol. 41:451.

46. Jagger, J., 1958: Bact. Rev. 22:99.

47. Blois, M. S., Jr. (ed.), 1960: Free Radicals in Biological Systems. Academic Press, New York.

48. Landsberg, H. E., April 1953: Sci. Am. 189:82.

49. Barrieau, R. E., 1957: Anal. Chem. 29:348.

50. Alexander, P., 1957: Atomic Radiations and Life. Pelican, London.

51. Gray, L. H., 1959: Radiation Biology (Martin, J. H., ed.). Proc. 2nd Australian Radiation Society. Butterworth, London.
52. Korff, S. A., 1957: Am. Scient. *45*:281.
53. Ginsburg, V., and Razoryonov, L., 1959: Am. Scient. *47*:562.
54. Newell, H. E., and Naugle, J. E., 1960: Science *132*:1465.
55. Hollaender, A., and Stapleton, G. E., Sept. 1959: Sci. Am. *201*:94.
56. Stanier, R., 1960: Harvey Lect. *54*:219.
57. Puck, T. T., April 1960: Sci. Am. *202*:142.
58. van Allen, J., March 1959: Sci. Am. *200*:39.
59. Wald, G., Oct. 1959: Sci. Am. *201*:92.
60. Rushton, W. A. H., 1961: *in* Life and Light (McElroy, W. D., and Glass, B., eds.). Johns Hopkins Univ. Press, Baltimore, p. 706. 1958: Ann. New York Acad. Sci. *74*:291.
61. Thimann, K., and Curry, G. M. *in* Life and Light, (McElroy, W. D., and Glass, B., eds.). Johns Hopkins Univ. Press, Baltimore, p. 646.
62. Bendix, S., 1960: *in* Comparative Biochemistry of Photoreactive Systems (Allen, M. B., ed.). Academic Press, New York, p. 107.
63. Deering, R. A., 1958: J. Bact. *76*:123.
64. Rupert, C. S., 1960: J. Gen. Physiol. *43*:573.
65. Brandt, C., and Giese, A. C., 1956: J. Gen. Physiol. *39*:735.
66. Jagger, J., 1960: Radiation Res. suppl. *2*:75.
67. Jagger, J., 1960: Radiation Res. *13*:521.
68. Stocken, L. A., 1959: Radiation Res. suppl. *1*:5?
69. Scientific American: issue on Ionizing Radiations Sept. 1959, *201*.
70. Biological Clocks, 1960: Cold Spring Harb. Symp *25*:87, 131, 149, 217.
71. Pittendrigh, C. S., 1960: Cold Spring Harb. Symp *25*:159.
72. Brown, F. A., Jr., 1959: Science *130*:1535. Am Sci. *47*:147.
73. Aschoff, J., 1960: Cold Spring Harb. Symp. *25*:11?
74. Bünning, E., 1960: Cold Spring Harb. Symp *25*:249.
75. Halberg, F., 1960: Cold Spring Harb. Symp *25*:289.
76. Hastings, J. W., and Sweeney, B. M., 1958: Biol Bull. *115*:440.
77. Sweeney, B. M., and Hastings, J. W., 1958: ? Protozool. *5*:217.
78. Hastings, J. W., 1959: Ann. Rev. Microbiol *13*:297.
79. Sweeney, B. M., and Hastings, J. W., 1960: Cold Spring Harb. Symp. *25*:87.
80. Bruce, V. G., 1960: Cold Spring Harb. Symp *25*:29.
81. A Symposium on Recovery of Cells from Injury 1961: J. Cell. Comp. Physiol. *58*; suppl., *1*:1—248.
82. Sparrow, A. H., and Miksche, J. P., 1961: Science *134*:282.
83. Tousey, R., 1961: Science *134*:441.

TEMPERATURE AS A FACTOR
IN THE CELL ENVIRONMENT

The Biokinetic Zone

All living cells are exposed to some thermal variation in their environment. Some are exposed to much less variation than others, since the temperature of the ocean varies much less than that of land and fresh water (see Chapter 7), but even when the temperature of the internal fluid (such as blood or body fluid) bathing the cells is closely controlled, as in warm-blooded animals, slight temperature changes occur. Because of its effect on life processes and because most cells have only a small range of adaptation to thermal changes, temperature is an important factor in the distribution of living things.

A temperature which is most favorable for one function of a cell, a function such as respiration, may not at the same time be favorable for another, such as the cell's growth or longevity. Furthermore, a temperature which may appear to be favorable for a given function during brief exposure of a cell may prove harmful on longer exposure. Temperature effects must therefore be examined rather fully, and it is a good experimental procedure when studying a given biological process to determine the effect of a temperature range on the process in order to select the temperature most favorable for the experiments.

The narrow range of temperatures within which the living cell carries on its life activities, called the *biokinetic zone*, lies approximately between 10° and 45° C. There are some organisms, however, that tolerate temperatures much higher than 45° C., and there are other organisms that tolerate temperatures much lower than 10° C. Most organisms when in a dormant state can withstand much greater temperature variations than when they are in an active state.[1] In addition, some organisms have been successfully adapted to heat by culturing them at progressively higher temperatures. For example, Dallinger[3] showed that over a period of 7 years, flagellates could become acclimatized to a temperature of 70° C.

Heat Resistance and Heat Death of Cells

Thermophilic (heat-loving) algae and bacteria are those which normally live at higher temperatures than their mesophilic relatives which live in the temperature range of the biokinetic zone. For example, some algae and bacteria live in hot springs at temperatures of 60° and 70° C., and the alga *Phormidium* has been reported to exist even at 89° C.[1, 2] These are temperatures which would kill most active cells.

The physiological basis of thermophily has been studied experimentally in only a few cases. However, it is common knowledge that the activities of organisms are primarily catalyzed by enzymes which are made up of proteins and that many proteins are altered by heat; for instance, egg albumin is quickly coagulated at temperatures between 60° and 100° C. It is also known that many enzymes are very easily inactivated by these temperatures. Some thermophilic bacteria withstand high temperatures perhaps because they appear to synthesize enzymes more rapidly than the high temperature destroys them.[4, 5] These bacteria are resistant to heat only when nutrients are available. In some cases at high temperature they require the amino acids and vitamins which they are able to make at lower temperatures, suggesting a partial breakdown of the synthetic mechanisms.[32] In the absence of appropriate nutrients, such bacteria are no more resistant to heat than mesophilic strains of the same species.[4] On the other hand, there are some thermophilic bacteria which are more resistant to heat because they possess enzymes which continue to function normally at high temperatures.[6] Stronger hydrogen bonding of the proteins of such organisms, demonstrated in a variety of experiments, is one of the reasons for their greater resistance to heat.[32] As a consequence, such thermophiles are unable to live at lower temperatures, presumably because the bonding then becomes too strong for normal catalytic action of the enzymes.

The high temperature required to kill an organism depends upon the temperature range to which the organism has been previously adapted, and upon the length of exposure of the organism. For example, arctic fish may die when the temperature is raised to 10° or 15° C., and marine animals of temperate zones may be killed when the temperature is raised to about 30° or 35° C., whereas fresh water and terrestrial animals may resist a temperature of 40° to 45° C. before death occurs. Detailed data on lethal temperatures and exposures for a wide variety of organisms are given by Bělehrádek.[1]

Lethal temperatures also depend upon the physiological state of the organism. Those in an active state are much more readily affected than those in a dormant state.

Heat death may conceivably result from thermal inactivation of enzymes in the cell. Many enzymes which are reversibly inactivated by mild heat are irreversibly inactivated by high temperatures. The action of heat on an enzyme is perhaps most clearly illustrated in the bioluminescent reaction in which the heat-stable substrate, luciferin, is oxidized in the presence of the enzyme, luciferase. The intensity of luminescence is a measure of the rate of the reaction. The intensity of luminescence increases when the temperature is raised up to a certain point. When the temperature is raised still higher, luminescence declines and is ultimately quenched. If the temperature is lowered, luminescence reappears, provided neither the temperature nor the time of exposure has been excessive. If left at 60° C. for a sufficient period, it will not luminesce on cooling, indicating that the enzyme has been inactivated (luciferin is heat stable). Similar experiments have been performed with luminous bacteria. Inactivation of the luminous system in the bacteria by heat is concomitant with inactivation of other enzymes as well and may result in the death of the bacteria.[7] High temperatures, therefore, shift the equilibrium of each thermolabile enzyme in favor of the denatured, inactive form.

$$\text{Native enzyme} \underset{}{\overset{\text{heat}}{\rightleftharpoons}} \text{denatured enzyme} \quad (10.1)$$

The time of exposure is also a factor and when the heat treatment is prolonged, even if the denatured enzyme is not irreversibly altered (e.g., at a temperature of 45° C. or lower), the processes required for life are probably suspended, and the cell dies.

Various enzymes of a cell have different temperature sensitivities, some even withstanding boiling. Killing curves for bacteria indicate that heat death is the result of a single event, probably inactivation of an enzyme system critical to cell reproduction. Since diploid yeast is much more resistant to heat than haploid yeast, the critical enzymes present in both chromosome sets must probably be inactivated before cell reproduction is blocked. The greater complexity of the killing curves for yeast than those for bacteria suggests that other factors, perhaps in the cytoplasm, play a part in determining heat resistance.[43] However, an alternative view is that possibly heat affects enzymes indirectly by degrading the aggregates of which they are a part. It is difficult experimentally to differentiate such an effect from a direct effect.

The possibility that derangements of the lipids of the cell are the cause of heat injury has also been suggested. As has already been shown (Chapter 3), lipids are important structural components of the cell and their disruption might well lead to death. The following evidence supports this interpretation: (1) High resistance of an organism to heat is correlated with a high melting point of the main lipids laid down in the organism and (2)

the melting point of lipids stored in animals adapted to higher temperatures is higher than that of lipids stored in control animals (for example, in fishes).[9, 36]

The liberation of a coagulating enzyme by heat is suggested as a third possible explanation for heat injury. Heat is found to release calcium from the outer portion of the cytoplasm of some cells, and this calcium is said to liberate a clotting enzyme which gels the cell.[10, 11] It is interesting in this respect that bacterial spores which are highly resistant to heat may have ten times as much calcium as the vegetative stages.[32]

Cold Resistance and Cold Death of Active Living Cells

Most cells become relatively inactive as the temperature falls to the lower limits they tolerate. Few remain active at the freezing point of water, although they may survive. Hypothermia, both naturally occurring in hibernators and induced in other organisms, results in decreased metabolism.[34] However, *cryophilic*, or cold-resistant organisms, arctic fishes and invertebrates carry on their life activities at a temperature of 0° C. or below.[12, 13] For example, some molds grow slowly even at −4° to −6.7° C.[14] and bacteria grow slowly in ice cream at −10° C.[42]

There is apparently an increase in rate of respiration of cells connected with cold adaptation of organisms, but the physiological changes which underlie such adaptation to cold have not been determined.[43]

Some organisms are injured or killed even when the temperature falls to points well above the freezing point of water. The cause of death in such cases is not known, but cells so injured by cold above freezing show altered respiration, which suggests that electrolyte balance is affected, since respiration furnishes energy for the exclusion of certain ions (see Chapter 13).

However, adequate tests of this possibility have not yet been made.[31, 35] It is a well-known phenomenon that water in contact with hydrocarbons forms "ice" at temperatures well above freezing, but again no evidence exists for such relations in cells.[35]

As an organism is slowly exposed to freezing temperatures, water freezes outside the cells, thereby concentrating the solution surrounding the cells. Consequently, water diffuses out of the cells into the bathing fluid, and the result is a concentration of solutes inside the cell. Such a high concentration of solutes inside the cell lowers the freezing point but is injurious to the cell whether achieved by freezing or by direct application of equally concentrated solutions to the cells.[15-17] In some cases as much as 60 to 90 per cent of the free cell water may be withdrawn.[33] Many cells, however, can endure being nearly frozen at $-5°$ C, reimbibing water on thawing without apparent injury.

The time factor here is also of great consideration. Rapid freezing results in ice formation (as small crystals) inside as well as outside cells which also may concentrate the dissolved materials to the point of injury. However, in rapid freezing the formation of ice crystals inside the cells may by itself disrupt the cytoplasmic structures and those of the nucleus beyond the point of recovery.[33] This is especially true if the cells are stored for a time, allowing for growth of large ice crystals from the small ones. After both slow and rapid freezing the nature of the thawing process proves especially important. For example, if the ice melts slowly, the cell will be exposed to a high electrolyte concentration at a higher temperature than that applied during freezing, allowing for more ready denaturing of proteins. During slow thawing, growth of ice crystals, especially inside cells, may kill them. Thus even if the cell initially survived freezing it might still be damaged

severely on thawing. Rapid thawing is therefore especially important.[33]

If glycerol is added to the suspending medium, some of it penetrates into the suspended cells and it lowers the freezing point of both the bathing medium and the fluid in the cells. But even if freezing occurs, less ice is produced than in the absence of glycerol, and the crystals formed are smaller because of the strong hydrogen binding of glycerol for water. Concentration of electrolytes by freezing is thereby reduced; for this reason glycerol is sometimes spoken of as an "electrolyte buffer." Bacteria and phages which are readily killed by freezing in broth have been shown to survive eight cycles of freezing and thawing (Fig. 10.1) in 15 per cent glycerol.[42] However, since glycerol itself is toxic, it must be removed by dialysis after thawing. Glycerol is especially useful in slow freezing procedures.[33] Treated in this manner, erythrocytes and other cells remain viable and can be stored at low temperatures for long periods. Even eggs in ovaries have been kept for months at temperatures well below freezing and then successfully transplanted.[41] When cells are frozen with glycerol the rate of thawing matters little.[33]

Arctic organisms are able to reduce susceptibility to cold death by dehydration before the onset of winter, some retaining between 80 and 90 per cent of the summer moisture, others only as little as 25 per cent. However, if subjected to very low temperatures, simpler forms of arctic organisms may be frozen, yet survive. Respiration continues at a much reduced rate. Ice crystals can be seen (e.g., in tissue spaces of midge larvae) or demonstrated in the organisms by a decrease in the specific gravity of the frozen material.[16, 40] Debris which allows contact for the organism, preventing physical disruption on freezing, as well as a line of entry for oxygen, may help preserve life in ice.[16] Some cells of vertebrates are

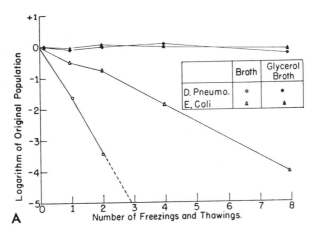

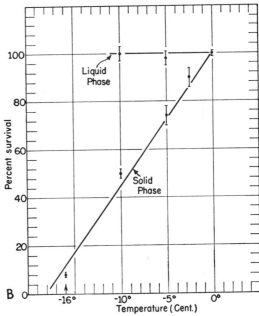

Fig. 10.1. *A,* survival of the colon bacillus (*Escherichia coli*) and the pneumonia coccus (*Diplococcus pneumoniae*) after repeated freezing (5 min. at $-80°$ C.) and thawing, with and without glycerol (15 per cent). (After Hollander and Nell, 1954.) *B,* survival of T-2 coliphage exposed to various temperatures for 45 minutes in both liquid (supercooled) and solid (frozen) phases. Note that when freezing is prevented and the phage remains in the liquid phase, little if any damage occurs, but when ice is formed (solid phase) damage is progressive with lowering of temperature. Since phage does not respire, the damage would appear to be direct, rather than from the accumulation of unnatural products. [From Wood, T. H., 1956: Biol. and Med. Physics. *4*: (*A*) p. 152; (*B*) p. 151.]

more susceptible to freezing, although hamsters have been frozen for an hour and revived.[41] The length of survival after freezing of such forms depends upon the extent of the injury during freezing. A fish completely frozen in ice has never revived, despite the stories to the contrary. It would thus appear that even the cells of arctic organisms are not free from injury by freezing, though they may be more resistant than temperate forms.[16]

Thermal Resistance of Dormant Cells

When unfavorable thermal conditions occur in the environment, many organisms suspend life activities and become dormant. Bacteria and lower plants form *spores*, protozoans and some invertebrates form *cysts*, and the cells in seeds of higher plants become dormant. The cold season of the polar, subpolar and north and south temperate zones is a period of dormancy for many organisms. The hot, dry season in desert and other arid habitats is a period of dormancy for many organisms which may dry up in the absence of water; these organisms renew their activity only when water becomes available again (e.g., rotifers, tardigrades, nematodes and mosses).

Cells of organisms in dormant states become dehydrated—in some cases to a considerable extent. The greater resistance of organisms to both heat and cold during their dormant stages is, in part, probably the result of the dehydrated state of their cells. Cysts and spores, for example, resist exposure to dry heat of over 100° C. Dry sterilization (as a means of killing dormant organisms), therefore, requires a temperature of 150° to 170° C. for half an hour or so. Moist sterilization, on the other hand, requires only 15 minutes at 115° C. (15 pounds pressure in an auto-

clave or pressure cooker). Boiling (100° C.) kills some cysts and spores, but it only induces germination of others, and following a time lapse a second boiling is necessary to kill the bacteria which have emerged from the spores. Repeated boiling for sterilization is called tyndallization. Pasteurization, or heating at 60° C. for half an hour, kills vegetative stages only, not spores.

The greater heat resistance of organisms in their dormant stages is not yet fully explained. It is known that the temperature required to denature proteins is higher the lower their water content. For example, at a relative humidity of 0 per cent, half of a given quantity of egg albumin is denatured when a sample is kept at a temperature of 140° C. for an hour;[21] at a relative humidity of 20 per cent, an hour at 124° C. suffices; at 47 per cent, an hour at 99° C.; at 75 per cent, an hour at 77° C.; and at 93 per cent, an hour at 57° C. (see Fig. 10.2). Similarly, a cyst, or seed, each highly resistant to heat, contains very little

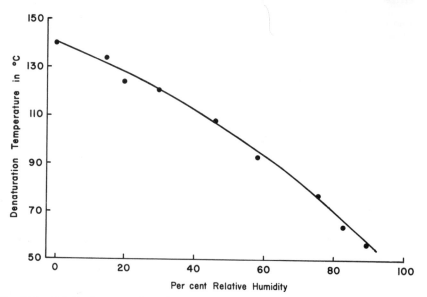

Fig. 10.2. Relation between relative humidity and temperature for denaturation of egg albumin. The data are for denaturation of half of the egg albumin in 60 minutes. (From Barker, H. A., 1933: J. Gen. Physiol. *17*:27.)

THE CELL ENVIRONMENT

water; for example, only 5 per cent of water is present in seeds of some desert plants,[22] whereas the active organism, highly sensitive to heat, contains 80 to 90 per cent water.

Some spores and cysts have been found capable of germinating after exposure to temperatures of between $-250°$ C. and $-272°$ C., which is close to absolute zero ($-273.18°$ C.), yet cells in active states do not survive even $-183°$ C.[16] In such dehydrated cells, little free water is available to form ice. This may account for their resistance to such low temperatures.[31] The fact that hibernating insects and cocoons of insects resist low temperatures even though they are not dehydrated suggests that factors other than dehydration may be involved.

The Rate of Thermochemical Reactions

The rate of reactions in the organism increases with the temperature up to a maximum; with further increase in temperature, the rate of activity declines. Therefore, for meaningful comparisons of the effects of temperature on the rates of various biological processes, the rates of reaction must be compared for the same temperature interval. Usually one determines the ratio of the rate of activity at a given temperature to the rate at a temperature 10° C. lower. This ratio, called the *temperature coefficient,* is designated Q_{10}. Four relatively different kinds of temperature coefficients have been found for cell processes, each corresponding to a distinctive mechanism of action: those which are about 2, those which are considerably higher than 2, those which are considerably less than 2 and those which are about 1. Illustrative data for a number of reactions are given in Table 10.1.

Examination of this table will disclose that, in comparable thermobiological reactions, as in thermochemical reactions, the rate increases at least twofold (i.e., 100 per cent) for each 10° C. rise in temperature, a relation which has sometimes been called van't Hoff's rule (see Appendix, 10.1, for equation). The fundamental cause underlying this principle is perhaps the same for both types of reactions. One possibility suggests itself, namely a comparable rise in kinetic energy of the system. However, calculation shows that a rise of 10° C. in temperature increases the average kinetic energy of the molecules only to a very limited extent—equal to $10/T$, where T is the absolute temperature. For instance, at room temperature the absolute temperature is about 300°; therefore, $10/T$ would be $10/300$ or 3.3 per cent. This trifling increase in the average kinetic energy of the molecules by itself is quite inadequate to explain the twofold rise in the rate of reaction which follows a 10° C. rise in temperature.

Arrhenius in 1889, however, proposed a plausible explanation for a twofold (or greater) rise in the rate of a thermochemical reaction with an increase in temperature of 10° C. He pointed out that not all the molecules in a population of a given kind of molecules, at a given temperature, have the same amount of kinetic energy. Following random collisions, some of the molecules accumulate more energy than others. Some become energy-rich, some energy-poor, and most are in the middle class between. Arrhenius suggested that it is the energy-rich molecules which are most likely to react on collision, and that the rate of reaction might therefore depend upon the concentration of such molecules. A molecule must have a certain amount of kinetic energy to undergo a thermochemical reaction. This critical amount of energy has been called the *energy of activation.* Arrhenius found means for determining experimentally this energy of activation (see Appendix, 10.2). He then used the Maxwell-Boltzmann distribution law to determine the number of molecules possessing the energy of activation before and after a 10° C. rise in temperature. The calculation shows that several times as many activated molecules are present at the higher temperature as at a temperature 10° C. lower (see Appendix 10.3 and Fig. 10.3). It seems most likely, therefore, that the increase in the rate of thermochemical reactions with a rise in temperature is attributable to the disproportionate increase in the fraction of molecules with the required energy of activation for a particular reaction.[7, 23]

Molecules, on absorbing energy, show increased movement, more rapid rotation and more rapid vibration, or higher electronic states. Absorption of heat usually results in the first two types of activation

TABLE **10.1.** *Increase in Rate of Reaction with a 10° Rise in Temperature*

TYPES OF REACTION	REACTIONS IN INANIMATE SYSTEM	Q_{10}	TEMP. RANGE °C.	REACTION IN ORGANISMS	Q_{10}	TEMP. RANGE °C.
Thermo-chemical	Reaction between peroxide and hydriotic acid	2.08	6–10	Photosynthesis at high light intensity	1.6–4.3	4–30
	Activity of malt amylase	2.2	10–20	Rate of cleavage of Arbacia eggs	3.9 3.3 2.6 1.7	7–17 8–19 15–25 20–30
	Most thermochem. reactions (van't Hoff rule)	2.3		Contractility of duodenum	2.42	28–38
				Respiration of pea seedlings	2.4	10–20
	Protein coagulation: egg albumin hemoglobin	635 13.8	69–76.3 60–70.4	Heat killing: spores bacteria protozoans rabbit leucocytes	2–10 12–136 891–1000 28.8	40–140 48–59 36–43 38–60
Diffusion and con-ductivity	Diffusion: strong electrolytes sugar dextrin	1.27 1.37 1.41	0–50	Penetration of molecules and ions into cells: Dyes into Arbacia	4.7	20–25
				Accumulation of bromine in Nitella same in light	1.57 2.4–2.7	10–20 10–20
				Water into Arbacia eggs	2.4	11–24.8
	Conductivity: KCl in water	1.22–1.24	10–25	Conductivity of living Laminaria	1.32–1.34	10–20
Photo-chemical	Photographic plate	1.05	—85–15	Bleaching of retinal pigment	1.0	5–36.1
	Decomposition of ozone	1.15	18–35	Killing of Staphylococcus by ultraviolet light	1.06	5–36
	$Cl_2 + H_2 \rightarrow 2HCl$	1.17	10–40	Killing infusoria by ultraviolet light	1.5–1.6	11–21
	Bromination of ethyl maleate ester	1.07 1.02	21.5–24.5 4–14	Photosynthesis, low light intensity	1.06	15–25

The data for coagulation of proteins are from Chick and Martin, 1910: J. Physiol. *40;* for photochemical reactions from Dhar, 1931: The Chemical Action of Light; for photosynthesis from Warburg, 1919: Biochem. Zeitschr. *100;* for killing of Staphylococcus from Gates, 1929: J. Gen. Physiol. *13;* all other data from Bělehrádek,[1] or directly from references cited by him.

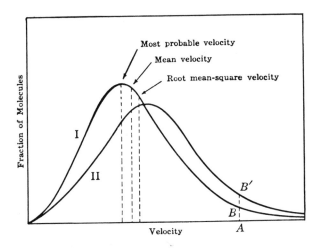

Fig. 10.3. Maxwell-Bolzmann distribution diagram (schematic) for increase in the number of molecules having energy equivalent to (or more than) the energy of activation (*ABB'*) with increase in temperature. The ordinate measures the fraction of molecules (or the probability for a given molecule) having the velocity (a function of the kinetic energy) corresponding to the abscissa. The abscissa measures the velocity of the molecules. Curve I represents the lower temperature; curve II, the higher temperature. The line *ABB'* marks the minimal activation energy. (Modified from Glasstone, 1946: The Elements of Physical Chemistry. Van Nostrand, New York, p. 267.)

and may result in the third as well. The velocity of a reaction is proportional to the frequency with which the state of activation is achieved by the molecules in a given system. Since an increase in temperature increases the chances for molecules to acquire a higher energy state, it increases the speed of thermochemical reactions.

As an example, let us consider a spontaneous reaction, that is, one which goes with a decrease in free energy. It will proceed rapidly if the molecules need to accumulate little energy before they are activated. If, on the other hand, the energy of activation is large, the reaction will proceed slowly. Anything (e.g., heat or catalysis) that increases the probability that the molecules will acquire the necessary energy of activation will increase the rate of the reaction.

These concepts might be summarized in the form of a diagram (Fig. 10.4). When a molecule moves from one energy level to another in a reaction, it must pass over an energy "barrier," even though the over-all effect is to decrease the free energy, and the reaction is, therefore, thermodynamically possible. The "barrier" is the energy of activation which a molecule must first accumulate. Anything which increases the chances of the molecule passing over this barrier increases its chances of reaction.[7]

Temperature Coefficients for Denaturation of Protein and Thermal Death of Cells

The temperature coefficient (Q_{10}) for denaturation of proteins is of a different order of magnitude from that in the

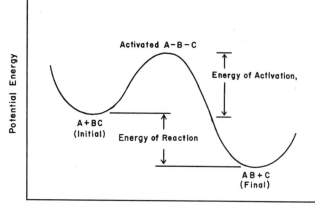

Fig. 10.4. Potential energy diagram for a thermochemical reaction. Before reacting, the molecules must accumulate sufficient kinetic energy (energy of activation) to pass over the energy barrier represented by the rising curve, even though the reaction occurs with a loss in free energy (approximately indicated by the energy of reaction).

thermochemical reactions just discussed. As seen in Table 10.1, the coefficient is very high, being higher at the upper range of temperatures used to denature the proteins. It must be realized that proteins are highly organized molecules and that denaturation involves the change from this highly organized structure to a much more random one. For this reason, even a small rise in temperature in the range which causes denaturation has a marked effect out of all proportion to the increase in the kinetic energy of the system (see Chapter 15).[26]

Exceedingly large temperature coefficients are also observed for thermal death. Values of the Q_{10} for thermal death range from about 10 to 100 or even 1000 for cells as diverse as bacteria, protozoa, eggs, sperm, vertebrate leucocytes and erythrocytes and cells of invertebrates and plants. (See Table 10.1.) These findings have been considered by many workers as corroboration of the hypothesis that heat death of organisms is attributable to the denaturation of certain critical proteins.[7]

Temperature Effects on the Rate of Diffusion and Conductivity

The Q_{10} for the rate of diffusion of nonelectrolytes and of electrolytes is less than 2.0; for example, it is 1.27 for electrolytes, 1.37 for sugar and 1.41 for dextrin (see Table 10.1). Since the kinetic energy of a system increases 3 to 4 per cent for each 10° C. rise in temperature, the increase of 30 to 40 per cent in rate of diffusion and of conductivity (movement of electrolytes in an electric field) must be attributed to some factor other than increase in kinetic energy of the system only. It has been suggested that perhaps changes in the viscosity of water may account for it, since the viscosity of water falls with a rise in temperature and the diffusion of molecules or ions dissolved in it is therefore enhanced. The values, as shown in Table 10.1, are of the same order of magnitude for both diffusion and conductivity.

Passage of molecules or ions through the cell membrane at times appears to be a simple diffusion process. Thus the Q_{10} for conductivity through the tissue of the alga *Laminaria* is similar to the Q_{10} for conductivity of a solution *in vitro* containing a concentration of electrolytes equal to that in the algal tissue. However, in other cases given in Table 10.1, the Q_{10} for passage of some materials into cells is often 2 or higher. A possible explanation of the high Q_{10} values for these examples is a change in the viscosity of the cell membrane through which the

202

ons or molecules must pass. However, here may be other explanations, since passage of molecules and ions through cell membranes is not always governed by the same mechanism (see Chapter 12).

Effect of Temperature on Photochemical and Photobiological Reactions

[except for long wavelengths]

The Q_{10} for photochemical and photobiological reactions is only slightly greater than 1.0, indicating that the rate of a photochemical reaction is little influenced by heat. As seen in Table 10.1, the Q_{10} for the bromination of ethyl maleate ester by light is 1.02. Similar low values are found for most of the photobiological reactions listed in the table; for instance, bleaching of visual purple in the eye by yellow light[24] is 1.0.

Absorption of light by a molecule leads to more rapid vibration or electronic excitation. The energy required for this purpose is larger than that which is usually supplied by heat. Absorption of light occurs, as already seen, in discrete units called quanta. The quantum is related to the wavelengths of radiations, being larger the shorter the wavelength (see Chapter 9). A molecule absorbs a quantum at a time; therefore, the rate of photochemical reactions is determined by the rate of uptake of light quanta. The probability that a molecule will capture a light quantum is not noticeably enhanced at all by increasing its kinetic energy (heat). Therefore, an increase in temperature has little effect on photochemical reactions. Consequently, the temperature coefficient for a photobiological reaction is low when the over-all process is limited by the rate of strictly photochemical reactions.

On the other hand, at the long wavelength limit for a photochemical reaction, where the energy in the quanta is insufficient for the reaction, an increase in temperature may in some cases increase the rate of the photochemical reaction. For example, the visual purple extracted from the vertebrate eye is bleached by violet to yellow light of the spectrum—even at low temperatures—but only slightly by red light (7000 Å). Increase in temperature has no effect on the rate of bleaching by violet or yellow light, but it accelerates the bleaching by red light. A 10° C. rise in temperature increases twofold or more the rate of bleaching by red light. Therefore, in this case, thermal energy appears to be effectively added to the photic energy.[24]

Temperature Coefficients and Limiting Reactions

Most biological reactions occur in a series of steps. Depending upon the conditions, one or another of these stepwise reactions may become the "bottleneck" or *rate-limiting reaction* (master reaction). The temperature coefficient for a biological process will therefore depend upon the conditions of the experiment. The temperature coefficient for photosynthesis is an interesting example. At low light intensities it is about unity. At high light intensities, however, it is found to be 2 or more (see Table 10.1). At low light intensity the rate at which the quanta of light are being absorbed (photochemical reaction) is the bottleneck that determines the rate of the over-all reaction. At high light intensity, however, when the chlorophyll molecules of the plant are saturated with light, the rate at which the light energy can be utilized in subsequent thermochemical reactions (such as the synthesis of carbohydrate) then becomes the bottleneck, limiting the rate of the over-all reaction. The nature of the photochemical (light) and the thermochemical (dark) reactions is considered in Chapter 20.

In like manner it is possible to distinguish whether a thermochemical reaction, a diffusion process or a protein denaturation is the bottleneck in a series of reactions in cells, because the differences in the temperature coefficients for these types of reactions are large enough to be measurable. Examples of the usefulness of temperature coefficients in analysis of reactions occurring in cellular activities will appear in subsequent chapters.

Crozier[25] attempted to make even wider use of temperature coefficients for identification of specific thermochemical reactions in cells. It is well known that biological thermochemical reactions, like those which liberate energy from food in the cell, occur in steps. If one step in a series becomes rate-limiting over some temperature range and has a constant temperature coefficient, it might be possible to match the coefficient for each temperature range with that of a biochemical reaction *in vitro* (in the test tube) and in this manner to identify each of the bottleneck or master thermochemical reactions, which are assumed to be occurring in the cell.[25] While temperature coefficients for chemical reactions in solution are fairly constant (see Table 10.2), temperature coefficients for enzymatic reactions *in vitro* (and presumably also in the cell) are quite variable with change in temperature (Table 10.2). Since biological reactions are usually enzymatic, it seems unlikely that their identification by this method would be possible even if the more refined methods suggested by Crozier were used (see Appendix 10.2).

While the possibility of identification of specific thermochemical reactions *in vivo* (in the cell) by temperature coefficient has great inherent appeal, it has not been considered valid by most workers,[26-2] even though the Q_{10} allows one to distinguish a thermochemical reaction from a protein denaturation, a photochemical reaction or a diffusion process.

APPENDIX

10.1   van't Hoff Equation for Q_{10}

When it is inconvenient to perform experiments at temperature intervals ten degrees apart, and data are gathered for smaller or larger temperature intervals the temperature coefficient may be determined by use of the van't Hoff equation:

$$Q_{10} = \left(\frac{k_2}{k_1}\right)^{10/(t_2-t_1)} \quad (10.2$$

where k_2 is the rate of the reaction at temperature t_2, and k_1 is the rate at t_1. This equation is more convenient to handle in the form:

$$\log Q_{10} = \frac{10}{t_2 - t_1} \log \frac{k_2}{k_1} \quad (10.3$$

TABLE 10.2.   *Variation in Temperature Coefficients over a Temperature Range*

TEMPERATURE INTERVAL	REACTION BETWEEN H_2O_2 AND HI	ACTIVITY OF A MALT AMYLASE	CO_2 PRODUCED BY PEA SEEDLINGS	FREQUENCY OF HEART BEAT (CAT)	PROTOPLASMIC STREAMING IN *Vallisneria*	DIVISION OF *Arbacia* EGG
0–10°	2.080	3.2	3.0	—	4.0	—
10–20	2.078	2.2	2.4	5.4	2.3	3.9
20–30	1.940	2.0	1.8	2.15	1.6	1.7
30–40	1.932	1.5	1.4	1.84	1.3	—
40–45	1.920	—	—	1.35	—	—

Data from Bělehrádek,[1] except for *Arbacia* which are from Harvey, 1932: Biol. Bull. *42*.

10.2 Determination of Energy of Activation

Arrhenius measured the rate of a thermochemical reaction at different temperatures and plotted the natural logarithm (ln) of the velocity, k, at each temperature against the reciprocal of the absolute temperature (T). He obtained a straight line. The equation for this relation is:

$$\frac{d\ln k}{dT} = \frac{a}{T^2} \qquad (10.4)$$

or

$$\ln k = c - \frac{a}{T} \qquad (10.5)$$

where a is the slope and c is the intercept on the temperature axis, $1/T$.

On the basis of theoretical considerations he considers that the rate of reaction is dependent on the number of molecules possessing a given amount of energy of activation, E. The slope, a, measures the rate of reaction. On the basis of theoretical deductions, the relation of a to E is given by Arrhenius as: $a = E/R$, where R is the gas constant. Substitution into the above equation gives:

$$\frac{d\ln k}{dT} = \frac{E}{RT^2} \qquad (10.6)$$

Integrated, this becomes:

$$\frac{k_2}{k_1} = e^{-\frac{E}{R}\left[\frac{1}{T_1} - \frac{1}{T_2}\right]} \qquad (10.7)$$

or,
$$\ln \frac{k_2}{k_1} = \frac{E}{R}\left[\frac{1}{T_1} - \frac{1}{T_2}\right], \qquad (10.8)$$

where E is the energy of activation; k_1 and k_2 are the velocity constants for the rates of the reaction at two different absolute temperatures, T_1 and T_2; ln is the natural logarithm and R is the gas constant. E may be determined from the plot of the logarithm of the rate of the reaction against $1/T$.[30] Strictly speaking, the E value determined in this manner is actually a much more complicated entity according to the transition state theory of Eyring and is preferably spoken of as the *temperature characteristic*, μ, rather than E, the energy of activation. The relationship is briefly considered in Appendix 10.4, but the original literature must be consulted for a full treatment.

Biologists have often used the Arrhenius equation instead of the van't Hoff equation for presenting their data on relations between temperature and the rate of a reaction. The μ or E is then considered to be the energy of activation for the limiting reaction, and is therefore a valuable index of the order of magnitude of the energy of activation required for a particular reaction. E values are sometimes found fairly constant over relatively wide temperature ranges in particular studies, which probably indicates that particular reactions are limiting the rates over those ranges. While such an index may not identify a limiting reaction, it may serve as the basis of inferences leading to fruitful experimentation by other procedures.[7]

10.3 Calculation of Number of Activated Molecules

From the Maxwell-Boltzmann distribution law one can calculate the relative number of molecules in a given population which possess a given amount of energy. N_1, the number of molecules having energy equal to or in excess of E (the energy of activation or the energy required for a given reaction), can be determined from the equation:

$$\frac{N_1}{N_0} = e^{-(E/RT)}, \qquad (10.9)$$

where N_0 is the total number of molecules, e the base of the natural system of logarithms, R the gas constant in calories and T the absolute temperature. E for a given reaction is determined experimentally as explained in Appendix 10.2.

10.4 Reaction Rate Theory

Reaction rates may be formulated according to the collision theory as shown above or by another approach, that of *transition states*. The collision theory is more familiar, but the newer theory has the advantage that by it all types of reactions may be formulated in a single way. The basic concept of the transition state theory (or absolute reaction rate theory) of Eyring[37] and his collaborators is that before molecules can react they must pass through a configuration known as the activated state which has an energy content greater than that of the normal reactants and a very short life of activation (about 10^{-13} sec.), the molecules either returning to the normal state or passing to the final state. The average of this energy increment is the activation energy (see Fig. 10.3 and 10.4). An equilibrium is established between the normal reactants and the activated complex, which is disturbed by the continuous passage of some activated molecules into the final state (lower trough, Fig. 10.4) of the reactants.

The specific reaction velocity, Vs, for the crossing of the energy barrier (the hump in Fig. 10.4) is given by the equation:

$$Vs = \frac{\alpha kT}{h} K^* \qquad (10.10)$$

Where K^* is the equilibrium constant between the normal reactants and the activated complex; kT/h is a frequency, k being the Boltzmann constant (the gas constant, R, per molecule, or R/N where N is Avogadro's number), h is Planck's constant (see Chapter 9), T is the absolute temperature and α is the transition coefficient and represents the probability of the system in the activated state (at the top of the hump) returning to the normal state or to the final state. The transition approaches unity in many reactions although it is a complicated function which cannot be considered here.

Since according to principles of thermodynamics:

$$RT \ln K^* = -\Delta F^* \qquad (10.11)$$

where F^* is the free energy or maximum work content of the system

or, $$\ln K^* = -\frac{\Delta F^*}{RT} \qquad (10.12)$$

Taking the antilogarithms to the base, e gives:

$$K^* = e^{-\Delta F^*/RT} \qquad (10.13)$$

Substituting this value of K^* into equation 10.9, gives:

$$Vs = \frac{\alpha kT}{h} \cdot e^{-\Delta F^*/RT} \qquad (10.14)$$

It is readily observable that equation 10.7 is much like equation 10.14, both being formulations for rates of reaction but on different grounds. However, the ΔF^*, the free energy of activation, is not exactly equal to E, the temperature characteristic, the latter incorporating many other factors which are separately considered in equation 10.14.

The reaction rate theory has shown usefulness in application to data on bacterial luminescence, growth, dehydrogenase activity, etc., and, in fact, is also applicable to rates of any molecular-rate process. However, it does not fit in some cases and the error may be large.[38]

GENERAL REFERENCES

Allen, M. B., 1960: Utilization of Thermal Energy by Living Organisms. Comp. Biochem. *1*:487–514.

Bělehrádek, J., 1935: Temperature and Living Matter. Protoplasma-Monographien, vol. 8, Verlag von Gebrüder Borntraeger, Berlin. See articles in Protoplasma *48*:53–71, 1957 and Annual Review of Physiology *19*:59–82.

Johnson, F. H. (ed.), 1957: Influence of Temperature on Biological Systems. Am. Physiol. Soc., Washington.

Johnson, F. H., Eyring, H., and Polissar, M. J., 1954: The Kinetic Basis of Molecular Biology. John Wiley and Sons, New York.

evitt, J., 1958: Frost, Drought and Heat Resistance. Protoplasmatologia VIII: 6 (Heilbrunn, L. V., and Weber, F., eds.) Springer-Verlag, Vienna.

recht, H., Christophersen, J., and Hensel, H., 1955: Temperatur und Leben. Springer-Verlag, Berlin.

rosser, C. L. (ed.), 1958: Physiological Adaptation. Am. Physiol. Soc., Washington.

mith, A. U., 1958: The Resistance of Animals to Cooling and Freezing. Biol. Rev. *33*:197–253.

Vood, T. H., 1956. Lethal Effects of High and Low Temperature on Unicellular Organisms. Adv. Biol. & Med. Phys. *4*:119–165.

LITERATURE CITED

1. Bělehrádek, J., 1935: Temperature and Living Matter. Protoplasma-Monographien. Vol. 8, Borntraeger, Berlin.

2. Brues, C. T., 1927: Quart. Rev. Biol. *2*:181.

3. Dallinger, W. H., 1887: J. Roy. Soc. London *7*:185.

4. Allen, M. B., 1950: J. Gen. Physiol. *33*:205.

5. Allen, M. B., 1953: Bact. Rev. *17*:125.

6. Militzer, W., Tuttle, L. C., and Georgi, C. E., 1951: Arch. Biochem. Biophys. *31*:416.

7. Johnson, F. H., Eyring, H., and Polissar, M. J., 1954: The Kinetic Basis of Molecular Biology. Wiley, New York.

8. Smith, E. L., 1949: Proc. Nat. Acad. Sci. U. S. *35*:80.

9. Hoar, W. S., and Dorchester, J. C., 1949: Can. J. Res. *27*:85.

10. Heilbrunn, L. V., Harris, D. L., LeFevre, G. E., Wilson, W. L., and Woodward, A. A., 1946: Physiol. Zool. *19*:404.

11. Heilbrunn, L. V., April 1954: Sci. Am., *190*:70.

12. Elkus, J., and Finnian, J. B., 1953: Exp. Cell. Res. *4*:69.

13. Sailer, R. I., 1950: Science *112*:743.

14. Berry, J. A., and Magoon, C. A., 1934: Phytopath. *24*:780.

15. Scholander, P. F., Hock, R., Walter, V., and Irving, L., 1950: Biol. Bull. *99*:259.

16. Scholander, P. F., Flagg, W., Hock, R. J. and Irving, L., 1953: J. Cell. Comp. Physiol., *42*:Supl. 1:1.

17. Lovelock, J. E., 1954: Nature *173*:659.

18. Luyet, B. J., and Gehenio, P. M., 1940: Life and Death at Low Temperatures. Biodynamica. Normandy, Missouri.

19. Parkes, A. S., and Smith, A. U. 1953: Proc. Roy. Soc., *B140*:455.

20. See review articles on physiological effects of heat and cold in the Annual Review of Physiology. Also, Prosser, C. L., 1958: Physiological Adaptation. Am. Physiol. Soc., Washington.

21. Barker, H. A., 1933: J. Gen. Physiol. *17*:21.

22. Christophersen, J., and Precht, H., 1953: Biol. Zentr. *72*:104.

23. Solomon, A. K., 1953: Adv. Biol. & Med. Phys. *3*:65.

24. St. George, R. C. C., 1952: J. Gen. Physiol. *35*:495.

25. Crozier, W. J., 1925: J. Gen. Physiol. *9*:525.

26. Johnson, F. H., et al., 1954: The Kinetic Basis of Molecular Biology. Wiley, New York, p. 200 ff. The Crozier Theory.

27. Burton, A. C., 1939: J. Cell. Comp. Physiol. *14*:327.

28. Morales, M. F., 1947: J. Cell. Comp. Physiol. *30*:303.

29. Booij, H. L., and Wolvekamp, H. P., 1944: Bibliotheca Biotheoretica D, *1*:145.

30. Arrhenius, S., 1915: Quantitative Laws in Biological Chemistry. Bell, London.

31. Fuhrman, G., and Fuhrman, F., 1959: J. Gen. Physiol. *42*:715.

32. Allen, M. B., 1960: Comp. Biochem. *1*:487.

33. Merryman, H. T., 1956: Science *124*:515.

34. Hock, R. J., and Covino, B. C., March 1958: Sci. Am. *198*:104.

35. Buswell, A. M., and Rodebush, W. H., April 1956: Sci. Am. *194*:77.

36. Henriques, V., and Hansen, C., 1901: Skand. Arch. f. Physiol. *11*:151.

37. Glasstone, S., Laidler, K. J., and Eyring, H., 1941: The Theory of Rate Processes. McGraw Hill, New York.

38. Belehrádek, J., 1957: Ann. Rev. Physiol. *19*:59.

39. Harris, R. J. C. (ed.), 1954: Biological Applications of Freezing and Drying. Academic Press, New York.

40. Smith, A. U., 1958: Biol. Rev. *33*:197.

41. Parkes, A. S., June 1956: Sci. Am. *194*:105.

42. Wood, T. H., 1956: Adv. Biol. & Med. Phys. *4*:119.

43. Prosser, C. L. (ed.), 1958: Physiological Adaptation. Am. Physiol. Soc., Washington.

EXCHANGE OF MATERIALS ACROSS THE CELL MEMBRANE

This section deals with the exchange of water, and materials dissolved in water, between the inside and the outside of the cell across the cell membrane. The cell membrane must permit the entry of cell foods and oxygen and the exit of cell wastes. The properties which enable the membrane to regulate entry and exit of materials are of prime importance because maintenance of life depends upon such exchanges. The movement of water and of dissolved materials through the cell membrane is a dynamic process; the living cell is never in equilibrium with the environment in terms of materials across its membrane. In fact, a cell in complete equilibrium with the solutes in its environment is dead.

At one time it was thought that movement of substances through the cell membrane was determined solely by the concentration gradient, i.e., a substance moved inward only when it was present outside in a concentration higher than inside, and vice versa. This is probably true in some instances, and numerous cases will be considered in Chapters 11 and 12, but movement against a concentration gradient has been observed in some other cases; that is, a substance which is present outside the cell in smaller amounts than inside is nevertheless absorbed. For example, potassium is usually accumulated in plant and animal cells to a concentration many times that in the medium surrounding the cells. Such transport requires expenditure of energy by the cell and has been called active transport. It is considered in Chapter 13. The physical and chemical nature of the cell membrane is discussed in Chapter 14.

Inasmuch as the topics discussed in each of the following chapters in this section are artificially separated from one another to simplify discussion, a certain amount of overlap is bound to occur. Such overlap is permitted only because it helps to elucidate the topic under discussion.

MOVEMENT OF WATER
ACROSS THE CELL MEMBRANE:
OSMOSIS

Water passes in and out through the cell membrane at all times, but no effect is demonstrable if the solute concentration is the same on both sides of the membrane. It is only when the concentrations of solute are different on the two sides that movement becomes apparent by shrinkage or swelling of the cell. Water moves in or out of the cell until the concentration of solute is equalized between the inside and the outside of the cell. Therefore, movement of water is often treated in terms of equilibrium conditions implied by the term *osmotic pressure*. Cells act as osmometers to the extent that they act as systems attaining equilibrium for water. *Osmosis is the diffusion of water (or more generally, a solvent) through a membrane in response to a concentration gradient*. The principles governing osmotic transfers have been studied with artificial, natural and living cell membranes.

Passage of Water Across
Artificial Membranes

Osmotic transfers may be best illustrated by a study of the movements of water through artificial membranes that are analogues to the cell membrane. Many artificial membranes have been devised to facilitate study of water movement. A membrane of copper ferrocyanide, formed by the interaction of potassium ferrocyanide and copper sulfate, has been a favorite artificial membrane since it was first introduced by Traube[4] in 1867. When a crystal of copper sulfate in a piece of gauze is suspended in a test tube filled with a solution of potassium ferrocyanide, the copper sulfate dissolves and interacts with the ferrocyanide, forming a membrane. Water enters this membrane causing the bag or "cell" to swell and burst. A new membrane precipitates in a new position as more of the copper sulfate is dissolved and additional water is taken up, and the process repeats itself until the copper sulfate is completely dissolved.

A similar and more effective membrane for experimental study was devised by Pfeffer[1] in 1877. Potassium ferrocyanide solution is placed inside an unglazed pottery jar surrounded by a solution of copper sulfate. An electric current is then passed between the two solutions. The membrane of copper ferrocyanide which is precipitated in the small pores of the unglazed jar allows only water to pass through it (see Fig. 11.1). If the jar is then filled with 1 molal NaCl and is suspended in a beaker of distilled water, water molecules pass through the mem-

brane but salts cannot, and since the water molecules cannot get out as readily as they enter, because they collide with sodium and chloride ions inside the jar, water accumulates inside the jar. If a tube is fitted to the mouth of the jar, water rises in the tube until the pressure developed by the rise of water equals the osmotic pressure (the tendency of the water molecules to enter the jar in response to the concentration gradient between the inside and the outside of the jar). Such a membrane, which is permeable to solvent only—in this case water—is said to be *semipermeable.*[1] In aqueous systems a semipermeable membrane implies a membrane permeable to water only.

A better way of measuring the osmotic pressure than by the height of water in a tube is by means of the mercury osmometer introduced by Pfeffer and illustrated in Figure 11.2. An osmometer is a device used to measure osmotic pressure. It must have a semipermeable membrane which allows water (solvent) but not the solute to pass.

The physical chemist usually employs still another device to determine osmotic pressure. It is the method by which the pressure that just prevents the entry of water (solvent) through the semipermeable membrane is measured; this is taken as a measure of the osmotic pressure.

Another artificial membrane often used in biological studies is cellophane dialysis tubing. If such a membrane is fastened over a thistle tube and the tube is filled with concentrated sodium chloride solution and immersed in distilled water, water will enter and the volume of solution in the thistle tube will increase as a consequence, indicating that cellophane is permeable to water. Tests for chloride in the distilled water outside, however, show that sodium chloride is also coming through the cellophane. But the rise in the level of the solution in the tube proves that entry of water is greater than

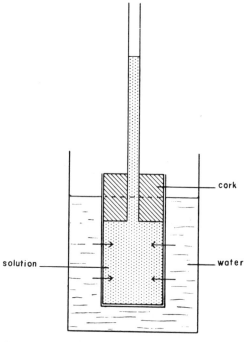

Fig. 11.1. A simple osmometer. The pores in the jar have been coated with a precipitate of copper ferrocyanide, which is permeable to water but not to solutes. Solute is dissolved in the jar, and after the cork with the tube is inserted, water enters faster than it leaves the solution; consequently, the level rises in the tube and indicates the level of osmotic pressure.

solution

cork

water

EXCHANGE OF MATERIALS ACROSS THE CELL MEMBRANE

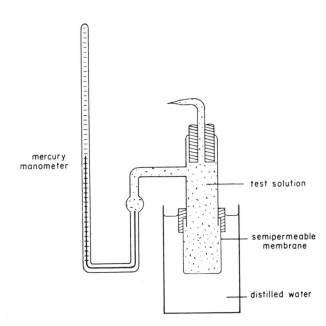

mercury
manometer

test solution

semipermeable
membrane

distilled water

Fig. 11.2. Pfeffer's osmometer with mercury manometer to measure the osmotic pressure. The test solution is kept inside the jar, in the walls of which has been precipitated a copper ferrocyanide membrane. Entry of water occurs until the osmotic pressure is counterbalanced by the pressure of the column of mercury.

outward movement of salt. Similar results are obtained with glucose, except that the outward movement of glucose is slower than that of salt. To show that passage of solute is not the result of a mechanical leak, Congo red, a colloidal dye, is added to the solution in the thistle tube during such an experiment. It will be recalled that colloids do not pass through cellophane (Chapter 4); therefore, the dye will be retained by an intact membrane, but the appearance of a pink color in the water surrounding the tube will indicate a tear in the membrane. A membrane which lets one material, like water, pass through more readily than another, like salt or sugar, is said to be *selectively permeable*.

Natural membranes, such as goldbeater's skin (the prepared outside membrane of the ox intestine) and "skin" (epidermis) from a scale of an onion bulb, can be used to study exchanges of water in the same manner as artificial membranes. Since the results for natural membranes are similar to those for cellophane, further discussion is omitted here.

Permeability of the Cell Membrane to Water

Experiments indicate that cells are generally highly permeable to water. For example, when a sea urchin egg is placed in sea water diluted with distilled water it swells, the swelling increasing with greater dilution of the sea water. Diluted sea water is said to be hypotonic to the egg, which is accustomed to undiluted sea water. Swelling continues with dilution until the membrane bursts and cytolysis occurs. When the egg is placed in sea water concentrated by evaporation or by addition of sucrose or salt, it shrinks, and the shrinkage increases as the medium becomes more concentrated. Such a medium is said to be hypertonic to the sea urchin egg. The egg in unaltered sea water does not swell or shrink, and the sea water is said to be isotonic.[2]

Experiments with red blood cells (erythrocytes) indicate that they also are permeable to water. If the erythrocytes are placed in a hypertonic solution they shrink in a characteristic way and are said to be crenated. When placed in a hypotonic salt solution they swell and may become spherical instead of discoidal. Erythrocytes become hemolyzed and lose their hemoglobin when placed in excessively dilute salt solutions.[3] A concentration of sodium chloride of approximately 0.7 per cent is isotonic to a red blood cell of a frog, and a concentration of 0.9 per cent is isotonic to mammalian erythrocytes.

Plant cells, too, are quite permeable to water. The cells of a fresh water plant like *Elodea* are normally turgid; that is, the protoplast is held firmly against the cell wall, and the entire leaf has a certain rigidity as a result of the collective rigidity of the individual cells. If the plant cells are placed in a concentrated salt solution, they become plasmolyzed (see Fig. 11.3), and the protoplast of each cell contracts about the shrunken vacuole. If the hypertonic salt solution is replaced by fresh water, each cell regains water and the protoplast again fills the space within the cell wall. When *Elodea* is placed in a series of solutions containing increasing concentrations of salt, plasmolysis occurs in its cells only when the concentration of a salt, such as potassium nitrate, reaches about 0.6 per cent. Less salt than this is present in the fresh water of ponds

and streams in which *Elodea* is found However, the rigid cell wall, limiting th volume, prevents excessive uptake c water.[1, 4]

Plant cells plasmolyzed by hypertoni solutions return in time to their initi volume (deplasmolysis). Deplasmolysis rapid in solutions of solutes which pene trate rapidly, and it is slow in solutions c solutes which penetrate slowly.[5] For ex ample, the initial shrinkage of an egg o of *Elodea* cells, when in hypertonic solu tions, indicates that water leaves the ce more readily than the solute molecule enter, but subsequent swelling shows tha the solute molecules have penetrated th cells. Solute molecules accumulate in th cell and water re-enters, causing the ce to swell. The membrane of a cell is there fore not semipermeable but selectivel permeable; that is, it is more permeabl to water than to other substances. This i found to be true of all living cells studied (For permeability to solutes, see Chapte 12.) It would appear that the cell mem brane is freely permeable to water anc permits water to enter when the cell i placed in hypotonic solutions and permit water to leave when the cell is placed i hypertonic solutions.

Bacteria, like plant cells, are also helc within cell walls and do not appear t swell in hypotonic solutions. However, i the cell wall is first digested off in th presence of the enzyme lysozyme[24], the protoplast which is liberated swells anc shrinks like any other cell.[16]

Osmotic Pressure of Nonelectrolytes

If a solution of a nonelectrolyte in a thistle tube is separated from distillec water by a semipermeable membrane water will pass through the membrane into the solution inside the tube. The in crease in volume of water will cause a rise of solution in the tube. The pressure exerted by the solution is proportional to the height (h) of the column and is called

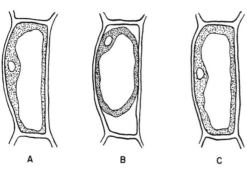

Fig. 11.3. A plant cell (A) undergoes plasmolysis (B) when it is placed in a hypertonic solution. Deplasmolysis (C) occurs after a period of time, but only if the solute can penetrate. Time for deplasmolysis depends upon the rate of entry of the solute.

A   B   C

EXCHANGE OF MATERIALS ACROSS THE CELL MEMBRANE

he osmotic pressure (π). Water will continue to increase the volume of solution until the pressure of the column on the membrane just compensates the entry of water into the membrane. At that time equilibrium will have been established, and

$$\pi = h \times k, \tag{11.1}$$

where k is a constant of proportionality for a given temperature and concentration. The higher the concentration of solute, the higher the rise of the water will be.

The plant physiologist, Pfeffer, made measurements of osmotic pressure of various solutes by using a copper ferrocyanide osmometer. He found that the osmotic pressure divided by the concentration of solute was constant (see Table 11.1), but he did not realize the full significance of his data.[1] The physical chemist, van't Hoff, showed that Pfeffer's data could be taken as evidence of the applicability of the gas laws to osmotic pressure. A gram molecular weight of a gas at atmospheric pressure occupies 22.4 liters of space. If it is compressed into the confines of a liter it exerts 22.4 atmospheres pressure. If a solute is compared to a gas, then a gram molecular weight of

TABLE 11.1. *Pfeffer's Data for Osmotic Pressure at Different Concentrations of Sucrose*

CONCENTRA-TION (C) IN PER CENT	OSMOTIC PRESSURE (π) IN ATMOSPHERES	$\dfrac{\pi}{C}$
1	0.70	0.7
2	1.34	0.67
4	2.74	0.68
6	4.10	0.68

To determine whether the rise in osmotic pressure is proportional to the concentration of the solution, Pfeffer divided the osmotic pressure (π) by the concentration (C) of the solution being tested. As seen in the third column, π/C is fairly constant. (After Glasstone.[6])

the solute in a liter of solution, if it acts like a gas, should exert a pressure of 22.4 atmospheres. When analyzed, Pfeffer's data showed that a gram molecular weight of a nonelectrolyte dissolved in a liter of water exerts an osmotic pressure of approximately 22.4 atmospheres, confirming van't Hoff's hypothesis.[6, 7] The agreement is only approximate, since exact agreement would occur only if the molecules of solute occupied no volume and the attractions between them were nil.

The gas law may be written PV = nRT, where P is the pressure in atmospheres, V the volume in liters, n the number of moles, R the gas constant (equal to 0.082 liter atmospheres per degree per mole) and T the absolute temperature. By rearrangement,

$$P = \frac{n}{V} \times RT \tag{11.2}$$

Since the number of moles of solute divided by the number of liters of solvent in which it is dissolved is equal to the molal concentration (moles in a kilogram of solvent), C may be substituted for n/V. Then,

$$P = CRT \tag{11.3}$$

For osmotic pressure this is usually written:

$$\pi = CRT, \tag{11.4}$$

in which π denotes the osmotic pressure.

For a gram molecular weight of osmotically active ideal nonelectrolyte, C is 1, R is 0.082 liter atmospheres per degree per mole, and the absolute temperature at 0° C. is 273°. Then

$$\pi = (1 \text{ mole/liter}) \cdot$$
$$(0.082 \text{ liter atm./degree/mole}) \cdot$$
$$(273°) \tag{11.5}$$
or $\pi = 22.4$ atmospheres

Since the gas laws were developed for perfect gases whose molecules have no volume and do not attract one another, their application to solutions is even more of an approximation than their application to gases. The gas law can be applied only to weak solutions at best. Deviations become marked at higher concentrations, and a more refined treatment is necessary.[6]

Osmotic Pressure of Electrolytes

Since electrolytes dissociate, each molecule gives rise to a number of ions. Because the osmotic pressure is determined by the number of particles present in the solution, for a given molal* concentration an electrolyte will exert a greater osmotic pressure than a nonelectrolyte. The magnitude of the difference depends on the number of ions produced by dissociation.

Therefore, the osmotic pressure of an electrolyte, calculated by the gas law, must be multiplied by a correction factor for dissociation. The correction factor is less than the total number of ions formed from a molecule of an electrolyte, because the activity of the ions, rather than their concentration, determines the osmotic pressure. Ionic interference reduces the effective concentration of the ions; e.g., unlike ions attract one another, reducing the number of ions free to act. The activity of a given electrolyte varies at different concentrations, being generally greater at low concentrations in which interference between ions is least. The determination of the activity for each concentration of an electrolyte is most easily done by cryoscopy (freezing point determination), which measures the number of particles active, not just the concentration. Then, by comparing the freezing point depression of an electrolyte with that of an ideal nonelectrolyte of the same concentration (usually 1 molal of each is used) a factor called the *cryoscopic coefficient*, G, may be obtained:

$$G = \frac{\Delta T_{fp}}{\Delta T_{\overline{fp}}}, \qquad (11.6)$$

where ΔT_{fp} is the freezing point depression produced by a given molal concentration of the electrolyte in question and $\Delta T_{\overline{fp}}$ is the lowering of the freezing point by the same molal concentration of an ideal nonelectrolyte. A few cryoscopic coefficients are given in Table 11.2. The osmotic pressure of an electrolyte can be calculated from the gas law equation (11.4), but the concentration term in the gas law equation must be multiplied by the cryoscopic coefficient, G, for each concentration of electrolyte

$$\pi = (C \times G)RT, \qquad (11.7)$$

since G measures the relative increase of number of particles by ionization and includes an activity correction.[6, 7]

Colligative Properties and the Determination of Osmotic Pressure

The methods already discussed for the direct measurement of osmotic pressure are not very suitable for the measurement of the osmotic pressure of cell contents because the materials are available only in relatively small quantities. Therefore, use has to be made of some properties of solutions that are functions of the same variable, namely, the *number* of particles in solution and not the *kind* of particles.

Those properties of a solution that depend upon the number of particles present per unit volume of solution are called its *colligative properties*, and they are a manifestation of a phenomenon common to all of them; i.e., solute molecules decrease the tendency of water to escape from one solution to another or from one phase to another. The *colligative proper-*

* The physical chemist uses molal concentrations in dealing with solutions. A molal (m) solution contains 1 gram molecular weight of a solute in 1000 grams of solvent, whereas a molar (M) solution is a liter of solution containing 1 gram molecular weight of a solute. Use of molal solutions has the advantage that molal solutions of different substances contain the same ratio of solute to solvent molecules. At very low concentrations, molar becomes equivalent to molal, since the effect of molecular volume becomes negligible.

EXCHANGE OF MATERIALS ACROSS THE CELL MEMBRANE

TABLE 11.2. *Cryoscopic Coefficients (G)* at Various Molal Concentrations*

ELECTROLYTE	0.02	0.05	0.1	0.2	0.5
MgCl$_2$	2.708†	2.677	2.658	2.679	2.896
MgSO$_4$	1.393†	1.302	1.212	1.125	—
CaCl$_2$	2.673†	2.630	2.601	2.573	2.680
LiCl	1.928	1.912	1.895	1.884	1.927
NaCl	1.921	—	1.872	1.843	—
KCl	1.919	1.885	1.857	1.827	1.784
KNO$_3$	1.904	1.847	1.784	1.698	1.551

Data from Heilbrunn, 1952: An Outline of General Physiology. 3rd Ed.

* $G = \dfrac{T_{fp}}{T_{\overline{fp}}}$, as defined in equation 11.6.

† 0.025 molal.

ies of solutions are (1) the osmotic pressure, (2) the freezing point depression, (3) the boiling point elevation and (4) the vapor pressure.

The dependence of osmotic pressure upon the number of active particles has already been discussed. The greater the number of particles, assuming that they are free to move, the greater will be their interference with outward passage of water molecules from a solution through a membrane. This interference with movement of water molecules also affects the freezing point, boiling point and vapor pressure in a like manner. The freezing point is lowered because solute molecules interfere with the formation of ice crystals. The boiling point is raised because the solute particles in solution interfere with the establishment of an equilibrium between the water molecules and the atmospheric pressure. Similarly, the vapor pressure, which depends upon the evaporation of water from the solution, is decreased by the interference of the solute particles with the escape of water molecules, and the decrease is proportional to the concentration of solute.[6, 7] It is self-evident, therefore, that if one of the colligative properties is known, any of the others can be calculated, since they are all related through the same variable.

The vapor pressure determination is perhaps the simplest, as seen from the following example. When two beakers containing aqueous solutions of different concentrations of solute are placed in an airtight enclosure (see Fig. 11.4), the water molecules leave and re-enter both solutions continuously, but because exit of water molecules is less impeded in the dilute solution, more water will leave it than leaves the more concentrated solution. Thus, the dilute solution loses more water than it receives and the concen-

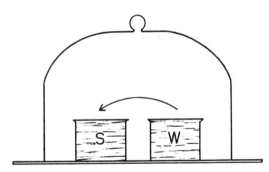

Fig. 11.4. Water distils over into a solution because of a difference in vapor tension between pure water (W) and the solution (S). The solute molecules reduce the escaping tendency of the water molecules in the solution. The temperature of pure water is lowered by evaporation from its surface. This lowering of temperature can be measured by a thermocouple (see Fig. 11.5).

trated solution receives more water than it loses until the two become equal in concentration, that is, until equilibrium is achieved. Since the temperature falls in the solution losing water, and since the change in temperature is proportional to the difference in concentrations of the

two solutions, the vapor pressure can b calculated from the change in tem perature.

Using this principle, an elegant method for determining osmotic pressures of ver small samples of fluid has been devel oped.[8] This method employs thermo couples to measure the temperature, be cause thermometers are unsatisfactory for such small samples of fluid. A thermo couple consists of a junction of two metals in which a change in temperature induces an electromotive force creating current measurable with a galvanometer (see Fig. 11.5). First the junctions are calibrated when one is placed in a solu tion of known concentration (and osmoti pressure) and the other in pure water. series of solutions of known osmotic pres sures are tested in this manner, and graph is constructed that relates galvano metric deflection to osmotic pressure The galvanometric deflection produced by a sample of unknown osmotic pressure is then determined in the same way and under the same conditions. This galvano metric deflection, placed on the standard curve, at once enables one to determine the osmotic pressure of the sample.

Another vapor pressure method for determining osmotic pressure is Barger' method. The fluid to be tested is taken up into one end of each of a series of capillary tubes. On the other end of each tube, a sample from a series of known concentrations is introduced, an air space remaining between the two solutions in the tube. The initial length of each solu tion in each tube is marked. The un known solution is tested in this way against the series of solutions of known concentrations. Each tube is examined periodically under a microscope to see if the test sample has gained or lost water This is continued until it is definitely established that a pair is found in which no water exchange occurs. If no water is exchanged between the two samples, the vapor pressures in the two solutions are

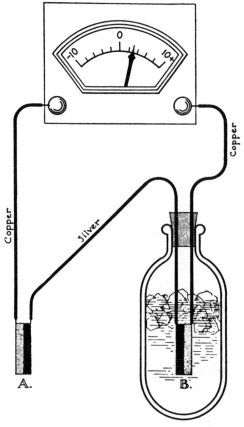

Fig. 11.5. An elementary form of thermocouple for measuring change in temperature. Junction B is always kept at some convenient known temperature, e.g., on ice. When junction A is placed on a substance of different temperature, the thermoelectric current produced deflects the galvanometer. Galvanometric deflection is calibrated with A at several known temperatures, and a calibration curve is constructed to relate the deflection to the temperature at A. Then junction A can be used to measure unknown temperatures within the range of the scale. (From Amberson and Smith, 1948: Outline of Physiology. Appleton-Century-Crofts, New York, p. 157.)

EXCHANGE OF MATERIALS ACROSS THE CELL MEMBRANE

qual. The osmotic pressures are also then equal in the two, and that of the unknown can be calculated in terms of the known. This method has the advantage of requiring a minimum of equipment,[10, 11] but it is somewhat tedious in operation.

In biological work, determination of the freezing point of a solution has been used most extensively for determining the osmotic pressure, because the equipment is generally available and the measurement can be made without altering the nature of the solution. It is known that the freezing point of an aqueous solution containing a gram molecular weight (1 molal) of ideal nonelectrolyte is depressed by 1.86° C. If an adequate quantity of solution is available it is placed in a freezing mixture with a thermometer, and the temperature is taken at the time ice crystals appear. The temperature is taken again when the crystals disappear on warming. From the depression of the freezing point the osmotic pressure is readily calculated with the following equation:

$$\frac{\Delta_x}{\Delta_m} = \frac{x}{22.4 \text{ atm.}} \qquad (11.8)$$

$$x = \frac{\Delta_x}{\Delta_m} \times 22.4 \text{ atm.} \qquad (11.9)$$

Here Δ_x = the depression of the freezing point produced by the "unknown" solution whose osmotic pressure is sought. Δ_m = the depression of the freezing point produced by a 1 molal solution of ideal nonelectrolyte and x = the osmotic pressure of the "unknown" solution.

A recently developed variant of the freezing point method is used for very small quantities of fluid. Test solutions are drawn up into capillary tubes and frozen. Their melting is then observed through crossed polaroids, under a microscope. Standards of known concentrations of sodium chloride (or other solute) are prepared in the same manner so that standard and test solutions can be exam-

ined together for comparison of the times required for the melting of the ice crystals. (See Fig. 11.6.) The times required for melting the ice in the known sodium chloride solutions are plotted against the concentrations of the solutions. From this standard graph the osmotic pressure of an unknown can be determined in terms

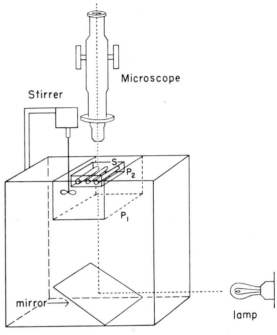

Fig. 11.6. Determining the melting point of minute quantities of biological materials. P_1 and P_2 are polaroid sheets suitably oriented so that the ice crystals appear bright against a dark background. Samples of several known concentrations of sodium chloride (S) are taken up into small capillary tubes and sealed with vaseline. Samples of unknown solutions (S) are taken up into similar tubes and sealed. Both are then placed in a rack and frozen. They are then placed in a water bath chilled with dry ice, and the time for melting the ice crystals is determined, the water in the bath being stirred the while. The crossed polaroids enable one to see the ice crystals clearly against a black field, since the crystals polarize the light. Disappearance of the ice crystals is indicated by the sudden blackening of the field. The melting points for all samples are plotted as in Figure 11.7, and the values of the unknown samples are determined from the curve. (After Gross, 1954: J. Exp. Biol., *31*:402.)

of the osmotic pressures of known concentrations of sodium chloride or other solute (see Fig. 11.7).[9]

Osmotic pressure can be determined by the rise in boiling point of a solution. When a nonelectrolyte is dissolved in water, the rise in boiling point is 0.52° C. per molal solution of the nonelectrolyte. However, this method is unsatisfactory for determining the osmotic pressures of biological solutions, because proteins coagulate when they are boiled, thus introducing an error into the determinations.

Cells as Osmometers

The living cell, having a selectively permeable membrane rather than a semipermeable membrane, could hardly be expected to behave like a perfect osmometer. However, a cell perhaps might show some approximation to an osmometer if in response to a concentration gradient, water were to pass through the membrane much more readily than would the solute. However, one correction must be made before such a test can be applied with fairness. The cell contains in its structures much protein and lipid, which add to the total volume of the cell and thereby excluding from that volume a corresponding volume of solution. The volume occupied by cell structures and called the *nonsolvent volume* (usually designated b), must be subtracted from the term for total volume in the equation for osmotic pressure: $\pi V = nRT$. The equation therefore becomes:

$$\pi(V - b) = nRT, \qquad (11.10)$$

where b represents the nonsolvent volume and the other terms have the meanings previously assigned. In Table 11.3 the nonsolvent volume is given as 12.5 per cent of the total volume of the cell, or 0.125. When correction for the nonsolvent volume is made, the sea urchin egg in diluted sea water is observed to behave reasonably well as an osmometer, the values in the fourth column being more nearly alike than those in the third column where no correction was made. In

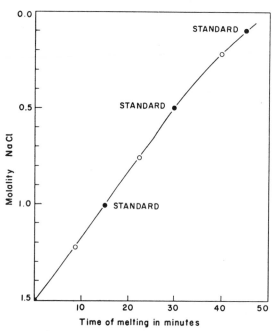

Fig. 11.7. Use of the melting method (shown in Fig. 11.6) for determination of osmotic pressure. A standard curve is first established by plotting data for the time required to melt frozen solutions of known concentrations of NaCl against the concentrations of the solutions. Three such points are shown as black dots, and the curve is drawn through these points. The concentration of an unknown solution, in terms of the standards, can be determined if the melting time (open circle) for a sample is placed on the curve.

TABLE 11.3. *Arbacia Egg as an Osmometer*

RELATIVE PRESSURE	VOLUME OBSERVED*	πV	$\pi(V - b)$
1.0	2,121	2,121	1,881
0.9	2,316	2,084	1,868
0.8	2,570	2,056	1,864
0.7	2,922	2,045	1,878
0.6	3,420	2,053	1,909
0.5	4,002	2,002	1,881

After Lucké and McCutcheon.[12]
* Volume in arbitrary units.

ther cells, where solutes pass through the membrane more rapidly than they do in the sea urchin egg, the cells do not act even approximately like osmometers.

To compare the relative permeabilities of different kinds of cells to water, it is necessary to obtain the volume of water entering per unit area of cell surface per unit time per unit difference in osmotic pressure between the inside and the outside of the cell. A permeability constant, k, for water is given in these terms by the following equation:[12]

$$\frac{dV}{dt} = k\, A(\pi_{in} - \pi_{out}) \qquad (11.11)$$

Here V is the volume of the cell, dV a small change in volume,
t is the time, dt a small change in time,
A is the area of the cell surface,
π_{in} is the osmotic pressure of the cell and
π_{out} is the osmotic pressure of the external medium.

The permeability constants for entry of water into several different cells, as determined primarily by swelling of cells in hypotonic media, are given in Table 11.4. Almost a two-hundredfold variation in permeability to water is observed in these cells. It is perhaps significant that the fresh-water forms, in which the greatest gradient is found between the inside and the outside of the cell, have the lowest permeability constants for entry of water. They are forced to void the constant excess of incoming water by means of contractile vacuoles. Having a low permeability to water, they reduce this work to a considerable degree.

Water movement into and out of a cell is not always as simple as the above discussion would lead one to believe.[18-22] It is important to point out that the permeability constant of a cell to water is only an approximation. For example, difference in osmotic pressure cannot be the only factor governing entry or exit of water, since in some cells, even the in-

TABLE 11.4. *Comparison of Permeabilities of Some Cells in Water*

SPECIES	PERMEABILITY CONSTANT*
Amoeba proteus	0.026–0.031
Pelomyxa carolinensis	0.023
Fresh water peritrichs	0.125–0.25
Arbacia egg	0.4
Human erythrocyte	3.0

From Prosser and Brown, 1961: Comparative Animal Physiology.
* In cubic microns of water, per square micron of surface area of cell, per atmosphere difference in pressure between the inside and outside of the cell, per minute.

ward and outward permeability to water is different,[12, 13] indicating operation of some biological factor as well. Furthermore, depending upon its physiological state, the same cell may show changes in its permeability to water. For example, the permeability of some echinoderm eggs to water doubles, triples or quadruples on fertilization of the eggs. After cell division occurs, permeability to water may fall back to the original value.[14, 15] It is curious that some cells are much more permeable to water than others and some cells even secrete water, for example gland cells in the carnivorous bladder plant *Utricularia*, which set the trap by this means.[23] All of these are interesting and fundamental problems involving the movement of water across the cell membrane.

GENERAL REFERENCES

Bennett-Clark, T. A., 1959: Water relations of cells, *in* Plant Physiology, a Treatise (Steward, C. F., ed.). Academic Press, N. Y., vol. 2, pp. 105–191.

Blum, G., 1957: Osmotischer Wert, Saugkraft, Turgor. Protoplasmatologia II, Springer-Verlag, Vienna.

Brooks, S. C., and Brooks, M. M., 1941: The Permeability of Living Cells. Verlag von Gebrüder Borntraeger, Berlin, Chapters 1 and 2.

Davson, H., 1959: Textbook of General Physiology. 2nd Ed. Little, Brown, Boston.

Davson, H., and Danielli, J. F., 1943: The Peremabil-
ity of Natural Membranes. Macmillan, New York.

Dick, D. A. T., 1959: Osmotic Properties of Living
Cells. Internat. Rev. Cyt. 8:388–448.

Glasstone, S., 1946: The Elements of Physical Chemistry. Van Nostrand, New York, Chapter 9.

Mitchell, P., and Moyle, J., 1956: Osmotic function
and structure in bacteria, in Bacterial Anatomy
(Spooner, T. C., and Stocker, B. A. D., eds.). Cambridge Univ. Press, Cambridge, pp. 150–180.

Ponder, E., 1948: Hemolysis and Related Phenomena.
Grune & Stratton, New York.

Ponder, E., 1955: Red Blood, Cells, Structure and
Function. Protoplasmatologia X, 2.

West, E. S., 1942: Physical Chemistry for Students of
Biochemistry and Medicine. Macmillan, New York,
Chapter 4.

LITERATURE CITED

1. Pfeffer, W., 1877: Osmotische Untersuchungen.
Engelmann, Leipzig.

2. Lucké, B., 1940: Cold Spring Harbor Symp.
8:123.

3. Ponder, E., 1948: Hemolysis and Related Phenomena. Grune & Stratton, New York.

4. Höber, R., et al., 1945: Physical Chemistry of
Cells and Tissues. Blakiston, New York, Chapter 14.

5. Davson, H., 1959: Textbook of General Physiology. 2nd Ed. Little, Brown & Co., Boston,
Chapter 7.

6. Glasstone, S., 1946: The Elements of Physical
Chemistry. Van Nostrand, New York.

7. West, E. S., 1942: Physical Chemistry for Students of Biochemistry and Medicine. Macmillan, New York, Chapter 4.

8. Lifson, N., and Visscher, M. B., 1944: in Medical
Physics (Glasser, O., ed.). Year Book, Chicago,
p. 871.

9. Gross, W., 1954: J. Exp. Biol. 31:402.

10. Barger, G., 1904: Trans. Chem. Soc. 85:286.

11. Krogh, A., 1939: Osmotic Regulation in Aquatic
Animals. Cambridge Univ. Press, London.

12. Lucké, B., and McCutcheon, M., 1932: Physiol.
Rev. 12:68.

13. Jacobs, M. H., 1952: Modern Trends in Physiology and Biochemistry (Barron, E. S. G., ed.).
Academic Press, New York, p. 149.

14. Lillie, R. S., 1918: Am. J. Physiol. 45:406.

15. Hobson, A. D., 1932: J. Exp. Zool. 9:69.

16. Gunsalus, I. C., and Stanier, R. Y., 1960: The
Bacteria. Academic Press, New York, I:143.

17. Kitching, J. A., 1956: Contractile Vacuoles of
Protozoa. Protoplasmatologia III, D, 3, a
Springer-Verlag, Vienna.

18. Kalman, S. M., 1959. J. Cell. Comp. Physiol.
54:155.

19. Grim, E., and Sollner, K., 1957: J. Gen. Physiol.
40:887.

20. Teorell, T., 1955: Exp. Cell. Res. suppl. 3:339.

21. Osterhout, W. J. V., 1956: J. Gen. Physiol.
39:963.

22. Robinson, J. R., 1953: Biol. Rev. 28:158. 1960
Physiol. Rev. 40:112.

23. Bennett-Clark, T. A., 1959: in Plant Physiology
a Treatise (Steward, C. F., ed.). 2:187. Academic Press, N. Y.

24. Acker, R. F., and Hartsell, S. E., June 1960: Sci.
Am. 202:132.

12

MOVEMENT OF SOLUTES
THROUGH THE CELL
MEMBRANE IN RESPONSE TO
A CONCENTRATION GRADIENT

Many substances other than water move in and out of cells in response to a concentration gradient, although only a few of them (carbon dioxide and oxygen) are able to move as freely as water. If a cell membrane allows a substance to move in or out through it, it is said to be permeable to that substance. Permeation of various solutes has been extensively studied by many investigators in an attempt to formulate general rules of permeability and develop from them a concept of the structure of the cell membrane.

Methods for Studying Permeability of Cell Membranes

Only a few of the methods employed in permeability studies will be discussed here. Some methods are only qualitative. For example, entry of dyes, such as neutral red, into cells like paramecia can be observed by the appearance of a pink color inside the cells.[1] Sometimes use is made of such dye penetration to study the permeation of other compounds. Thus the entry of a base like ammonia into paramecia stained with neutral red may be observed because the pink paramecia become yellowish as soon as the base has entered. However, it is virtually impossible to measure quantitatively the rate of entry of dyes or other substances by such a method, because if the penetration is very slow, no color is seen unless the experiment is carried over a long period, or if only a minute quantity enters, no color change is noticed. Furthermore, the method depends upon a personal element—judgment of color—which is likely to vary from one person to another. The same criticism applies also to other visual methods, such as the formation of an insoluble precipitate inside cells; e.g., the formation of calcium oxalate crystals in cells of *Elodea* as an indication of the penetration of oxalic acid.[3]

223

Volume Change. A quantitative method much more satisfactory for studying the permeability of cell membranes is the observation of the rate of deplasmolysis of plasmolyzed cells.[2,4] A cell plasmolyzed in a hypertonic solution of glycerol, for example, swells again after a lapse of time during which glycerol enters and the cell re-absorbs water (see Chapter 11). The relative rates of entry into cells of different substances used in hypertonic solutions may be tested by a study of rates of deplasmolysis as the cells reabsorb water. For example, when equimolal hypertonic solutions of several substances like ethylene glycol, glycerol and glucose are applied to cells, they will plasmolyze the cells. Deplasmolysis will occur first among the cells in ethylene glycol and last among those in glucose. This means that ethylene glycol penetrates the fastest of the three and glucose the slowest (see Fig. 11.3).

Similarly, a marine egg which has been shrunk by a hypertonic solution gradually resumes its initial volume as the solute penetrates and water is taken up. Measurement of the time required to resume the initial volume again serves as a measure of the rate of entry of the solute (see Fig. 12.1). If the cell remains shrunken in a solution, the solute has failed to enter the cell or changes in the cell structure have occurred.

A similar method, particularly useful for the study of the permeability of the cell membranes of minute cells, is the determination of the volume of a mass of cells before and after immersion in hypertonic solutions. The volume of the cell mass is determined after the cells have been packed together by centrifugation. This is a favorite method for the study of permeability of red blood corpuscles. A special centrifuge tube called the hematocrit, with a calibrated fine cylindrical portion 1 or 2 millimeters in diameter, is used for this purpose. If the series of experiments on different substances is carried out under similar conditions and with the same centrifugal force applied for the same time, quantitative data on

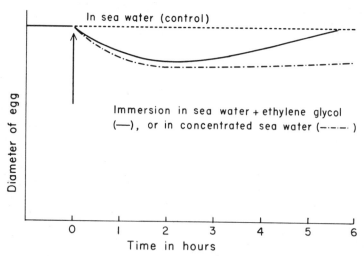

Fig. 12.1. Return to normal volume as a measure of permeability. Sea urchin eggs placed in sea water rendered hypertonic by addition of ethylene glycol in one case and by evaporation of water in the other case. Ethylene glycol enters more rapidly than salts; therefore, the eggs return sooner to their initial volume in ethylene glycol than in sea water.

EXCHANGE OF MATERIALS ACROSS THE CELL MEMBRANE

he rate of entry of the various substances can be readily obtained by the volume changes of the packed cells.[5]

Hemolysis. Hemolysis, indicated by the sudden appearance of a clear red solution instead of the previously murky suspension of red blood cells, has also been used as a measure of the rate of penetration of substances into erythrocytes. For this purpose red blood cells are placed in hypertonic solutions such as ethylene glycol. At first water leaves the cells, causing crenation, but in time ethylene glycol molecules enter. This entry increases the store of osmotically active molecules inside the cells, which results in a corresponding uptake of water. The cell membrane can stretch only to a limited extent without altering its properties, however, and the cells undergo hemolysis when this limit has been passed. In solutions of glucose, erythrocytes are hemolyzed only after a much longer time than when they are in ethylene glycol.[5, 6] The relative rates of entry of various kinds of molecules may therefore be measured by the rates of hemolysis. However, some question exists whether this method can be used for comparisons of hemolysis in red blood cells of different species, because the strength of the membrane may vary in different species, and thus hemolysis rates may not have the same meaning.

Quantitative Analyses. Perhaps the most direct method for measuring permeability is the quantitative analysis of the internal contents of a cell exposed to a solute for a known period. For this purpose large coenocytic (multinucleate) plant cells, such as *Valonia*, *Chara* and *Halicystis*, are ideal, because the uptake of the materials can be measured by analysis of the contents of the large central sap vacuoles.[7] The vacuole of *Valonia* or *Halicystis* often contains more than 1 milliliter of sap, making possible microchemical tests on the sap of a single cell.

Few animal cells are large enough to permit chemical analyses of a single cell, but the squid giant axon has been so employed. The chemical method is especially valuable because the data lend themselves to calculation of permeability constants in terms of the quantity of material transported per unit time across a unit area of cell membrane per unit osmotic gradient. Data obtained on one cell for a variety of substances may therefore be quantitatively compared with data on another cell.

Still another method used to measure permeability of a cell to a given substance is the rate of uptake of that substance from solution after a suspension of cells is added. This is an especially valuable quantitative method for study of the rate of entry of solutes into yeast or other small, active cells, because the internal contents of such cells are too minute for quantitative analysis. The cells are readily centrifuged off from the test solution, leaving a supernatant fluid which may be subjected to quantitative analysis. To illustrate, a suspension of 10^8 yeast cells per milliliter removes about 6 milligrams of sugar from solution in the first hour. The rate of removal may be measured by sampling the supernatant fluid 15, 30 and 60 minutes after yeast is first exposed to a known concentration of the glucose solution (in phosphate buffer). A small correction has to be made for the glucose respired during the course of the experiment. Another possible source of error is adsorption of some solutes to the surfaces of the cells.

Another important quantitative method is that employing radioactive tracers.[8, 9] Cells may be exposed to solutions containing radioactive isotopes, e.g., $_{11}Na^{24}$. After the superficial solution is rinsed off, the amount of radioactive ion which has been taken up may be measured with a Geiger counter (see Fig. 12.2). By making readings after varying the exposures to

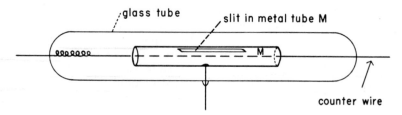

Fig. 12.2. A Geiger-Müller counter (diagrammatic). The counter wire and the metal tube are at a difference in potential of about 1000 to 1500 volts, so that absorption of even a single electron or quantum by the metal leads to an electric discharge from the metal to the wire. This is registered as a "plunk" by the relay-driven counter, which in simplest form resembles a cyclometer or tally counter.

radioactive sodium, one may determine the rate of ion uptake. Moreover, periodic readings taken subsequent to removal of the cells from radioactive solutions, indicate the rate of loss of ions. Valuable quantitative data have been obtained by this method. For instance, unique data not obtainable by other methods have thus been gathered for sodium. Previous experiments suggested that sodium does not enter cells, or enters so slowly that it cannot be measured, for example, by quantitative analysis of vacuolar contents of large plant cells. Exposure of cells to radioactive sodium, however, demonstrated that sodium ions enter and leave cells at the same readily measurable rate; therefore, no net change occurs in the cell content of sodium ions. Consequently, movement of sodium ions could not have been demonstrated by even the most precise quantitative chemical determinations.[8]

The radioactive isotope method has been confined largely to study of the entry of a number of electrolytes which have radioactive isotopes with sufficiently long half-life periods to permit measurement. H^3, C^{14}, Na^{24}, P^{32}, S^{35}, Cl^{36}, K^{42}, Ca^{45}, Fe^{59}, Cu^{64}, Zn^{65}, Br^{82}, Sr^{89} and I^{131} are isotopes now available for tracer studies. However, the tracer method

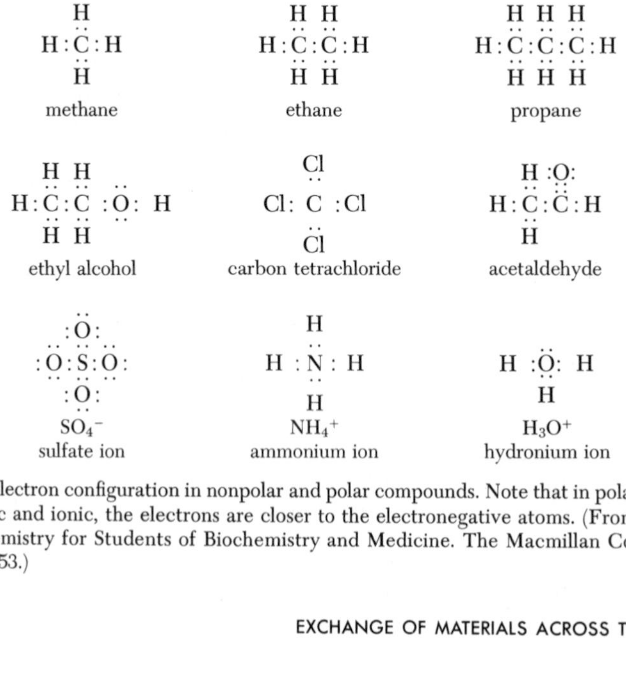

methane

ethane

propane

ethyl alcohol

carbon tetrachloride

acetaldehyde

SO_4^-
sulfate ion

NH_4^+
ammonium ion

H_3O^+
hydronium ion

Fig. 12.3. Electron configuration in nonpolar and polar compounds. Note that in polar compounds, both nonionic and ionic, the electrons are closer to the electronegative atoms. (From West, 1942: Physical Chemistry for Students of Biochemistry and Medicine. The Macmillan Company, New York, pp. 45–53.)

226   EXCHANGE OF MATERIALS ACROSS THE CELL MEMBRANE

need not be confined to electrolytes, since organic molecules may be labeled with radioactive carbon.[9]

The Correlation of Permeability with Partition Coefficients

A definite rationale lies behind the groups of compounds tested in permeability studies. By testing various groups of compounds, each with certain properties in common, it has been possible to find some correlation between these properties and movements of each solute through the cell membrane. Each of the main classes of compounds is considered below.[2]

Nonpolar compounds are compounds in which electrons are equally shared by the two atoms forming a bond (see Fig. 12.3), as in the paraffins, olefins and cyclic compounds. They have a high solubility in fats or fat solvents, but a low solubility in water.

In *nonionic polar compounds* the electrons of the bond between two atoms are attracted more to one of the atoms (e.g., to the strongly electronegative atoms, such as oxygen, nitrogen and chlorine) than to the other. As a consequence, the molecule acts as a dipole and orients in an electric field. Nonionic polar compounds are derivatives of nonpolar compounds into which electronegative atoms or radicals have been introduced. Thus, methyl alcohol is a derivative of methane, ethyl alcohol a derivative of ethane, and so on (see Fig. 12.3).

In *ionic compounds* the electrons of a valency bond are held by only one of the atoms or radicals, so that ions are present even in the crystalline state of such compounds. In the crystal the ions are bound together by electrostatic forces. A liquid of high dielectric constant, like water, stabilizes the attractive forces between pairs of ions, allowing them to separate from one another and act as individual particles. Ionic compounds are of two kinds—*weak electrolytes*, such as weak acids and bases, and *strong electrolytes*, such as salts and strong acids and bases. The stronger the electrolyte the greater will be its solubility in water and the less its solubility in oil. In a homologous series such as the organic acids, the strength (ionization) of the acids decreases as the chain length increases; for instance, formic acid is stronger than acetic, the latter is stronger than propionic, and so on. As the degree of ionization declines, the oil solubility increases, and the higher fatty acids are freely soluble in oils or oil solvents but only slightly soluble in water (see Table 12.1).

The ratio of solubility of a compound in oil or fat solvent to its solubility in water is called the *partition coefficient.* The more nonpolar a compound is, the more soluble it is in fats or fat solvents (i.e., the more lipophilic it is). Such compounds usually have slight, if any, solu-

TABLE 12.1. *Partition Coefficients of a Homologous Series of Acids*

ACID	NUMBER OF CARBONS	MOLECULAR WEIGHT	DISSOCIATION CONSTANT	WATER SOLUBILITY IN GRAMS/100 ML.	PARTITION COEFFICIENT, BENZENE : WATER
Formic	1	46.03	1.76×10^{-4}	very high	—
Acetic	2	60.05	1.75×10^{-5}	very high	0.055
Propionic	3	74.08	1.40×10^{-5}	very high	0.28
Butyric	4	88.10	1.48×10^{-5}	5.62 at $-1.1°$ C.	1.08
Caproic	5	116.14	1.32×10^{-5}	0.4	3.73
Caprylic	6	144.21	—	0.25 at 100° C.	16.10

Data from Handbook of Chemistry and Physics, 35th Ed., and Höber.[10]

bility in water. Their partition coefficients are therefore high. On the other hand, polar derivatives of nonpolar compounds are usually less soluble in fats or fat solvents, in correspondence to their degree of polarity. With increase of polarity comes increasing solubility in water. To illustrate, lower alcohols like methyl alcohol and ethyl alcohol are highly polar, and they are only slightly soluble in fats or fat solvents but completely miscible with water. Conversely, higher alcohols like butyl alcohol and amyl alcohol are sparingly soluble in water but miscible with fat solvents in all proportions. Lower alcohols have low partition coefficients; higher alcohols have high ones. Ionized compounds are polar and correspondingly less soluble in fats but usually highly soluble in water. Weak electrolytes with lipophilic radicals, like the long chains of the higher fatty acids mentioned above, are soluble in fats and have high partition coefficients, while the lower fatty acids (formic acid, acetic acid, etc.) are highly soluble in water and have low partition coefficients. Strong electrolytes are sparingly soluble in fats but highly soluble in water. Their partition coefficients are therefore low.

The entry of a large number of compounds into the cells of *Chara*, a plant with large coenocytic cells, was studied by Collander and Bärlund,[7] and some of their results are cited in detail here because they constitute the most extensive study of its kind. The amount of a substance entering a *Chara* cell per unit time was determined by chemical analysis, and the permeability constant in terms of the quantity of compound entering per unit time per unit area of cell surface per unit osmotic gradient was then calculated. These data are given graphically in Figure 12.4. The approximate molecular diameters of the compounds are indicated by the size of the circles in the figure, the largest circles designating the largest molecules. Scrutiny of the graph discloses that usually molecules with the largest partition coefficients enter the cell most readily, regardless of molecular size.

The relation between partition coefficient and molecular size is most clearly

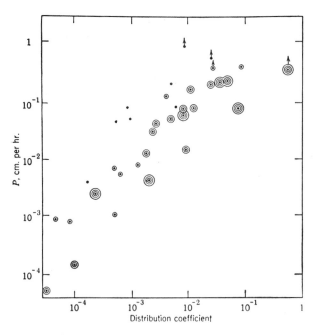

Fig. 12.4. Relation between partition coefficient (distribution coefficient) of a substance between oil and water and its penetration (P) into the *Chara* cell. The small dots indicate small molecules, and successive circles about these indicate corresponding increases in molecular size. Note that even large molecules of high solubility in oil penetrate the cell readily. (From Collander, 1937: Trans. Faraday Soc. 33:986.)

EXCHANGE OF MATERIALS ACROSS THE CELL MEMBRANE

brought out by comparing the rates of penetration of members of a homologous series such as the alcohols. If the narcotic action of the alcohols on respiration is used to measure their penetration, higher alcohols with greater oil solubility are observed to enter cells much more readily than lower alcohols of less oil solubility, even though the molecular sizes of the higher alcohols are considerably larger[10] (see Table 12.2).

Another example showing that entry of molecules into cells increases with increase in partition coefficient, even though correlated with an increase in molecular weight, is that of the urethans. Comparing the effects of urethans (alkyl carbamates) on the resting potential of frog nerves as a measure of their penetration into cells, one can demonstrate that urethan (ethyl carbamate) penetrates less readily than the substituted urethans in which methyl, ethyl or other radicals are substituted for some of the hydrogen atoms. The substituted urethans have higher oil-to-water partition coefficients than ethyl carbamate.[11]

In the latter two examples permeability increases with increase in partition coefficient, even when the molecular size increases at the same time. This indicates that lipoid solubility of a molecule is a factor of greater moment than its size in determining rate of entry into a cell.

The question arises whether partition coefficient alone determines if a molecule shall pass through the cell membrane. Permeability, however, is not so simple a phenomenon as the correlation between permeability and partition coefficients would lead one to believe. Further experiments demonstrate that molecular size does influence the passage of substances through the cell membrane and that many other factors, such as hydrogen ion concentration, salts, temperature and physiological state, also have an effect on the movement of solutes through the cell membrane.

The Effects of Molecular Size upon Permeability

In studying the effects of molecular size on permeability, one should note that in general the molecular weight of a substance gives some idea of the approximate diameter of its molecules; the greater the molecular weight, the larger will be the molecule. Molecular diameters also depend upon steric configuration, especially in organic molecules. Symmetry, or its lack, also influences the effective diameter of a molecule, an asymmetrical molecule having a larger effective diameter than a symmetrical one.

TABLE 12.2.   *Partition Coefficients (Ratio of Solubility in Oil to Solubility in Water) of a Series of Homologous Alcohols*

ALCOHOL	MOLECULAR WEIGHT	SOLUBILITY IN GM. PER 100 ML. WATER	PARTITION COEFFICIENT, OIL : WATER	NARCOTIC CONCENTRATION
Methyl	31.06	∞	0.0097	5.0
Ethyl	46.07	∞	0.0357	1.6
Propyl	60.09	∞	0.156	0.8
n-Butyl	74.12	7.9	0.588	0.15
i-Amyl	88.15	slight	2.13	0.045

Data from Handbook of Chemistry and Physics, 35th Ed.; and Höber.[10] The narcotic concentration is in moles needed to give 50 per cent inhibition of oxygen consumption by goose erythrocytes.

It is understood that very large molecules probably have only a slight chance of entering a cell. Sucrose, for example, penetrates cells in very small amounts, if at all. Larger carbohydrate molecules, such as starch, glycogen or inulin, do not pass through cell membranes; for this reason they serve effectively as food stores. The probability that a protein molecule will pass through a cell membrane is also very slight, although the absorption of antigens indicates that penetration occurs in some instances.[13]

On the other hand, it has been found that, provided the partition coefficients of the compounds are the same, the molecular size, even if small, has some effect upon permeability. For example, cyanamide, propionamide, succinamide and diethylmalonamide have about the same partition coefficients, but their molecular diameters increase in the order given (see Fig. 12.5). When these compounds were tested on *Chara* it was found that their ability to penetrate the cell membrane decreased with increase in molecular diameter. Size is, then, also an important factor in determining whether or not a molecule will pass into a cell and in determining the rate of penetration, but it appears that the partition coefficient is of primary importance and size is of secondary importance in

determining passage through the membrane of most cells.[7]

However, there are cases in which molecular size, though small, may even be of greater importance than the partition coefficient in determining the penetration of molecules into some cells. This is illustrated by the data in Figure 12.6 for *Beggiatoa*,[12] a large sulfur bacterium, tested with compounds similar to those used with *Chara*. Here the correlation between permeation and molecular size is much more decisive than the correlation between permeation and partition coefficient (see Fig. 12.7). This case is instructive because it illustrates the individuality of cells.

Another example of the influence of molecular size on permeability is shown in the penetration of aldehydes into a dark mutant strain of luminous bacteria, which lacks the ability to form its own aldehydes needed for luminescence, but will luminesce if aldehyde is supplied. By using the first phase of luminescence (when luminous intensity increases linearly with the concentration of aldehyde) as a measure of entry, the data for rate of penetration of a homologous series of aldehydes was obtained, as shown in Table 12.3. The permeability constants calculated for the rate of entry of aldehydes into bacteria is of the same order of magnitude as for entry of nonelectrolytes into plant cells.[41]

It is apparent that macromolecules such as polypeptides, proteins and polysaccharides cannot, by virtue of their very size, pass through the pores in a cell membrane by which smaller molecules enter and leave the cell if their passage through the cell membrane is governed by the same rules as determine the passage of the smaller molecules tested.[42] Another method has been developed by cells for uptake of such macromolecules, e.g., *pinocytosis*, which is discussed in Chapter 13.

Cyanamide $CN \cdot NH_2$
Propionamide $CH_3 \cdot CH_2 \cdot CO \cdot NH_2$
Succinamide $NH_2 \cdot CO \cdot CH_2 \cdot CH_2 \cdot CO \cdot NH_2$

Diethylmalonamide
$$C_2H_5 - \overset{\displaystyle CO \cdot NH_2}{\underset{\displaystyle CO \cdot NH_2}{C}} - C_2H_5$$

Fig. 12.5. Compounds of like partition coefficient but of different molecular size. Penetration into *Chara* is inversely correlated with molecular size, the permeability decreasing in the order given. (After Collander and Bärlund, 1933: Acta Bot. Fennica, *11*:1.)

230

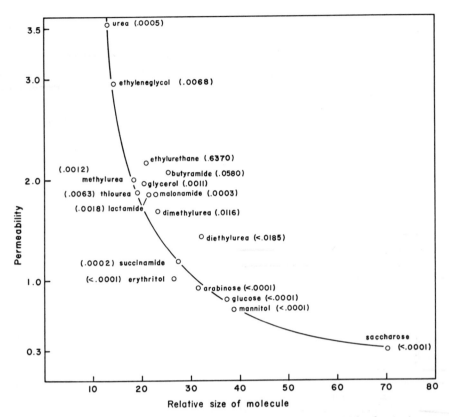

Fig. 12.6. Relation between molecular size and permeability in *Beggiatoa*. Molecular size is measured by molecular refraction in yellow light. Permeability is measured by the $\log_{10}$ ($10^4 \times$ the threshold plasmolytic concentration in moles per liter). Partition coefficients in ether:water are given in parentheses. Correlation is clearly with molecular size. (Data from Ruhland and Hoffmann, 1925: Planta, *1*:1.)

The Effect of Ionization upon Permeability

Electrolytes enter cells more slowly, in general, than nonelectrolytes of similar molecular dimensions, weaker electrolytes entering more rapidly than strong ones. The relation between charge and penetration is best seen by studying the rate of entry of weak electrolytes as affected by their degree of ionization. The degree of ionization of a weak electrolyte is determined by the pH. By varying the pH, within limits safe for the organism, one may determine what effect

the charge on an electrolyte has upon its ability to penetrate a cell membrane.

In Figure 12.8 is shown the effect of pH on the penetration of carbon dioxide or carbonic acid. At pH 6.11 one half is dissociated. As the pH rises, the dissociation increases but the entry of CO_2 decreases. Conversely, with fall in pH the amount of dissociation decreases and the entry of carbon dioxide into the cell increases.[14] Similar relations hold for hydrogen sulfide, hydrocyanic acid, auxins (plant growth hormones), dinitrophenol (metabolic stimulant) and other biologically active weak acids. The entry of

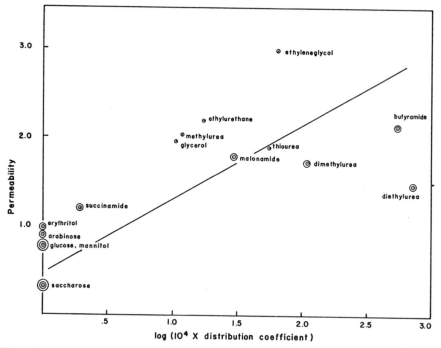

Fig. 12.7. Relation between partition coefficient and permeability of *Beggiatoa* to various organic substances. While the permeability increases with the partition coefficient, the correlation is not nearly so good as that found in *Chara* (see Fig. 12.4). Permeability is measured by $\log_{10}$ ($10^4 \times$ threshold plasmolytic concentration in moles per liter). The abscissa is $\log_{10}$ ($10^4 \times$ partition coefficient between ether and water). (Data from Ruhland and Hoffmann, 1925: Planta, *1*:1.)

weak bases such as the amines and alkaloids is governed by the same principles, except that in their case the rise in pH suppresses dissociation and enhances penetration. The principle has practical

TABLE 12.3. *Rate of Penetration of Aldehydes into Luminous Bacteria*

NUMBER OF CARBONS	NAME	PENETRATION IN CM. PER SEC. $\times$ 10^{-6}	Q_{10}
7	heptanal	10.6	1.13
8	octanal	6.4	1.19
9	nonanal	1.68	1.26
10	decanal	0.95	1.26
11	undecanal	0.85	1.42
12	dodecanal	0.7	1.89
14	tetradecanal	0.31	1.78

Data from Rogers and McElroy.[41]

value to the pharmacologist, since the rate of entry of such a drug may be controlled at will by varying the pH of the solutions to which the cells are exposed.[15, 19]

The effect of degree of ionization on the entry of electrolytes into cells is further illustrated by comparing the rates of entry of members of a homologous series such as the weak organic acids illustrated in Table 12.1. As judged by criteria such as color changes in cells with natural pigments, penetration of the anions increases in the order given in the table.[16] It appears that in spite of the increase in molecular size, the entry of the acids is more rapid, the smaller their degree of dissociation. However, lipoid solubility plays a role here also, since the rate of entry increases with a rise in the partition coefficient, a factor previously

EXCHANGE OF MATERIALS ACROSS THE CELL MEMBRANE

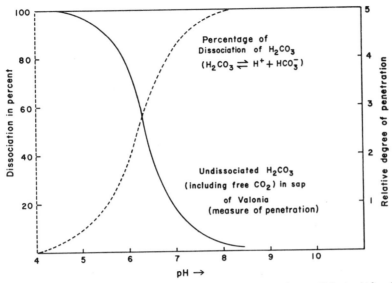

Fig. 12.8. Relation between pH and penetration of a weak electrolyte in *Valonia*. (After Oster-hout and Dorcas, 1926: J. Gen. Physiol., 9:259.)

emphasized as of paramount importance.

Presumably, permeation is proportional to the number of undissociated molecules, and a change in pH in the direction which increases the proportion of undissociated molecules will enhance penetration. The data indicate that the presence of a charge on an ion decreases its chance of entry.

If the presence of an electric charge is indeed a disadvantage for entry of ions into the cell, then the stronger the charge on an ion the less probable should be the ion's entry into a cell. This is found to be true. In studies on a series of strong electrolytes (completely dissociated) some ions are found to enter more readily than others. Monovalent cations such as Na^+ and K^+ enter more readily than bivalent cations such as Ca^{++} or Mg^{++}, and bivalent cations enter more readily than trivalent cations such as Fe^{+++}. Similarly, monovalent anions such as I^- or Cl^- enter more readily than divalent anions such as $SO_4^=$ or tartrate.[17]

Not all ions of the same valency enter cells at the same rate. For example, the ammonium ion enters more rapidly than potassium, potassium more rapidly than sodium, and sodium more rapidly than lithium. This might be explained on the basis of the relative size of the hydrated ions. As was explained in Chapter 4, ions bear charges which attract and orient water molecules about themselves in hydration spheres. The resultant particle is therefore much larger than the ion itself. Hydration is not equal in all ions. For instance, the nucleus of potassium is surrounded by several shells of electrons; therefore its net charge density is lower than that of lithium, which has one shell of electrons. Consequently, less water is attracted to potassium than to lithium. Hydration must always be taken into account when one considers the effective size of an ion, since the size of a hydrated ion determines the diffusion rate as much as it determines the ease of the ion's passage through the cell membrane (see Table 12.4). For the entry of anions into cells, a similar explanation has been applied to explain the differential entry of ions of the same valency, e.g., SCN > I > NO_3 > Cl.[1, 17] Thus permeability to

TABLE 12.4. *Penetration and Properties of Some Cations*

PROPERTY	ION		
	Li	Na	K
Atomic weight	6.939	22.997	39.096
Degree of hydration	most	intermediate	least
Effective diameter	largest	intermediate	smallest
Entry into cells	slowest	intermediate	fastest

ions is dependent to some extent upon a "sieve" action of the cell membrane. However, it can be demonstrated that the hydration sphere does not electrically neutralize the ion. The residual charge still acts as a hindrance to penetration as does, in addition, the particle size resulting from hydration.

The fact that uncharged particles enter a cell more readily than ions do, as illustrated above for weak electrolytes, suggests an electric charge on the cell membrane. Anions are attracted to positively charged areas and cations to negatively charged ones. Since both anions and cations are affected, the cell membrane is considered to be a *mosaic* of negative and positive charges. However, the over-all charge on the cell membrane is positive, so that anions would be expected to enter cells more readily than cations. This is found to be the case.[18]

Some cells appear to be freely permeable to anions while at the same time they largely exclude cations. Other cells may be freely permeable to cations but may largely exclude anions. The passage of an ion from an external medium into a cell is thought to be in exchange for an ion inside the cell. Hydrogen ions resulting from metabolic activity are always available for exchange with cations, and bicarbonate ions of similar origin are available for exchange with anions. For maintenance of the electric potential across the cell membrane, equal numbers of anions and cations need not be taken up by the cell, but the exchange of ion for ion must be equal.[19]

All of these considerations on the permeability of cells to ions apply only to situations in which no marked accumulation occurs and where no transport mechanism seems to be involved. When marked accumulation occurs, as for example, that of potassium in most cells, an active transport system is involved (Chapter 13).

Osmotic Relations in the Presence of Protein

Proteins form ions that penetrate neither natural nor artificial membranes with small pores. When a potassium proteinate solution, at the appropriate pH, is placed in a cellophane bag and immersed in a solution of potassium chloride, the initial distribution of ions is similar to that shown in Figure 12.9A. At this time the initial concentration of potassium ions inside is designated as C_i, the concentration of chloride is zero, and the concentration of proteinate is designated as C_i. The initial concentration of potassium ions outside at this time is designated as C_o, and the concentration of chloride ions is designated as C_o.

Since chloride ions penetrate the membrane, they diffuse inward in response to the concentration gradient. To maintain electric neutrality, potassium ions accompany them. At equilibrium, therefore, a certain concentration, X, of potassium and chloride ions will have entered the membrane (Fig. 12.9B). At that time the concentration of potassium ions inside the membrane will be $(C_i + X)$, while

EXCHANGE OF MATERIALS ACROSS THE CELL MEMBRANE

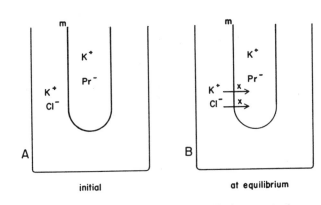

initial	at equilibrium
Initial concentration	Final concentration

inside	inside
$K^+ = C_i$	$K^+ = C_i + X$
$Pr^- = C_i$	$Pr^- = C_i$
$Cl^- = 0$	$Cl^- = X$
outside	outside
$K^+ = C_o$	$K^+ = C_o - X$
$Cl^- = C_o$	$Cl^- = C_o - X$

Fig. 12.9. Donnan equilibrium. The membrane (m) within which the protein solution is contained is impermeable to protein ions but permits all the other ions to pass. NOTE: Because salts are taken up into the tube containing the protein, the osmotic pressure will rise and water will enter.

that of the chloride ions inside will be X. The concentration of potassium ions outside the cellophane bag will be $(C_o - X)$ and that of the chloride ions outside the bag will be $(C_o - X)$.

Donnan,[39] by applying the law of mass action, found that at equilibrium the product of the concentrations of the diffusible ions inside the bag equals the product of the concentrations of the diffusible ions outside the bag:

$$[K^+]_{in} [Cl^-]_{in} = [K^+]_{out} [Cl^-]_{out} \quad (12.1)$$

Substituting for these symbols the concentration terms used above, one can write the following equation:

$$(C_i + X) X = (C_o - X) (C_o - X) \quad (12.2)$$

Solving for X:

$$X^2 + C_i X = C_o{}^2 - 2C_o X + X^2 \quad (12.3)$$

$$X = \frac{C_o{}^2}{C_i + 2C_o}. \quad (12.4)$$

Knowing the initial concentrations of ions inside and outside a membrane, one can use this equation to solve for X, the

concentration (at equilibrium) of the diffusible ions which have entered the membrane. The equilibrium is called the *Donnan equilibrium* in honor of its discoverer.[39]

If a mixture of uni-univalent, diffusible and membrane-penetrating electrolytes such as NaCl, KNO_3, LiBr and HI is used instead of KCl inside and outside the tube containing the protein (Fig. 12.9), the following relations hold:

$$\frac{[Na^+]_i}{[Na^+]_o} = \frac{[K^+]_i}{[K^+]_o} = \frac{[Li^+]_i}{[Li^+]_o} = \frac{[H^+]_i}{[H^+]_o} =$$

$$\frac{[Cl^-]_o}{[Cl^-]_i} = \frac{[NO_3{}^-]_o}{[NO_3{}^-]_i} = \frac{[Br^-]_o}{[Br^-]_i} = \frac{[I^-]_o}{[I^-]_i} \quad (12.5)$$

The Effects of Temperature and Radiations on Permeability

If certain substances enter a cell in response to a concentration gradient between the outside and inside of the cell, and if the molecules are freely able to enter and leave the cell membrane, the temperature coefficient for entry of these substances into cells should be like that found for free diffusion, namely, 1.3–1.4 (Table 10.1). Experiments show this to be true in a few cases. For example, a temperature coefficient of this order is found for the entry of propyl alcohol into erythrocytes and of some aldehydes into luminous bacteria[41] (Tables 10.1 and 12.3), suggesting that these molecules move freely through these cell membranes.

However, in many other cases, e.g., the entry of dyes into *Arbacia* or into frog skin (Table 10.1), the rate of entry of compounds into a cell is increased several fold by a ten degree rise in temperature. It would appear that most molecules have to be activated to cross some barrier in the cell membrane (see Chapter 14). A ten degree rise in temperature increases by several fold the number of molecules with the energy of activation (see Chapter 10) required to cross the barrier. The temperature coefficient for permeability in such cases may well be between 2 and 4.[22, 23]

The effects of visible light, ultraviolet radiations and ionizing radiations upon the penetration of substances into cells has been studied, and some literature on this topic exists.[33–37] Some of the findings are controversial, and therefore they will not be reviewed here, but it is known that when cells are sufficiently injured by radiations their permeability to various solutes increases as it does following any other injury.

The Effects of Salts on Permeability— Salt Antagonism

The salt environment to which a cell is subjected affects the permeability of the cell membrane to other substances. To study these effects, the electrical conductivity of plant cells has been measured as an index of entry of ions. For this purpose the kelp *Laminaria*, which has a broad blade, has been used extensively. With a cork borer, disks of tissue cell are cut from the blade. These are put together, like a roll of coins, between two electrodes, and the resistance (the reciprocal of the conductivity) is determined (see Fig. 12.10). A decrease in resistance means that the ions are passing through the cells more readily and that the permeability has therefore been increased. A few samples of the many interesting studies performed are cited below.

When *Laminaria* disks are immersed in sodium chloride solutions isotonic with sea water (0.52 molar), their electrical resistance gradually decreases, indicating an increase in permeability. After extended exposure the cells, having become injured, are somewhat freely permeable to sodium chloride, suggesting that the plasma membrane of the cells now presents little resistance to entry and exit of the sodium and chloride ions. If not subjected to too long an exposure to the sodium chloride, the *Laminaria* disks recover when immersed again in sea water, and their electrical resistance increases to some extent (see Fig. 12.11).

When this experiment is repeated with calcium chloride isotonic to sea water (0.278 molar solution), the electrical resistance of the disks first increases,

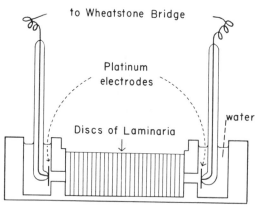

to Wheatstone Bridge

Platinum electrodes

Discs of Laminaria

water

Fig. 12.10. Apparatus for conductivity studies. (After Osterhout, 1922: Injury, Recovery and Death in Relation to Conductivity and Permeability. Lippincott, Philadelphia, p. 24.)

EXCHANGE OF MATERIALS ACROSS THE CELL MEMBRANE

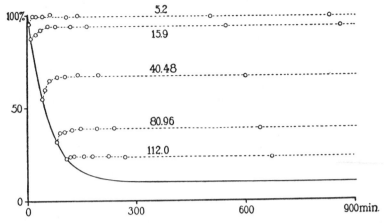

Fig. 12.11. The effects of isotonic NaCl on the permeability of disks cut out of the kelp *Laminaria*. The curves show the net electric resistance (ordinate) in per cent of the initial resistance of *Laminaria agardhii* in 0.52 molar NaCl (unbroken line) and recovery in sea water (dotted lines). The figure attached to each recovery curve denotes the time of exposure (in minutes) to the solution of NaCl. (From Osterhout[24].)

ndicating decreased permeability to the alt (see Fig. 12.12), and then falls, showng that the cells, having become injured re now more permeable to the ions.

Isotonic potassium chloride produces effects similar to those of sodium chloride,

and isotonic magnesium chloride produces effects similar to those of calcium chloride.

When *Laminaria* disks are placed in an isotonic mixture of sodium chloride and calcium chloride, in the same proportions as present in sea water, the elec-

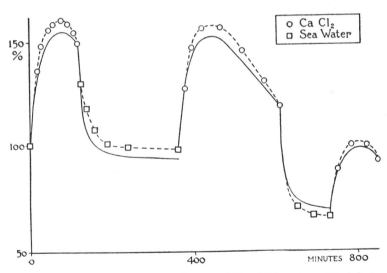

Fig. 12.12. The effect of isotonic $CaCl_2$ on the permeability of disks cut out of the kelp *Laminaria*. The curves show the net electric resistance (ordinate) in per cent of the initial resistance of *Laminaria agardhii* in 0.278 molar $CaCl_2$ and in sea water. The unbroken line represents calculated values, and the broken line represents observed values. The curves are based on an average of ten or more experiments. (From Osterhout[24].)

MOVEMENT OF SOLUTES THROUGH THE CELL MEMBRANE

trical resistance remains (17 hours, in one test) about the same as that of the control in sea water, indicating that the permeability is practically normal and that the cells have not been injured. Since calcium and sodium chlorides have opposite initial effects on the permeability of the cell membrane, calcium chloride decreasing it and sodium chloride increasing it, these two ions are said to antagonize each other. The net effect is that a mixture of the two salts maintains a practically normal permeability of the membrane. The permeability of the membrane is completely normal if potassium and magnesium chlorides also are added to the solution of sodium and calcium chlorides in the proportions in which the cations are found in sea water: in other words, if artificial sea water is used. Salt antagonism appears to be the antagonistic action of different salts upon one another in maintaining normal permeability of the cell membrane.

Similar salt antagonism is also observed on cells of animal tissues. For instance, a frog heart placed in pure sodium chloride solution ceases beating, but if calcium chloride is added in the proportion found in blood (or sea water), the heart revives. However, the beat is not normal unless potassium chloride and a buffer are added also (see Fig. 12.13). Ordinarily glucose is also added to the solution to supply nutrient to the heart muscle cells. Such a balanced salt solution was developed for frog heart and tissue cells by Sidney Ringer, a British physician, and is called Ringer's solution in his honor.[2] Many similar solutions have been developed since.[26]

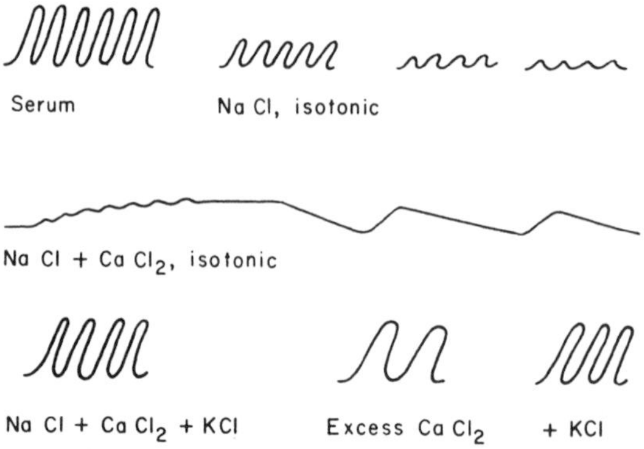

The antagonistic relations between various cations are more complex than would be suggested by these discussions. They have been extensively studied,[4] but a satisfactory interpretation in terms of molecular interactions in the cell membrane has not been found. While anions of salts, used in balanced media, probably also affect the life of the tissue cells suspended in them, antagonism is thought to be essentially a cationic phenomenon. On the other hand, anions such as nitrates, which are not normally found in animal tissue fluids or blood, have been found in some cases to have a marked effect.[27]

It is also possible that calcium is needed in the bathing fluid because it plays such an important part in irritability of cells as emphasized by Heilbrunn in presenting his general theory of stimulation.[40, 4] According to this theory, calcium is bound to cell proteins but also exists as a free cation in the cell. Stimulation of cells is followed by release of calcium from its bound condition in the cortex of the cells and its passage into the endoplasm. In muscle cells such a release of calcium is followed by contraction, and injection of solutions of calcium similarly is followed by strong contraction. However, the absence of calcium in the bathing medium or its presence in excess has been shown to interfere with stimulation and response in the cell.[40, 43]

The fact that calcium decreases the

Serum   Na Cl, isotonic

Na Cl + Ca Cl$_2$, isotonic

Na Cl + Ca Cl$_2$ + KCl   Excess Ca Cl$_2$ + KCl

Fig. 12.13. The effects of salts on a frog's heart. The heart stops in isotonic NaCl, but beats slowly when CaCl$_2$ is added in the proportions found in blood (the heart must be stimulated once). The beat is almost normal when KCl is added in the proportion found in blood and when the mixture contains a buffer. Excess CaCl$_2$ prolongs the beat of the heart and is antagonized by KCl. (After Ringer, 1882–83: J. Physiol., 4:29, 422.)

ermeability of the cell membrane to
water and to other substances is of great
importance, especially in the water rela-
ons of cells of fresh water organisms.
uch organisms must maintain within
hem a certain amount of salt for normal
unctioning even though little salt is
vailable in the bathing medium, and
ven though such cells continuously take
p water and lose salts. Salt is replenished
nd the necessary balance achieved by
ptake from food, and excess water is
oided in a urine hypotonic to blood. In
nany fresh water animals the surfaces
ermeable to water have been restricted
o cells of the gills. Experiments show
hat calcium ions in water reduce the
ermeability of the gill cells to both
vater and salts and some gill cells have
leveloped the capacity to take up salts
ven against a gradient (see Chapter
3).[28]

The problem of regulating the perme-
bility of cells in the gills is acute for
rackish water animals like crabs, which
nigrate into highly diluted sea water or
ven fresh water. When such animals are
laced in distilled water they may lose
alts and gain water so rapidly that they
lie. In hard fresh water, on the other
and, they are able to get along because
calcium reduces the permeability of the
cell membranes to both solutes and water.

The Effect of Narcotics and Anesthetics
upon Permeability

Narcotics and anesthetics generally exert their characteristic effects on cell
sensitivity and respiration in proportion
to their lipoid solubility, indicating that
they may need to enter the cell to affect
it. Some values for the narcotic action of
a number of compounds, correlated with
their solubility in olive oil, are given in
Table 12.5.

Anesthetics also affect the permeability
of cells in an interesting manner. For example, butyl alcohol decreases the pene-

TABLE 12.5. *Relation Between Narcotic
Action and Lipoid Solubility*

COMPOUND	VOL. % REQUIRED TO NARCOTIZE MICE	SOLUBILITY IN OLIVE OIL AT $37°$ C.
Ethane	80	1.3
Acetylene	65	1.8
Dimethyl ether	12	11.6
Methylchloride	6.5	14.0
Dimethyl acetal	1.9	100
Chloroform	0.5	265

Data from Höber.[10]

tration of glycerol into the red blood cells
of human beings, rats, rabbits, guinea
pigs and birds, but it increases the penetration of glycerol into the red blood cells
of sheep, horses, dogs, bats, pigs, reptiles
and fishes. Thiourea, on the other hand,
has effects opposite to that of butyl alcohol on the penetration of glycerol into
the red blood cells of the two series of
animals tested.[29] Furthermore, the same
anesthetic, at different concentrations,
may have the reverse effects on the permeability of a given type of cell. For example,
urethan in low concentration decreases
the permeability of disks of algal tissue,
whereas at high concentrations it has the
opposite effect when first applied. In
both instances prolonged exposure results
in injury and increased permeability.[24]

Such diverse effects of anesthetics on
the permeability of cells are difficult to
explain. Perhaps the anesthetic molecules,
being highly lipoid soluble, accumulate at
the surface of the cell, thus altering the
properties of the membrane by either increasing or decreasing the ease of entry
of other molecules. For example, if the
solution of anesthetic in the membrane
makes the membrane more lipoidal in nature, molecules of high partition coefficient will enter more readily than before,
while those of low partition coefficients
will enter less readily. The converse
would also be possible.[30]

The Effect of the Physiological State

Movement of solutes through the cell membrane is dependent on the physiological state of the cells. Active cells utilize cell foods and accessory materials more rapidly than inactive cells; therefore, they maintain a continuous diffusion gradient for these substances, enabling the substances to enter the cell readily.

When a muscle cell or nerve cell is shocked and stimulated, its permeability to ions is increased. An active muscle cell is permeable to amino acids, glucose and other materials, whereas a resting one is not.[31] Electric stimulation of cells of various tissues, plant and animal, results in an increase in their permeability to solutes at the negative electrode, as shown by increased conductivity (decreased resistance). The leakage of potassium ions at this electrode in *Nitella* and the squid giant axon may be sufficient even for measurement by microchemical methods.[32] As shown by experiments with radioactive sodium, sodium ions also pass through the membrane of a stimulated cell more freely than they do through the membrane of a resting cell. Injury of the cell by heat, radiations,[33-37] overstimulation, anesthetics, pH change, salt unbalance, or any other means,[38] results in an increased permeability of the cell. By use of the conductivity method Osterhout[24] has made an extensive study of the effects various degrees of injury have on permeability of *Laminaria* and other algae. If the injury is slight there is only a slight increase in the conductivity, indicating that the permeability of the cells has increased slightly. If the injury is large, the increase in conductivity is greater. If exposure to any of the above injurious factors has not been excessive before the cells are returned to normal conditions, complete recovery of normal permeability often follows. However, as shown in Figures 12.11 and 12.12, only partial recovery may occur, and the permeability may be permanently increased by injury. All gradations of change are possible, depending upon the degree of exposure and damage to the cells. Studies of permeability changes following injury of a variety of cells indicate a similar action however, the data on cells other than *Laminaria* are neither as extensive nor as readily presented graphically.

Death, as measured by permeability, is a quantitative phenomenon. Osterhout's monograph should be consulted for a more detailed account of the changes following injury by various means and of the degree of reversibility which occurs when the injury is slight.[24]

Comparison of the Permeability of Different Kinds of Cells

The relative permeability of different kinds of cells to a particular substance may be compared by any method which is equally applicable to all of the cells. For example, the rate of hemolysis has been used for comparison of the permeability of different erythrocytes. Erythrocytes of various species of mammals, when tested in this manner for their permeability to glycerol, show differences covering a range of 240 fold (see Table 12.6). Similar differences are observed for entry of sodium ions, potassium ions, urea and glucose.

When comparing the permeability of various kinds of cells to a given substance, and the same method cannot be applied to all of the cells, then it is necessary to measure the amount of the substance entering a unit area per unit of time and per unit concentration difference between the insides and outsides of the cells. Calculation of a permeability constant, incorporating these quantitative data has been made possible by means of certain equations.[21] These are based on Fick's law of diffusion, which states that a substance, S, will diffuse through an

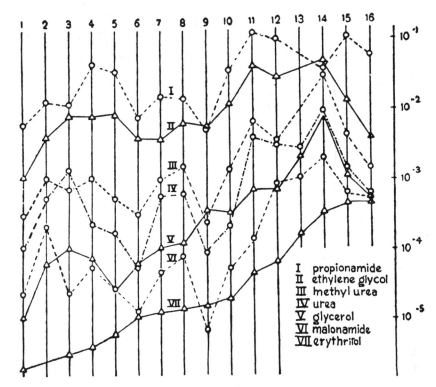

Fig. 12.14. Permeability constants of plant cells to nonelectrolytes. Cells from 16 species are represented: 1, Leaf cells of *Plagiothecum denticulatum;* 2, *Oedogonium sp.;* 3, root cells of *Lemna minor;* 4, *Pylaiella litoralis;* 5, *Zygnema cyanosporum;* 6, sub-epidermal cells of *Curcuma rubricaulis;* 7, *Spirogyra sp.;* 8, leaf cells of *Elodea densa;* 9, epidermal cells of *Rhoeo discolor;* 10, epidermal cells of *Taraxacum pectinatiforme;* 11. "leaf cells" of *Chara ceratophylla;* 12, internodal cells of *Ceramium diaphanum;* 13, *Bacterium paracoli;* 14, *Oscillatoria princeps;* 15, *Melosira sp.;* 16, *Licmophora sp.* (From Collander, 1937: Trans. Faraday Soc., 33:989.)

TABLE 12.6. *Variation in Permeability of Erythrocytes of Various Mammals, Measured by Time for 75 Per Cent Hemolysis in 0.3 Molar Glycerol in 0.12 Per Cent NaCl.*

ANIMAL	TIME	ANIMAL	TIME
Rat	3.5	dog	253
Man	5.1	pig	340
Mouse	12.9	cat	459
Rabbit	21.8	ox	612
Guinea pig	38.2	sheep	850

Data from Höber.[10]

area, A, at a rate, dS/dt (amount, dS, per unit time, dt), which is dependent upon the difference in concentration between the substances at a certain distance apart.

$$\frac{dS}{dt} = DA \frac{dC}{dx} \qquad (12.6)$$

In this equation D is the diffusion coefficient and is given in moles per unit area per unit concentration gradient, and dC is the difference in concentrations ($C_1 - C_2$) over the distance dx.

For passage through a membrane such as that of a cell, the above equation becomes

$$\frac{dS}{dt} = \frac{DA}{M}(C_{out} - C_{in}) \qquad (12.7)$$

Here C_{out} represents the concentration of the substance, S, outside, and C_{in} is its concentration inside the cell. A is the area of the membrane, and M—which is substituted for dx in equation 12.6—represents the thickness of the membrane.

Since the amount of substance (S) per volume (V) of the cell is C_{in}, $C_{in}V$ may be substituted for S. When k, the permeability constant, is substituted for D/M, the equation is written as follows:

$$\frac{dC_{in}}{dt} = k \frac{A}{V} (C_{out} - C_{in}). \qquad (12.8)$$

If the volume of fluid outside the cell is large, integration of equation 12.8 and solution for k gives

$$k = \frac{V}{At} \ln \frac{C_{out} - C_{in}}{C_{out} - C^1_{in}} \qquad (12.9)$$

Here C_{in} and C^1_{in} are the concentrations inside the cell before and after time t. The permeability constant, k, is therefore given in moles of the substance entering per square micron of cell surface per second per mole difference in concentration of substance S outside and inside the cell.[21]

The permeability constants for entry of a variety of substances into cells of a given species of plant or animal are different because some substances enter readily, others slowly. While for any one substance tested the permeability constant is different for cells of each of a number of species of organisms, the cells of each of these various species often show the same relative differences in permeability constants for different substances tested on each of them. This is illustrated in a study on penetration of a number of substances into cells of sixteen species of plants[20] illustrated in Figure 12.14. This finding gives greater confidence that the rules of permeability, developed from experiments on the cells of a fair sample of organisms, are likely to apply to other cells in a qualitative way. No method yet exists for predicting permeability quantitatively.

GENERAL REFERENCES

Brooks, S. C., and Brooks, M. M., 1941: The Permeability of Living Cells. Protoplasma Monographie 19, Borntraeger, Berlin.

Collander, R., 1959: Cell Membranes: Their Resistance to Penetration and Their Capacity for Transport in Plant Physiology, a Treatise (Steward, C. F., ed. Academic Press, New York, 2:3–102.

Danielli, J. F., 1950: Cell Physiology and Pharmcology. Elsevier, Houston.

Davson, H., 1959: A Textbook of General Physiology, Little, Brown, Boston, Section 3. The transfer of water and solutes, pp. 198–352.

Davson, H., and Danielli, J. F., 1952: The Permeability of Natural Membranes. 2nd Ed. Macmillan, New York. Especially Chapters 16, 17.

Höber, R., 1945: Physical Chemistry of Cells and Tissues. Blakiston, New York, Chapter 23.

Miles, A. A., and Pirie, N. W., (ed.), 1950: The Nature of the Bacterial Surface. Thomas, Springfield, Ill.

Osterhout, W. J. V., 1922: Injury, Recovery and Death in Relation to Conductivity and Permeability. Lippincott, Philadelphia. Especially Chapter 4.

LITERATURE CITED

1. Brooks, S. C., and Brooks, M. M., 1941: The Permeability of Living Cells. Protoplasma Monographien 19, Borntraeger, Berlin, Ch. 12.
2. West, E. S., 1942: Physical Chemistry for Students of Biochemistry and Medicine. Macmillan, New York, Ch. 2.
3. Mazia, D., and Clark, J. M., 1936: Biol. Bull. 71:306.
4. Baptiste, E. C. J., 1935: Ann. Bot. 49:345.
5. Ponder, E., and Saslow, G., 1930: J. Physiol. 70:18, 169. 1931, 73:267.
6. Ponder, E., 1948: Hemolysis and Related Phenomena. Grune & Stratton, New York.
7. Collander, R., and Bärlund, H., 1933: Acta Bot. Fennica 11:1.
8. Brooks, S. C., 1938: J. Cell. Comp. Physiol. 11:247. 1951: 38:83.
9. Ussing, H. H., 1953: Ann. Rev. Physiol. 15:1, also 1952: Adv. Enzymol. 13:21.
10. Höber, R. (ed.), 1945: Physical Chemistry of Cell and Tissues. Blakiston, New York, p. 357.
11. Crescitelli, F., 1948: J. Cell. Comp. Physiol. 32:187.
12. Ruhland, W., and Hoffmann, C., 1925: Plant 1:1.

3. Coons, A. H., 1952: Symp. Soc. Exp. Biol. *6*:166.
4. Osterhout, W. J. V., and Dorcas, M. J., 1926: J. Gen. Physiol. *9*:255.
5. Höber, R., 1945: Physical Chemistry of Cells and Tissues, Blakiston, New York, Ch. 12.
6. Harvey, E. B., 1915: Papers of Marine Dept. Biol., Carnegie Inst. of Wash., Publ. 212, *8*:145.
7. Ussing, H. H., 1954: Symp. Soc. Exp. Biol. *8*:407.
8. Höber, R., 1936: Physiol. Rev., *16*:52.
9. Brooks, S. C., 1929: Protoplasma *8*:389.
10. Collander, R., 1937: Phys. Ökonom. Ges. Konigsberg *50*:53.
11. Davson, H., 1959: A Textbook of General Physiology. Little, Brown, Boston.
12. Davson, H., and Danielli, J. F., 1952: The Permeability of Natural Membranes. 2nd Ed. Macmillan, New York, Ch. 17.
13. Bělehrádek, J., 1935: Temperature and Living Matter. Protoplasma Monographien *8*, Borntraeger, Berlin, p. 31.
14. Osterhout, W. J. V., 1922: Injury, Recovery and Death in Relation to Conductivity and Permeability. Lippincott, Philadelphia, Ch. 4.
15. Ringer, S., 1880–86: J. Physiol. *3*:380; *4*:29; *7*:291.
16. Prosser, C. L., and Brown, F. A., Jr., 1961: Comparative Animal Physiology. 2nd Ed. Saunders, Philadelphia, Table 12, p. 75.
17. Feigen, G.: Personal Communication.
18. Krogh, A., 1939: Osmotic Regulation in Aquatic Animals. Cambridge Univ. Press, London, p. 130–153.

29. Jacobs, M. H., 1952: *in* Modern Trends in Physiology and Biochemistry (Barron, E. S. G., ed.). Academic Press, New York, p. 149.
30. Danielli, J. F., 1950: Cell Physiology and Pharmacology. Elsevier, Houston.
31. Steinbach, H. B., 1954: Symp. Soc. Exp. Biol. *8*:438.
32. Hodgkin, A. L., and Keynes, R. D., 1953: J. Physiol. *119*:513; *121*:403.
33. Heilbrunn, L. V., and Mazia, D., 1936: *in* Biological Effects of Radiations (Dugar, B. M., ed.). McGraw-Hill, New York, Ch. 18.
34. Green, J. W., 1954: Anat. Rec. *120*:707.
35. Reed, E. A., 1948: J. Cell. Comp. Physiol. *31*:261.
36. Shepard, C. W., and Stewart, M., 1952: J. Cell. Comp. Physiol. *39* (suppl. 2.) 189.
37. Ting, T. P., and Zirkle, R. E., 1940: J. Cell. Comp. Physiol. *16*:269.
38. Mullins, L. J., 1949: Exp. Cell. Res. suppl. *1*:328.
39. Donnan, F. G., 1911: Zeitschr. Elektrochem. *17*:572.
40. Heilbrunn, L. V., 1952: An Outline of General Physiology. 3rd Ed. Saunders, Philadelphia, Ch. 33.
41. Rogers, P., and McElroy, W. D., 1958: Arch. Biochem. Biophys. *75*:87, 106.
42. Solomon, A. K., Dec. 1960: Sci. Am. *203*:146.
43. Heilbrunn, L. V., June 1951: Sci. Am. *184*:60.
44. Davson, H., 1959: A Textbook of General Physiology. 2nd Ed. Little, Brown, Boston, Sect. 3: 198–352.

ACTIVE TRANSPORT THROUGH THE CELL MEMBRANE AND PINOCYTOSIS

Active Transport

When a substance moves through a cell membrane against a concentration gradient, either into or out of a cell, it is at once apparent that such movement could not be by a simple process of diffusion. To move the molecules of a substance against a concentration gradient and an electrochemical gradient requires a mechanism other than—or in addition to—diffusion, and a source of energy for such movement. The cell must do work in moving the substance through the cell membrane against a concentration gradient. Any movement of substances through the cell membrane which requires work on the part of the cell is called *active transport.**

The phenomenon of active transport is perhaps best illustrated by the activity of the cells of the kidney tubule. Pieces of kidney tubule, separated with a micromanipulator from a chick embryo, often round up into spheres one cell layer thick (see Fig. 13.1). When such spheres are immersed in dilute solutions of phenol red,

dissolved in embryonic tissue fluid, each sphere accumulates the dye in its internal cavity so that the cavity becomes deep pink in color. The dye may be seen passing through the cells of the tubule in which it lingers in transit and where it becomes orange in color,[1] a change to be expected of phenol red at the pH (about 6.7 to 6.8) inside the cells. If phenol red were diffusing through the cells in response to the difference between the concentrations of the dye in the bathing solution and in the vesicle, it would move inward until equilibrium was established. The appearance of the dye in much higher concentration inside the cavity of the vesicle than elsewhere means that the dye is passing through the cells and is being extruded or secreted into the cavity against a concentration gradient.

If the kidney cell preparation is placed on ice at the time phenol red is added, it

---

* The term active transport is used in different ways by various authors, no definition being at present satisfactory to everyone. For a discussion consult references 2 and 35.

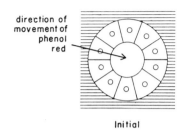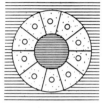

direction of
movement of
phenol
red

Initial   After lapse of time

Fig. 13.1. Accumulation of phenol red in sections of proximal kidney tubules of embryo chick (diagrammatic). Phenol red moves inward until it becomes more concentrated in the inside of the vesicle than on the outside.

fails to accumulate the dye. If it is placed on ice after accumulation of the dye inside the vesicle, the dye then diffuses out and distributes itself equally between the medium and the lumen of the vesicle. Warmed up to chick body temperature (39° C.), the vesicle again accumulates the dye. The experiment demonstrates that while the dye continues to diffuse through tubule cells even at low temperature, it is no longer accumulated, probably because some process essential to accumulation is inhibited. Measurements show that the respiration of the kidney tubule cells comes virtually to a halt when the tubule is placed on ice. Since respiration is the source of the energy by which cellular work is accomplished, the inference is drawn that the movement of the dye against a concentration gradient requires cellular work. This inference is corroborated by experiments, again using dyes, in which respiration of the kidney tubule cells, even though at 39° C., is inhibited by a metabolic poison. When respiration virtually ceases, dye is no longer accumulated. Diffusion, however, continues in response to the concentration gradient, and a preparation which is poisoned after it has already accumulated dye is still able to lose it to the medium.

These experiments demonstrate that kidney tubule cells can do work against a concentration gradient only if they are able to liberate energy. Energy, then, is needed to carry molecules of dye against a concentration gradient, just as energy is needed to climb a hill. The work which is done in transporting a dye against a concentration gradient can be calculated. It is proportional to a constant multiplied by the natural logarithm of the ratio of the concentration of the dye inside and outside the cell, the difference in concentration representing the height of the concentration "hill" (see Fig. 13.2). (When ions are being transported,[35] a term for the work done against the electrochemical gradient must be added to this.) From the respiratory rate of the kidney cells it is also possible to determine how much energy has been released by the cell during the time that a given amount of solute has been transported. The calculations show that the energy released in respiration is more than enough to do this work.

Since a cell of the kidney must do work in moving phenol red, and since the molecules are taken in as a result of activity on the part of the cell, rather than in response to a diffusion gradient, the movement of the dye is clearly an example of active transport.[2]

Two criteria have often been used to determine whether a substance moves across the cell membrane by active transport: first, whether it moves against a concentration gradient; second, whether it requires metabolic energy for the movement.

If a substance moves against a concentration gradient, transport is probably active, although not all active transport

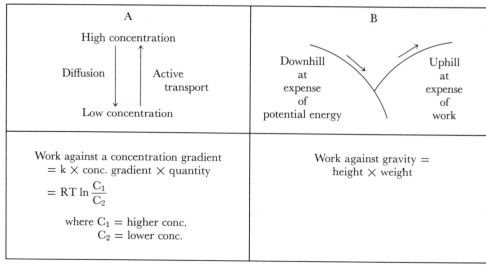

A	B
High concentration Diffusion Active transport Low concentration	Downhill at expense of potential energy Uphill at expense of work
Work against a concentration gradient $= k \times$ conc. gradient $\times$ quantity $= RT \ln \dfrac{C_1}{C_2}$ where $C_1 =$ higher conc. $C_2 =$ lower conc.	Work against gravity $=$ height $\times$ weight

Fig. 13.2. Analogy between concentration gradient (left half of A) and potential gradient (left half of B) and between movement against a concentration gradient (right half of A) and work done in moving uphill (right half of B). Equations for work against a concentration gradient (osmotic work) and for work in lifting a weight up a height are given at the bottom of the figure.

need be against a concentration gradient, as will be shown later. However, it is usually necessary to demonstrate that the substance in question is osmotically active inside the cell and that its movement really occurs against a concentration gradient. Because some substances are present inside cells in a concentration greater than outside (Fig. 3.1) does not necessarily imply that they enter the cell by an active process against a concentration gradient. For instance, a substance may be rendered osmotically inactive inside the cell in any of a number of ways. If ionic, it might unite with another ion to form an insoluble compound (e.g., calcium oxalate). Or it might possibly be dissolved in lipid and therefore be unavailable for action in the aqueous continuum of the cell. Organic substances like glucose may be polymerized to form insoluble glycogen or starch, and glucose molecules could thus be trapped, that is, taken out of solution, and a concentration gradient favorable for uptake might be maintained in spite of extensive entry.

Since active transport depends on release of energy from metabolic reactions, the effect of respiratory activity on uptake of the materials by a cell should be tested. If the accumulation of a substance ceases after respiration is stopped by respiratory inhibitor (e.g., cyanide), active transport is highly probable. If accumulation is slowed by a lowering of the temperature (which decreases the rate of respiration), active transport is probable. Likewise, greatly reducing the oxygen tension decreases the aerobic respiration of the cell and usually decreases active transport. In cases where blocking aerobic respiration does not inhibit active transport, the energy for the process perhaps is supplied by anaerobic metabolism.[3] If this is so, blocking the remaining anaerobic metabolism, for example with iodoacetic acid, will stop the active transport. It is likely that active transport always occurs at the expense of either aerobic or anaerobic metabolism, but ceases when both are stopped.[3]

As much as 30 per cent of the metab-

EXCHANGE OF MATERIALS ACROSS THE CELL MEMBRANE

olism of a mammalian red blood cell and 15 per cent of the metabolism of an ascites (tumor) cell is thought to be expended in active transport processes.[41]

Examples of Active Transport

Not much is known of the mechanism of active transport, but many examples have been described and the process seems to be quite general in plant cells, animal cells, and microorganisms. It is thought that probably more solutes enter cells actively than passively.[38] A number of interesting cases are cited here.

Accumulation of Potassium in Cells. The great accumulation of potassium in many plant and animal cells and in microorganisms is difficult to explain except as a result of some form of active transport. For example, *Nitella*, a fresh water plant with large cells, has 1065 times as much potassium as the water in which it grows; *Valonia*, another large plant cell has 41.6 times as much; and *Chara* has 63 times as much.[4] While the concentration of potassium is not always this much greater inside than outside the cell, such concentrations are characteristic of plant cells generally. A somewhat similar difference in concentration of potassium between the inside of the cell and the bathing medium is found in the muscle and the nerve cells (Fig. 3.1) and in microorganisms such as yeast. In most cells, then, potassium is the dominant monovalent cation, although the erythrocytes of a few species of mammals (e.g., dog and cat) present an exception, accumulating sodium instead of potassium.[5]

That potassium is present in cells as an ion and is osmotically active is demonstrated by electrical measurements. The conductivity of large single cells or of suspensions of small cells is of such a magnitude as to indicate that potassium exists in the cells in dissolved, ionic form; otherwise, the conductivity would be much lower since potassium is the main cation of the cell. The potassium gradient between the inside of the cells and the medium is therefore the converse of that required for passive uptake, and it could be maintained only by active transport. If this is the case, potassium should leak out of the cells, in response to the concentration gradient, if metabolism is inhibited. This, in fact, is observed in many cases. For example, if either a squid giant axon or a *Halicystis* cell is placed under anaerobic conditions, potassium leaks out because the energy liberated by aerobic metabolism is no longer available to keep it inside.[6] If oxygen is bubbled through the water, it enables the cells to take up potassium again. In these cells anaerobic metabolism apparently does not provide the energy required for active uptake of potassium.

Lowering the temperature to near the freezing point causes potassium to leak out of human erythrocytes, presumably because the metabolic reactions required for potassium uptake are suspended. When the temperature is raised, potassium is again taken up.[7] On the other hand, the human erythrocyte continues to hold its potassium even when the oxygen tension is greatly decreased at room or body temperature. This implies that in this case anaerobic processes (called glycolysis in animal cells) liberate the energy for active transport of potassium. Such a postulate is corroborated by the finding that poisoning the anaerobic glycolysis with fluoride causes potassium to leak out of the cells, even at room or body temperature.

Yeast holds its potassium under anaerobic conditions, provided glucose is present. It is unable to liberate energy anaerobically (by fermentation) unless nutrient is present in the bathing medium; i.e., it does not use its stored food for this purpose. Therefore, when yeast is washed free of glucose, and kept in the absence of oxygen, it loses its potassium. When glucose is restored, potassium also is recovered. A similar phenomenon is observed for the bacterium *Escherichia coli*.[4]

A normal, healthy cell membrane is necessary for maintenance of the difference in concentrations of potassium between the inside and the outside of the cell. Alteration of the membrane or of the cell leads to potassium leakage. For example, when the giant axon of the squid is stimulated, potassium leaks out.[9] The same is true of *Nitella*. In other words, when the membrane is temporarily altered, ions can get through. On recovery, however, potassium is reabsorbed. Potassium leakage following stimulation of cells has been the subject of a number of studies.

It has been found that potassium is not the only ion which moves through the membrane of a stimulated cell. By carefully timing the movements of radioactive sodium and potassium in separate experiments one can observe that in a stimulated cell sodium moves in, then potassium leaks out. The sodium subsequently leaves and the potassium once again enters. Analysis of this occurrence suggested, as a possible explanation, that potassium is not accumulated by active transport, but rather that sodium is extruded by active transport, this process being referred to as the *sodium pump*. Elimination of sodium in this manner presumably goes on in all cells which accumulate potassium, and supposedly the elimination of the sodium creates a cation gradient favorable for the passive uptake of potassium, because sodium is the only other readily diffusible cation present in the environmental waters. In such a case, when potassium leaks out of cells which have been inhibited by metabolic poisons, cold, or anaerobiosis, it could be considered that the sodium pump is temporarily out of action and sodium enters the cells by diffusion. Sodium can be extruded only when metabolic energy for this purpose is liberated by the cell (in the absence of poisons and at appropriate temperatures).[10]

However, newer evidence indicates that the sodium pump explanation alone is not in keeping with the facts.[10, 33-37] Not only is sodium actively extruded in many cases, but potassium is actively transported into the cell as well. For example, in the red blood cell the electrochemical gradient is inadequate to bring in the potassium, and active transport is physically necessary.[37] It would also appear likely, in some cases, that one mechanism handles both sodium and potassium because changing the concentration of one of the ions outside the cell also affects the transport of the other ion.[41] Evidence from use of tracers is accumulating that potassium is actively transported in muscle and nerve cells as well, even though the electrochemical gradient is favorable for passive entry. Somewhat similar data are found for the cells of the red alga, *Porphyra perforata*.[47] In yeast, potassium is taken up by active transport in exchange for hydrogen ions.[35]

It is probable that the ion transport is not the same in cells of different species or even in cells of different tissues in the same species. For example, the epithelial cells of the small intestines transport actively both sodium and chloride ions while cells of the kidney tubules transport sodium actively and chloride moves passively in response to concentration gradients.[35]

Root Pressure and Guttation. Considerable information has accumulated on the development of root pressure in plants. Experimental analyses of the sap indicate that the root hair cells are capable of taking up, against a concentration gradient, the various necessary salt ions such as potassium, magnesium, calcium and nitrate.[11, 13] From the root hair cells the salts are transferred to the cortical cells and from the cortical cells they are actively secreted against a concentration gradient into the xylem ducts. From there

EXCHANGE OF MATERIALS ACROSS THE CELL MEMBRANE

he salts may readily be distributed by diffusion to any cells where they are required in the plant. Accumulation of salts in the root cells, thus leading to a high osmotic pressure, accounts for bleeding of a cut stem and for guttation, the phenomenon in which, under humid conditions, droplets of water appear from water-secreting glands along the edge of a leaf. Although a detailed discussion of bleeding and guttation is out of place here, such phenomena indicate that the plant cells actively transport some materials against concentration gradients.[12] The role these processes play in the plant economy is discussed in textbooks of plant physiology.[8]

Vacuolar Function. It is thought that fresh water protozoans make use of active transport in voiding water.[14] The water surrounding them contains less salt than the protozoan protoplasm does; therefore, water enters in response to the concentration gradient but must leave the protozoans against the concentration gradient. The magnitude of the elimination of water becomes evident when it is realized that every 15 or 20 minutes a *Paramecium* empties through its contractile vacuole a quantity of water equal to its entire volume.

On the other hand, a brackish water protozoan in slightly diluted sea water may take in little water, in which case the activity of its contractile vacuole may be very low. However, if the medium is greatly diluted, as after a heavy rain, the rate of vacuolar contraction may be greatly increased. The contractile vacuole appears to beat faster with greater dilution of the medium.

When a fresh water protozoan is poisoned with cyanide, and its respiration thus suspended, the contractile vacuoles fail to function and the cell swells (Fig. 13.3). If it is not washed free of cyanide, it bursts.

Active transport is likely in these examples, but the mechanism has not been investigated adequately to state whether, in the formation of the vacuole, salts are first secreted against a concentration

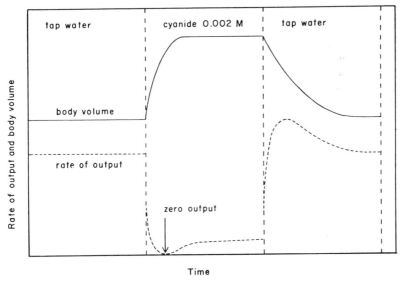

Fig. 13.3. The effects of cyanide on the swelling and vacuolar output of the fresh water protozoan *Zoothamnion*. The time of a complete experiment is about two hours. (After Kitching, 1938: Biol. Rev., *13*:423.)

gradient so that then water enters passively into the vacuole, or whether water is actively passed into the vacuole directly against a concentration gradient.[36]

Active Transport in Cells of the Gut. When there is a high concentration of sugars in the gut of a dog, a concentration gradient exists from the cells of the lumen of the gut to the blood stream favorable to transport of sugar by simple diffusion through the cell membranes. To test whether such movement does occur, the metabolism of the gut cells must be inhibited by appropriate metabolic poisons, so that the source of energy necessary for active transport can be stopped. When this is done in isolated loops of the intestine, pentoses move as freely as they did before, but though some glucose and galactose still move into the blood stream, they do so at a much lower rate than in the absence of poison. This experiment suggests that the movement of glucose and of galactose depends upon active transport. To test this hypothesis, the blood stream is loaded with glucose (or galactose) so that any movement of glucose from the unpoisoned gut cells to the blood must then occur against a concentration gradient. The fact that it continues at a relatively rapid rate indicates that active transport is involved. A similar experiment is one in which a concentration of glucose (or galactose) less than that in the blood is placed in the gut so that any movement from gut to blood must occur against a concentration gradient. It still does, further supporting the hypothesis. Whatever the transporting mechanism is, however, it has a limited capacity. For example, if the glucose concentration in the gut is increased, the rate of its transport into the blood rises until a definite concentration limit is reached, beyond which further increase in its concentration has no effect on the rate of its transport. The rate of transport is therefore seemingly limited by that amount which some mechanism can carry per unit of time.

The conclusion from all of these experiments is that some sugars, like some pentoses, probably move from gut to blood by simple diffusion and therefore only when the concentration gradient in that direction is favorable. So also do glucose and galactose to a small extent but in addition, they are actively transported even against a concentration gradient, much of the transport of glucose occurring apparently in this manner.[15]

Active Transport in the Cells of the Nephric Organs. Active transport against a concentration gradient is most readily demonstrable in the tubules (nephrons) of the aglomerular kidney found in only a few marine fishes (such as the pipefish and the goosefish), because fluid can enter such a tubule only through the membranes of the cells. The only way in which the tubule of a nephron can form urine in this case is by transport of materials, across the cells of the tubule, from the blood into the lumen[16] (see Fig. 13.4). If the concentration of a given compound in the tubule is less than that in the blood, entry of that compound into the tubule can occur by simple diffusion through the cell. On the other hand, the urine of aglomerular fishes is found to contain creatine, creatinine, uric acid, magnesium, potassium, chloride and sulfate, each of them often in a concentration considerably greater than in the blood. The aglomerular kidney also concentrates in the urine a variety of foreign materials, such as nitrate, thiosulfate, sulfocyanides, indigo carmine, neutral red and phenol red, that have been experimentally injected into the blood. Moreover, this activity ceases when oxygen is withheld or when the metabolism of the kidney cells is inhibited by appropriate poisons. All evidence, therefore, indicates active transport against a concentration gradient, requiring metabolic energy.

The glomerular kidney, which is characteristic of all vertebrates except the fishes cited above, contains a glomerulus or tuft of blood capillaries in an epithelial up for filtration of water and of dissolved constituents of the blood other than the proteins (see Fig. 13.4). While the fluid passes along the length of the tubule, part of the water and some of the other filtered constituents are reabsorbed.[17, 18] Although active transport is more difficult to demonstrate in the tubules of glomerular kidneys, it occurs in the reabsorption process (which often takes place against a concentration gradient) as well as in the secretion of certain wastes into the tubules. Inhibition of the metabolic processes in the cells of the kidney inhibits both of these reactions. Also some wastes are found concentrated in the urine to a greater extent than would have been possible only by reabsorption of water from the filtrate. These must have been voided into the urine by active transport against the concentration gradient. Decisive and direct proof of such secretion against a gradient has already been shown in sections of the kidney tubules of a chick embryo. Proof of the active transport in glomerular kidney cells is more involved and the interested student is referred to textbooks of animal physiology for a discussion of the functioning of the kidney.[16]

Accumulating evidence indicates that active transport occurs also in the cells of tear glands of marine birds,[49] and in cells of the nephric organs of some invertebrates.[19-22] For example, in some fresh water invertebrates the urine is found to be hypotonic to the blood. This indicates either the elimination of water against a concentration gradient or the selective uptake of salts against a concentration gradient. When certain species of crabs (or other invertebrates), capable of tolerating brackish water, are transferred from sea water to diluted sea water, they void more urine, and their respiration increases correspondingly. The increase in each case is larger if the dilution is greater. The increased respiration has been interpreted as a result of the increased amount of energy required for

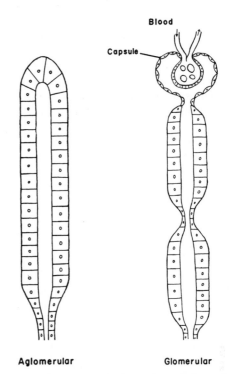

Fig. 13.4. Diagram of aglomerular and glomerular kidney tubules (nephrons). Both are copiously supplied with blood capillaries along the outside. Only the glomerular tubule has a capillary tuft in a capsule.

eliminating the excess water taken up osmotically by the gills.

In general, studies on the movement of various materials against concentration gradients in the kidney cells indicate that the materials move at different rates. The rules governing such movements resemble the rules of permeability previously discussed. Thus, very large molecules are not eliminated (e.g., an aglomerular kidney never passes sucrose, inulin or albumin); movement is related to lipoid solubility, size playing a lesser role; and so on.

Active Transport of Organic Nutrients into Cells

Glucose appears to enter yeast and erythrocytes only when energy is expended, even in the presence of a favorable concentration gradient. However, the evidence for this consists mainly of the finding that heavy metals, such as copper and uranium, inhibit glucose uptake in these cells. It is postulated that enzymes at the cell surface are necessary for uptake of glucose, and that these enzymes are selectively poisoned by copper, uranium and other heavy metals.[23, 24]

Evidence of a chemically and metabolically coupled transport system (in these respects different from the permease system described below) for uptake of some substances, such as amino acids, into bacteria has also been presented.[40] The entry of these substances shows pH dependency and it is poisoned by typical metabolic poisons (see Chapter 17), and the transport is competitive with analogues. Furthermore, the transport system can be saturated; that is, an increase beyond a critical level in concentration of the material whose entry is being studied, e.g., amino acids, does not affect the rate of entry of the material into the bacteria. Presumably the enzymes are already carrying all the molecules they can. Such a system is feasible for bacteria where all the enzymes required for aerobic metabolism are located in the surface of the protoplast (see Chapters 2 and 5). In such cases an enzyme would probably bring in a molecule by coupling with it at the surface and handing it on to another enzyme in the metabolic main line[25, 40] (see Chapter 17).

The Permease System

In some bacteria, e.g., the colon bacillus, *Escherichia coli*, sugar transport occurs through a special transport system known as the permease system.[46] Such a system can be demonstrated most readily in cases where it must be induced—that is, where it is not a *constitutive* enzyme system (one always present and demonstrable) but rather develops or is *induced*

after the addition of a substrate. The following examples serve to illustrate the phenomenon. The wild-type strain of *E. coli*, placed in a solution of lactose, a disaccharide, does not use this sugar at once but only after a lapse of time. This delay in utilization could be interpreted as the time required either for the entry of the sugar into the cell or for the induction of the enzyme (β-galactosidase) necessary to digest the disaccharide into monosaccharides before its use in metabolism. It can readily be demonstrated that in wild-type *E. coli* the digestive enzyme is always present in the cell. The cells need only be lysed and the digestive enzyme can be isolated. The time lapse noted above, in utilization of lactose, must be due to failure of the lactose to enter the cell until some change occurs. The nature of this change has been analyzed by the use of a number of mutant strains.

A mutant of *E. coli* was isolated which lacks the constitutive digestive enzyme since the enzyme could not be detected in extracts of the bacteria. As a consequence, the mutant presumably cannot use lactose in its metabolism. Yet after an induction period it is able to remove lactose from the medium, as shown by quantitative determinations before and after the induction period. Mutant cells from which the cell walls are removed accumulate lactose to the point that the protoplasts swell extensively and even burst, taking up water in response to the increased osmotic pressure. As much as 22 per cent of the dry weight of the bacteria consists of lactose at this time. Entry of lactose in this case in not passive but enzyme controlled.

Still another mutant of *E. coli* has been found which possesses the digestive enzyme (as demonstrated in extracts of the bacteria) but is unable to use the lactose because, even after an inductive period, it is unable to develop the permease system. There is thus no doubt

252

that separate systems are involved in uptake and in digestion of lactose.

The separateness of uptake-mechanism and utilization can be shown in yet another way, i.e., by the use of a metabolically inactive analogue which is structurally similar to lactose, such as thiomethyl-D-β-galactoside. This lactose analogue is not normally used by wild-type E. coli, but when supplied to the wild-type divested of cell walls, the protoplasts take up the analogue to the point of swelling and even bursting. Thus they can neither digest nor utilize the lactose analogue, but they can accumulate it—the permease system fails to distinguish between it and lactose.

Even more convincing are experiments demonstrating that induction of the permease system, as that of any other induced system, is poisoned by protein-synthesis inhibitors such as chloramphenicol. Ultraviolet radiation, which inhibits various cell syntheses (see Chapter 9), also inhibits its development, as it does other enzyme inductions.

It is apparent in the above example that uptake of lactose occurs against a concentration gradient and must require work.[46] One might therefore expect it to be blocked by metabolic poisons which generally block active transport. Azide and dinitrophenol are indeed found to stop accumulation of nutrients in permease systems. Since these poisons prevent the formation of high-energy phosphate bonds during respiration, it is possible that such bonds are involved in uptake of materials by permease systems.

Monod has concluded that the permease system is a specialized enzyme transport system which, once formed, is independent of and does not participate in metabolism—it only brings the sugar (or other nutrient) through the cell membrane. Any coupling with metabolism is, therefore, physical, not chemical. Permeases have been postulated for a variety of substrates, each one specific to a sub-

strate. E. coli is thought to have 30 to 60 such systems. It is conceivable that some, if not all, are coupled to energy donors. The permease presumably combines with the substrate molecule, aiding it through the osmotic barrier.

Permeases have been described for a number of species of bacteria and for yeast. They may occur in plant and animal cells but are much more difficult to demonstrate in such materials.[46]

Conclusion

While active transport of water has been considered a possibility by some workers,[36, 39] others are unwilling to accept the evidence presented.[35] True, water is voided in hypotonic urine, but filtration of the blood and active reabsorption of the solutes in the filtrate during the countercurrent flow between uriniferous tubules and the parallel small blood vessels, into which the solutes are absorbed, would account for this satisfactorily.[35] The metabolic cost to the cell of active extrusion of the quantity of water involved alone is considered prohibitive, making a search for alternative mechanisms desirable in other cases as well.

The various examples cited give some idea of the great variety of biological processes which are dependent upon active uptake of compounds or ions against concentration gradients. Such active uptake occurs in plant cells, animal cells and microorganisms. It may appear surprising that cells bring in many substances by active transport when some of them might enter on the basis of their own kinetic energy, i.e., when present outside the cell in higher concentration than inside. However, active transport makes it possible for the cell to take in these substances at a rate determined solely by the needs of the cell at any time, regardless of how favorable or unfavorable the concentration gradient may be for uptake at that time. And even when the concentration gradient is unfavorable for entry, that is, the substance is present outside the cell in a concentration lower than inside, active transport enables the cell to accumulate the substance. Thus, to a cell, active transport of a substance has considerable advantage over its diffusion through the cell membrane in answer to a concentration gradient. This fact probably accounts for the widespread occurrence of active transport in spite of its cost in metabolic energy to the cell.

The Effect of Environment upon Active Transport

Because temperature affects metabolic processes it is expected to influence the rate of active transport. If a substance is carried through a cell membrane by active transport, the rate of liberation of energy by respiration is likely to be the limiting factor. Therefore, a temperature coefficient characteristic of thermochemical reactions is to be expected for active transport; that is, the rate of entry of such a compound should be doubled or tripled by a rise of ten degrees centigrade. However, a high temperature coefficient obtained for uptake of any substance would not by itself prove that the substance is taken in by an active process. It must be corroborated by other means as well (see Chapter 14).

Other environmental factors which affect the metabolic system are likely to affect active transport: for example, narcotics and anesthetics, heavy metals, radiations, salts and pH. Analysis of the effects of the environment on active transport, although necessary, has not yet been extensive enough for a fruitful discussion.

Possible Mechanism of Active Transport

Many suggestions for the actual mechanisms of active transport, including an effective working model for ion transport,[32] have appeared in the literature during recent years, but without general agreement. Among these are suggested the following:

1. The folding of protein molecules that have picked up the material at the cell surface.[26] A contractile protein molecule is conceived to attach to the membrane, extending and contracting (coiling). Uncoiling involves the breaking of intramolecular bonds, thus forming affinities which can be satisfied only by adsorption of foreign molecules or ions. When the protein is recoiled the original bonds are re-formed and the foreign matter desorbed inside the cell. The protein molecules may also act as enzymes capable of liberating energy from high-energy phosphate compounds by which the work necessary for active transport is accomplished.

2. Nucleic acid molecules attaching themselves to incoming molecules or ions.[27]

3. Electroendosmosis or mass movement of fluid (fluid circuit) through a fixed membrane as a result of a difference in potential on both sides of it. It is difficult to see how such movement could be selective; this hypothesis is mentioned only for the sake of completeness.[43]

4. Enzyme carriers which in the reduced state act as carriers and release the ions when oxidized.[28, 35, 41] This has also been called electron-linked transport and the prototype is Lundegard's theory.[42] Electrons are transferred along a chain of enzymes in the main line of oxidations (see Chapter 17) as the iron in the cytochromes and cytochrome oxidase changes in valency from two to three. Cation transport is supposed to be accomplished by the exchange of hydrogen ions for the cations in question. The source of energy is the drop in potential of the electrons. While appealing, the theory is not in quantitative agreement with the other findings.

5. Carriers other than respiratory enzymes. Only this theory is considered in detail below.

Consider Figure 13.5. A cell of a nephric tubule is bathed with a solution in which a certain compound (A) is present in lesser concentration on the outside than in the lumen of the tubule. The problem is to get A through the cell and into the lumen of the tubule against the concentration gradient. Suppose that in the outer surface of the cell (O) there is present a compound with a high energy bond ($\sim$B), continuously produced by metabolic reactions. When the compounds A and $\sim$B meet in the presence of a certain enzyme (E_1), they form a complex (AB). As the complex forms at the outer surface of the cell it diffuses through the cell down a concentration gradient. When AB reaches the inner surface (i) of the cell, bordering the lumen, it meets another enzyme (E_2) which decomposes it into A and B. Compound A, present in high concentration locally at the surface of the cell along the lumen of the tubule, diffuses into the lumen of the tubule. The complex AB is thus continually produced at O and decomposed at i by enzymatic reactions. Compound B, the molecular carrier, is conceived of as a large molecule which cannot readily pass through the cell membrane; consequently it and its complex with A remain inside the cell. This formulation has the appeal of simplicity since the complex formed at the cellular surface farthest from the lumen diffuses through the cell in a concentration gradient, and A diffuses from the cell in a concentration gradient when it is liberated from the complex at the inner surface of the cell where it is locally present in high concentration. This scheme requires polar localization of enzymes, such as E_1 and E_2, for which some evidence has been presented in both kidney tissues and gut. Formation of some substances like $\sim$B is well known in the metabolic

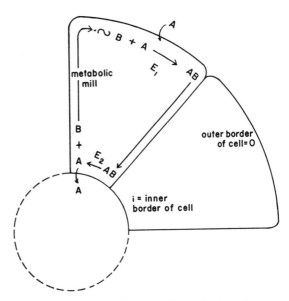

Fig. 13.5. Diagram of a possible mechanism of active transport. See text for explanation.

cycles of cells. However, identification of enzymes or compounds involved in active transport has so far not met with success.[30, 31]

The same hypothesis might explain unidirectional active transport through the cell membrane against a concentration gradient, as in the accumulation of ions in cells. In that case "O" (see Fig. 13.5) will be thought of as the outside surface of the cell membrane and "i" as the inner one, bordering on the cytoplasm.

Some attempts have been made to determine the identity of the carrier molecule (or molecules) in active transport of this type. From studies on the salt-secreting cells of glands in the eyes of marine birds (e.g., the albatross) good evidence has accumulated that phosphatidic acid (glycerol esterfied with two molecules of fatty acid and one molecule of phosphoric acid) might be the carrier of sodium and possibly of hydrophilic molecules and ions generally. Phosphatidic acid has the property of ready solubility in the lipid phase, while at the same time it has a minus charge which can bind the sodium. It does not leave the lipid phase but makes contact with the aqueous phase, there releasing the aqueous soluble material. The energy required for the movement is believed to be supplied by the high energy phosphate bond. Additional data are required to test this, and other interesting suggestions, more exhaustively.[44, 45, 48] From studies with the slime mold *Physarum* a carrier of a different chemical nature has been proposed.[74] It is possible that a variety of carriers occurs in different types of cells.

Pinocytosis

Edwards,[51] in 1925, working with *Amoeba*, noticed the formation of small channels in the cell membrane followed by the separation of small vacuoles, or *pinosomes*, in the cytoplasm (see Fig. 13.6). Lewis[52] in 1931 described the same phenomenon which he saw in tissue culture and gave it the name *pinocytosis*. Little work then appeared upon the topic[53] until recently when workers in a number of laboratories developed an intense interest in the process. There are comprehensive reviews of the growing literature[54, 72] on pinocytosis in a variety of cells.

Occurrence. The study of pinocytosis has been much facilitated by modern technological methods. For example, the development of the electron microscope has made possible resolution of much smaller channels and pinosomes. Also they can be seen by the use of labeled molecules, such as proteins marked with dyes which fluoresce in the ultraviolet. Such proteins, when used to induce pinocytosis experimentally, can be identified readily inside the cell by fluorescence microscopy.[57] They can be traced, following pinocytosis, in the large number of minute vacuoles scattered in the cytoplasm. Organic molecules marked with radioactive tracers such as C^{14} may also be employed. In this case, radioautographs are made of the cells and if pinocytosis has occurred, small vacuoles containing radioactive material are evident. Ferritin, a protein containing much iron, has also been used. The iron, having a high density, is opaque to electrons and following pinocytosis, electron micrographs reveal it in small vacuoles in the cytoplasm.

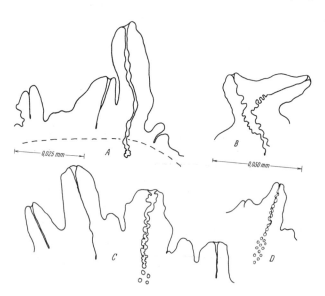

Fig. 13.6. Pinocytosis channels in *Amoeba proteus*: *A*, channels in small pseudopods in various stages of formation. *B*, convoluted channels. *C*, channels beginning to disintegrate at the inner end. *D*, further disintegration showing that many drops of fluid are ingested in the formation of each channel. (After Mast, S. O., and Doyle, W. L., 1934, Protoplasma, *20*:555.)

EXCHANGE OF MATERIALS ACROSS THE CELL MEMBRANE

It has been shown that pinocytosis occurs in ameba and ameboid cells, such as leucocytes (white blood cells), brush border cells of the kidney (active in fluid exchanges), epithelial cells of the intestine, reticuloendothelial cells, Kupfer (phagocytic) cells of the liver, cells lining the walls of the capillaries, some malignant cells in tissue culture and in some other cells in tissue culture. Pinocytosis was not observed (using labeled protein) in cardiac, smooth or skeletal muscle cells or in cells of a number of other tissues, or in some tissue culture cells, including fibroblasts and human amnion cells.[57, 58]

In cells of plant roots, evidence has been found for pinocytosis,[59, 60] although the formation of pinosomes has not been seen. Marked proteins and enzymes were found to penetrate into these cells from the outside and to appear in the cytoplasm around the nucleus. Electron micrographs of plant cells in some instances indicate canals leading from the surface into the cytoplasm which might be interpreted as pinocytosis channels.

Indirect evidence also indicates that pinocytosis probably occurs on a wide scale in cells of embryos, since many proteins are known to pass through the placenta and immunologically specific proteins have been found to enter a wide variety of tissue cells, even into the cell nuclei.[61] The entry into many types of cells of the enzyme ribonuclease has also been demonstrated indirectly by its hydrolysis of the cellular RNA, as revealed by the subsequent decreased staining by basic dyes and the decreased absorption of ultraviolet radiation by the cells.[62] Pinocytosis has also been observed in the developing eggs of *Lymnaea stagnalis*.[62]

Some workers are of the opinion that pinocytosis is perhaps a general phenomenon and the negative evidence is discounted on the basis that the appropriate conditions may not have been supplied to the cells. Others believe that the phenomenon is limited to cells capable of forming pseudopodia or at least having highly mobile membranes.

Induction of Pinocytosis. Mast and Doyle[53] showed that in *Amoeba proteus* pinocytosis is induced by salts and proteins. It is now known that amino acids and viruses are also effective, but that neither carbohydrates nor nucleic acids can induce pinocytosis. In some instances dyes have also induced pinocytosis.[68]

The proteins found most effective for induction of pinocytosis in *Amoeba* are gamma globulin and gelatin. The enzyme lysozyme (a protein) is also an effective inducer.[70] For leucocytes, solutions of 1 to 4 per cent albumin and globulin were effective, although even less than 1 per cent would suffice.[63, 70]

Salts induce pinocytosis also, cations being more effective than anions, as shown in Figure 13.7. Potassium, sodium and magnesium salts cause induction more readily than calcium. Sodium and magnesium induce narrower channels than potassium. A pH of 6.5 to 8.0 and a temperature between 12 and 22° C. are most favorable.[64] The optimal concentration is different for each salt, although 0.1 M solutions are adequate in most cases. The upper limit of concentration, however, is set by the toxic action of the salt upon the cytoplasm and lies between 0.25 and 1.0 M. Since pinocytosis has been seen in the eleocytes of the sea urchin,[54] it would be interesting if the salt relations in such a form were to be tested since the cells are already accommodated to a concentration of about 0.5 M.

Once pinocytosis has been induced, in amebas, it goes on actively for 15 to 45 minutes, then decreases.[54] It was found necessary to wash the amebas free of ionic medium and then to reimmerse them in the salt or protein solutions in order to induce another period of activity.

It is interesting to note that, even in the absence of excess salts or proteins, ultraviolet radiations induce pinocytosis

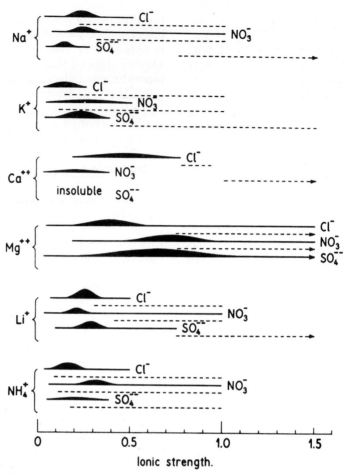

Fig. 13.7. Pinocytosis and toxicity in relation to concentrations of salts expressed in terms of ionic strength (the ionic strength is half of the sum of the terms obtained by multiplying the molality of each ion in the solution by the square of its valence). Dotted line indicates toxicity, solid line indicates pinocytosis, the width of the lines giving an indication of the intensity of the reaction. (From Chapman-Andresen, 1958: Comp. Rend. Lab. Carlsberg, *31*:77.)

in amebas. However, the number of channels is small and they appear about 1 hour after strong irradiation.[65] At this time, extrusion of water from the ameba has been increased. No difference in induction was shown in nucleate and enucleate halves of an ameba.

The Pinosomes

When an ameba is placed into a solution favorable for induction of pinocytosis it forms a rosette, most of its surface being covered by small active pseudopodia, each made up almost entirely of clear ectoplasm (Fig. 13.8). In the pseudopodia (Fig. 13.9) may be seen the clear channels which are the forerunners of the pinosomes. By the use of proteins marked with fluorescent dyes, the pinosomes, formed by the pinching off of the vacuoles, may be readily seen inside the ameba.

The vacuoles which form as a result of

EXCHANGE OF MATERIALS ACROSS THE CELL MEMBRANE

inocytosis contain within them the same solutes as the external medium. Holter[54] has shown that the vacuoles in an ameba do not centrifuge down soon after engulfment but rather stay at the centripetal end with the lighter materials of the cell. If the ameba is centrifuged after a lapse of time, the vacuoles are carried down to the centrifugal end with the heavier materials in the cell. Presumably in the meantime the material in the vacuoles has been concentrated by the withdrawal of water. This can be shown by the use of fluorescent proteins which gradually become concentrated into a brilliant densely fluorescent globule. Finally, only a fluorescent granule remains when most of the water is withdrawn.

It is of interest to know whether the membrane of the vacuole is like the cell membrane, and whether other materials besides water can also enter the cytoplasm from the vacuole. As a test case, glucose marked with C^{14} was included in the inducing solution containing protein. Radioautographs, following pinocytosis, indicated that the glucose had entered into the vacuoles and later radioautographs showed that the glucose became dispersed in the cell. Ultimately, about 15 per cent of the radioactive carbon became incorporated into the cytoskeleton of the cell and about 75 per cent of the radioactive carbon was given off by the ameba as carbon dioxide. Similar experiments carried out with methionine marked with S^{35} showed it to enter into the cytoplasm also.

Less has been learned about the fate of proteins taken into the cell, primarily because marking methods have not been adequate. That water is withdrawn from the vacuole and the protein is concentrated into a granule has been mentioned above. The fluorescein labeling on the protein is removed from the cell much more rapidly than the C^{14} label on glucose, but whether the protein is digested

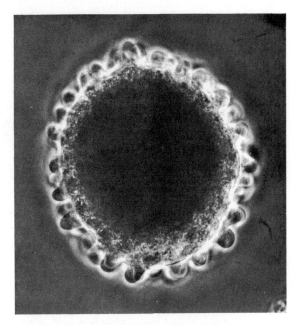

Fig. 13.8. Induction of many round pseudopods in *Amoeba* placed in strong protein solution. (From Rustad, April 1961: Sci. Am. *204*:121.)

or the labeling material is just voided is not known.[54]

Pinocytotic vacuoles have been seen to shrink, coalesce and even divide, but never to disappear. Whether the membrane of a vacuole is digested is not known. Some workers have even inferred that pinocytosis might be a way of building the laminated structures in the cytoplasm.[54]

Mechanism of Pinocytosis

Pinocytosis in the ameba, *Chaos chaos*, has been described as a result of movement of the cell membrane, which is considered to be an elastic structure fitting closely to the underlying cytoplasm. The cell membrane wrinkles, not being freed completely from the gel below it as a new flow of a pseudopod begins. This leads to invagination of parts of the cell membrane which are consequently separated from the larger advancing portion

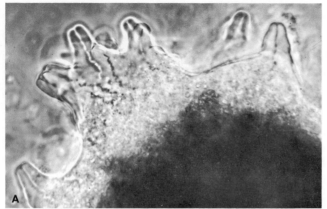

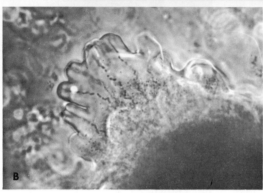

Fig. 13.9. A, pinocytosis in Amoeba proteus as seen under phase contrast microscopy. The Amoeba was starved for 24 hours then immersed into 1 per cent egg albumin in balanced salt solution. The pinocytotic channels are clearly visible in the pseudopodia. In some of the channels deep inside the cell small pinosomes may be seen forming from the engulfed fluid. B taken 35 seconds later during which time the ameba has moved; therefore, the pseudopodia do not match. The most prominent channels in A have become the most prominent chains of vacuoles (pinosomes) in B. (From Holter, 1960, Intern. Rev. Cytol. 8:484–485. Photographs courtesy of Dr. David Prescott, Oak Ridge National Laboratory.)

of the membrane. It is thought that the charged solute particles, used to induce pinocytosis, may weaken the structural rigidity of the membrane, allowing parts of it during movement to be drawn into the cytoplasm by its remaining attachments to the gel sheet. These vacuoles or channels are then separated from the membrane and released into the interior of the cell as pinosomes.[66]

Bennett,[67] on the other hand, postulated that pinocytosis does not involve just the engulfment of fluid but that there is need for attachment of materials on the surface of the cell before the vacuole can form, as shown in Figure 13.10. Decisive evidence for this mechanism has been obtained, using protein as the inducer of pinocytosis. The amebas were immersed in an antigen protein for varying periods. They were then freeze-dried and sectioned. The sections were exposed to an antibody protein labeled with fluorescein. The sections so treated showed a brilliant fluorescence under ultraviolet radiation, indicating that the surface of the ameba was heavily coated with the antigen to which the antibody containing fluorescein had become attached.[66, 68, 73] Further proof of attachment of protein came from studies using protein labeled with radioactive material.[68] In 5 minutes an ameba binds 50 times the amount of protein contained in its own volume (of solution). It would therefore appear that such binding may play an important role in pinocytosis and may be a necessary first step, so that pinocytosis is not just "cell drinking" but a process consisting of several steps.

EXCHANGE OF MATERIALS ACROSS THE CELL MEMBRANE

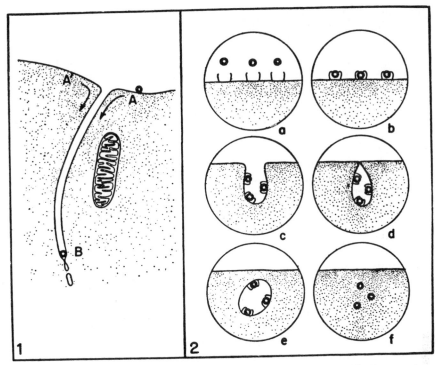

Fig. 13.10. Induction of pinocytosis by attachment of particles as envisaged by Bennett. A particle (1A) induces membrane flow, forming a channel containing the particle (1B) which is taken inward into a pinosome such as those illustrated forming. The series of figures illustrates the approach (2a) and attachment (2b) of a particle, invagination of the cell membrane (2c), formation of a pinosome (2d, e), and finally, incorporation of the particulate material into the cytoplasm (2f). (From Bennett, 1956: J. Biophys. Biochem. Cytol. 2:Part 2 (suppl.), 99.)

Basic dyes are found to induce pinocytosis also and can be shown to be bound to the surface of an ameba, most likely by electrostatic forces. Proteins compete for the surface of an ameba in this reaction. Some photomicrographs indicate that the surface of an ameba has hair-like projections which greatly increase the area of the surface available for binding.[68] Experiments show that to these structures, as a first step in pinocytosis, particles become attached.

Binding, or surface adsorption, of protein on the surface of the cell continues even in the presence of carbon monoxide or cyanide, either of which is inhibitory to the oxidative metabolism of the cell. It also continues at low temepratures which are inhibitory to pinocytosis. This indicates that the first step in the process of pinocytosis is a simple physical reaction.

The reaction which follows the surface binding of the protein, however, including the formation of channels and vesicles, is stopped by such metabolic inhibitors as cyanide and carbon monoxide and also by low temperatures. It is therefore dependent upon the oxidative metabolism of the cell. Thus it seems that there are at least two processes involved in pinocytosis.

Significance of Pinocytosis

Evidence from many different kinds of animal and plant cells indicates that macromolecules such as proteins, polypeptides and hormones enter cells. Embryologists have shown by delicate and specific tests that proteins also enter into cells of embryos. Pinocytosis is thought to be the mechanism by which entry of such macromolecules is made possible, since it is difficult to consider that the small pores in the cell membrane (measured in a number of ways) could possibly permit such macromolecules to enter freely. Pinocytosis might also be a means for entry of other relatively large molecules, e.g., glucose, which the cell might incidentally engulf along with the medium containing the pinocytosis-inciting particles or ions.

Is Pinocytosis Active Transport? If active transport is defined as the selective uptake of a particular solute against a concentration gradient performed at the expense of metabolic energy, then pinocytosis does not truly qualify as active transport. In pinocytosis the active step requiring energy is the formation of a vacuole or channel and its separation from the cell membrane. This phase of the process is not selective because it is a random sampling of the enviromental fluid. The only selective phase appears to be the binding of proteins and perhaps other molecules to the surface of the cell and this may or may not require metabolic energy. When the vacuole is formed these materials are included and they may move passively against a concentration gradient. It might even be that the entering proteins differ from those inside the cell, in which case they therefore move along with a concentration gradient, not against it.

Solutes other than the particles inducing pinocytosis, included in the engulfed vacuole as a random sample of the environmental fluid, are concentrated only as a result of subsequent processes, possibly active ones, not yet studied. Whether these solutes pass by diffusion or by active transport through the por-

tion of the cell membrane which forms the vacuolar wall, and whether the solutes are concentrated by removing the water from the vacuole by osmosis or active transport is not known, but some solutes are readily incorporated into the cytoskeleton or used in metabolism, e.g., C^{14} glucose, mentioned above. Some cells also void secretory vacuoles or granules —presumably by the reverse of pinocytosis.

Pinocytosis appears to be more complex than active uptake through the cell membrane, and until more is known about the process of pinocytosis it is fruitless to try to classify it.

GENERAL REFERENCES ON ACTIVE TRANSPORT

Anderson, B., and Ussing, H. H., 1960: Active Transport. Comp. Biochem. 2:371–402.
Christensen, H. N., 1955: Mode of Transport of Amino Acids into Cells; Symposium on Amino Acid Metabolism. Johns Hopkins Press, Baltimore.
Clark, H. T. (ed.), 1954: Ion Transport Across Membranes. Academic Press, New York.
Conway, E. J., 1955: Evidence for a Redox Pump in Active Transport of Cations. Internat. Rev. Cyt. 4:377–396.
Danielli, J. F. (ed.), 1954: Active Transport and Secretion. Symp. Soc. Exp. Biol., no. 8. Academic Press, New York.
Davson, H., 1959: A Textbook of General Physiology. 2nd Ed. Little, Brown, Boston, Ch. 10–14.
Fuhrman, F., 1959: Transport Through Biological Membranes. Ann. Rev. Physiol. 21:19–48.
Harris, E. J. (ed.), 1956: Transport and Accumulation in Biological Systems. Academic Press, New York.
Kitching, J. A., 1956: Contractile Vacuoles of Protozoa. Protoplasmatologia III, D, 3, a. Springer-Verlag, Vienna.
Kleinzeller, A. and Kotyk, A., (eds.), 1961: Membrane Transport and Metabolism. Academic Press, New York.
Mitchell, P., 1959: Biochemistry of Microorganisms. Ann. Rev. Microbiol. 13:407–440.
Robinson, J. R., 1953: The Active Transport of Water in Living Systems. Biol. Rev. 28:158–194; 1960: Metabolism of Intracellular Water. Biol. Rev. 40:112–149.
Robertson, R. N., 1960: Ion Transport and Respiration. Biol. Rev. 35:231–264.

EXCHANGE OF MATERIALS ACROSS THE CELL MEMBRANE

Roche, M. (ed.), 1960: Symposium on Active Transport. J. Gen. Physiol. *43*:5, part 2.

Teorell, T., 1955: A contribution to the Knowledge of Rhythmical Transport Processes of Water and Salts. Exp. Cell. Res. suppl. *3*:339–345.

GENERAL REFERENCES ON PINOCYTOSIS

Holter, H., 1960: Pinocytosis. Internat. Rev. Cyt. *8*:481–504.

Holter, H., 1961: The Induction of Pinocytosis: *in* Biological Approaches to Cancer Therapy (Harris, R. J. C., ed.), Academic Press, New York.

Rustad, R. C., April 1961: Pinocytosis. Sci. Am. *204*:120–130.

LITERATURE CITED

1. Chambers, R., Beck, L. V., and Belkin, M., 1935: J. Cell. Comp. Physiol. *6*:425.
2. Rosenberg, T., 1954: Symp. Soc. Exp. Biol., *8*:27.
3. Harris, E. J., and Maizels, M., 1951: J. Physiol. *113*:506.
4. Davson, H., 1959: Textbook of General Physiology, 2nd Ed. Little, Brown, Boston.
5. Ponder, E., 1948: Hemolysis and Related Problems. Grune & Stratton, New York.
6. Blinks, L. R., 1949: Proc. Nat. Acad. Sci. U. S. *35*:566.
7. DeGowin, E., et al., 1940: J. Am. Med. Assoc. *114*:885.
8. Steward, C. F., ed., 1959: Plant Physiology, a Treatise. Vol. 2, Academic Press, New York.
9. Huxley, A. F., and Stämpfli, R., 1951: J. Physiol. *112*:496.
10. Conway, E. J., 1953: Internat. Rev. Cyt. *2*:419.
11. Hoagland, D. R., 1940: Cold Spring Harbor Symp. *8*:181.
12. Hoagland, D. R., 1944: Lectures on the Inorganic Nutrition of Plants. Chronica Botanica, Waltham, Mass.
13. Stewart, F. C., and Miller, F. K., 1954: Symp. Soc. Exp. Biol., *8*:367.
14. Kitching, J. A., 1954: Symp. Soc. Exp. Biol. *8*:63.
15. Davson, H., 1954: Symp. Soc. Exp. Biol., *8*:16.
16. Smith, H. W., 1951: Physiology of the Kidney. Oxford Univ. Press, London.
17. Robinson, J. R., 1953: Biol. Rev. *28*:158.
18. Robinson, J. R., 1954: Symp. Soc. Exp. Biol., *8*:42.
19. Ramsay, J. A., 1954: Symp. Soc. Exp. Biol., *8*:1.
20. Koch, H. J., 1954: *in* Recent Developments in Cell Physiology. (Kitching, J. A., ed.) Academic Press, New York, p. 15.
21. Treherne, J. E., 1954: J. Exp. Biol., *31*:386.
22. Fretter, V., 1955: J. Marine Biol. Assoc. of the United Kingdom *34*:151.
23. LeFevre, P. G., 1954: Symp. Soc. Exp. Biol. *8*:118.
24. Rothstein, A., 1954: Symp. Soc. Exp. Biol. *8*:165.
25. Gale, E. F., 1954: Symp. Soc. Exp. Biol. *8*:242.
26. Goldacre, R. J., 1952: Internat. Rev. Cyt., *1*:135.
27. Lansing, A. L., and Rosenthal, T. B., 1952: J. Cell. Comp. Physiol. *40*:337.
28. Conway, E. J., Ryan, H., and Carton, E., 1954: Biochem. J. *58*:158.
29. Wilbrandt, W., 1954: Symp. Soc. Exp. Biol., *8*:136.
30. Steinbach, H. B., 1951: Ann. Rev. Physiol. *13*:21.
31. Conway, E. J., 1955: Internat. Rev. Cyt. *4*:377.
32. Teorell, T., 1953: Progress in Biophysics and Biophysical Chemistry. Academic Press, New York, vol. 3, p. 305.
33. Harris, E. J., (ed.), 1956: Transport and Accumulation in Biological Systems. Academic Press, New York.
34. Ling, G., 1955: Fed. Proc. *14*:93–94.
35. Anderson, B., and Ussing, H. H., 1960: Comp. Biochem. *2*:371.
36. Kitching, J. A., 1956: Contractile Vacuoles of Protozoa. Protoplasmatologia III, D, 3, a.
37. Ussing, H. H., 1952: Adv. Enzymol. *13*:21.
38. Le Fevre, P. G., 1955: Active Transport through Cell Membranes. Protoplasmatologia VIII, D, 3, a.
39. Robinson, J. R., 1960: Physiol. Rev. *40*:112.
40. Mitchell, P., 1959: Ann. Rev. Microbiol. *13*:407; 1957: Nature *180*:134.
41. Stein, W. D., 1960: The Transfer Mechanism in Active Transport in New Approaches in Cell Biology (Walker, P. M. B., ed.). Academic Press, New York, pp. 125–138.
42. Lundegard, H., 1954: Symp. Soc. Exp. Biol. *8*:262.
43. Abrahamson, H. A., and Moyer, L. S., 1937: Trans. Electrochem. Soc., p. 137.
44. Hokin, H. A., and Hokin, M. R., 1959: Nature *184*, suppl. 14:1068.
45. Hokin, L. E., and Hokin, M. R., 1960: J. Gen. Physiol. *44*:61. Hokin, M. R., Hokin, L. E., and Shelp, W. D., *idem.* p. 217.
46. Cohen, G., and Monod, J., 1957: Bact. Rev. *21*:169.
47. Eppley, R. W., 1959: J. Gen. Physiol. *43*:29.
48. Hokin, L. E., and Hokin, M. R., 1960: Internat. Rev. Neurobiol. *2*:99.
49. Schmidt-Nielsen, K., Jan. 1959: Sci. Am. *200*:109.
50. Klemperer, H. G., 1957: Biochem. J. *67*:381.
51. Edwards, J. G., 1925: Biol. Bull. *48*:236.
52. Lewis, W. H., 1931: Johns Hopkins Hosp. Bull. *49*:17.

53. Mast, S. O., and Doyle, L., 1934. Protoplasma 20:555.
54. Holter, H., 1959: Internat. Rev. Cyt. 8:481; 1959: Ann. New York Acad. Sci. 78:524.
55. Palade, G. E., 1956: J. Biophys. Biochem. Cyt. 2 (suppl. 2):85.
56. Moody, M. D., Goldman, M., and Thomason, B. M., 1956: J. Bact. 72:357.
57. Holter, H., and Holtzer, H., 1959: Exp. Cell. Res. 18:421.
58. Holtzer, H., and Holtzer, S., 1960: Comp. Rend. Lab. Carlsberg 31: no. 26, 373.
59. McLaren, A. D., Jenson, W. A., and Jacobson, L., 1960: Plant Physiol. 35:549.
60. Jensen, W. A., and McLaren, A. D., 1960: Exp. Cell. Res. 19:414.
61. Schechtman, A., 1956: Internat. Rev. Cyt. 5:303.
62. Brachet, J., 1957: Biochemical Cytology. Academic Press, New York.
63. Chapman-Andresen, C., 1958: Comp. Rend. Lab. Carlsberg 31: no. 6, 77.
64. DeTerra, N., and Rustad, R. C., 1959: Exp. Cell Res. 17:191.
65. Rinaldi, A. R., 1959: Exp. Cell. Res. 18:70.
66. Brandt, P. W., 1958: Exp. Cell. Res. 15:300.
67. Bennett, H. S., 1956: J. Biophys. Biochem. Cyt. 2, Part 2 (suppl.):99.
68. Rustad, R. C., April 1961: Sci. Am. 204:120.
69. Elbers, P. F., and Bluemink, J. B., 1960: Exp. Cell. Res. 21:619.
70. Chapman-Andresen, C., and Prescott, D. M., 1956: Compt. Rend. Lab. Carlsberg 30:57.
71. Holter, H., and Marshall, J. M., Jr., 1954: Compt. Rend. Lab. Carlsberg 29:7.
72. Holter, H., 1961: in Biological Approaches to Cancer Chemotherapy (Harris, R. J. C., ed.), Academic Press, New York.
73. Marshall, J. M., Schumaker, V. N., and Brandt, P. W., 1959: Ann. New York Acad. Sci. 78:515.
74. Anderson, J. D., 1962: J. Gen. Physiol. 45:567.

CHAPTER 14

THE CHEMICAL NATURE
OF THE CELL MEMBRANE

Extraneous Membranes

Although it is often stated that the cytoplasm of a cell is bounded by a *cell membrane* or *plasma membrane*, extraneous coats in addition may surround the delicate plasma membrane and protect it.[1] In a sea urchin egg a *jelly layer* covers the *vitelline membrane* within which is the plasma membrane, as shown in Figure 14.1. Both of these layers are secreted by the ovary and both may be removed without damaging the plasma membrane. Thus the jelly coating, which in some cases is hyaluronic acid,[2] may be dissolved by treatment with acidified sea water. The vitelline membrane, which is a tough elastic coating, may be lifted and stretched with a needle and can be removed by microdissection or by washing in isotonic KCl solution. An egg, denuded of the jelly and the vitelline membrane, becomes sticky and the membrane then separating the egg from the medium is believed to be the plasma membrane. The "naked" egg is much more susceptible to injury than when it is protected by the vitelline membrane and the jelly, but it nevertheless develops normally when fertilized.

When an egg is fertilized the vitelline membrane is raised as a fertilization membrane, and a space then separates it from the surface of the egg.[3] This space is filled with fluid except for some strands connecting the membrane to the surface of the egg. About the surface of the egg is then secreted a *hyaline plasma layer*. This becomes prominent as the cement which binds the blastomeres together when the egg undergoes cleavage. It is probably mucopolysaccharide in nature.[2]

The presence of a plasma membrane on a naked sea urchin egg can be demonstrated by microdissection. When the surface is depressed by the application of a microdissection needle, it visibly crinkles.[1, 2] If the egg, freed of its extraneous membranes, is sawed in two with a needle, two spheres are obtained, indicating that the cut surface has developed a membrane which holds the cell material in place. Even when the egg in sea water is torn with a needle, a new membrane forms, indicating that the material required for the formation of the membrane

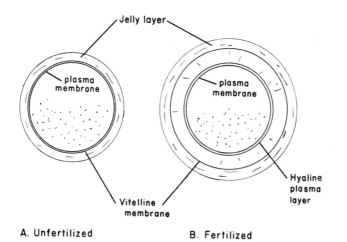

A. Unfertilized   B. Fertilized

Fig. 14.1. Diagrams of unfertilized and fertilized sea urchin eggs to show extraneous layers. The plasma membrane is indicated, although it is not actually possible to see it. The vitelline membrane is raised during fertilization.

is present in the interior of the egg (see Fig. 14.2A). However, if the membrane is torn in calcium-free sea water, the contents of the egg disperse in the solution (see Fig. 14.2B). Calcium appears to be essential for the formation of the membrane, which is presumably formed by the precipitation of the cell material in the presence of calcium. Heilbrunn has called this reaction the surface precipitation reaction.[5]

As the cells differentiate into tissues they are cemented together by a material much like the hyaline plasma layer which binds together the blastomeres of an embryo. In capillaries the cellular cement acts like a filter through which blood plasma passes into the surrounding tissue spaces (some molecules, however, also pass through the cell membranes).[36]

In ciliate protozoans the plasma membrane is protected by a tough proteinaceous pellicle which, superficially, resembles the wall of a plant cell. However, when a protozoan is placed in hypertonic solution the pellicle decreases in size to fit the shrunken protozoan, which indicates that the pellicle is elastic in nature. Details of the organization of the pellicle have been studied with the electron microscope.[4, 47]

The pellicle can be removed from some protozoan cells. For example, the pellicle of *Blepharisma undulans* is shed when the ciliates are placed in a solution of 0.05 per cent strichnine sulfate. The *Blepharisma* withdraws in from its pellicle and then swims out of the pellicular sack through the mouth opening or by enlarging the contractile vacuole opening. Freed of its pellicle, the *Blepharisma* becomes pear shaped, as if unable to maintain its long slender form without the rigid pellicle. A new pellicle is regenerated within a day or two and the cell gradually resumes its normal shape.[42]

In lieu of the pellicle an ameba is coated with a slime, as are even some cells with a pellicle or a cell wall (e.g., desmids and diatoms). An ameba pushed with a microneedle and released may snap back to its original position as a result of contraction of the elastic slime.[52]

Plant Cell Walls. In a plant cell a *cell wall* is always present, protecting the cell membrane. The cell wall is composed chiefly of cellulose (in most plants) secreted by the cell. The adjacent cell walls of abutting cells are cemented together by pectin. Old cell walls may be thickened by lignin, a ring compound (see Chapter 3), and surfaces of epidermal cells may be covered with a waxy covering which reduces water loss.

EXCHANGE OF MATERIALS ACROSS THE CELL MEMBRANE

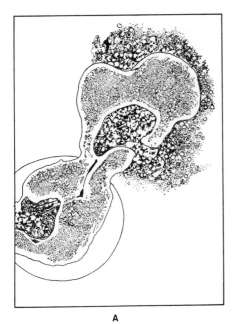
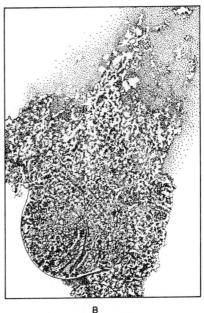

Fig. 14.2. *A*, surface precipitation reaction in an egg of a starfish (*Partiria miniata*) crushed in sea water. *B*, the membrane fails to develop when the egg is crushed in calcium-free sea water. (After a photograph by Richard Boolootian.)

Extensive studies by x-ray diffraction, polarized microscopy and electron microscopy have been made of the architecture of the plant cell wall, and it would appear that the cytoplasm lays down an interwoven network of fibers (primary wall) to which lamellar deposits (secondary wall) are later added. Spaces remain between the cellulose fibers, and the network design gives maximal strength for a minimum of material.[37]

The first rudiment of a future cell wall in a cell about to divide is seen as a series of droplets on the midline between the two daughter cells and at right angles to the spindle. Half an hour later birefringence is observed, probably at the moment of formation of the cellulose fibrils on either side of the pectic materials forming the middle lamella.[45]

In *Valonia*, the unit fibers are composed of α cellulose and may be quite long, about 10 μ, and astonishingly constant in diameter—150 to 300 Å. The fibers are ribbon-like and lie with the broader face in the plane of the cell wall. X-ray evidence indicates "periods" of 500 glucose residues, each one 2500 Å long.[45, 46] X-ray mapping before and after stripping of these fibers revealed two sets of fibers: one meridional and the other following a shallow, spiral path; the two kinds of fibers were laid down in layers following a definite pattern of succession, a total of 200 to 300 layers being present.

The primary cell wall of many other plant cells, however, has fibers which are distinctly interwoven, not in plane sheets as in *Valonia*, indicating that the secreting cytoplasm penetrates the fibril meshwork. The secondary cell wall has parallel fibers of constant thickness laid down in close texture and forming lamellae (Fig. 14.3). The intimacy of contact between cytoplasm and cell wall is shown

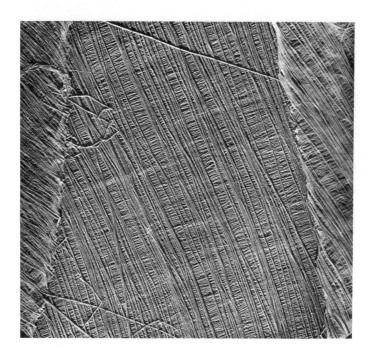

Fig. 14.3. Electron micrograph of the arrangements of cellulose fibers in the cell walls of *Cladophora rupestris* (green alga). ($\times$ 24,000) Note the three directions in which the fibers run. Smaller units, of which the fibers are composed, may be seen in the isolated fibers at the top and the bottom. (Courtesy of Preston, R. D., 1961: Proc. Roy. Soc. *B 154*:70–94.)

also by the adhesion of the cytoplasm upon plasmolysis to the growing tips of cell walls.[45, 46]

The cell wall may have a degree of plasticity. For example, the stamen hair cells of *Tradescantia,* placed in hypotonic solutions, may extend 100 per cent and again return to their original size on replacement into isotonic solutions.[45] In the growing tip the cell walls must be plasticized before they can elongate, there being as much as a sixfold increase in dry weight of the wall substance during maximal extension.[45]

The cell wall composition is not always the same. For example, while the cotton hair is 90 per cent (by dry weight) cellulose, only 2 per cent of a red algal cell wall is cellulose, other polysaccharides of complex nature making up the remainder. The cell walls of fungi, including yeast, are made up largely of chitin, a glucosamine polymer (see Table 3.1). In chitinous cell walls of some invertebrate animal cells self-tanning proteins are also present.[45]

In bacteria the separateness of the cell wall and the cell membrane is readily demonstrated by plasmolysis (Fig. 2.6). The structure of the cell wall, as shown by electron microscopy, in most cases appears to be made up of minute rectangular or hexagonal units about 120 to 140 Å in dimension (Fig. 14.4). In some cases, however, it consists of many stranded curving cables. The chemical composition of the cell wall is somewhat different in the two major divisions of bacteria. In bacteria, e.g., *Staphylococcus,* reacting positively to the gram stain (crystal violet followed by iodine which probably reacts with magnesium ribonucleate in the cell wall), the wall amounts to 20 per cent of the dry weight of the bacterium and is made up of a small number of amino acids, including diaminopimelic acid (unique to bacteria and blue-green algae), hexosamine and 1 to 3 per cent of lipid. The cell walls of bacteria which are negative to the gram stain, e.g., *Escherichia coli,* are thinner and contain much more lipid, proportionally, and are chemically

Fig. 14.4. Electron micrographs of cell walls of bacteria. *Left*, cell walls of *Streptococcus fecalis*, after splitting the cells by grinding to permit the contents to escape. (× 12,000) *Right*, a portion of a *Spirillum rubrum* cell, showing the regular pattern of bodies of which this wall is constructed. (× 42,000) (Salton and Williams; Salton and Horne.)

more elaborate than in the gram-positive group. Two layers are found in the cell wall of *E. coli*. One is extractable with phenol and is made up of lipoprotein, accounting for 80 per cent of the dry weight of the wall; the other is chemically much like the wall of the gram-positive types, containing lipopolysaccharide, lysine and hexosamine.[43]

Penicillin is bacteriostatic to gram-positive bacteria because it inhibits development of the cell wall in the growing bacteria. Streptomycin is bacteriostatic to many gram-negative forms.[44]

Outside the cell wall of most, if not all, bacteria is found other material encapsulating it in slime or firmer matter made up of polysaccharides, lipid and sometimes other materials. These materials are important to bacteriologists as antigens, but encapsulating material is of use to bacteria primarily as additional mechanical protection.[44]

Cell walls, vitelline membranes, fertilization membranes arising from vitelline membranes, and the hyaline plasma layer have a porosity such that most materials (except very large molecules) can pass through them. It is the cell membrane that determines what shall enter or leave the cell. An analysis of the cell membrane is therefore most pertinent to an understanding of the transport of materials into and out of cells.

Chemical Content of Cell Membranes

A single cell membrane is too small for microchemical analysis, but such an analysis is possible with a mass of cell membranes. The ghosts of erythrocytes,[6] and more recently of bacteria,[7, 8] have been subjected to biochemical analysis in an attempt to determine some of their constituents.

Upon hemolysis, an erythrocyte liberates hemoglobin, and the ghost which is left behind appears to consist of nothing but the cell membrane, although the membrane may continue to swell and shrink in response to osmotic stresses.[21] Analysis of a mass of ghosts indicates that they consist of lipid and protein in the ratio of 1.0 to 1.7 by weight. The protein, called stromatin, has a high molecular weight and is fibrous in nature. The lipids are mainly cholesterol and phospholipids. Cholesterol makes up between 15 and 32 per cent of the total lipid content. The phospholipids, which make up between 55 and 75 per cent of the total lipid content, consist primarily of lecithin and cephalin. On the average the membrane has 75 to 90 molecules of lipid for every molecule of protein, enough lipid to cover the surface of the red blood corpuscle with a layer two to three molecules thick.[6]

Some investigators question these analyses of the chemical contents of the cell membrane on the basis that perhaps more than the plasma membrane may be present in the ghost, especially since the nature of the ghost varies with its mode of preparation.[12] For instance, it is possible that the erythrocyte ghost includes some of the internal structure upon which the hemoglobin has been bound. However, the data from ghosts of bacteria generally corroborate those on erythrocytes.[7, 8] Similar experiments have not yet been feasible with other types of cells.

Some workers, using staining methods, have identified nucleic acid in the membrane of the *Arbacia* egg,[9] and the same has been claimed in other instances. It is difficult to be sure that some of the endoplasmic reticulum with ribosomes is not being included. Another group of workers, using a similar technique, have evidence for the presence of carbohydrates in the plasma membrane of *Amoeba*.[10] Carbohydrates probably are generally present in the cell membrane conjugated with proteins to form mucoproteins (see below).

Salts are also present in cell membranes, and microincineration tests suggest that some of these are present in higher concentration in the membranes than elsewhere in cells.[38] Water is also present in the cell membrane, as in all cell materials.

Additional evidence of the chemical nature of the cell membrane has been obtained from less direct experiments on cells. Some of these experiments are outlined below.

Evidence for Lipids in the Cell Membrane

The general correlation between lipoid solubility and entry of various compounds into the cell (see Fig. 12.4) is strong presumptive evidence for the presence of lipoidal material in the cell membrane. Overton, more than 50 years ago, carried away by the strong correlation which he found between lipoid solubility and permeability of substances,[13] postulated that the plasma membrane was made up entirely of lipids, a view not acceptable today. Many other experiments demonstrate the presence of lipoidal material in the plasma membrane, but none of them excludes the possibility that other materials are also present.

The high electric resistance of cells (e.g., 100,000 ohms per square centimeter of surface in *Nitella*, and 1000 ohms in the squid giant axon) is best interpretable on the basis of the presence of a lipoidal layer at the surface of the cell. Ions penetrate through the lipoidal layer only with difficulty; consequently, conduction of electricity through the membrane is slight and the resistance large. It has been calculated that a layer of lipids about 50 Å thick, consisting of two layers of molecules, is sufficient to give such resistance.[14]

A third line of circumstantial evidence for the presence of lipid in the surface of the cell is the coalescence of oil with the cell membrane.[15, 16] Oil, forced out of a micropipette under the microscope, is brought next to the cell to be tested. It may engulf the cell completely if the surface of the cell (such as an erythrocyte) contains lipids. A small drop of oil brought next to *Amoeba dubia* forms an oil cap on it. Because of the rigid nature of the ectoplasm, the oil cap is not taken into the *Amoeba*. An oil cap also forms on an *Arbacia* egg freed of extraneous coats (see Fig. 14.5), but if no protein is present in the sea water, the oil droplet pops inside the cell because the surface tension within the cell is less than at the surface of the oil. When the vitelline membrane is present the oil does not coalesce with an *Arbacia* egg, since the lipoidal layer of the cell membrane of the

Fig. 14.5. Diagrams illustrating
the behavior of oil drops brought
into contact with the cell surface.
The arrows indicate the internally
directed force in the droplets due
to interfacial tension.[From Danielli,
Bourne, ed.), 1951: Cytology and
Cell Physiology. Oxford Univ. Press,
London, p. 161.]

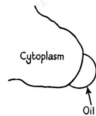

Cytoplasm

Oil

Oil cap on an Amoeba

Oil droplet on Arbacia egg membrane
Final position   Initial position

egg cannot make contact with the oil through the vitelline membrane. When an egg, from which the extraneous membranes have been removed is fertilized, the hyaline plasma layer is secreted over the plasma membrane, and oil again will not cap the egg.

A fourth line of evidence for lipids in the cell membrane is the lysis (breakdown) of the cell membrane by lipolytic agents. For example, the cell membrane is lysed by benzene and carbon tetrachloride, both of which are lipoid solvents. Digitonin, sodium and potassium salts of fatty acids, and paraffin sulfonates, all of which lyse the cell membrane, act as lysins primarily because of their effect on cell lipids. Digitonin, for example, is thought to form a complex with membrane sterols. Much more specific is the lysis of the cell membrane by lecithinase, an enzyme which catalyzes the hydrolysis of lecithin in the cell membrane.[6, 17]

If the cell membrane contains lipids, calculation of the rate of penetration of various substances through an artificial but similar lipid layer should give permeability constants for these compounds comparable in magnitude to those found for the penetration of the same compounds into cells. This has been found to be true. Permeability constants calculated for compounds penetrating a layer of lipid 50 Å thick are of the same order of magnitude as those found for the same compounds penetrating many cells. Calculation of the penetration of the same substances through an aqueous layer of this thickness gives permeability constants

of an entirely different order of magnitude,[14] as seen in Table 14.1.

Evidence for Protein in the Cell Membrane

A number of lines of evidence point clearly to the presence of protein in the plasma membrane of the cell. The elasticity of the plasma membrane of the cell and its strength strongly suggest that the lipids in the cell membrane are bound together by some other type of compound. A membrane made up exclusively of lipids would lack mechanical strength. The fibrous proteins of large molecular weight found in erythrocyte ghosts contain hydrophobic and hydrophilic groups and could well perform such a role. The hydrophobic groups of the molecule bind lipids, while the hydrophilic groups bind water-soluble substances. Proteins could therefore bind the lipids to the aqueous cytoplasm. The protein at the surface allows for stretch and compression, providing the elasticity of the cell membrane observed and measured.[18, 19]

Evidence for the presence of protein in the plasma membrane of the cell comes from measurement of surface tension between the cell membrane and the surrounding medium. By measuring the force necessary to distort an egg with a gold fiber it is possible to determine the surface tension at the surface of the egg. Determination of the centrifugal force required to break an egg in two may also be used for this purpose. Regardless of the type of cell tested and of the method

TABLE 14.1. *Comparison of the Permeability of Water and Oil Films and a Variety of Cells to Three Substances*

SUBSTANCE	5 mμ WATER	5 mμ OIL	ARBACIA EGG	*Chara cera-tophylla*	*Pylaiella litoralis*	OX ERYTHROCYTE
Ethylene glycol	1.7×10^9	0.1	0.73	1.2	0.1	0.2
Glycerol	1.4×10^9	0.002	0.005	0.02	0.002	0.002
Erythritol	1.2×10^9	0.00005	—	0.001	0.0001	—

Data from Danielli.[14] The permeability is given in moles of a substance entering a square micron of surface area per second for a unit mole per liter difference in concentration between the inside and the outside of the cell (multiplied by 10^{16} to give a number which can be handled more conveniently than can small fractions). The permeability was calculated for water and oil films and was taken from experimental data for the cells. Note that the permeability of cells to these compounds is of the same magnitude as the permeability of an oil film to them.

used, the surface tension of the cell membrane appears to be low. The values found for *Arbacia* are between 0.2 and 0.08 dynes/cm.; the value for the *Triturus* erythrocyte is 0.1; for *Amoeba dubia*, 1.3; for the slime mold *Physarum*, 0.45; for the egg of *Triturus*, 0.1. The surface tension of oil against water is about 15 dynes/cm. However, when some protein is spread on an oil, the surface tension against water falls to values of 1.0 or less. The low surface tension at the surface of cells suggests the presence of protein.[20] Some uncertainty exists, however, as to whether the term surface tension really applies in making measurements on an elastic membrane such as the cell membrane.

Lysis of the cell membrane by agents which act specifically upon proteins offers further corroborative evidence of the presence of proteins in the surface of the cell. Cells injected into an animal act as antigens against which antibodies are formed in the serum. Lysis of the foreign cells by such antibodies implies action on their membranes. Antibodies are not known to be produced against lipids, but they are demonstrable against proteins and carbohydrates. Since both are present in cell membranes, the evidence is indecisive.[19] Also, the polymerized polyhydroxyphenols are known to denature proteins but not to affect carbohydrates

or lipids. When such a substance is applied to a cell, the structure of the membrane is disrupted, leading to lysis.[21, 22] This too suggests the presence of protein in the cell membrane. Evidence from electron micrographs of erythrocyte ghosts also indicates the presence of proteins in the cell membrane. This evidence will be discussed later.

Among the proteins of the cell membrane are glycoproteins and mucoproteins, conjugates of carbohydrates and proteins. They are very widespread, perhaps universal, and may form a considerable component of the membrane protein. These are of considerable importance as antigens. An example is the agglutination (precipitation) of red blood cells by influenza virus, as a result of reaction between enzymatically active groups on the surface of the virus particles with surface mucopolysaccharides on the red blood cells. The widespread nature of immunological reactions to all types of cells indicates the general presence of such mucoids in their surfaces. The mucoids of the foreign cells serve as antigens against which the host organism develops antibodies.[41, 48, 52]

The cell membrane must also be the site of receptor proteins in bacteria containing permease systems. In any cells where active transport occurs, and this is probably universal, it is likely that en-

mes occur in the surface of the cell. It
ay be that part of the structural protein
f a cell membrane is enzymatic
rotein.[41, 48, 52]

hickness of the Cell Membrane

The thickness of the plasma membrane
as been measured with a leptoscope, an
istrument used to measure the thickness
f thin films.[23-25] For this purpose a metal
iirror is passed into and out of a
arium stearate solution a number of
mes. Each time the plate is passed into
ie solution a layer of barium stearate is
eposited upon the plate. It is found that
1 the first layer the hydrophilic barium
; toward the plate and the hydrophobic
iyer outward; in the second layer the hy-
rophobic portion faces inward, because of
s attraction to the preceding hydrophobic
roup; and so on (see Fig. 14.6 and 14.7).
)n successive parts of the plate different
iumbers of layers of barium stearate are
leposited. On a similar metal mirror eryth-
ocytes are deposited, and the two mir-
ors are viewed side by side under a
nicroscope. The degree to which the re-
lected light is attenuated by the erythro-
:ytes is matched against attenuation
:aused by graded layers of barium
tearate. It is possible to calculate the
hickness of the membrane of the erythro-
:yte ghost by knowing the thickness of a
tearate layer, and by knowing the match-
ng point for the ghost and a particular
iumber of layers of stearate on the test
)late. Estimates determined in this man-
ier for the thickness of cell membranes
)f different types of erythrocytes vary
rom 140 to 250 Å. About half this thick-
iess is left after the lipids are extracted,
ndicating a residue of protein.

Estimates obtained by dividing the
:otal amount of protein and lipid in the
membrane by the area of the membrane
ndicate a thickness of the same order of
magnitude as was obtained by the above

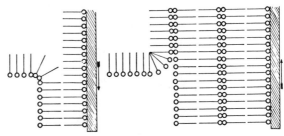

Fig. 14.6. Diagram representing the building up of
monomolecular films at an air-water interface. *Left*,
a glass slide previously coated with a film of barium
stearate (see the polar groups attached to the glass
surface) is dipped in water having a monomolecular
film of barium stearate at the interface. The second
monomolecular layer attaches to the first by the nonpolar ends. *Right*, several bimolecular layers of barium
stearate have been deposited on the glass slide by
successive dips into the water. (Courtesy of Professor
D. Waugh.)

method; namely, about 120 to 140 Å for
the cell membrane of the erythrocyte.[6]

Still another approach used for esti-
mating the thickness of the cell membranes of a variety of cells is that of
measuring the thickness of an oil film required to duplicate the electric properties
characteristic of the cell membrane. The
resistance of a 50 Å oil film is found to
be of the same order of magnitude as
that of the cell membrane.[19] From experiments with polarized light somewhat
thicker cell membranes are estimated,
but still of the same order of magnitude
as determined by other methods.[24]

Since the dimensions of the cell membrane are within the limits of resolution
by the electron microscope, considerable
effort has been made to study the cell
membrane by this means. Such studies
made of flattened entire cell membranes
and of thin sections of cell membranes
indicate a thickness of about 75 Å for the
cell membrane[45, 48] (see Fig. 14.11).

Some confidence, therefore, may be
placed in the values found, since from all
experimental approaches they are found
to be at least of the same order of magni-

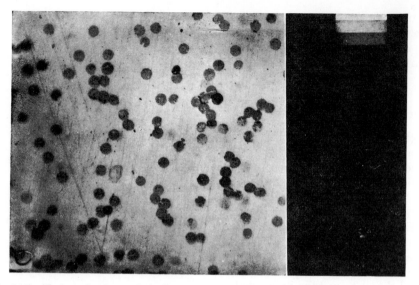

Fig. 14.7. Photograph taken with the leptoscope, in which may be seen the stroma of hemolyzed erythrocytes. The standard step intensity gauge (increasing monomolecular layers of barium stearate) is seen in the upper right corner. (Courtesy of Professor D. Waugh.)

tude. However, more precise data are desirable.

Structure of the Cell Membrane

The structural arrangement of proteins and lipids in the cell membrane has interested many workers, but the molecular pattern cannot be seen even with the electron microscope and no direct method for its study is yet available. The structure of the cell membrane can only be inferred from indirect evidence.

The striking correlation between lipoid solubility and permeability led Overton to postulate a cell covered with lipid. Since, as shown by Langmuir, molecules of fatty acids, at an interface, stood at right angles to the surface of the water, the same was thought to be likely in cell membranes. When, in 1925, Gorter and Grendel showed that all the extracted lipids from a red blood cell occupied an area twice that for a single molecular film, it was postulated that there was a membrane with a double layer of lipid molecules, each with its hydrophobic end

to the other,[20] standing at right angles to the surface. Because the surface tension of an egg cell membrane is much lower than that expected for a lipid, but approximately equal to the value for a lipid with a coating of proteins, it was thought by many workers that proteins may cover, though not necessarily completely, the outer surface of the cell membrane.[19, 20]

Most of the evidence for the arrangement of lipids and proteins in the plasma membrane comes from studies using the x-ray diffraction method[26, 27] and polarized light.[12, 20, 25] For interpretation of the data it is necessary first to describe briefly the use of the polarizing microscope in such studies.

It is well known that light, passing through a doubly refracting crystal such as calcite, is separated into two rays which vibrate at right angles to one another. Such light is said to be polarized. The *Nicol prism*, one of the best known polarizers, is made by cutting a rhomb of Iceland spar (a pure, transparent form of calcite) in halves along the line of one of

EXCHANGE OF MATERIALS ACROSS THE CELL MEMBRANE

he optical faces, polishing the cut faces nd cementing them together with Canada balsam. As seen in Figure 14.8 unpolarized light entering one end is eparated by the prism into two beams, ne vibrating in the plane of the figure, he other at right angles to it. One of hese beams is totally reflected by the ayer of Canada balsam and is usually bsorbed by the opaque case covering art of the rhomb. The other beam is ransmitted. Hence, a Nicol prism transmits plane-polarized light. If a second Nicol prism is used in series with the first, nd in the same position, the polarized ight is transmitted. If, however, the second prism is rotated through 90° in relation to the first prism, the light fails to pass. But if an object like quartz, which polarizes light, is placed in the beam of ight between the two prisms, and if the wo Nicols are at right angles to each other (crossed), instead of a plain dark ield, a brilliantly lit object is seen against a dark background, indicating that the object has polarized the light passing through it. If the second prism is then rotated away from 90°, the field suddenly becomes dark. The angle required to rotate the second prism in order to extinguish the light is a measure of the degree to which the plane of polarized light has been rotated by the interposed object. The second prism is called an analyzer because by moving it one can analyze the degree to which the plane of polarized light has been rotated by an object inserted in the light path. In the polarizing microscope a polarizer is present in the condenser and an analyzer is present in the ocular.

Various natural substances are observed to be *isotropic;* that is, light passes through them equally well in all directions. Others, which affect the passage of light unequally in different directions, are *anisotropic* or *birefringent.* The ray passing directly through a crystal is called the *ordinary ray* while the ray which is deviated is called the *extraordinary ray.* If the velocity of the extraordinary ray passing through such a material is less than the velocity of the ordinary ray, the crystal is said to be negative (e.g., quartz). If the extraordinary ray has a velocity greater than the ordinary, the crystal is said to be positive. *Crystalline* or *intrinsic birefringence* is found where the bonds between molecules (or ions) have a regular asymmetrical arrangement. The birefringence in this case is independent of the refractive index of the medium.

Dichroism occurs when the absorption of a given wavelength of polarized light changes with the orientation of the object. For example, the degree of absorption at wavelength 2600 Å by nucleic acids depends upon whether the light is parallel to, or at right angles to, the oriented purine and pyrimidine residues.

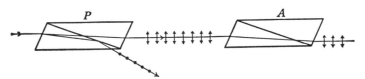

Fig. 14.8. Polarization of light by a Nicol prism. Only the beam in the plane of the sheet has been permitted to pass, that at right angles being deflected. The second Nicol prism, if oriented like the first, has no effect on the polarized light. However, if it is rotated through 90° the beam will be extinguished. (From Stewart and Gingrich, 1959: Physics. 6th Ed. Ginn and Company, Boston.)

Dichroism is a sensitive indicator of orientation of molecules in a structure. However, it is seldom seen in biological objects in the visible spectrum except in some stained preparations where it results from orientation of dye molecules. It may be seen at 2600 Å in the sperm nuclei where the concentrated nucleic acids appear to be oriented.

Birefringence of inanimate objects, then, is the result of their crystalline nature. Birefringence of biological materials indicates that their molecules are oriented with respect to one another much as in a crystal. Some particles—for example, nucleoprotein molecules—line up only if the solution is flowing; what they show is therefore called *flow* or *streaming birefringence*. This indicates that the molecules are elongate and line up in the path of least resistance to a current, just as sticks line up in a brook. Organisms are more likely to show *form birefringence*, because of regular orientation of tiny particles (rods or planes) differing in refractive index from their surrounding medium. Birefringence in such cases disappears when the material is immersed in a medium of the same refractive index. Oriented rods have different refractive indices for directions parallel to and at right angles to the major axis. Therefore, by making observations with polarized light one may determine in which direction in a given structure the rods lie. Studies with the polarizing microscope suggest that the protein molecules in the cell membrane are parallel to the surface of the cell and that the lipids are radially arranged.[23, 26, 27] However, according to the investigators presenting the data, this cannot be considered an established fact because the evidence may be interpreted in other, though less likely, ways.

The cell membrane is visualized by Danielli and Davson[19, 20, 29] as consisting of two layers of lipid molecules arranged radially with their hydrocarbon chains toward each other, and with their respec-tive polar groups arranged outwardly and inwardly, the entire double layer of lipid molecules being sandwiched between two layers of protein bounding the outside and the inside of the membrane (see Fig. 14.9 and 14.11). The layers and pores are considered to be dynamic, not static, and at times a lipid chain appears to make contact with the outside of the cell, at least in some spots, because lipase (e.g., lecithinase) lyse cell membranes, indicating that they are able to reach the lipids.[14, 19, 20, 28] Conversely, some investigators propose that in this dynamic membrane protein-lined "pores" periodically appear through the lipid layers, giving rise to a protein continuum from outer to inner protein layers in the cell membrane.[29]

Another hypothesis suggests that the protein of the cell membrane may form a lattice of fibrous protein between the meshes of which the lipid component is distributed.[30, 31] For instance, electron micrographs show that erythrocyte ghosts from which the lipids had been extracted with solvents have a fibrous structure interrupted by holes which are assumed to be the places where the lipids had previously been located. Untreated ghosts show no such cavities. Therefore, since both polar and nonpolar groups are found in proteins, the cell membrane may be visualized as a mosaic of patches in which polar groups of lipids are attached to polar groups of proteins, and other patches in which the nonpolar groups of proteins are attached to nonpolar groups of lipids. The first type of patch would permit water-soluble materials to enter the cell membrane, and the second type would permit oil-soluble materials to enter the membrane. Several other models of cell membranes have recently been described.[28, 40] For example, an alternate view is that of an all-lipid membrane with protein pores. However, studies of thin cross sections of cell membranes by electron microscopy do not show a homogeneous membrane

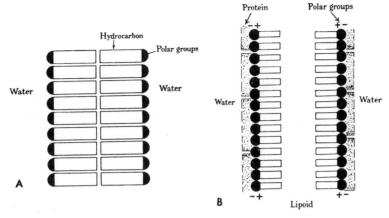

Fig. 14.9. Diagrams of hypothetical structures of the cell membrane. (*A*, from Gorter and Grendel. *B*, from Danielli in Davson and Danielli, 1943: The Permeability of Natural Membranes. Cambridge Univ. Press, London, pp. 62, 64.)

with radial heterogeneity such as might be expected of this structure, although the radii of protein might conceivably be below the limit of resolution. However, the tripartite nature of the unit membrane seen in electron micrographs favors, although it does not prove, the validity of the Danielli-Davson model shown in Figure 14.9.[45, 48]

Much of the basic electron microscopic work leading to the present concept of cell membrane structure has come from a study of the myelin sheath of the neuron (nerve cell). As shown diagramatically in Figure 14.10, the axon of the neuron depresses the cell membrane of the Schwann cell (sheath cell) and, rotating in the cell (or being spirally wrapped in the cell), it gradually accumulates around it a number of double membranes in which it lies. The myelin sheath, therefore, consists essentially of numerous cell membranes derived from the Schwann cell and wound around the axon of the neuron, including some material between the membranes.[48]

Analysis of the sheath by methods of x-ray diffraction and polarizing microscopy had already led to an understanding of the existence of repeating units of great regularity. Electron micrographs confirmed and extended these studies. High resolution on ultra-thin cross sections of the neuron and its myelin sheath indicates a unit membrane of 75 Å consisting of two osmophilic layers (i.e., staining with osmium tetroxide) each about 25 to 40 Å wide and a less dense band between them about 20 to 25 Å wide (Fig. 14.11). Because of the way the myelin sheath is formed during development (Fig. 14.10), such unit membranes occur in pairs, in apposition to each other within the sheath. Many such pairs with some material between them (shown between membranes in Fig. 14.10) make up the myelin sheath.

Such a basic unit membrane as seen in the sheath appears to be general for a wide variety of cells, e.g., cells of intestinal epithelium, nerves, skin, liver, pancreas, kidney, endothelium, blood and muscle of a variety of species of vertebrates and invertebrates including ciliates and amebas. Even more remarkable is the finding of a similar unit in plant cell membranes as well.[48] Since the membranes of the endoplasmic reticulum and mitochondria and even the Golgi apparatus show the same unit structure, it

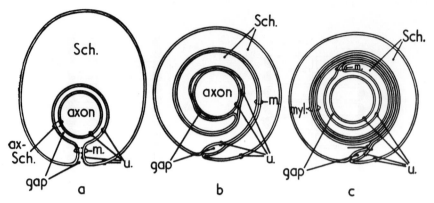

Fig. 14.10. Three stages in the development of nerve myelin are indicated. The earliest recognized stage is shown in (*a*). Here a single axon is embedded in a Schwann cell (Sch.). The enveloping lips of the Schwann cell come together around the axon to form a double membrane known as the mesaxon (m.). There is usually a small gap between the Schwann cell membranes (u.) forming the mesaxon, which is continuous with the gap between the axon and the Schwann cell membranes making up the axon-Schwann membrane (ax.-Sch.). At a later stage of myelination represented by (*b*) the mesaxon is elongated in a spiral around the axon and its central gap is largely obliterated. The gap of the axon-Schwann membrane is also partially obliterated. At a later stage (*c*) the mesaxon is elongated further and the cytoplasmic surfaces of the spiral mesaxon loops come together to form the major dense lines of compact myelin (myl.). (From Robertson, 1959: Biochem. Soc. Symp. 16. Cambridge Univ. Press.)

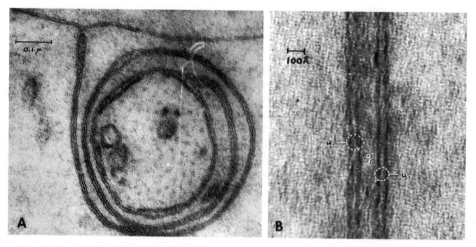

Fig. 14.11. Electron micrographs of unit membranes in the myelin sheath. *A*, unit membranes are clearly seen at the top of the figure and pairs of such membranes are seen beyond the point at which the unit membranes meet. Each unit membrane is made up of three layers. *B*, higher magnification of a pair of unit membranes, each member of the pair being indicated by (u); (g) shows the material between the pair of unit membranes. The three layers of the unit membrane probably correspond to the three layers shown in the Davson-Danielli of Fig. 14.9, the outer layers being, perhaps, protein; the inner, lipid material. (Robertson, J. D., 1959; Biochem. Soc. Symp. *16*:3. Cambridge Univ. Press.)

EXCHANGE OF MATERIALS ACROSS THE CELL MEMBRANE

ould appear to be a fundamental unit common to all cell membranes[48] (see g. 5.9).

Electron microscopic studies also real extensions of the cell membranes by lds. The intestinal epithelium cell may ave as many as 3000 microvilli, and milar structures are seen in brush border cells of the kidney tubules. These icrovilli are believed to increase the urface of the cell for exchange with the aterials in the bathing medium. In her cells, invaginations and irregularities so occur, but not to the spectacular deree as they do in the cells in which a ajor activity is the exchange of materals with the environment. All these xtensions have the thickness (75 Å) of a nit membrane.[41]

It has been claimed that in some fungal ells connections between the cell membrane and the nuclear membrane can be en.[49] It is also thought that possibly all ie membrane systems in the cell have ieir origins as invaginations of the cell iembrane, hence the similarity. The inidings are then considered as a means or communication from surface to endolasmic reticulum and nucleus.[48] Because ie membranous systems in the cytolasm vary with conditions it is assumed iat they are in a state of dynamic equibrium, forming and breaking down connually. Because all of these studies were iade with fixed materials, and not on ie living cells, it is difficult to pass judgient on these provocative ideas.[41, 48]

The Nuclear Membrane

The nuclear membrane is of profound nportance because during interphase he nucleus can pass information to the ytoplasm only through the nuclear memrane. Knowledge of the nature of the uclear membrane would make it possile to explain in what way the nucleus overns the synthetic activities occurring n the cytoplasm of the cell.

Early studies suggested that the nuclear membrane was a selectively permeable membrane, much like the membrane of the cell.[32, 33] The nucleus accumulates labeled sodium (Na^{22}).[54] Supporting this view were observations on changes in nuclear volumes of cells placed in hypertonic and hypotonic solutions. For instance, when marine eggs are placed in hypertonic solutions, the nucleus shrinks along with the general shrinkage of the cell. In hypotonic solutions, the nucleus swells as does the cytoplasm. It was later recognized that these experiments do not constitute adequate support for this view because a highly porous nuclear membrane would also permit the nucleus to swell or shrink when the cytoplasm does.[45]

Meantime some experiments indicated that the nuclear membrane was more porous than the cell membrane. For example, heparin and sulfated polymanuronic acid, added to a suspension of isolated nuclei from rat liver cells, displace highly polymerized DNA, a very large molecule, which then passes out of the nucleus through the nuclear membrane. Furthermore, nucleases are able to penetrate isolated nuclei of rat liver cells and to digest the nucleic acids in very short periods, indicating that these large molecules have entered the nuclei rapidly. Partially hydrolyzed gelatin and albumin, both of which are large molecules, appear to penetrate such nuclei as well.[34] Also, when isolated nuclei of amphibian eggs are immersed in a solution of hemoglobin, hemoglobin accumulates within them.[45] However, it can be argued that such nuclei removed from the cytoplasm of cells are abnormal.[39] Thus in nuclear transfer experiments, great care must be taken to prevent contact of the nuclei with the medium, lest the nuclei be injured. Even a short stay of the nuclei in the medium prevents their normal functioning.[45, 48] The ready passage of macromolecules through the membranes of isolated nuclei cannot, therefore, be considered conclusive evidence that the normal nuclear membrane is equally porous.

However, experiments performed with nuclei still inside the cytoplasm avoid the criticism leveled against those performed on isolated nuclei. Such experiments have demonstrated that nuclear membranes of some cells are more porous than cell membranes and that they permit macromolecules to enter and leave the nuclei. Thus, in cases where RNAase or DNAase is able to penetrate an intact cell, they also enter the nucleus and hydrolyze the nucleic acids in the nucleus. Changes in function and in the staining properties of the nuclei are then observed.[53] The appearance of fluorescent antibodies (proteins) in nuclei of embryos also indicates that the nuclear membrane has a greater porosity than the cell membrane.[45] It is difficult to accumulate such evidence for all types of cells since the large molecules to be tested do not penetrate the cell membrane except presumably by pinocytosis, a process which may not be general (see Chapter 13).

The most direct evidence on the nature of the nuclear membrane is from electron micrographs (Fig. 6.5). These clearly show two unit membranes of somewhat greater thickness than the unit cell membranes. According to some workers the nuclear membranes might be considered modified extensions of the endoplasmic reticulum or the cisterna surrounding the nucleus.[50] The outer nuclear membrane has pores 400 to 700 Å in diameter and these have been seen in cells of a variety of tissues to extend through the inner membrane as well.[50] On the other hand, in some electron micrographs such pores are not seen as clearly in the inner membrane, and, considering the differences in techniques employed by different workers, the status of these pores in some cells must be considered uncertain until resolved by further study.[45] Pinocytosis or evidence for it from cytoplasm to nucleus has not been described.[50]

Isolated membranes from nuclei of amphibian cells show an outer layer of protein and lipid and an inner one containing a relatively insoluble protein. The protein in both appears to be elastin-like and capable of being stretched reversibly.

The possibility of another kind of communication between nucleus and cytoplasm has been suggested, namely, out-pouching from chromosomes forming blebs on the nuclear membrane which separate into the cytoplasm as vesicles or laminae. These structures are covered by membranes derived from the nuclear membranes.[51]

Relation between Structure of the Cell Membrane and Permeability

How can permeability be explained in terms of the structure of the cell membrane? Assuming that the cell membrane is a sandwich of two layers of lipid between an outer and an inner layer of protein, the following illustration will perhaps exemplify some of the problems in permeability encountered in our discussion.

The membrane of the cell (see Fig. 14.12) presents the main hurdles to any entering molecule which must pass from the aqueous external medium into the cell membrane, through the cell membrane and, finally, from the cell membrane into the aqueous medium of the cytoplasm within the cell. The membrane contains a considerable amount of lipoidal material, as was seen above. If a molecule entering a cell has a high lipoid solubility (that is, a high partition coefficient), neither its entry into nor its transport through the membrane presents an obstacle. However, entry of the molecule from the membrane into the aqueous cytoplasm does present an obstacle because the cohesive bonds it has formed with the lipoid molecules of the membrane must be broken before it can leave the membrane.

If, on the other hand, a molecule en-

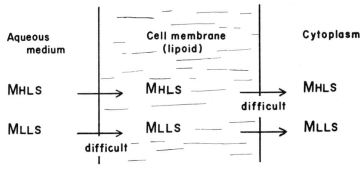

Fig. 14.12. Hurdles encountered by a molecule with high lipoid solubility (M_HLS) and a molecule with low lipoid solubility (M_LLS) when passing through the cell membrane to the cytoplasm. (After Davson and Danielli, 1952: The Permeability of Natural Membranes. 2nd Ed. Cambridge University Press, London, ch. 17.)

ering a cell membrane is highly soluble n water (that is, it has a low partition coefficient), its strong hydrogen bonds with the water in which it is dissolved outside the cell must be broken before he molecule can enter the lipoid membrane. Its movement through the lipoid membrane also presents an obstacle. However, such a molecule passes readily rom the membrane into the aqueous cytoplasm inside the cell where it forms new hydrogen bonds. In this case, therefore, passage into and through the cell membrane is the most difficult hurdle.

If the energy required to get across any of these hurdles is large, only the molecules with the required energy of activation are successful in moving through the membrane.[20] For this reason, temperature coefficients for permeability may be quite large even when active transport is not involved.

Although much interesting information has accumulated, much more evidence is needed before the problem of the structure of the cell membrane and the nuclear membrane and the problem of their permeability can be resolved.

GENERAL REFERENCES

Chambers, R., and Chambers, E., 1961: Explorations into the Nature of the Living Cell. Harvard Univ.

Press, Cambridge, Parts I (Extraneous coats) and III (The protoplasmic surface film).

Danielli, J. F., 1954: Morphological and Molecular Aspects of Active Transport. Symp. Soc. Exp. Biol. 8:502.

DeRobertis, E. D. P., Nowinski, W. W., and Saez, F. A., 1960: General Cytology. 3rd Ed. Saunders, Philadelphia.

James, A. M., 1957: The Electrochemistry of the Bacterial Surface. Progr. Biophys. 8:92.

Muhlethaler, K., 1961: Plant Cell Walls, in The Cell (Brachet, J., and Mirsky, A. E., eds.). Academic Press, New York 2:85.

Picken, L., 1960: The Organization of Cells. Clarendon, Oxford. Ch. 8, The Cell Surface and Cell Membranes.

Ponder, E., 1961: The Cell Membrane and Its Properties, in The Cell (Brachet, J., and Mirsky, A. E., eds.). Academic Press, New York 2:1.

Preston, R. D., 1959: Wall Organization in Plant Cells. Internat. Rev. Cyt. 8:33.

Robertson, J. D., 1959: The Ultrastructure of Cell Membranes and Their Derivatives. Biochem. Soc. Symp. 16:3.

Robertson, J. D., 1960: The Molecular Structure and Contact Relationships of Cell Membranes. Progr. Biophys. 10:343.

Robertson, J. D., April, 1962: The Membrane of the Living Cell. Sci. Am. 206:65.

Roche, P. (ed)., 1960: Physiology of the Cell Membrane. J. Gen. Physiol. 43: no. 5, part 2 (suppl.).

Weiss, L., 1960: The Adhesions of Cells. Internat. Rev. Cyt. 9:187.

LITERATURE CITED

1. Chambers, R., 1940: Cold Spring Harbor Symp., 8:144.
2. Chambers, R., 1949: Biol. Rev., 24:246.
3. Runnstrom, J., 1952: Symp. Soc. Exp. Biol. 6:39.

4. Sedar, A. W., and Porter, K. R., 1955: J. Biophys. Biochem. Cyt. *1*:583.
5. Heilbrunn, L. V., 1930: Proc. Am. Phil. Soc. *69*:295.
6. Parpart, A. K., and Ballantine, R., 1952: *in* Modern Trends in Physiology and Biochemistry (Barron, E. S. G., ed.). Academic Press, New York, p. 135.
7. Dubos, D. J., 1947: Exp. Cell. Res. suppl. *1*:192.
8. Miles, A. A., and Pirie, N. W., 1950: The Nature of the Bacterial Surface. Thomas, Springfield, Ill.
9. Lansing, A. I., and Rosenthal, T. B., 1952: J. Cell. Comp. Physiol. *40*:337.
10. Bairati, A., and Lehmann, F. E., 1952: Exp. Cell. Res., *5*:220.
11. Teorell, T., 1952: J. Gen. Physiol., *35*:669.
12. Ponder, E., 1952: J. Exp. Biol., *29*:605.
13. Overton, E., 1902: Arch. Ges. Physiol., *92*:115.
14. Danielli, J. F., 1951: *in* Cytology and Cell Physiology (Bourne, G. H., ed.). Oxford Univ. Press, London, p. 163.
15. Chambers, R., and Kopac, M. J., 1937: J. Cell. Comp. Physiol. *9*:331.
16. Kopac, M., 1940: Cold Spring Harbor Symp., *8*:154.
17. Ponder, E., 1953: J. Gen. Physiol. *36*:723.
18. Mitchison, J. M., and Swann, M. M., 1954: J. Exp. Biol. *31*:443.
19. Danielli, J. F., 1952: Symp. Soc. Exp. Biol., *6*:1.
20. Davson, H., and Danielli, J. F., 1952: Permeability of Natural Membranes. 2nd Ed. Cambridge Univ. Press, London.
21. Ponder, E., 1948: Hemolysis and Related Problems. Grune & Stratton, New York.
22. Ponder, E., and Ponder, R. V., 1954: J. Gen. Physiol., *37*:411.
23. Waugh, D. F., and Schmitt, F. O., 1940: Cold Spring Harbor Symp., *8*:233.
24. Waugh, D. F., 1950: Ann. New York Acad. Sci. *50*:835.
25. Mitchison, J. M., 1953: J. Exp. Biol.. *30*:397.
26. Schmitt, F. O., Barr, R. S., and Ponder, E., 1938: J. Cell. Comp. Physiol. *11*:309.
27. Schmitt, F. O., and Palmer, K. J., 1940: Cold Spring Harbor Symp. *8*:94.
28. Ponder, E., 1954: Blood *9*:227.
29. Danielli, J. F., 1954: Recent Developments Cell Physiology. 7th Colston Symp., pp. 1–1
30. Wolpers, C., 1941: Naturwiss. *29*:416.
31. Hillier, J., and Hoffman, J. F., 1953: J. Ce Comp. Physiol. *42*:203.
32. Shapiro, H., and Parpart, A. K., 1937: J. Ce Comp. Physiol. *10*:147.
33. Churney, L., 1942: Biol. Bull., *82*:52.
34. Anderson, N. G., 1953: Science *117*:517.
35. Caspersson, T. O., 1950: Cell Growth and Ce Function. Norton, New York.
36. Pappenheimer, J. R., 1953: Physiol. Rev. *33*:38
37. Frey-Wyssling, A., 1953: Submicroscopic Mo phology of Protoplasm. Elsevier, Amsterdar
38. Scott, G. H., 1933: Am. J. Anat. *53*:243.
39. Allfrey, V. G., Mirsky, A. E., and Stern, H., 195 Adv. Enzymol. *16*:411.
40. Ponder, E., Jan. 1957: Sci. Am. *196*: *1*:95.
41. Robertson, J. D., 1959: Biochem. Soc. Symp *16*:3.
42. Nadler, J. E., 1929: Biol. Bull. *56*:327.
43. Robinow, C. F., 1960: The Cell (Brachet, J., an Mirsky, A. E., eds.). Academic Press, Ne York *3*:45.
44. Carpenter, P. L., 1961: Microbiology. Saunder Philadelphia, pp. 40, 125.
45. Picken, L., 1960: The Organization of Cell Clarendon, Oxford, p. 353.
46. Preston, R. D., 1959: Internat. Rev. Cyt. *8*:33.
47. Ehret, C. F., 1960: Science *132*:115.
48. Robertson, J. D., 1960: Progr. Biophys. *10*:343.
49. McAlear, J. H., and Edwards, G. A., 1958: Exp Cell Res. *16*:689.
50. Watson, M. L., 1959: J. Biophys. Biochem. Cy *6*:147.
51. Gay, H., Jan. 1960: Sci. Am. *202*:126.
52. Chambers, R., and Chambers, E. L., 1961: E: plorations into the Nature of the Living Cell Harvard Univ. Press, Cambridge, Mass., p. 4C
53. Brachet, J., 1957: Biochemical Cytology. Aca demic Press, New York.
54. Allfrey, V. G., Meudt, R., Hopkins, J. W., an Mirsky, A. E., 1961: Proc. Nat. Acad. Sci. U. ! *47*:907.

CONVERSIONS OF ENERGY AND MATTER IN THE CELL

It is evident that the cell can perform its work only at the expense of chemical energy obtained from nutrient molecules. All cells require certain cell foods: soluble nutrients such as glucose, amino acids, and certain vitamins, and salts which can penetrate the cell membrane. All cells except anaerobes require free oxygen. It is in the cells that conversions of matter and transfers of energy occur, during which wastes are produced which must be removed if life is to be maintained.

For the unicellular organisms the problem is relatively simple. They absorb or engulf nutrients, and oxygen is taken directly from their environment. They eliminate their metabolic waste products directly into it.

In a multicellular plant or animal, in which the individual cells are often removed from immediate contact with the exterior, a cellular environment is provided by specialized supply systems, e.g., digestive, respiratory, circulatory and excretory systems. Through the services of these supply systems, each and every cell is thus supplied with the nutrients and oxygen it needs and is washed free of its metabolic waste products. For example, the animal must eat plants or other animals which ultimately depend upon plants for food. The food so ingested is digested in the alimentary tract. The cell foods are absorbed and taken by the blood to all parts of the organism, where the tissue fluids bathe and supply the cells. Oxygen, which enters through the respiratory system, also reaches the cells by way of the blood, and the metabolic reactions result in the formation of cell wastes which are removed by the tissue fluid and carried by the blood to the excretory system which extracts and voids them. The following scheme shows the conversions which occur in the course of these processes.

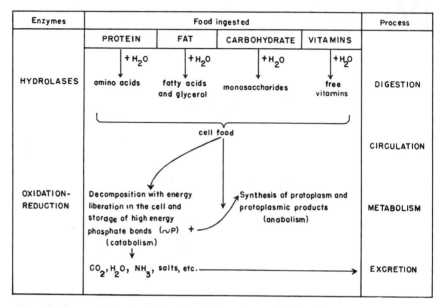

General scheme of animal nutrition. For colorless plants a similar scheme could be drawn. Such plants do not ingest food, however; instead, they secrete digestive enzymes, and they absorb the digested material. Green plants synthesize their own carbohydrates in the process of photosynthesis, and they synthesize other foods from carbohydrates and salts.

The nutrition pattern of green plants differs from that of animals in certain fundamental respects. Green plants contain chlorophyll, manufacturing their own carbohydrates which they store for future use, and from carbohydrates and salts they synthesize the various compounds they need. Digestion here (except in a few carnivorous plants) serves exclusively for mobilization of insoluble foods in storage depots (e.g., starch to sugars) and not for preparation of ingested food. As a consequence of the over-all synthetic character of plant metabolism, excretion of nitrogen compounds is limited, and much of the waste nitrogen resulting from cellular metabolism is recycled via the amides. Carbon dioxide, oxygen and sometimes water enter and leave by way of the stomata in the leaves. Water, nitrates, sulfates and other minerals are absorbed by the root cells. Some nonmetabolizable wastes are carried out to the bark or other tissues and deposited there. In the plant the xylem transports water and salts, and the phloem system distributes such cell foods as amino acids, glucose and vitamins so that each cell is adequately supplied by the sap.

The nutritional problems of an individual cell in a multicellular plant or animal organism are, in the final analysis, the same as the nutritional problems of a unicellular organism. It is these cell functions which particularly interest the cell physiologist.

The laws of thermodynamics which underlie all considerations of energy exchanges in cells are considered in Chapter 15. The nature of enzymes and their functions are considered in Chapter 16. The energy-liberating reactions of metabolism which provide the energy for maintenance of life in the cell are outlined in Chapter 17. The nature of oxidation-reduction in cells is dealt with in Chapter 18. Cell respiration, glycolysis and bioluminescence are discussed in Chapter 19 and photosynthesis in green plant cells, in Chapter 20.

APPLICATION OF THE LAWS OF THERMODYNAMICS TO THE CELL

Energy and Matter

Energy is the capacity to do work. There are two main types of energy: kinetic and potential. Kinetic energy of moving bodies is dealt with in physics and is of less concern at this point than the kinetic energy of molecules. *Kinetic energy of molecules (or heat) is energy of random motion.* The amount of molecular kinetic energy in a system is proportional to the absolute temperature of that system, and at absolute zero ($-273.18°$ C.) kinetic energy ceases to exist. For every $10°$ rise in temperature the kinetic energy increases by 10/absolute temperature (in degrees). The kinetic energy of molecules may be inferred from the Brownian movement (see Fig. 15.1) of very small but microscopically visible particles which move about more actively as the temperature rises. The random nature of Brownian movement is attributed to the random motion of molecules colliding with the visible particles and imparting to them sufficient energy for movement.[8] *Potential* energy (or generalized mechanical energy) is energy of position or bound energy, which can be released to produce kinetic energy. Potential energy may be electric, chemical, photic (light) or positional, such as that of a stone on the top of a hill.

That conversions between kinetic and potential energy occur should be obvious in a qualitative way to anyone who has ever lit a fire or hoisted a heavy object to a shelf. Any attempt to investigate these relations quantitatively, however, depends on the operation of the fundamental principles embodied in the first and second laws of thermodynamics.

Matter is that which occupies space and of which objects are made. Matter is converted to energy in nuclear fission and fusion, as, for example, in the atomic bomb and in the sun, but in ordinary chemical reactions this does not occur.

The Law of Conservation of Energy; the First Law of Thermodynamics[3, 4]

The law of conservation of energy states that energy can be neither created

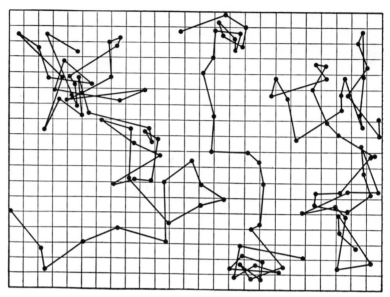

Fig. 15.1. Brownian movement of three particles. (From Perrin, 1913: Les Atomes. Alcan, Paris.)

nor destroyed but can be transformed from one form to another. For example, light absorbed on a black area, or electric energy in the resistance wire of a toaster, is converted to heat, and the energy in oil is converted to heat in an oil burner.

If energy is neither created nor destroyed, but only converted from one form to another, it follows that the total energy in a system isolated from the environment will neither increase nor decrease. This is another way of stating the first law of thermodynamics. When a given amount of chemical, electrical or photic energy disappears in an isolated system it is transformed into an equivalent amount of heat.

An *isolated system* is one which does not exchange energy with the surrounding environment. The universe itself may be considered an isolated system. On a smaller scale, a perfectly insulated container across the boundaries of which heat neither enters nor leaves can be used to isolate a chemical system. A thermos bottle or Dewar flask approximates such a container. Hot liquid placed in it will remain hot because the liquid is to some extent isolated from the surrounding environment by the vacuum between the two walls of the bottle. The greater the vacuum, the better the insulation, since heat is conducted only very slowly by the few molecules of air which remain in the vacuum. The degree of imperfection in the insulation is indicated by the time required for the liquid to cool. Heat is lost to the environment chiefly through the plug, although some is also lost by radiation.

For a study of energy exchanges in chemical systems a *calorimeter* is used. This may be nothing more than a large Dewar flask, or it may be a more elaborate piece of equipment following the same essential plan (see Fig. 15.2). The outermost jacket of the calorimeter is a good insulator and surrounds a chamber filled with water which absorbs the heat released by the sample in the combustion chamber, the innermost chamber. The water is actively stirred and its temperature is determined with a thermometer. Since perfect insulation of a calorimeter

CONVERSIONS OF ENERGY AND MATTER IN THE CELL

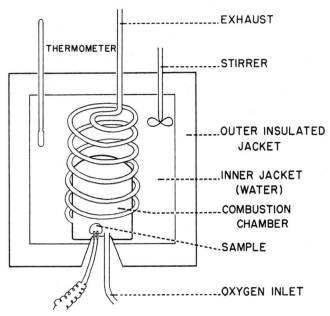

Fig. 15.2. A bomb calorimeter for determining heat of combustion of compounds.

...as not been attained, corrections must be made for the slight thermal leaks. Adequate corrections can be made by measuring the amount of electric energy required to produce an equal change in temperature in a comparable time lapse.

Degradation of Energy and the Second Law of Thermodynamics[1, 3, 4]

Although the total energy in an isolated system neither increases nor decreases, the transformations of energy from one form into another proceed in such a fashion that the capacity of the total energy to perform work decreases. That high grade potential energy in the system capable of performing work tends to become degraded to kinetic energy incapable of doing as much work is in essence a statement of the second law of thermodynamics.

High grade potential energy is often spoken of as energy with a high degree of orderliness, while low grade or molecular kinetic energy is said to be energy

of random movement. As potential energy changes to kinetic energy, the randomness or disorder increases. A thermodynamic function known as *entropy* is used by the physical chemist to measure the randomness of the energy of a system. Randomness of arrangement in nature is a more probable state than a special arrangement; entropy is a measure of the randomness of arrangement in atomic mechanics. Therefore, entropy may be defined in terms of probability. Entropy tends to increase because an increase in randomness is more likely in the molecular world than the reverse.

At absolute zero the entropy of a crystalline system is zero since the probability of randomness is nil. Entropy can therefore be measured, using absolute zero as a base line. The second law of thermodynamics might then be restated in terms of entropy; the entropy of an isolated system tends to increase.

Stated in still other terms, the second law of thermodynamics stipulates that in any transformation of one type of high grade potential energy into another type of potential energy, the efficiency of the process is not perfect because kinetic energy also always tends to be produced. The inefficiency of potential energy conversions is simply an expression of this tendency. It is exceedingly difficult to run against this tendency and to transform kinetic energy back into potential energy. Obviously this transformation can occur, as it does in the steam turbine or in the internal combustion engine, but in all of these cases only a small fraction of the kinetic energy is converted into useful work (see Appendix 15.1). Thus, whenever potential energy is degraded to kinetic energy, most of the work-producing capacity of the degraded portion is lost forever. Ultimately all the potential energy available in a system may be degraded to kinetic energy or heat, and, considering our universe as an isolated system, it is possible that over an almost infinite period the storehouse of high grade potential energy may become exhausted.

If all the potential energy in an isolated system is converted into heat, and no work is done by the system, the total energy conversion can be measured by the amount of heat evolved, using the calorimeter described (see Fig. 15.2). In such a system the chemical potential energy is first completely transformed to heat by combustion of the substance held in a platinum container and ignited electrically. Oxygen, usually under pressure, is supplied to the *combustion bomb* as needed. The carbon dioxide released in the reaction can be measured in the exhaust. If the volume of the water in the calorimeter is known and its rise in temperature is measured, the heat produced in the reaction can be determined. The *calorie* (often written cal.) is the amount of heat required to raise 1 gram of water 1 degree centigrade. For example, complete combustion of glucose ($C_6H_{12}O_6$) releases 673,000 calories per mole. By use of the calorimetric method, the caloric content of a large number of compound has been measured. Some of these values are given in Table 15.1.

The fundamental principle of the second law is part of the daily experiences of mankind. Everyone knows, for instance that water runs downhill and not uphill, its potential energy and capacity to do useful work decreasing the while. Everyone knows that the light energy of the sun is converted to heat on absorption but that production of light from heat requires the high heat of incandescence, indicating the relatively small likelihood of heat being converted to light. No means in fact, exists for storing light energy as such except transiently, although it is converted to, and stored as, chemical energy in green plants (Chapter 20) Electrical energy also may be stored only briefly and in small amounts in condensers. Chemical compounds, although often serving as good stores of potential chemical energy, also decompose, releasing their energy stores by such processes as oxidation. High grade energy, such as light, electric or chemical potential energy, having a high capacity for doing work, then, tends to become degraded to

TABLE 15.1. *Heats of Combustion of Various Organic Compounds in Calories per Mole*

Stearic acid	2,711,000
Sucrose	1,349,000
Glucose	673,000
Glycerol	397,000
Alanine	387,000
Ethyl alcohol	327,000
Lactic acid	326,000
Acetaldehyde	279,000
Acetic acid	209,000
Pyruvic acid†	279,100

Data from Handbook of Chemistry and Physics 35th Ed.
† From the International Critical Tables V: 165 1929.

ow grade or molecular kinetic energy capable of performing less work. Ultimately, all the potential energy in a system is degraded to kinetic energy or heat.

Chemical compounds are, relatively speaking, the best stores of potential energy, provided they are kept dry and away from catalysts which speed their decomposition. It is this fact that makes life possible. Plant cells trap the vast reserves of the sun's light energy, transforming the light into chemical potential energy of carbohydrates for later use. The carbohydrates may be converted to other foods for storage in the plant. Animals and microorganisms tap this reserve of chemicals in plants from which they obtain the energy necessary for their life activities. Man uses such energy reserves from his crops, and he exploits the energy reserves of coal and oil, plant products of ancient geologic eras. An attempt is being made at present to convert chemical and photic energy directly to electrical energy for special use in space satellites. Because such direct conversions occur with higher efficiency than indirect conversions (e.g., conversion of chemical energy of coal to heat and then conversion of the heat to electrical energy in a conventional electric plant), such studies may have vast practical applications in the future.[7] Man is also learning to use atomic energy effectively, opening an entirely new energy reserve.

Free Energy

The physical chemist is unable to assess the total energy content of an isolated system, but he is more interested in the changes in energy that occur within it, because from these he can learn a great deal about the reactions concerned.

The heat of reaction, ΔH (energy content of the products minus the energy content of the reactants), is written with a negative sign, $-\Delta H$, if heat is lost to the environment and with a plus sign, $+\Delta H$, if heat is gained from the environment. For example, for the combustion of glucose in a calorimeter in which no external work is done:

$$C_6H_{12}O_6 + 6\,O_2 \rightarrow 6\,CO_2 + 6\,H_2O \quad (15.1)$$

ΔH = energy content of products— energy content of reactants
= $-673,000$ cal./mole (at 25° C.).

Of greater theoretical interest than the heat of reaction is the *change in free energy* (ΔF), which represents the maximum work that can be obtained from a given reaction. The change in free energy (free energy of products minus the free energy of reactants) of a reaction occurring reversibly at constant temperature and pressure may be defined in terms of changes in entropy (ΔS) and the heat of reaction:

ΔF = free energy of products— free energy of reactants, or
$$\Delta F = \Delta H - T\Delta S \quad (15.2)$$

where T is the absolute temperature.

The free energy change (ΔF) of a reaction bears no simple relation to the change in energy content (ΔH). Though the two quantities are often similar in size and sign, they are sometimes very different. This difference between ΔF and ΔH arises from the difference in entropy between reactants and products.

The change in free energy (ΔF) of a reaction may be greater than the ΔH. Thus if heat is absorbed from the surroundings during the course of a reaction, more useful work may be accomplished than would be possible if only the energy liberated in the reaction were available for performance of work. For instance, in the combustion of glucose, ΔF (at 25° C.) is $-688,160$ calories per mole compared to a ΔH of $-673,000$ calories per mole. On the other hand, when the work performed during a reaction is less than the energy liberated in the reaction, the ΔF of the reaction is less than the ΔH.

If the ΔF of a reaction is negative; that is, if the free energy decreases, the reaction is spontaneous. If the ΔF of a reaction is positive, the reaction will not occur spontaneously, and high grade energy must be supplied in some manner to make it go.

It is possible to relate the change in free energy to the equilibrium constant for a reaction.[3] Thus, in the reaction:

$$A + B \rightleftharpoons C + D \qquad (15.3)$$

at equilibrium, application of the law of mass action gives the following expression:

$$\frac{[C] [D]}{[A] [B]} = K \qquad (15.4)$$

where K is the equilibrium constant.

If K is 1, no reaction will occur when equivalent concentrations of the reactants are mixed. If K is less than 1, the reaction will proceed to the right; if K is more than 1, it will proceed to the left.

The change in free energy (ΔF) for the reaction is related to its equilibrium constant (K) in the following way:

$$\Delta F = -RT \ln K \qquad (15.5)$$

where R is the gas constant (about 2.0 cal./mole/degree), T is the absolute temperature and ln is the natural logarithm (2.3 times the logarithm to the base 10).

Coupled Reactions

A reaction which occurs with a decrease in free energy ($-\Delta F$) is said to be *exergonic*. One which occurs with an increase in free energy ($+\Delta F$) is said to be *endergonic*. The oxidation of glucose is an example of the first, and photosynthesis is an example of the second. In biochemical reactions in the cell the free energy is not truly liberated but is conserved as special bond energy in high energy bonds and is thus passed on to other molecules to be used by them to form new bonds. This is illustrated in Figure 15.3 for a whole series of biological reactions, in which cell work is accomplished at the expense of such bond energy. Each of these cases is dealt with in more detail elsewhere.

In many synthetic biological reactions the energy is supplied in the form of labile high energy phosphate bonds (see Chapter 17) from exergonic reactions coupled with endergonic reactions. By this means a complex compound may be synthesized seemingly in contradiction to the second law of thermodynamics. However, the energy of the exergonic reaction is utilized in the synthesis so that the net effect is the degradation of free energy available in the system consisting of all the components entering into the coupled reactions. We shall consider one specific example of coupled exergonic and endergonic reactions. The reaction between coenzyme A and acetic acid to form the compound acetyl-coenzyme A proceeds with an increase in free energy and is therefore not spontaneous. However, if adenosine triphosphate is present the reaction between coenzyme A proceeds spontaneously with a decrease in free energy, the triphosphate being degraded to a diphosphate with the liberation of inorganic phosphate (low energy form). The acetic acid is meanwhile coupled to coenzyme A by virtue of the energy transferred from the adenosine triphosphate.

In such coupled reactions occurring in the cell, the participants normally share atoms. The major problem, however, is to determine, at the molecular level, the nature of the constraint which prevents the reaction from merely going downhill without doing work and which makes possible instead coupling and transference of the energy. In some cases the constraint is the stability of the high energy molecule, which "forbids" the uncoupled breakdown. For example, in the presence of the appropriate enzyme, creatine phosphate readily transfers its high energy phosphate to adenosine diphosphate,

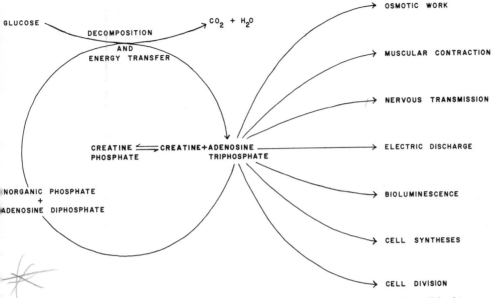

Fig. 15.3. High energy phosphate bonds and cell work. Energy from glucose (or other cell foods) made available during its anaerobic and aerobic decomposition in the cells is transferred to an inorganic phosphate which is thus linked by a resonant, high energy phosphate bond to adenosine diphosphate (ADP) making it into adenosine triphosphate (ATP). The ATP may donate its high energy phosphate ($\triangle$F = about 8000 calories per mole) to creatin (C) forming creatin phosphate (CP) as a storage depot of high energy bonds; or it may transfer the energy in coupled reactions performing all kinds of cell work. Only osmotic work has already been considered (Chapter 13); other types of cell work are discussed in subsequent chapters. High energy phosphate bonds are probably stored in metabolizing parts of all cells. (For other high energy phosphate compounds, see Chapter 17.)

forming, as a result, adenosine triphosphate. But it does not do this by itself without the enzyme. Enzymes thus facilitate reactions along pathways useful to the cell (see Chapter 16).

Entropy and the Second Law of Thermodynamics

As already pointed out, the change in total energy content (ΔH) is not a measure of the free energy change (ΔF) in a reaction. The total energy change consists of two components—the utilizable energy change (ΔF) and the nonutilizable energy change ($T\Delta S$), or change in entropy times the absolute temperature (T):

$$\Delta H = \Delta F + T\Delta S \qquad (15.6)$$

Equation 15.6, rearranged, is the same as equation 15.2.

For a specific reaction $A \rightleftharpoons B$ (15.7)

the ΔH can be determined if the heat of combustion of each of the reactants, A and B, is determined. This can be done in a bomb calorimeter (Fig. 15.2). If, for this hypothetical example, the heat of combustion of A is taken to be 5000 calories per mole and that of B, 2000 calories per mole, then for the reaction at the arbitrary temperature of 27° C. (300 degrees absolute):

$$(A - B) = (5000 - 2000) \text{ or}$$

3000 calories of heat would be given up; therefore $\Delta H = -3000$ calories per mole.

If we assume that the entropy change on going from A to B was 10, substituting this value into equation 15.2:

$$\Delta F = \Delta H - T\Delta S,$$
$$\text{or } (-3000) - (300 \times 10) =$$
$$-6000 \text{ calories per mole.}$$

In this case the entropy term contributes significantly to the free energy change.[15] The entropy term may be large or small.

While some reactions can be performed in such a way that they are practically reversible, all spontaneous reactions are largely, if not completely, irreversible, and the change in entropy in a reaction indicates its degree of irreversibility. If the symbol S designates entropy, and ΔS, the difference in entropy between the beginning and the end of the reaction, then:

$$\Delta S = S_b - S_e = q/T, \text{ where} \tag{15.8}$$

S_b is the entropy at the beginning of a reaction,
S_e is the entropy at the end of the reaction,
q is the heat absorbed from the surroundings
and T is the absolute temperature.

The second law of thermodynamics may now be stated in terms of entropy: the entropy of a system increases with the progression of spontaneous reactions. Part of a system may show a decrease of entropy while another part shows an increase. This is true in coupled reactions and occurs in many biological syntheses. However, the entropy of the entire system always shows an net increase.

The Cell and the Laws of Thermodynamics

Biological reactions all take place in solution—gases are dissolved before being used in the cell; therefore, with few exceptions, such reactions may be considered as systems occurring at constant pressure and at constant volume (changes in volume being negligible). Even more important, cells can function when they are at uniform temperature. Thermal gradients may occur temporarily in cells of a tissue when heat is produced and thermal conductivity is limited, but the thermal gradients are incidental, not essential to cellular functions. The second law of thermodynamics, therefore, can be applied in a simplified form because, in a system at constant temperature, it is impossible to convert heat into work. Comparing a cell to a heat engine is thus misleading, since a heat engine converts heat into work only because of the thermal gradients within it (see Appendix 15.1).

High grade energy capable of doing work in the cell is continuously converted into heat during cell reactions, and since the opposite cannot occur, the change is irreversible. Although the different kinds of free energy (e.g., mechanical work, electrical energy, chemical energy, light, etc.) can be freely interconverted from one form to another, the interconversion is never complete. That part of the free energy not converted into a new form must appear as heat (in accordance with the first law of thermodynamics). The degree to which free energy is degraded to heat is therefore a measure of the inefficiency of the conversion process. Consequently, free energy must be continuously supplied to the cell from the outside if the cell is to remain alive.

When there are no coupled reactions, no work is done and the heat produced (ΔH) equals the sum of the entropy term ($T\Delta S$) and the free energy term (ΔF). When coupling between two reactions is perfect and no free energy is degraded, as in a reversible process, the work done equals the free energy change (ΔF). In the cell, only a fraction of the free energy, whose size (ϵ) depends upon the effectiveness of the coupling mechanism, is made available for work:

$$\text{Work done} = -\epsilon\Delta F \tag{15.9}$$

The remainder of the free energy is then given off as heat.

One simple rule which emerges from such studies is that actual absorption of heat can occur only if an entropy term is nvolved. The free energy term can lead to evolution of heat or to no heat change at all.[14] It is important to realize that when heat is measured experimentally, it comes from these two sources which are quite different and distinct. The first ($T\Delta S$) is incidental and reversible, the second (ΔF) is irreversible.

It should also be obvious from a thermodynamic point of view that a living cell must obtain as food some simple molecules with considerable energy. These can be built into any of the complex and improbable molecules (molecules of low entropy) characteristic of living materials. Such molecules are the proteins which are denatured with a large increase in entropy, indicating that the structure becomes random during denaturation.[14] It is for this reason that the temperature coefficient for protein denaturation is so high (see Chapter 10).

The cell is never in equilibrium with its environment, except perhaps in death. Rather, the cell maintains a *steady state* and constitutes an *open system* in continuous energy exchange with its environment. Since classical thermodynamic relationships were developed for a system in equilibrium, the question arises whether such reasoning is applicable to a particular reaction occurring in a cell.

The problem of accumulation, storage and expenditure of free energy (i.e., energy with maximum work capacity) by cells is independent of whether these cells are in a steady state condition or in equilibrium states. A given reaction occurring in the cell cannot liberate more energy or less energy than it liberates in the test tube, where its thermodynamics can be used to determine only whether a reaction of known ΔF will or will not occur. Such thermodynamic properties of the reaction in the cell cannot be determined by the classical methods because the cell is not in equilibrium with its environment and the reactions do not therefore come to equilibrium. A new and different approach is necessary for this purpose, and

the subject of thermodynamics of irreversible processes or open systems is being intensively studied at the present time. This is one of the instances where a biological problem has prompted physical scientists to explore a neglected field of physical-chemical theory.[9, 16]

Classical thermodynamics is limited in another respect. While it predicts, for a reaction of known ΔF, whether the reaction will or will not occur, it can predict nothing as to the rate of the reaction. A new physical-chemical reaction-rate theory (see p. 206), which relates the free energy change to the rate of reaction, has been used for such studies. The relationship between the reaction rate and the free energy change is linear only when the reaction proceeds near equilibrium.[14] From reaction-rate studies it can be shown that an open system, in which several reactions are proceeding, does not show sustained oscillations. Indeed, because each individual reaction continues to proceed at a constant rate the over-all reactions settle down to a stationary state in which the amounts and concentrations of the various reactants remain constant even though the reactions are proceeding. This stationary state is also one in which occurs the lowest possible rate of energy dissipation, or entropy production. When extraneous changes are introduced into the system such a system likewise alters spontaneously in such a way as to reduce to a minimum its energy dissipation, or entropy production. The stationary state thus has somewhat the appearance of an equilibrium, and is very similar to what goes on in the living cell.[14]

The Laws of Energy Exchange and Life

When a gram molecular weight of glucose is burned in a calorimeter, 6 moles of oxygen are used, 6 moles of carbon dioxide are evolved, and 673,000 calories of heat are liberated. If the organism obeys the laws of thermodynamics, it should also use 6 moles of oxygen, evolve

6 moles of carbon dioxide and liberate 673,000 calories of heat in a calorimeter for each gram molecular weight of glucose burned. This is on the assumption, however, that only carbohydrate is being used by the living cells of the organism, a subject which will be further discussed in Chapter 19.

At about the time of the American Revolution, and even before the law of conservation of energy was fully appreciated by physical scientists, the great French scientists, Lavoisier and Laplace, devised a primitive calorimeter to study the nature of energy conversions in living organisms. (See Figure 15.4.) Around a cage containing a guinea pig they placed an ice jacket which absorbed heat produced during the experiment, and the heat was measured by the amount of water obtained from the melted ice. They isolated this system by surrounding it with another ice jacket, which absorbed all heat entering from the environment. So long as ice was present, both ice jackets remained at a temperature of 0° C.; therefore no heat was transferred from one jacket to the other although some ice melted in each, as shown by control tests, and the inner chamber was, therefore, effectively isolated. Lavoisier and Laplace collected the water from the ice melted in the inner chamber, and from its volume (heat of fusion is 79.7 calories; that is, 79.7 calories are required to melt one gram of ice) they determined the total amount of heat produced by the guinea pig in 10 hours (enough to melt 341 grams of ice). In a parallel experiment they determined the amount of carbon dioxide produced in the same period and from this calculated the amount of carbon oxidized.[2, 5] Comparison of the energy liberated by the oxidation of the same amount of carbon, on the one hand, in chemical combustion (enough to melt 326.7 grams of ice), and, on the other, in the animal, indicated that the values were of the same order of magnitude. The difference in the values prob-

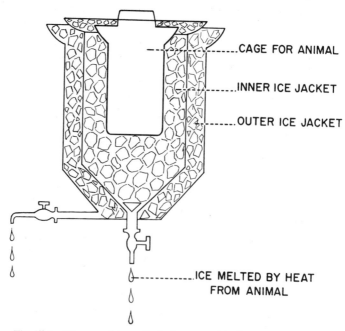

CAGE FOR ANIMAL

INNER ICE JACKET

OUTER ICE JACKET

ICE MELTED BY HEAT FROM ANIMAL

Fig. 15.4. Diagram of type of calorimeter used by Lavoisier and Laplace.

bly stems chiefly from calculation of the combustion on the basis of carbon alone. In the organism carbohydrate is burned. When this is taken into consideration, as in modern calorimetry, the agreement is much closer.

The calorimeters in use today for biological research are considerably more elaborate, but the essential plan is still the same—to isolate a given system by good insulation and to measure the heat evolved, the oxygen consumed and the carbon dioxide produced. Figure 15.5 is a diagram of a modern calorimeter. The heat is caught in water passed through the chamber at a constant rate, the temperature of the water being determined at the entry and exit points by thermocouples. The amount of oxygen entering is determined by flow meters, the amount of carbon dioxide is determined after absorption in soda lime (a mixture of sodium hydroxide and calcium hydroxide) and water vapor is absorbed in sulfuric acid.

It is now known from data obtained by calorimetry that, whether a given amount of carbohydrate is oxidized completely to carbon dioxide and water by an organism or in a bomb calorimeter, the same amount of heat is produced. Undoubtedly the oxidation of a given compound in the organism occurs by pathways different from those in the bomb calorimeter. However, it has been demonstrated that in a bomb calorimeter, regardless of the pathway by which the combustion occurs, if the compound is oxidized to the same degree (in the case of the carbohydrate cited, completely to carbon dioxide and water), the amount of energy released is the same. Since energy is neither created nor destroyed (first law of thermodynamics), this could have been inferred.

The findings of calorimetry are of profound significance since they indicate that in living cells, as in the inanimate world, the energy transformations are described by the same physical-chemical laws. Since energy transformations underlie all the work done by the organism, they are basic to our further studies in cell physiology.

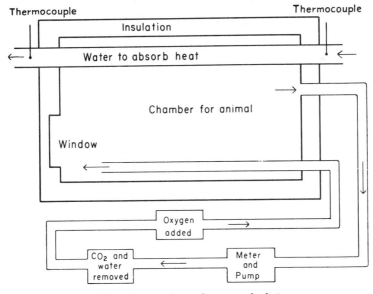

Fig. 15.5. Diagram of a modern type of calorimeter.

The organism oxidizes only a fraction of the food it obtains; much chemical potential energy is stored in compounds in organisms as reserve potential energy for future use. These reserves accumulate in different places in different organisms. In unicellular organisms and cells, excess food is stored in the form of oil globules and starch or glycogen granules. Occasionally protein is also stored. Multicellular plants store reserves in bulbs, tubers, roots, seeds and fruit as starches, sugars, fats or even proteins. Multicellular animals usually store glycogen in the muscles, and fat in fat bodies. In man, glycogen is stored in the liver and muscles while fat is stored subcutaneously and in the greater and lesser omenta that suspend the digestive organs. When the diet provides insufficient food for the organism to maintain itself, the reserves are utilized first, and when these are gone the cell substance is attacked.

Heat is produced not only by warm-blooded animals but by all living things. Witness the heat of the manure pile, resulting from the action of microorganisms; notice the warmth of germinating seeds, accumulated from the metabolic activities of the cells, or the heat produced in a beehive by the muscular activities of bees. Even fish produce heat when actively swimming, but this is rapidly dissipated into the environment since water is a fair conductor of heat.

The Law of Conservation of Matter in the Living World

It has been known for a long time that in the course of chemical reactions elements enter into various combinations with one another, but that the elements can always be recovered from the compounds. There is neither an increase nor a decrease in the amount of each of the elements participating in the reactions; in other words, matter is neither created nor destroyed but is only transformed

from one form to another. This is a statement of the law of conservation of matter. In atomic fission, matter is converted into energy, but in ordinary chemical reactions the law has been established as a fundamental principle.

Elements enter into various combinations in the course of the chemical reactions which occur in the cells of organisms. Organic compounds are produced by green plants in photosynthesis. Carbohydrates, among the earliest products of photosynthesis, may be converted by a plant into amino acids, fatty acids and a multitude of other organic compounds. The plant may be eaten by an animal which uses the organic compounds from the plant as cell foods to convert them into compounds necessary for the activities of its own cells. The animal cell may in turn serve as food for another animal. Both animal and plant, on death, serve as food for microorganisms of decomposition and decay. This series of interconversions of carbon compounds is known as the *carbon cycle* and is illustrated in Figure 15.6. The details of some of these conversions are omitted here but will be discussed to some extent in Chapters 17 and 20 on metabolism and photosynthesis.

Plant cells build nitrogen-containing compounds such as amino acids and proteins by adding an amino group to the carbon compounds produced in photosynthesis. The nitrogen in nitrates or ammonia obtained from the soil is used for this purpose. The animal uses plant proteins to build its own cells and voids the excess nitrogen thus acquired, as well as other metabolic nitrogenous wastes, as urea, uric acid or ammonia. An animal may also obtain proteins by using another animal as food. On death, both plants and animals are used as food by microorganisms of decay and their nitrogen is again put into circulation. This set of relations, known as the *nitrogen cycle*, is shown in Figure 15.7. Details of some of

CONVERSIONS OF ENERGY AND MATTER IN THE CELL

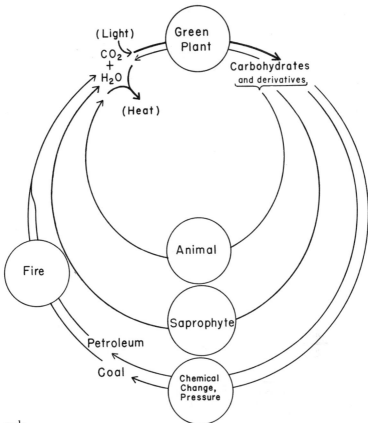

(Light)

CO_2
+
H_2O

Green
Plant

Carbohydrates
and derivatives,

(Heat)

Fire

Animal

Saprophyte

Petroleum

Coal

Chemical
Change,
Pressure

Fig. 15.6. The carbon cycle.

hese conversions will be discussed in Chapter 17 on metabolism.

Cycles similar to the carbon or nitrogen cycles could be outlined for phosphorus, sulfur and other elements used by the living cell, but the two cycles presented illustrate the major features: namely, that a given element is shuttled from compound to compound and from organism to organism, all the while forming various combinations with other elements.

No reason has ever been found to doubt that the law of conservation of matter applies to the living world. Many experiments, especially recent ones using compounds marked with radioactive carbon or isotopes of nitrogen, indicate that the carbon or nitrogen in the conversions of the carbon, nitrogen or other cycles can be accounted for quantitatively. Balance sheets for experiments show that the amount of an element, supplied in nutrients, that is taken up by an organism can be traced in the organism and recovered in the various compounds synthesized or excreted by it.

Since life has existed for millions of years, it may be inferred that conservation of matter is necessary for continuance of life; the same elements must be used over and over again, and, in fact, turnover rates have been calculated for some of them (see Chapter 20 for carbon and oxygen turnover). Atoms which today form part of one organism may have formed part of another organism years ago and some day may form part of still

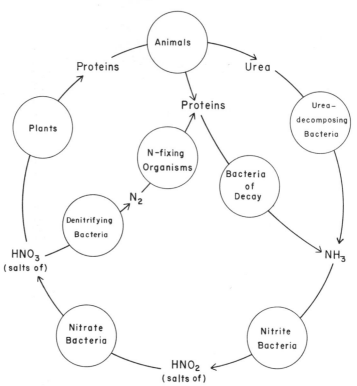

Fig. 15.7. The nitrogen cycle. While some animals excrete urea as the main nitrogenous waste (along with small amounts of ammonia and uric acid), others void uric acid as the main nitrogenous waste. Still others void ammonia. Uric acid, like urea, is decomposed by bacteria to ammonia and carbon dioxide.

another. Material transformations in the living cell and the organism are, therefore, governed by the same physical-chemical laws that apply to the inanimate world. Indeed, the very fact that metabolic studies are possible is an expression of the applicability of the laws of conservation of matter and energy.

Conversion of Mass to Energy, and the General Law of Conservation

According to Einstein's theory of relativity, the equivalence of mass and energy can be represented by the equation,

$$E = mc^2, \qquad (15.10)$$

where E is the energy, m the mass converted in the atomic shrinkage and c the velocity of light. If m is given in grams and c is taken as 3×10^{10} cm. per sec., then E will be in ergs: $E = m(9 \times 10^{20})$. To convert to calories, the value for E (in ergs) is divided by 4.18×10^7.

The total mass of a uranium 235 nucleus and a neutron is known to be greater than the mass of the immediate products resulting from atomic fission. For fission of a kilogram of uranium 235, the decrease in mass is just about 1 gram. This amounts to about 2.1×10^{13} calories and is equivalent to 20,000 tons of TNT (trinitrotoluene), or to the daily output of the Hoover Dam (2.3×10^7 kilowatt hours of electricity).[6] For the mechanism of fission the student is referred to textbooks of modern physics.

The conversion of matter to energy indicates that perhaps the laws of conservation of matter and energy should be

300

tated in even broader terms than has been the custom in the past, namely that matter and energy can neither be created nor destroyed although under certain conditions they can be converted from one to another. This implies that matter may also be created from energy, a view for which some evidence exists. However, it must be remembered that in the ordinary reactions which occur in the living cell, the laws of conservation of energy and matter apply in the strict and conventional sense.

Whereas matter circulates between the environment and living things, coming in to form parts of cells and then returning to the environment upon their death, and again finding its way into another organism at a future time, the movement of energy is unidirectional. High grade energy comes into the green plant cell as light from the sun; some of it is stored as chemical energy in carbohydrates and other foods, while some of it is degraded to low grade energy in which form it leaves the living cell. Thus, in nature the flow of matter is cyclic, whereas, essentially, the flow of energy is not.

APPENDIX

15.1 Heat Engines and the Carnot Cycle

The Carnot engine is a theoretical machine in which all the processes are carried out under ideal conditions and without losses of heat energy by radiation or conduction. The machine receives the energy at T_H which is cooled to T_L in doing work. The maximal efficiency, $ef.$, of a Carnot engine has been shown to be:

$$ef. = \frac{T_H - T_L}{T_H} \qquad (15.11)$$

Here T_H represents the high temperature and T_L the low, and the values are given in degrees Kelvin or absolute temperature. For example, if steam at $200°$ C.

(473° K.) is cooled to 40° C. (313° K.) while driving a steam engine, the maximum efficiency achievable is:

$$ef. = \frac{473 - 313}{473} = 0.34$$

In practice a maximum of about 23 per cent efficiency is obtained, and it may be considerably less.

GENERAL REFERENCES

von Bertalanffy, L., 1952: Problems of Life. Wiley, New York, p. 126, Open Systems.

Blum, H. F., 1955: Time's Arrow and Evolution. 2nd Ed. Princeton Univ. Press, Princeton, New Jersey, Ch. 3, Energetics and Kinetics of Chemical Reaction.

Edsall, J. T., and Wyman, J., 1958: Biophysical Chemistry, in Thermodynamics, Electrostatics and the Biological Significance of the Properties of Matter. Academic Press, New York, Vol. I.

Eyring, H., Boyce, R. P., and Spikes, J. D., 1960: Thermodynamics of Living Systems. Comp. Biochem. 2:15.

Florkin, M., and Mason, H. S. (eds.), 1960: Sources of Free Energy. Comp. Biochem. 1:1.

Prigogine, I., 1962. Introduction to Thermodynamics of Irreversible Processes. 2nd Ed. Thomas, Springfield, Ill.

Wilkie, D. R., 1960: Thermodynamics and the Interpretation of Biological Heat Measurements. Progr. Biophys. 10:260.

LITERATURE CITED

1. Blum, H. F., 1955: Time's Arrow and Evolution. 2nd Ed. Princeton Univ. Press, Princeton, New Jersey, Ch. 3.
2. Gabriel, M., and Fogel, S., 1955: Great Experiments in Biology. Prentice-Hall, New York.
3. Glasstone, S., 1960. Elements of Physical Chemistry. 2nd Ed. Van Nostrand, New York.
4. Höber, R. (ed.), 1945: Physical Chemistry of Cells and Tissues. Blakiston, Philadelphia, Ch. 3.
5. Suner, A. P., 1955: Classics of Biology. Pitman, London, Ch. 1.
6. Los Alamos Scientific Laboratory, 1950: The Effects of Atomic Weapons. U. S. Government Printing Office, Washington.
7. Egli, P. H., 1960: Am. Scient. 48:311.

8. Alder, B. J., and Wainwright, T. E., Oct. 1959: Sci. Am. *201*:113.
9. Eyring, H., Boyce, R. P., and Spikes, J. D., 1960: Comp. Biochem. *1*:15.
10. Pasynskii, A. G., 1957: Uspekhi Sovremenmoi Biol. *43*:263.
11. Baas-Becking, L. G. M., and Kaplan, I. R., 1956: Koninkl. Ned. Akad. Wetenschap., Proc. Ser. B *59*:85, 97.
12. von Bertalanffy, L., 1952: Problems of Life. Wiley, New York.
13. Wilson, P. W., 1955: Perspectives in Microbiology (Waksman, S. ed.) Rutgers Univ. Press, New Brunswick, New Jersey, p. 110.
14. Wilkie, D. R., 1960: Progr. Biophys. *10*:260.
15. McElroy, W. D., 1961: Cellular Physiology and Biochemistry. Prentice-Hall, Englewood Cliffs, New Jersey, Ch. 4.
16. Prigogine, I., 1962: Introduction to Thermodynamics of Irreversible Processes. 2nd Ed. Thomas, Springfield, Ill.

CHAPTER 16

CELLULAR ENZYMES

Lowering the Energy of Activation by Enzymes

An *enzyme* is a biocatalyst made up of protein, and like other catalysts* it accelerates the rate of a reaction without itself being used up, except incidentally in side reactions. It is safe to assume that most hydrolytic, oxidative or other reactions occurring in the cell are catalyzed by enzymes. Only a few reactions, some examples of which will be cited later, may be rapid enough without them.[1] The main function of a catalyst is to lower the energy of activation (kinetic energy) required of a molecule before the molecule can proceed in a particular reaction. In other words, the catalyst lowers the energy barrier over which a molecule must pass (Fig. 16.1). It thus increases the rate of the reaction because at any given temperature there is the probability that the number of molecules having a lower amount of energy will be greater than the number having a larger amount of energy (see Fig. 10.3). Enzymes function in this manner in the cell. For example, the energy of activation for the decomposition of hydrogen peroxide to water and oxygen is 18,000 calories per

mole. In the presence of the enzyme catalase, which occurs in all aerobic cells, it is only 5500 calories per mole. The advantage of enzymes to the cell, which must operate at what a chemist would consider a relatively low temperature, is self-evident. It is therefore not surprising that almost all the reactions in the cell are catalyzed by enzymes.

A very important aspect of enzyme action is the channeling of reactions along certain pathways. Thus many reactions may be thermodynamically possible (spontaneous) but do not occur at a finite rate. Selected reactions may be promoted by supplying the appropriate enzymes. Thus, in a sense, by supplying the required enzymes the cell achieves control over a series of possible reactions[25] (see p. 292).

It is not known whether it is possible for the cell to make enzymes to catalyze any chosen reaction, or whether they can be made only for certain types of reactions. If the latter is true, then the meta-

---

* The term "catalyst" is used by the physical chemist for a substance which alters the rate of a reaction. Consequently, negative catalysis is possible. The word is used here in the popular sense, i.e., a substance which accelerates a reaction.

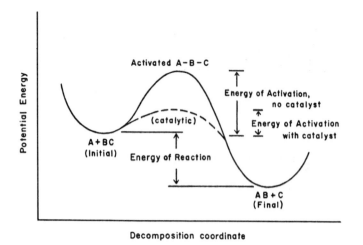

Fig. 16.1. Potential energy diagram for a reaction occurring in one case in the absence and in another case in the presence of a catalyst. Before reacting, the molecules must accumulate sufficient kinetic energy (energy of activation) to pass over the energy barrier represented by the rising curve, even though the reaction occurs with a loss in free energy (approximately indicated by the heat of reaction). In the presence of a catalyst the energy of activation is considerably less than in its absence.

bolic chain of reactions not only must satisfy the energetic requirements, but it must be channeled by means of such enzymes as are possible.[25]

Although an enzyme cannot increase the amount of energy obtainable from a given chemical reaction, it can enormously increase the efficiency with which the energy is obtained. The effect of the enzyme is thus to raise what might be called the chemical conductance, thereby permitting a given rate of energy production with a lower dissipation of free energy.

Hydrolytic Enzymes—Hydrolysis

Hydrolysis is the process by which a compound is split into fragments by the addition of water. The manner in which proteins, fats and polysaccharides are hydrolyzed is of special importance because all these compounds are necessary for maintenance of life, yet they are large molecules and thus usually do not penetrate through the cell membrane. Such hydrolyses are illustrated in Figure 16.2.

Hydrolyses are spontaneous reactions in which a small amount of energy is liberated; that is, they occur with a net decrease in free energy. However, in the absence of a catalyst, they often proceed too slowly to be measured. For instance, it is an everyday experience that a piece of meat placed in water does not noticeably hydrolyze into its consituent amino acids, nor does starch seemingly hydrolyze to sugar when suspended in water, provided that growth of microorganisms is prevented. This means that the number of molecules having the requisite energy of activation is too small to give a perceptible change. However, addition of a small amount of acid to either of the above substances catalyzes their hydrolysis, which occurs especially rapidly if heat is also applied. In animals, plants and microorganisms, hydrolyses are catalyzed by enzymes.

Enzymes which help to hydrolyze or split complex foods such as proteins, carbohydrates and fats into smaller residues are known as hydrolytic enzymes (i.e., hydrolases) or digestive enzymes, and the process of hydrolysis is also spoken of as digestion. Hydrolases are present inside all cells and make possible intracellular movements of proteins, lipids and carbohydrates.

In unicellular organisms, hydrolysis or digestion is often intracellular. For example, Amoeba and Paramecium form food vacuoles that enclose the food which

CONVERSIONS OF ENERGY AND MATTER IN THE CELL

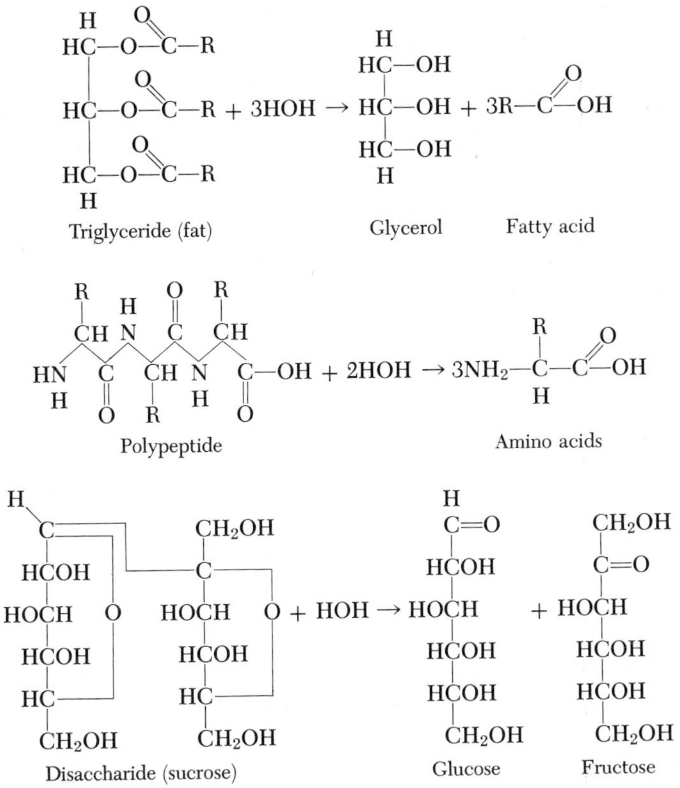

$$
\begin{array}{l}
\text{HC—O—C—R} \\
\text{HC—O—C—R} + 3\text{HOH} \rightarrow \text{HC—OH} + 3\text{R—C—OH} \\
\text{HC—O—C—R}
\end{array}
$$

Triglyceride (fat) Glycerol Fatty acid

Polypeptide $+ 2\text{HOH} \rightarrow 3\text{NH}_2\text{—C—C—OH}$

Polypeptide Amino acids

Disaccharide (sucrose) $+ \text{HOH} \rightarrow$ Glucose $+$ Fructose

Fig. 16.2. Diagrams of the digestion of food by hydrolysis.

s hydrolyzed there; the cell foods resulting from hydrolysis pass through the vacuolar membrane into the cell, and the indigestible residues are voided into the medium. Bacteria, however, digest their foods by secreting enzymes onto the substrate, which is then liquefied during hydrolysis, and the cell foods are absorbed by the bacteria.

In multicellular animals, digestion of a food may occur in steps, each of which may be localized in a separate part of the digestive system. For example, starch digestion in man (and a few other vertebrates) begins in the mouth, being catalyzed by an enzyme secreted by the cells of the salivary glands. Starch digestion continues further along the pathway, aided by the action of enzymes from the cells of the pancreas and the walls of the

small intestine. Proteolysis, or protein hydrolysis, in all vertebrates begins in the stomach (acid phase) and then continues in the small intestine (alkaline phase), assisted by the action of pancreatic juice and later by the action of intestinal wall juices. Fat digestion, however, occurs in one step, catalyzed in the small intestine by enzymes from cells of the pancreas. In some insects and higher mollusks, the digestive tract is divided into distinct regions, each with its specific functions and enzymes. In the lower invertebrate, digestion is more variable. It may occur intracellularly or by amebocytes. When it occurs in the lumen of the gut, it is likely to be localized in a single stomach-intestine, the separation of phases usually being less distinct than in the vertebrates.

Digested foods pass into the blood

stream of an animal and are distributed to all the cells of the body. Food in excess over immediate needs is deposited in places of storage, usually after polymerization or combination with other compounds into insoluble forms, e.g., glycogen (in liver and muscle), fat (in adipose tissue) and protein (in muscle).

In multicellular green plants, digestion is intracellular, and digested foods move into the sap and are thus carried to each cell. Excess of manufactured food goes into storage, e.g., sugar (in fruit), starch (in potatoes), fat (in nuts), protein (in beans), etc. Here digestion is concerned mainly with hydrolysis of foods into a form suitable for transport from regions of storage to regions of growth. An exception is found in carnivorous plants, in which digestion, resembling the process in animals, may occur at the tips of glandular hairs, as in the sundew, *Drosera*, or in a cavity, as in a modified leaf of the pitcher plant, *Darlingtonia*. Furthermore, by the activities of hydrolytic enzymes, foods in storage depots can be mobilized when need arises. They then move into the blood for intercellular relocation to places where foods are required.

Specificity of Hydrolytic Enzymes

Proteins are essentially polymers of amino acids; carbohydrates, such as polysaccharides, are polymers of monosaccharides; and fats are conjugates of glycerol and fatty acids. Large molecules such as these are usually hydrolyzed in several steps, each step being catalyzed by a specific enzyme.

For example, a protein molecule is split first by the *endopeptidases* into smaller fragments from the ends of which amino acids are hydrolyzed by the *exopeptidases*. The exopeptidases perform their work more effectively after the action of endopeptidases, since more ends of protein fragments then become available upon which they may act.

Three familiar endopeptidases are pepsin, secreted by cells of the stomach a vertebrate, and chymotrypsin and trypsin, present in the pancreatic juice. The high degree of specificity is shown by the fact that each one attacks a particular linkage between amino acids. Pepsin attacks protein, or protein fragment, on the amino side of the peptide bond between tyrosine (or phenylalanine) and other amino acids. Chymotrypsin attacks the carboxyl end of the bond between tyrosine (or phenylalanine, tryptophan and methionine) and other amino acids (see Fig. 16.3). Trypsin acts at the carboxyl end of lysine or arginine residues.[2]

Exopeptidases are also specific in action. Aminopolypeptidases attack a polypeptide on the end where a free amino group exists; carboxypolypeptidases attack a polypeptide on the end where a free carboxyl group exists. The result of each reaction is the production of a free amino acid and a polypeptide molecule reduced in molecular weight. Dipeptidases attack only dipeptides, producing amino acids as products. Many dipeptidases probably exist, each one specific to a particular dipeptide.[3]

The *carbohydrases*, which catalyze hydrolysis of carbohydrates, are also specific. Between the glucose molecules in starch there are two types of linkage, one of which is attacked by alpha amylase and the other, by beta amylase. The net effect of digestion of the various hexosans (polymerized hexoses, see Table 3.1) is the formation of monosaccharides, primarily glucose. However, plant cells also produce and store pentosans (polymerized pentoses) and have enzymes by which these are hydrolyzed into pentoses.

Certain animals and plants have a variety of special carbohydrases which enable them to cope with hexosans or pentosans. Some protozoans in termites possess a cellulase that enables them to digest cellulose in wood to glucose. Some of the bacteria in cattle and other

protein + carbohydrate hydrolases - very specific
fat - hydrolytic enzymes - not specific

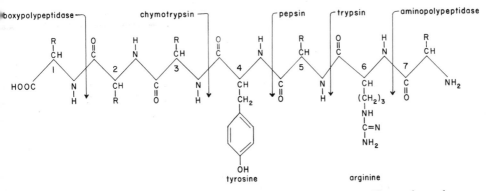

Fig. 16.3. A diagram to indicate the specificity of various proteolytic enzymes. The numbers refer to the amino acid residues only two of which, tyrosine and arginine, are labeled below. The polypeptidases are specific, one to the free carboxyl end (left) of a protein molecule or peptide, the other to the free amino end (right) of such molecules. Pepsin is specific to the amino side of tyrosine (or phenylalanine) residues inside a protein molecule; chymotrypsin is specific to the carboxyl side of such residues; and trypsin is specific to the carboxyl side of arginine or lysine residues.

erbivores also secrete cellulases. These rganisms are in symbiotic relation with heir hosts, directly or indirectly provid-g the host with nutrients resulting from he digestion of cellulose.[1] Plants like the erusalem artichoke store inulin, a fruc-se polymer. An enzyme, inulase, creted by cells in the tubers, enables hem to digest the stores of inulin to fruc-se when necessary for growth.

Lipases, which hydrolyze fats by at-acking the ester linkages between alco-ols (such as glycerol) and fatty acids, are elatively unspecific in action. Provided he acid is organic, its chemical identity nd that of the alcohol radical with vhich it is combined do not appear to natter. One lipase usually acts catalyti-ally upon all of them, presumably be-ause the steric configuration of the onds is similar in all of them. However, hough lipases from different organisms nay perform similar functions, they are ot quite identical since their pH optima ary. For example, the pancreatic lipase f man acts best at pH 7.0, while that of he castor bean has an optimum at pH .0. But in either case the products of he complete digestion of fats in general re fatty acids and glycerol.[1] The prod-

ucts of digestion of phospholipids, on the other hand, include, in addition to fatty acids and glycerol, phosphoric acid and an organic base. For example, lecithin (see Fig. 3.12) yields, on hydrolysis, fatty acids, glycerol, phosphoric acid and choline.

An enzyme only accelerates a reaction; it cannot make a reaction proceed which is otherwise impossible. If a reaction is reversible the enzyme accelerates the re-action in both directions, and at a given time the direction of the reaction de-pends upon the law of mass action. For example, it has been demonstrated that the hydrolysis of fat by a lipase proceeds to an equilibrium, at which time there is a mixture of fat, fatty acid and glycerol. If more fatty acids and glycerol are then added to this mixture, the same lipase will synthesize fat until a new equilib-rium is reached (see Fig. 16.4). Such a reversal is not found, however, in car-bohydrates and proteins. For instance, disaccharides and polysaccharides can be synthesized only by phosphorylases from monosaccharides possessing a high en-ergy phosphate bond. This indicates that energy is necessary for the synthesis[4] as well as an enzyme other than a hydro-

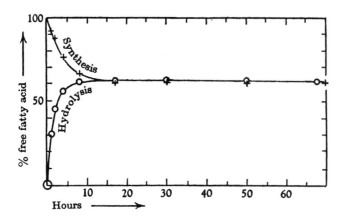

Fig. 16.4. Hydrolysis and synthes of triolein by *Ricinus* lipase. (Aft Parsons; data of Armstrong an Gosney.)

lase. Enzymes other than the hydrolases are necessary to catalyze such syntheses since polymerization occurs by a pathway entirely different from that of hydrolysis. The synthesis of proteins requires phosphorylated amino acids and enzymes other than the hydrolases (see Chapters 6 and 25).

The Chemical Nature of Hydrolytic Enzymes

Sumner, in 1926, first succeeded in crystallizing urease from jack bean seeds. Urease is a hydrolytic enzyme which decomposes urea to carbon dioxide and ammonia. In 1930, Northrop crystallized pepsin from the gastric juice of the cow, and he and Kunitz soon thereafter crystallized trypsin from the pancreas of the same animal. Since then many hydrolytic and other types of enzymes have been crystallized and purified.[5]

Several methods have been used in the purification of enzymes. For example, enzymes may be purified by salting out the proteins from digestive juice or from a mash of digestive tissue, and subsequently comparing the activities of the supernatant and the precipitated materials. Since some proteins in a mixture are precipitated by a low concentration of a salt (like ammonium sulfate), and others by a higher concentration, separation of the proteins in a mixture is possible by suc-

cessive salting out operations. Each frac tion obtained in this manner is the tested for enzymatic activity. The activ material is dissolved and the precipitatio procedure is repeated with smaller con centration intervals until the enzyme ac tivity is confined largely to one of th fractions. The salt may then be remove from the protein by dialysis (e.g., throug cellophane) and the active concentrate material is crystallized.

Even crystalline enzymes often contai impurities, but they may be further free of minute quantities of contaminatin protein impurities by electrophoresi (Tiselius apparatus[12]). This method take advantage of the fact that a protein mole cule is positively charged on the acid sid of its isoelectric pH and negativel charged on the alkaline side; therefore, i migrates in an electric field except at it isoelectric pH. Three factors affect th mobility of a protein: its size, symmetry and charge density. Movement is there fore hindered by large size, by asym metry and by decrease in charge density As a result, proteins in a mixture movin in response to an electric field are "sorte out," and the concentration of each on in a gradient may be measured opticall (e.g., with ultraviolet light or, more com monly, by the change in the index o refraction (Schlieren optics)). Each pro tein may be separately removed from th electrophoresis tube or from the appro

iate region of the filter paper when
per electrophoresis is used. Each frac-
on can then be tested for enzyme
tivity.

Even electrophoretic separation is not
al proof of purity since two proteins
ay form an aggregate and move to-
ther. Such proof can be obtained, how-
er, by the method called *end group
alysis*. This is based on the knowledge
at any one peptide chain has only one
rminal amino (and one terminal car-
oxyl) group. The terminal amino group
n be tagged, for example, with the dye
4-dinitrofluorobenzene (and comparable
ethods are available for identifying the
rboxyl group). If the protein consists of
single polypeptide strand, only one
gged amino acid should appear per
olecule when the protein is hydrolyzed
d chromatographed (or separated on
ion exchange column). If the protein
nsists of two (or more) chains, two (or
ore) terminal amino acids should ap-
ear per molecule, but always in the
me stoichiometric ratios in each sample
sted. If a mixture of proteins occurs in
aggregate, an exact stoichiometric
tio is unlikely.

All samples of enzymes purified by
ese methods show properties and reac-
ons characteristic of proteins: color re-
ctions, ultraviolet absorption spectra,
activation by heat and radiations, and
nsitivity to pH and salts, etc. It is there-
re evident that all enzymes are com-
osed of proteins and that the specific
roperties of an enzyme probably depend
pon the kind of protein of which it is
omposed. However, in some enzymes
e proteins have other ions or molecules
ttached to them.

ctivation of Hydrolytic Enzymes

Many hydrolytic enzymes appear to as-
ociate with a variety of salts which have
n important function in the catalytic ac-
ivity of these enzymes. It has been
hown that upon dialysis some purified
hydrolytic enzymes become inactive or
greatly reduced in their catalytic activity.[2] For example, when ptyalin (salivary
amylase) loses its associated sodium chloride during dialysis, neither the protein
portion nor the sodium chloride alone
has catalytic activity. When the two
are mixed together again, the preparation once more becomes catalytically
active. It has been shown that in this
case it is the chloride ion in sodium
chloride which is essential for the enzyme
activation. Many of the elements needed
for enzymatic reactions are present in
minute quantities in cells of plants and
animals, and may be associated in a similar manner with such enzymes (see Table
3.4 and Table 16.1). However, not all hydrolytic enzymes are activated by salts.
Some, like pepsin, trypsin and chymotrypsin, are not known to require salt ions for
their catalytic action.

Hydrolases are often in an inactive state
when they leave the cells in which they
are manufactured. In such a case they
must be activated before they can catalyze hydrolyses. For example, *pepsinogen*,
the inactive forerunner of pepsin, is
secreted from cells (chief cells) in the
stomach lining into the lumen, where it
is activated by hydrochloric acid (H^+ ions)
coming from other secretory cells (parie-
tal cells) nearby and also by the auto-
catalytic action of pepsin itself. Activation in this case involves removal of a
polypeptide, since the molecular weight
of pepsinogen differs from that of pepsin
by an amount equivalent to the molecular
weight (4000) of a small polypeptide as
shown in Fig. 16.5.[13] The suggestion has
been made that the polypeptide masks
the active spots of the enzyme.

Enzymes which require free sulfhydryl
groups (—SH) for catalytic activity must
be reduced after purification to restore
the activity lost on oxidation of these
groups during the purification process.
For example, the protease *papain*, as extracted from the papaya, is inactive until
it is treated with reducing agents such as

TABLE 16.1. *Specific Metal Activation of Various Hydrolytic Enzymes*

ENZYME	HYDROLYSES CATALYZED BY ENZYMES	METAL REQUIRE
Prolidase	Glycylproline + HOH → proline + glycine	Mn
Dehydropeptidase	Glycyldehydrophenylalanine + HOH → glycine + NH_3 + phenylpyruvic acid	Zn
Carboxypeptidase	Carbobenzoxyglycyl-l-leucine + HOH → carbobenzoxyglycine + leucine	Mg
Glycylglycine dipeptidase	Glycylglycine + HOH → 2 glycine	Zn

These hydrolyses will proceed only if the metals are present in small quantities, indicating that the metals are catalytic in action. The peculiar substrates of the second and third reactions are used because analytic procedures are easier with such synthetic compounds. (From McElroy and Nason,[18] and from Smith and Hanson, 1949: J. Biol. Chem. *179*.)

glutathione, hydrogen cyanide or hydrogen sulfide, which convert the disulfid bonds (S—S) in the enzyme to thiol o sulfhydryl bonds (—SH), the enzyme be ing active only when one of these bond is present in the reduced state. Cathepsir a protein-digesting enzyme in the liver is also activated by reduction. Suc enzymes are inactivated when oxidized This may occur even by exposure to ai during extraction or purification.

Enzymes Involved in Cellular Oxidation-Reductions

In addition to the hydrolases whic catalyze hydrolysis of organic compound a number of other kinds of enzymes— isomerases, transferring enzymes, addin and splitting enzymes, oxidases and de hydrogenases—take part in the synthesi and degradation of nutrients in the cell.[1, While some of these enzymes are know only in impure state in cell fragments others have been crystallized an purified.[13]

The *isomerases* catalyze interna changes in the molecules of compounds such as the shift from glucose-1-phos phate to fructose-6-phosphate. Quite number of isomerases catalyze suc changes in both the anaerobic and aero bic phases of metabolism.

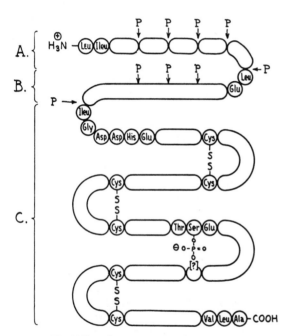

Fig. 16.5. The structure of pepsinogen. The principle attack by hydrogen ions (of HCl) and pepsin is at points marked *P*, releasing miscellaneous peptides (A), pepsin inhibitor (B), and pepsin (C). The undetermined sequences are actually much larger in relation to the known sequences than is indicated. The location of the phosphoserine residue with respect to the disulfides is also uncertain. (From Boyer, Lardy and Myrbäck.[13])

310

Transferring enzymes catalyze trans- ference of various radicals, such as the high energy phosphates (a transference catalyzed by phosphorylases), methyl groups, acetyl groups and amino groups. For instance, the enzyme hexokinase catalyzes the phosphorylation of glucose, in the course of which a high energy phosphate bond is transferred from an adenosine triphosphate (ATP; see Fig. 7.3) to a glucose molecule. Dehydro- genases and related enzymes (e.g., flavo- proteins) are a special group of transfer- ing enzymes by which hydrogen is transferred.

Adding and *splitting enzymes* catalyze addition of a fragment to a molecule or splitting of a fragment from a molecule; e.g., the addition of CO_2 to a molecule, with the formation of a new carboxyl group, or the splitting out of CO_2 from a carboxyl group.[16] As an illustration, pyruvic acid may be carboxylated to form oxaloacetic acid or decarboxylated to form an acetyl fragment and CO_2. Some transferring enzymes catalyze the addi- tion or removal of water. However, such enzymes differ from hydrolases in that they do not split molecules.

Oxidases and *dehydrogenases* are con- cerned with electron and hydrogen ion transfers. Examples are cytochrome oxidase, which transfers electrons, and coenzyme I (diphosphopyridine nucleo- tide or DPN; see Fig. 16.6), which trans- fers hydrogen ions and electrons.

Although a large number of different and specific types of enzymes are con- cerned with oxidation-reduction reactions in the cell, all of them have some proper- ties in common.[1, 8] Each oxidative en- zyme studied has been found to consist of a protein carrier and a prosthetic group. The prosthetic group is an organic radical, sometimes of considerable com- plexity, which is attached to the protein. Neither the protein nor the prosthetic group alone is enzymatically active, as can be demonstrated by separating the

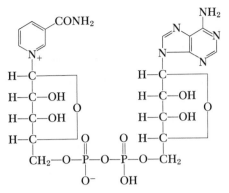

Fig. 16.6. Diphosphopyridine nucleotide (DPN), the coenzyme or prosthetic group of some of the de- hydrogenases. Triphosphopyridine nucleotide (TPN) is similar in structure except that it has an extra phos- phoric acid residue attached to the pentose of adenosine (right side of the molecule).

two components. For example, when the flavoprotein enzyme (the yellow enzyme) is dialyzed against distilled water, a yel- low compound diffuses out, leaving the protein in the cellophane bag. The yellow compound, containing riboflavin or vita- min B_2, is the prosthetic group of the enzyme (see Fig. 16.7). Neither the pro- tein part inside the cellophane bag nor the prosthetic group outside shows enzymatic activity. The two when mixed become active, together forming the en- zyme. In the cell the two are probably present mostly in the associated form, since the dissociation constant for this enzyme is small.

In some other enzymes, like the *dehy- drogenases*, the prosthetic group is usu- ally dissociated from the protein and associates with it only when acting on the substrate. When the dissociation con- stant is large, as in this case, the pros- thetic group is generally called a coenzyme. Two prosthetic groups (see Fig. 16.6) are known for dehydrogenases —coenzyme I, or diphosphopyridine nucleotide (DPN^+), and coenzyme II, or triphosphopyridine nucleotide (TPN^+). TPN^+ is most frequently the coenzyme in synthetic reactions. It also functions in

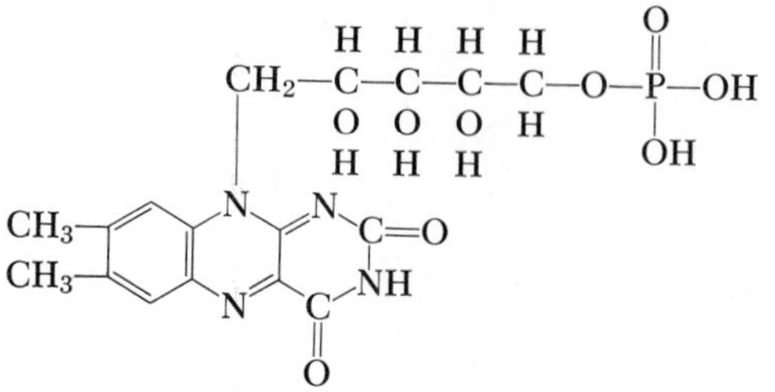

H H H H   O
CH₂—C—C—C—C—O—P—OH
    O O O H |
    H H H   OH

$$CH_2-\underset{\underset{H}{O}}{C}-\underset{\underset{H}{O}}{C}-\underset{\underset{H}{O}}{C}-\underset{H}{C}-O-\underset{OH}{\overset{O}{P}}-OH$$

CH₃— (ring) N, N, C=O
CH₃— (ring) N, C, NH
O

Riboflavin phosphate
(flavin mononucleotide)

↓ + ATP

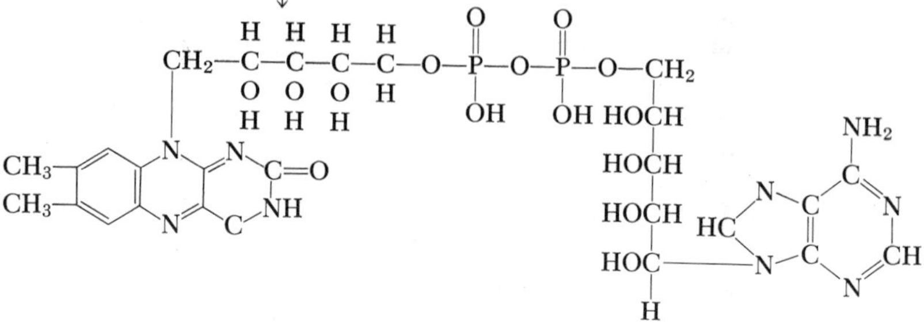

H H H H   O   O
CH₂—C—C—C—C—O—P—O—P—O—CH₂
    O O O H   OH OH HOCH
    H H H   HOCH
CH₃— N, N, C=O   HOCH HC
CH₃— N, C, NH   HOC
                           H

NH₂
N—C—C—N
HC—N—C—CH—N

Flavin adenine dinucleotide (FAD)

$$DPNH + FMN \longrightarrow DPN + FMNH_2$$
or   or
FAD   FADH₂

Fig. 16.7. Riboflavin prosthetic groups of "yellow" enzymes. Both of the yellow enzymes partici-pate primarily for transport of hydrogen ions and electrons from prosthetic groups of one of the dehydrogenases (e.g., diphosphopyridine nucleotide) to the cytochromes. Each prosthetic group has specific functions, e.g., FMN is the prosthetic group of lactic dehydrogenase while FAD is the prosthetic group of aldehyde oxidase, D-amino oxidase and fatty acyl-CoA dehydrogenases. (From McElroy, 1960: Cellular Physiology and Biochemistry, Prentice-Hall, Englewood Cliffs, New Jersey, p. 50.)

the pentose oxidative shunt (Fig. 17.13) while DPN^+ is the coenzyme for most degradative dehydrogenations. All the de-hydrogenases formed by union of these prosthetic groups with various proteins are highly specific as to substrate. Disso-ciation appears advantageous since the same prosthetic group can thus associate with various proteins, each combination being specific to some substrate. The specificity of a dehydrogenase, therefore, must be due largely to the protein moiety of the enzyme with which the coenzyme associates.[2]

Cytochromes are enzymes which trans-fer electrons from flavoproteins or other carrier enzymes to cytochrome oxidase. The cytochrome oxidase in turn passe the electrons to oxygen, activating it an enabling it to combine with the hydroge ions and form water. The cytochrome (Fig. 16.8), of which there are a numbe in all aerobic cells, are cell pigments wit a prosthetic group resembling the hem of hemoglobin. Cytochrome oxidase als has a similar prosthetic group. In cyto chromes and cytochrome oxidase the iro changes from the oxidized (Fe^{+++}) to th reduced (Fe^{++}) state as an electron i received, and from the reduced to th oxidized state as an electron is passed o to oxygen. In hemoglobin the iron is a

CONVERSIONS OF ENERGY AND MATTER IN THE CEL

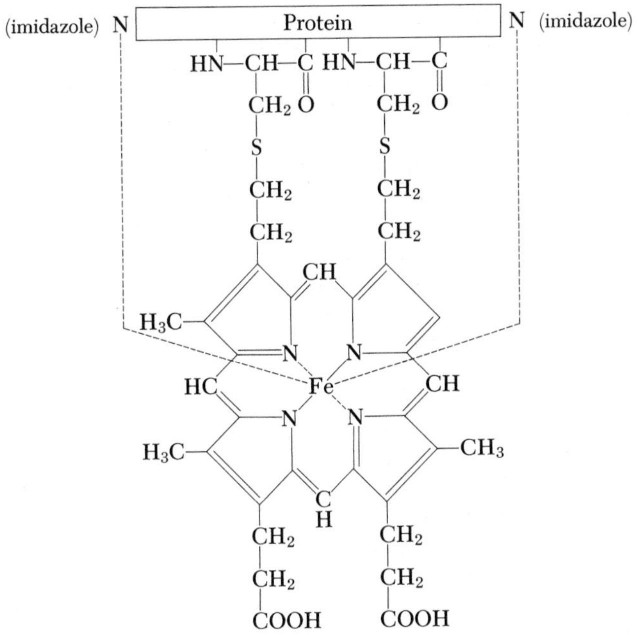

Fig. 16.8.   Reduced cytochrome-*c*. (From Florkin, 1960: Unity and Diversity in Biochemistry. Pergamon Press, London, p. 119.)

ways in the reduced state and adds oxygen only loosely (becomes oxygenated) without changing in valence.

The cytochromes and cytochrome oxidase are tetrapyrrole compounds, four pyrroles surrounding the iron. Tetrapyrroles without the metal are called porphyrins. When a metal is present they are called metalloporphyrins. Cytochrome and heme are examples of metalloporphyrins in which iron is present. It is interesting to note that the plant pigment chlorophyll (see Fig. 20.8) is a metalloporphyrin in which magnesium is present.[2]

As already pointed out, many of the enzymes catalyzing the oxidation-reduction reactions are quite specific in action; e.g., succinic acid dehydrogenase catalyzes dehydrogenation of succinic acid only, and malic acid dehydrogenase catalyzes dehydrogenation of malic acid only. However, enzymes exist which catalyze a number of reactions, being specific not to an individual molecule but to a particular steric configuration of atoms, which may occur in a number of different molecules. For instance, isocitric dehydrogenase catalyzes dehydrogenation of both isocitric and oxalosuccinic acids in the Krebs cycle.[2]

Some of the enzymes participating in oxidation-reduction reactions, like some of the enzymes participating in hydrolyses, are activated by various elements.[18] Some of these elements are listed in Table 16.2, along with the enzymes for which they are necessary.

It is interesting to note the presence of members of the vitamin B complex as components of the prosthetic groups of the enzymes involved in cellular oxidations and syntheses. This accounts for the presence of certain B vitamins in all organisms examined; e.g., vitamin B_1, or thiamine, which forms part of the prosthetic group of cocarboxylase (see Fig.

TABLE 16.2. *Elements Necessary for Some Oxidative Enzymes*

ENZYME	REACTION	META
Carbonic anhydrase	$CO_2 + H_2O \rightleftarrows H_2CO_3$	Zn
Inorganic pyrophosphatase	Pyrophosphate $+ H_2O \rightarrow PO_4$	Mg*
Catalase	$2H_2O_2 \rightarrow 2H_2O + O_2$	Fe
Cytochromes	Electron transport	Fe
Tyrosinase	Tyrosine $+ \frac{1}{2}O_2 \rightarrow$ hallachrome	Cu
Laccase	Phenols $\rightarrow$ ortho and paraquinones	Cu
Ascorbic acid oxidase	Ascorbic acid $\rightarrow$ dehydroascorbic acid	Cu

From McElroy and Swanson, Jan. 1953: Scient. Am. *188*. A much more complete account is given in McElroy and Nason, 1954.[18]

* Magnesium is indicated to be an activator for a large variety of enzymes—kinases, mutases, etc.

16.9), an enzyme important in the metabolism of pyruvic acid. Some of the pertinent information on the metabolic role of these vitamins is summarized in Table 3.10, along with a summary of the gross superficial symptoms which result from lack of the vitamins in the diet. These pathological symptoms are the cumulative effects of prolonged metabolical disturbances.[19, 20]

Effect of Environment on Enzyme Activity

The rate of an enzyme-catalyzed reaction, in most cases, increases proportionally with increasing concentration of the enzyme, provided the substrate is present in excess and is therefore not a rate-limiting factor.

The effect of variation in substrate concentration upon the rate of an enzyme-catalyzed reaction (the enzyme being present in excess and therefore not rate limiting) depends upon the individual circumstances. The relation between the rate of the reaction and substrate concentration has been formulated most general terms as follows:

$$\text{Rate} = k\,[S]^n \qquad (16.$$

In this equation k and n are constan and S is the concentration of th substrate. In some cases increasing th substrate concentration (in the lower pa of the concentration range) proportio ally increases the rate of the reaction. that case the exponent n in the abov equation has the value of unity (fir order). When a high concentration substrate proves inhibitory, as it does i some cases, the exponent n is said to hav a negative value. In some other case much more complex relations than th above exist between the concentration substrate and the rate of the enzyme catalyzed reaction.[8]

When the concentration of enzyme i low enough so that it is rate limiting, an the concentration of substrate is varie the rate of the reaction may prove inde pendent of the substrate concentratio In that case n in equation 16.1 is zerc and the term for the substrate drops ou

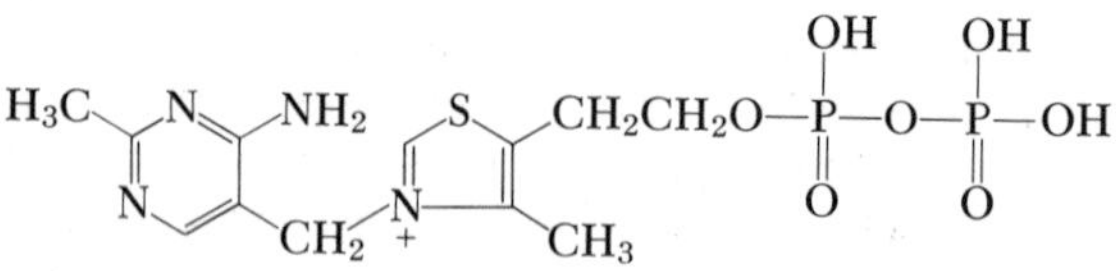

Fig. 16.9. Thiamin pyrophosphate, or cocarboxylase.

the equation. Qualitatively speaking, e enzyme becomes saturated with sub-rate or nearly so. This becomes the oottleneck" determining the rate of the action, and further increase in substrate oncentration has a negligible effect.

If the substrate concentration is varied, it the enzyme concentration kept con-ant, a limiting rate is reached which is e maximal turnover rate or work rate the available enzyme at the particular mperature and pH of the experiment. xamples of the effect of concentration enzyme and substrate on rate of reac-on are given in Figures 16.10 and 16.11. hese data suggest that an enzyme-sub-rate complex is formed as the first step any enzyme catalyzed reactions.[8] (For more complete formulation of enzyme inetics see Appendix 16.1.)

Temperature also is a factor in enzyme tivity. Experiments with hydrolytic en-ymes indicate that the greatest rate of ydrolysis occurs at the temperature opti-al for the hydrolase. The optimal temper-ure is different for enzymes from different rganisms. It is usually low for enzymes

from plants and cold-blooded animals of the Arctic, very high for enzymes from some thermophilic bacteria and inter-mediate for enzymes from cells of other forms. In a warm-blooded animal, body temperature is the optimal temperature for the catalytic activities of its hydrolytic enzymes.

A rise in temperature up to the op-timum is accompanied by a correspond-ing increase in the rate of hydrolysis be-cause of the increase in the number of molecules with the required energy of activation, as shown in Figure 16.12. An increase in temperature above the opti-mum is accompanied by a decrease in the rate of hydrolysis. This has been ex-plained in the following manner. Only the native or unaltered form of an en-zyme is catalytically active; therefore, other things being equal, the rate of a hydrolytic reaction will depend upon the concentration of the native enzyme. At all temperatures, within a range charac-teristic of the organism, an equilibrium exists between native and denatured en-zyme. This equilibrium can be shifted in

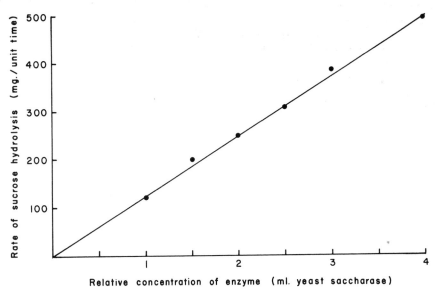

Fig. 16.10. Effect of enzyme concentration on the rate of a reaction when an excess of enzyme is present. (After Baldwin.[1])

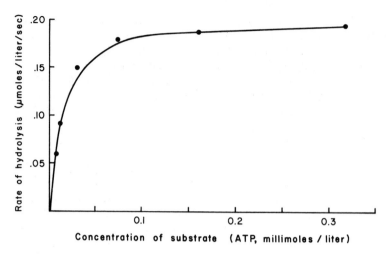

Fig. 16.11. Effect of substrate concentration on the rate of reaction when a limited amount of enzyme is present. Note that the enzyme becomes saturated with substrate so that further increase in concentration of substrate has no effect. (After Ouellet *et al.*, 1952: Arch. Biochem. and Biophys. 39:41.

either direction. As the temperature rises, more of the enzyme goes into the denatured state, as shown in Table 16.3. Therefore, as the quantity of native enzyme decreases, the rate of the hydrolytic reaction catalyzed by the enzyme declines. The temperature coefficient, Q_{10}, for denaturation of enzymes between 70° and 80° C. is several hundred, indicating a tremendous rate of denaturation at these temperatures.

Most enzymes are denatured irreversibly at a temperature between 50° and 80° C. Others, however, are very resistant to high temperature. For example, crystalline trypsin is reversibly denatured even at 100° C. and so is Taka-Diastase. The latter is irreversibly denatured only above 140° C. Each enzyme is inactive catalytically while at the limit of its high temperature tolerance but resumes its activity when cooled.[7]

Enzymes are also inactivated by salts of heavy metals such as copper or mercury. These metals are often used in fixing agents for preserving cell proteins, because they act as denaturants and protein precipitants. Their action on en-

TABLE 16.3. *Denaturation of Trypsin by Heat*

T° C.	PER CENT DENATURED	T° C.	PER CENT DENATURED
42	32.8	45	57.4
43	39.2	48	80.4
44	50.0	50	87.8

Data from Northrop, Kunitz and Herriott: Crystal line Enzymes.

zymes is, therefore, not unexpected. The same might be said of an alkaloidal re agent such as phosphotungstic acid which is often used to precipitate proteins in biochemical procedures.

One of the most interesting environ mental influences on enzymatic activity is the effect of pH. Each enzyme is cata lytically active over a limited range o pH (see Fig. 16.13). For example, the optimum range for the activity of pepsin is between pH 1.5 and 2.5; for trypsin between 8 and 11; for salivary amylase between 6.7 and 6.8; for malt amylase, a 5.2; for pancreatic lipase, at 7; for casto bean lipase, at 5. In all these cases activ

CONVERSIONS OF ENERGY AND MATTER IN THE CELL

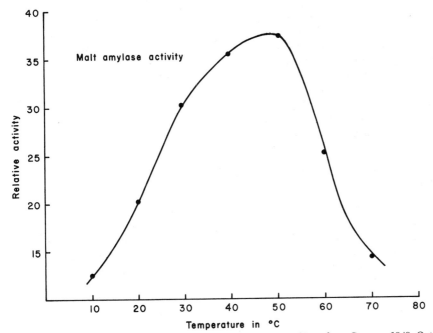

Fig. 16.12.   Effect of temperature on the rate of enzyme activity. (Data from Gortner, 1949: Outlines of Biochemistry. 3rd Ed., Wiley, New York.)

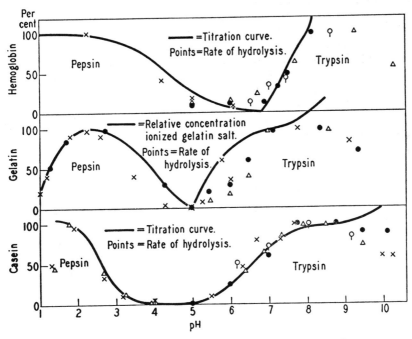

Fig. 16.13.   The effect of pH upon the activity of pepsin and trypsin. The ordinate measures the relative rates of hydrolysis. Note that the pH effect varies with the protein. (From Northrop 1939: Crystalline Enzymes. Columbia Univ. Press, New York, p. 8.)

ity declines gradually on either side of the optimum. The pH sensitivity of enzymes probably results from the necessity of a particular charge distribution about the active center for optimal activity. Since different enzymes are composed of amino acids in different proportions, the optimum pH of an enzyme is apt to be a characteristic property dependent upon its composition.

Mechanism of Enzyme Action

As we have seen in Chapter 10, the rate of a thermochemical reaction is proportional to the number of molecules possessing the required energy of activation. If at a given temperature the number of activated molecules is small, the rate of the reaction will be low. A catalyst is thought to increase the rate of a reaction because the energy of activation is decreased (Fig. 16.1) when the reactant molecules are adsorbed to its surface and subjected to the stress of adsorption, which may amount to a compression of several hundred atmospheres pressure. Consequently, even at low temperatures, in the presence of a catalyst the number of molecules having energy sufficient to react is vastly increased. After the adsorbed molecules react they are less attracted to the catalyst, and as they leave the adsorbing surface, room becomes available on it for more reactant molecules.

An enzyme appears to act in much the same way as an inorganic catalyst. It is known that an enzyme adsorbs the substrate upon which it acts, forming an intimate union of it,* as shown diagrammatically for pepsin in Figure 16.14 and for an amylase in Figure 16.15. In this case it would seem that the positive and negative charges present on the protein of the enzyme attract the oppositely charged radicals of the substrate. The precise nature of the union is not known with certainty and may vary with different enzymes. In general, enzymes lower

the energy of activation for cellular reactions, making possible, at a temperature favorable for cells, reactions which would otherwise require very high temperatures and would be impossible. For example, the energy of activation for hydrolysis of cane sugar by acid is 25,600 calories per mole, while for its hydrolysis in the presence of the enzyme invertase, it is only 9080 calories per mole.[7]

The hydrolysis of a polypeptide by peptidase, in which a metal ion is often associated with a protein (see Tables 16.1 and 16.2), has been envisaged in the following manner. The metal ion attaches itself by residual valency to a polypeptide molecule on one side of the peptide bond, while the protein portion of the enzyme attaches itself on the other side of the same peptide bond. A stress like the pull of the two claws of a crab is thereby placed on the peptide bond, weakening the bond between the amino and carboxyl groups of the two amino acid residues of the polypeptide. Thereby the energy required for breaking the peptide bond is reduced, and the hydrogen ions, always present, then catalyze its hydrolysis, even at room temperature.[1] In the absence of an enzyme a high temperature is required for this hydrolysis.

Experimental evidence indicates that oxidation-reduction enzymes, like hydrolytic enzymes, combine with the substrate.[1] For example, peroxide, which absorbs light maximally in the visible spectrum at wavelengths 498, 538, 548 and 645 mμ, on addition of peroxidase shows maximal absorption at 561 and 630.5 mμ. Such a change in absorption spectrum indicates that the union between substrate and enzyme must be rather intimate, since the absorption

---

* The possibility that enzymes may act at long range (200 Å) through a plastic film was suggested by Rothen.[11] However, evidence has accumulated that such action occurred through cracks in the film clearly visible in electron micrographs.

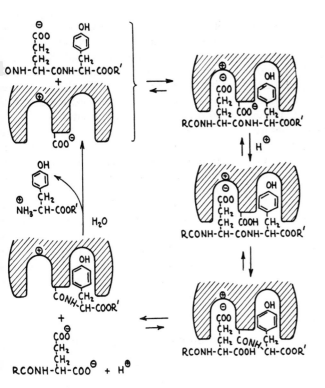

Fig. 16.14. A proposed mechanism of action of pepsin; N-acyl-L-glutamyl-L-tyrosine ester represented as substrate. (From Boyer, Lardy and Myrbäck.[13])

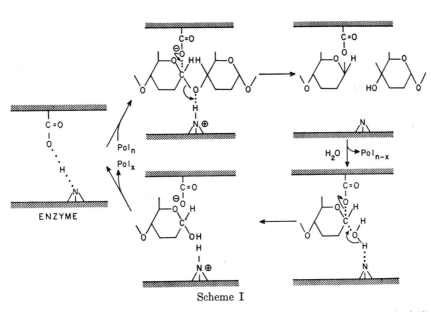

Scheme I

Fig. 16.15. Proposed mechanism of action of amylases. (From Boyer, Lardy and Myrbäck.[13])

spectrum of a compound is not so altered except by a chemical change.

Evidence of union between enzyme and substrate is also indicated by bioluminescence. An enzyme, luciferase, catalyzes the oxidation of a substrate, luciferin, with the emission of light. If the luciferin and luciferase are mixed before oxygen is admitted, the oxidation will take less time than if the oxygen is first added to each separately and the two are then mixed (see Fig. 16.16). It therefore seems most likely that first there is the formation of a complex of luciferin and luciferase followed by the oxidation of the complex by atmospheric oxygen:

$$\text{luciferin} + \text{luciferase} \rightarrow$$
$$\text{luciferin-luciferase complex} \quad (16.2)$$

$$\text{luciferin-luciferase complex} + O_2 \rightarrow$$
$$\text{oxyluciferin} + \text{luciferase} + \text{light} \quad (16.3)$$

Because the formation of the complex, luciferin-luciferase, is a slower reaction than its oxidation, a mixture of luciferin and luciferase in which the complex has already formed will give off light more rapidly on admission of oxygen than will the reaction upon addition of luciferin and oxygen to luciferase and oxygen. The difference in time in the two cases measures the time required for the association of luciferin and luciferase.[21]

From such evidence as the above it is thought that the substrates involved in oxidations and reductions are bound selectively to the surfaces of the enzyme concerned. It is conceivable that as a result of molecular distortion and stress resulting from such adsorption, the energy of activation required for dehydrogenation or other oxidative enzymatic reactions is lowered (see Fig. 16.1) so that the reactions can proceed at temperatures in the biokinetic zone (see Chapter 10).

Inhibition of Enzymes by Poisons

Since enzymes have sites (one or more by which they combine with a substrate) inactivation of those sites prevents the

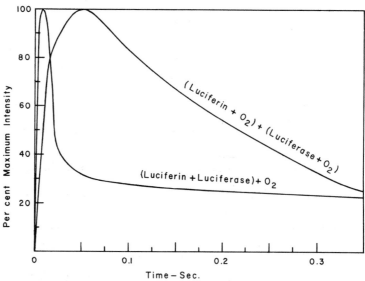

Fig. 16.16. Rate of emission of light when *Cypridina* luciferin (oxidizable substrate) is mixed with luciferase (enzyme) before admission of oxygen, and when each solution is mixed with oxygen before the two are mixed together. (After Chance, *et al.*[21])

CONVERSIONS OF ENERGY AND MATTER IN THE CELL

ctivity of the enzyme upon its substrate.
n agent inactivating an enzyme is an
nzyme poison. Poisons are effective to
lifferent degrees and act upon enzymes
n different ways.

When a nonmetabolizable molecule,
\, resembles a metabolizable molecule, B,
ufficiently to be bound to the enzyme,
hen A remains attached to the enzyme
nd prevents the attachment of B, thus
ompeting with B for space on the en-
yme surface. Its inhibition of the reac-
ions of B is called *competitive inhibi-
ion.*[22] For example, malonic acid
esembles succinic acid (see Fig. 16.17)
ecause both have two carboxyl groups.
Aalonic acid inhibits the action of suc-
inic dehydrogenase on succinic acid by
'clogging the active spots" on the en-
yme, and since the malonic acid is not
netabolized it remains attached to the
nzyme. However, the complex of malo-
iic acid and succinic dehydrogenase does
lissociate at a finite rate given by the dis-
ociation constant. Therefore, an excess
f succinic acid will reverse the action of
nalonic acid (law of mass action). In
;eneral, where competitive inhibition
iccurs, an excess of substrate reverses the
iction of the poison, as shown in Figure
l6.18. An experiment in which the substrate concentration is varied generally
enables one to distinguish between competitive and noncompetitive inhibition.[22]

Some molecules which are metabolic
antagonists to particular substrates exhibit
noncompetitive inhibition of enzyme reactions. In such cases also, the inhibitor
resembles the metabolizable substance,
but it is apparently attached to the enzyme at some point other than the one
which binds the original substrate, and by
its antagonistic action it prevents the
expected enzyme reaction (see Fig. 16.19).
Sometimes such inhibition is not relieved
under any conditions, and high substrate
concentration even at low inhibitor concentration has no effect. In other cases,
however, when the inhibitor concentra-

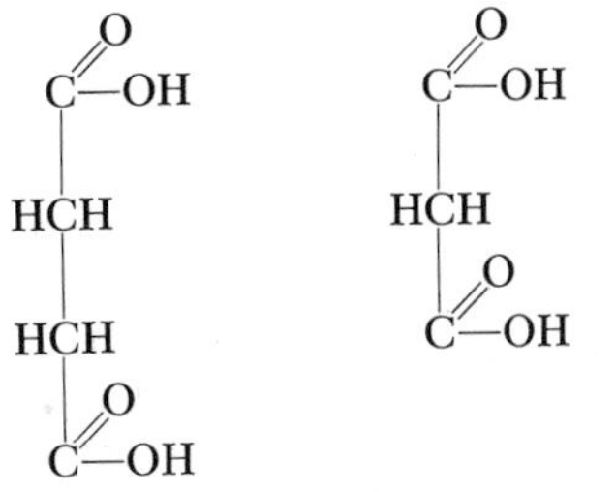

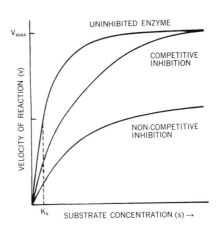

Fig. 16.17. The structural formulas of malonic and succinic acids.

tion is low, a high concentration of substrate reverses the inhibition. For instance,
inhibition of bacterial metabolism by a
small concentration of sulfonamide is
relieved by a high concentration of folic
acid.[8]

Enzymes which depend upon the presence of sulfhydryl (—SH) groups for their
activity are inactivated by salts of heavy
metals or alkylating agents. Mercury and
copper salts inactivate some hydrolases by
combining with the sulfhydryls. Iodoacetic
acid inhibits some oxidative enzymes by
reacting with their sulfhydryl groups (al-
kylation). Some of the enzymes in the

Fig. 16.18. The rate of a catalyzed reaction as
a function of substrate concentration is plotted for an
active enzyme and for an enzyme inhibited by either
a competitive or a noncompetitive inhibitor. (From
Sizer.[22])

Enzyme Inhibition and Activation

⌣ = enzyme surface
S = substrate
I = inhibitor
A = activator. This might consist of a salt in hydrolyses or of an electron acceptor
     (second substrate) in oxidations.
● = active spot on enzyme
x = auxiliary active spot

Note: Interaction (electron transport) between ● and x might occur through a protein.

Competitive inhibition:

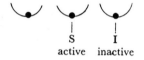

Noncompetitive (independent) inhibition—no interference of I with the attachment of S:

Independent activation:

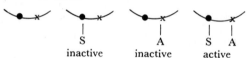

Activation through binding:

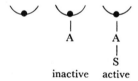

Activation through removal (e.g., pepsinogen to pepsin):

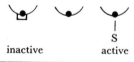

Fig. 16.19. Enzyme inhibition and activation. (Based on a number of sources, part by courtesy of Dr. B. Hofstee, Palo Alto Medical Research Foundation.)

aerobic phase of sugar decomposition require active sulfhydryl groups and are therefore readily inhibited by iodoacetic acid. This type of inhibition depends upon the concentration of the poison, not on the ratio of poison to substrate, and is a noncompetitive inhibition.[8]

Members of a class of enzymes which require for their activity metal ions such as Mg^{++}, Mn^{++}, Co^{++}, Zn^{++} or Fe^{++} are inactivated by substances which combine with these.[8] For example, cyanide forms an almost nondissociable complex with the copper in the prosthetic group of polyphenol oxidase, an enzyme catalyzing the oxidation of polyphenols in plant cells. In a similar manner, cyanide also binds the iron in cytochrome oxidase, an enzyme in the main pathway of oxidation-reduction in the cell (see Chapter 17). In this case inhibition depends upon the concentration of the poison, not on the ratio of poison to substrate.[22]

Many other types of enzyme poisons exist besides the ones considered above. For example, some enzymes not affected by sulfhydryl poisons or metal poisons are affected by diisopropylfluorophosphate (DFP), e.g., acetylcholine esterase. Again, the coupling between oxidative reactions and formation of high energy phosphates is affected by dinitrophenol (DNP). Some of these enzyme poisons will be cited later when discussion of them is pertinent.

APPENDIX

16.1 The Michaelis-Menten Law

Assuming the formation of a complex between enzyme and substrate in enzyme-catalyzed reactions:

enzyme + substrate $\longrightarrow$ complex, or

$$E + S \underset{K_2}{\overset{K_1}{\rightleftharpoons}} ES \qquad (16.4)$$

where K_1 is the velocity constant of the formation of complex (ES), and K_2 is the velocity constant for dissociation of (ES).

If complex $\longrightarrow$ enzyme + products, or

$$ES \xrightarrow{K_3} E + P, \qquad (16.5)$$

then K_3 is the velocity constant for decomposition of the complex (ES) with the formation of reaction products (P).

Under certain conditions, the rate of the enzymatic reaction will be dependent upon the concentration of the substrate. This relation has been formulated quantitatively by Michaelis and Menten[9] on the basis of the law of mass action. The following derivation follows that given by Bull.[24]

If E_0 represents the total concentration of enzyme, E the total concentration of free enzyme, and ES the concentration of bound enzyme, then

$$E = E_0 - ES \qquad (16.6)$$

The dissociation constant of the enzyme-substrate complex is:

$$K_m = \frac{E \times S}{ES} = \frac{(E_0 - ES)S}{ES} \qquad (16.7)$$

or, by rearrangement:

$$ES = \frac{E_0 \times S}{K_m + S} \qquad (16.8)$$

The velocity of the reaction for the formation of each product is:

$$v = K_3 \times ES \qquad (16.9)$$

where K_3 has the same meaning as in equation 16.5.

Then substitution of equation 16.9 into equation 16.8 gives:

$$v = \frac{K_3 \times E_0 \times S}{K_m + S} \qquad (16.10)$$

If the substrate concentration is increased to the point where the surface of the enzyme is saturated with substrate, the maximum velocity of the reaction is:

$$V = K_3 \times E_0 \qquad (16.11)$$

which, substituted into equation 16.10, gives:

$$v = \frac{V \times S}{K_m + S} \quad (16.12)$$

Taking the reciprocals of the terms of equation 16.12, gives:

$$\frac{1}{v} = \frac{K_m}{V \times S} + \frac{1}{V} \quad (16.13)$$

A plot of $1/v$ against $1/S$ should yield a straight line, the slope of which is K_m/V and the intercept is $1/V$.

Integration of equation 16.12 gives:

$$S - S_0 + K_m \ln \frac{S}{S_0} = Vt \quad (16.14)$$

where S_0 represents the total concentration of substrate, S the concentration of free substrate and ln is the natural logarithm. When S is large and K_m is small, the reaction will be essentially independent of concentration (zero order). When S is small and K_m is large, the reaction will depend upon the concentration of S (first order).

K_m is not a dissociation constant in the usual sense of the term. The rate of formation of ES is:

$$\frac{dES}{dt} = K_1 (E_0 - ES)S \quad (16.15)$$

and the rate of decomposition of ES is:

$$\frac{dES}{dt} = -(K_2 \times ES + K_3 \times ES) \quad (16.16)$$

If the rate of the over-all reaction is constant, then ES must be constant and

$$K_1 (E_0 - ES)S = K_2 \times ES + K_3 \times ES \quad (16.17)$$

Solving equation 16.17 for ES gives:

$$ES = \frac{S \times E_0}{S + \dfrac{K_2 + K_3}{K_1}} \quad (16.18)$$

Comparing equation 16.18 with equation 16.8 shows that K_m is really equal to $(K_2 + K_3)/K_1$, and it is only when K_3 is very much smaller than K_2 that K_m becomes equal to the true dissociation constant of the complex.

The Michaelis-Menten substrate-enzyme complex is not the activated complex, the latter being present in much lower concentration. The substrate-enzyme complex must pass into an activated form before it can decompose into the final products of the reaction.

Tests of the above expression of the velocity on many biological reactions, as affected by substrate in the lower concentration range, indicate good quantitative agreement with prediction. This gives assurance that the kinetics of enzymatic reactions are subject to the law of mass action and indicates the incisiveness of the formulation of the relationships between enzyme and substrate by Michaelis and Menten.

GENERAL REFERENCES

Advances in Enzymology and Related Subjects in Biochemistry, annual since 1941.

Baldwin, E., 1957: Dynamic Aspects of Biochemistry. 3rd Ed. Cambridge Univ. Press, London.

Boyer, P. D., Lardy, H., and Myrback, K., 1960: The Enzymes. 2nd Ed. Academic Press, New York, 4 volumes.

Bray, H., 1957: Kinetics and Thermodynamics in Biochemistry. Academic Press, New York.

Colowick, S. P., and Kaplan, N. D., 1955–1959: Methods in Enzymology. Academic Press, New York, 6 volumes.

Dixon, M., and Webb, E. C., 1958: Enzymes. Longmans Green, London.

Graebler, O. H. (ed.), 1956: Enzymes, Units of Biological Structure and Function. Academic Press, New York.

Johnson, F. H., Eyring, H., and Polissar, M. J., 1954: The Kinetic Basis of Molecular Biology. Wiley, New York.

Kaplan, N. D., Ciotti, M. M., Hamolsky, M., and Bieber, R. E., 1960: Molecular Heterogeneity and the Evolution of Enzymes. Science 131:392.

Laidler, K. J., 1954: Introduction to the Chemistry of Enzymes. McGraw-Hill, New York.

McElroy, W. D., and Glass, B. (eds.), 1954: A Symposium on the Mechanism of Enzyme Action. Johns Hopkins Press, Baltimore.

Northrop, J. H., Kunitz, M., and Herriott, R. M., 1948: Crystalline Enzymes. Columbia Univ. Press, New York.

einer, J., 1959: Behavior of Enzyme Systems. Burgess, Minneapolis.

umner, J. B., and Myrback, K. (eds.), 1950–52: The Enzymes. Academic Press, New York, 2 volumes, 2 parts.

LITERATURE CITED

1. Baldwin, E., 1957: Dynamic Aspects of Biochemistry. 3rd Ed. Cambridge Univ. Press, London.
2. Cantarow, A., and Schepartz, B., 1962: Biochemistry. 3rd Ed. Saunders, Philadelphia.
3. Smith, E., 1949: Proc. Nat. Acad. Sci., U. S. 35:80.
4. Hassid, W., and Doudoroff, M., 1950: Adv. Enzymol. 10:123.
5. Northrop, J. H., Kunitz, M., and Herriott, R. M., 1948: Crystalline Enzymes. Columbia Univ. Press, New York.
6. Giri, K. V., Prasad, A. L. N., Devi, S., and Ram, J. S. R., 1952: Biochem. J. 51:123.
7. Johnson, F. H., Eyring, H., and Polissor, M., 1954: The Kinetic Basis of Molecular Biology. Wiley, New York.
8. Laidler, K. J., 1954: Introduction to the Chemistry of Enzymes. McGraw-Hill, New York.
9. Michaelis, L., and Menten, M. L., 1913: Biochem. Zeitschr. 49:333.
10. Smith, E., 1951: in Enzymes and Enzyme Systems (Edsall, J. T., ed.). Harvard Univ. Press, Cambridge, p. 47.
11. Rothen, A., 1947: J. Biol. Chem. 168:75.
12. Tiselius, A., 1937: Trans. Faraday Society 33:524.
13. Boyer, P. D., Lardy, H., and Myrback, K., 1960: The Enzymes. Academic Press, New York, vol. 4, Chaps. 4 and 5.
14. Frieden, E., Aug. 1959: Sci. Am. 201:119.
15. Smith, E. L., 1960: in The Enzymes (ref. 13 above), vol. 4, Chap. 1.
16. Ochoa, S., 1951: Physiol. Rev. 31:56.
17. Theorell, H., 1956: Science 124:467.
18. McElroy, W. D., and Nason, A., 1954: Ann. Rev. Plant Physiol. 5:1.
19. Sebrell, W. H., and Harris, R. S., 1954: The Vitamins: Chemistry, Physiology, Pathology. Academic Press, New York.
20. Szent-Györgyi, A., 1939: On Oxidation, Fermentation, Vitamins, Health and Disease. Williams & Wilkins, Baltimore.
21. Chance, B., Harvey, E. N., Johnson, F., and Milliken, G., 1940: J. Cell. Comp. Physiol. 15:195.
22. Sizer, I., 1957: Science 125:54.
23. Meister, A., 1955: Adv. Enzymol. 16:185.
24. Bull, H., 1951: Physical Biochemistry. 2nd Ed. Wiley, New York.
25. Wilkie, D. R., 1960: Progr. Biophys. 10:260.

CHAPTER 17

THE RELEASE OF ENERGY
IN CELLS

Cell foods are the source of all the building materials and energy available to the cell. Upon the breakdown of these foods the energy, stored therein as chemical energy, is released and used for carrying out all the functions of life. The release of energy is achieved through oxidation-reduction reactions. The elucidation of the nature of these reactions and of the pathway of oxidation-reduction reactions in the cell is one of the most exciting developments of the biochemistry and physiology of the cell in the last two decades. The sum total of all the chemical changes occurring in the cell constitutes its *metabolism*. While the decomposition (catabolism) of some substances in the cell is usually linked with the synthesis (anabolism) of other substances necessary to the life of the cell, in this chapter attention is centered on the decomposition of cell foods with the release of energy, cell syntheses being discussed in Chapter 25.

The Nature of Oxidation-Reduction Reactions

The very word *oxidation* implies a process in which a substance combines with oxygen—for example, the union of hydrogen and oxygen in the formation of water—and the early workers so defined it. Hydrogen gives up electrons to oxygen and is thereby oxidized, while oxygen taking up the electrons, is thereby reduced:

$$2H_2 + O_2 \rightarrow 2H_2O \qquad (17.1)$$

In many cases, however, electrons are given up even when oxygen is not present; for example, in the formation of ferric from ferrous iron.

$$Fe^{++} \underset{\text{reduction}}{\overset{\text{oxidation}}{\rightleftharpoons}} Fe^{+++} + e. \qquad (17.2)$$

Fe^{++} is the electron donor which is oxidized to Fe^{+++}. In the reverse reaction Fe^{+++} is the electron acceptor which is reduced to Fe^{++}. Oxidation, in its most generalized sense, is at present defined as the donation of electrons from one molecule (ion, atom, radical) to another, and reduction is defined as the acceptance of electrons by one molecule (ion, atom, radical) from another. The two processes always occur simultaneously.

In many of the oxidation-reduction reactions which occur in the cell, not only electron transfer but also hydrogen trans-er occurs. For example, when succinic acid is oxidized to fumaric acid, two hydrogen ions and two electrons are removed. In this case, oxidation consists of the removal of the hydrogen ions and electrons from the succinic acid to the enzyme catalyzing the reaction:

$$
\begin{array}{ccc}
\text{COOH} & & \text{COOH} \\
| & & | \\
\text{CH}_2 & \xrightarrow{\;-(2\text{H}^+ + 2e)\;} & \text{CH} \\
| & & \| \\
\text{CH}_2 & \text{Succinic} & \text{CH} \\
| & \text{dehydrogenase} & | \\
\text{COOH} & & \text{COOH} \\
\text{Succinic} & & \text{Fumaric} \\
\text{acid} & & \text{acid}
\end{array}
\qquad (17.3)
$$

The donor of the hydrogen ions and electrons is a reductant called the *hydrogen donor*. On giving up hydrogen ions and electrons it is oxidized. The enzyme catalyzing the reaction and accepting the hydrogen ions and electrons is an oxidant called the *hydrogen acceptor*. It is reduced in the process. A generalized equation for such an oxidation-reduction reaction may be written as follows:

$$ (17.4) $$

$$
\begin{array}{ccccc}
\text{H}_2\text{B} & + & \text{A} & \xrightarrow{\;\text{oxidation}\;} & \text{B} & + & \text{H}_2\text{A} \\
\text{H-donor} & & \text{H-acceptor} & & \text{Oxidized} & & \text{Reduced} \\
& & & & \text{H-donor} & & \text{H-acceptor}
\end{array}
$$

When oxygen is present in a cell, it generally acts as the terminal hydrogen and electron acceptor, becoming reduced in the process. Oxygen readily accepts electrons from molecules (or from ions, radicals, etc.) and it is because of this property that the oxidations in which oxygen participates were studied first, and the process was called oxidation. In the main line of oxidation in the cell, oxygen serves as the final hydrogen acceptor, and water (H_2O) is the end product.[42] When flavoproteins pass hydrogen ions and electrons to oxygen in other than the main line of oxidation, H_2O_2 is usually formed.[2]

Stepwise Release of Energy During Oxidation-Reduction Reactions

Whereas many hydrolyses (see Chapter 16) generally proceed with small energy releases, involving a few hundred calories per mole, oxidation-reduction reactions in the cell usually are accompanied by the release of considerable amounts of energy (see Fig. 17.1). The work of the cell is directly or indirectly accomplished by this energy. This energy is usually stored in compounds containing high en-

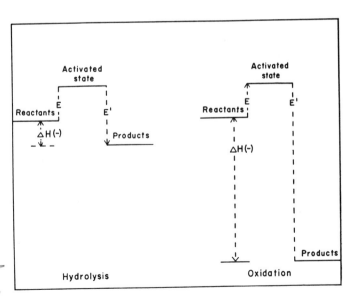

Fig. 17.1. A comparison of the amounts of energy liberated in hydrolysis and in oxidation. Note the small energy change ($\triangle$ H) in hydrolysis, compared with the large change ($\triangle$ H) in oxidation.

ergy phosphate bonds (e.g., adenosine triphosphate), from which the energy can be liberated for synthesis of other necessary compounds in the cell.

The energy available in a nutrient molecule is never liberated by the cell in one burst as in a calorimeter, where, for example, the burning of a gram mole of glucose liberates 673,000 calories of energy. The cell has no way of using this much energy liberated in one step; it could efficiently convert only a very small fraction of it. Rather, the cell degrades the glucose stepwise, a small amount of energy being liberated in each step, with each step generally catalyzed by a specific enzyme. The merit of a series of stepwise reactions is that they can be coupled energetically, and in certain steps the energy liberated is transferred to high energy phosphate bonds in which it is stored. Kept close to reversibility and equilibrium, the energy releases and transfers are made efficiently. A sequence of reactions involving small energy exchanges is therefore advantageous to the organism. The over-all efficiency, as indicated by the formation of 38 high energy phosphate bonds during the decomposition of 1 mole of glucose (see Tables 17.1 and 17.3), is about 50 per cent.[2, 39, 40]

Pathway of Oxidation-Reduction Reactions in the Cell

Table 17.1 shows a general scheme[2, 17] for the oxidation-reduction of glucose in the cell, during which glucose is decomposed, with the evolution of energy, into carbon dioxide and water as the end products. Glucose is phosphorylated, and after atomic rearrangements in the molecule, it is split into two triose phosphates. Each triose phosphate, in the presence of dehydrogenases and other enzymes, is oxidized to pyruvic acid. This phase of glucose decomposition can also occur in the absence of oxygen, and is discussed in more detail later as the anaerobic decomposition of glucose.

In the second phase of glucose decomposition, which occurs only in the presence of oxygen, the pyruvic acid formed as the end product of the first series of reactions described above is first decarboxylated (CO_2 being given off) and the 2-carbon fragment, called acetyl, is combined with a coenzyme called *coenzyme A*, or CoA (see Fig. 17.2). The acetyl-CoA is further oxidized, only after combination with a 4-carbon acid, to form a 6-carbon acid which is subsequently decarboxylated[10] and oxidized to again form a 4-carbon acid, carbon dioxide and water being given off in the process. As a result of this entire series of reactions glucose is completely decomposed to carbon dioxide and water.[2] These reactions are discussed in more detail later as the aerobic decomposition of glucose.

Part of the energy transferred in the oxidation of glucose in the cell is stored in *phosphorylated organic compounds*. The high energy phosphate bond (usually written $\sim P$) in such compounds is easily transferred from one organic compound to another in the presence of the proper enzyme.[56] Therefore, it serves as a convenient means of storing and distributing the energy in cells. When the energy of such a phosphate bond (about 8000 calories per mole, the exact amount depending upon the conditions of the reaction, such as pH and salt environment) is utilized in a reaction (e.g., a synthesis of a compound) inorganic phosphate appears (low energy bond).

Some high energy phosphate compounds of importance are listed in Table 17.1. *Adenosine triphosphate* (ATP), a nucleotide, is composed of a pentose sugar, three phosphoric acids, and the nitrogenous base, adenine (see Fig. 17.3). The bond between the pentose and the first phosphoric acid residue is an ordinary low energy bond, but the bonds between the other two phosphoric acid residues are high energy phosphate bonds. These are sometimes indicated

CONVERSIONS OF ENERGY AND MATTER IN THE CELL

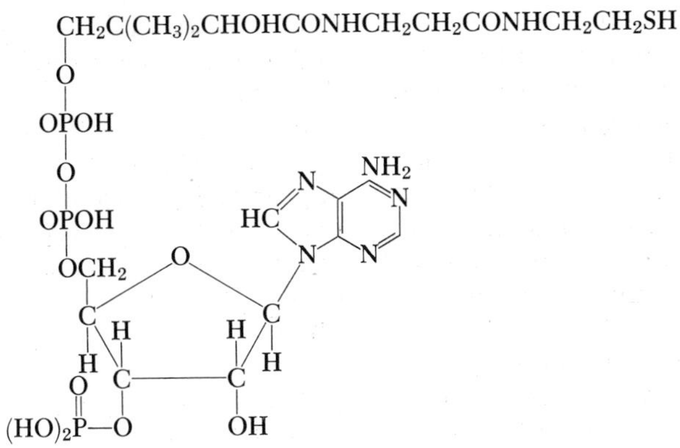

$CH_2C(CH_3)_2CHOHCONHCH_2CH_2CONHCH_2CH_2SH$

O

OPOH

O

OPOH

OCH$_2$

(HO)$_2$P—O

OH

NH$_2$

HC

Fig. 17.2. Coenzyme A.

TABLE 17.1. *General Scheme of the Decomposition of Glucose*

PROCESS	O$_2$ NEED	REACTIONS	CLASSES OF ENZYMES INVOLVED	HIGH ENERGY PHOSPHATES*
Glycolysis	—	Glucose (hexose) + ↓ ATP Hexose-phosphate ↓ 2 triose phosphates ↓ 2 pyruvic acid + energy as ∼ P	Phosphate-transferring enzymes Phosphate-splitting enzymes Isomerases Dehydrogenases Phosphate-transferring enzymes	∼ P + ADP → ATP ATP + C → ADP + CP
Krebs Tricarboxylic Acid Cycle	+	CO$_2$ + H$_2$O + energy as ∼ P	Dehydrogenases Isomerases Flavoproteins Cytochromes Cytochrome oxidase Decarboxylase Phosphate-transferring enzymes	∼ P + ADP → ATP ATP + C → ADP + CP

* The phosphates are identified as follows:
ATP = adenosine triphosphate (adenine–pentose–phosphate ∼ phosphate ∼ phosphate)
ADP = adenosine diphosphate (adenine–pentose–phosphate ∼ phosphate)
CP = creatine phosphate (creatine ∼ phosphate)
C = creatine
  In some cells arginine takes the place of creatine.

by a characteristic symbol as shown in Figure 17.3 for creatine phosphate. In *adenosine diphosphate* (ADP), which has two phosphoric acid residues, only one high energy phosphate bond is found. When energy is released from ATP, one high energy bond is broken and one ADP is formed. The two are therefore always present together. In muscle cells a relatively small amount of adenosine triphosphate is present, but a larger supply of another phosphate, known as creatine phosphate (CP), exists as the high energy phosphate reservoir (Fig. 17.3). Muscle cells may contain up to 0.5 per cent, wet weight, of creatine phosphate. Creatine phosphate in the presence of the appro-

priate enzyme (a kinase) may transfer it high energy bond to ADP forming crea tine and ATP, and conversely, creatin may accept one ~ P from ATP, formin CP and ADP; therefore, ATP and AD appear to be distributors of high energ phosphate bonds. In cells of many inverte brates *arginine phosphate* takes the plac of creatine phosphate. Creatine phos phate and arginine phosphate are calle *phosphagens.*[2]

Although high energy phosphate bond are usually outlined as a category distinc from low energy bonds, this is somewha deceptive since a whole series of bond: of different energy content occurs, a: shown in Figure 17.4. Although the trans

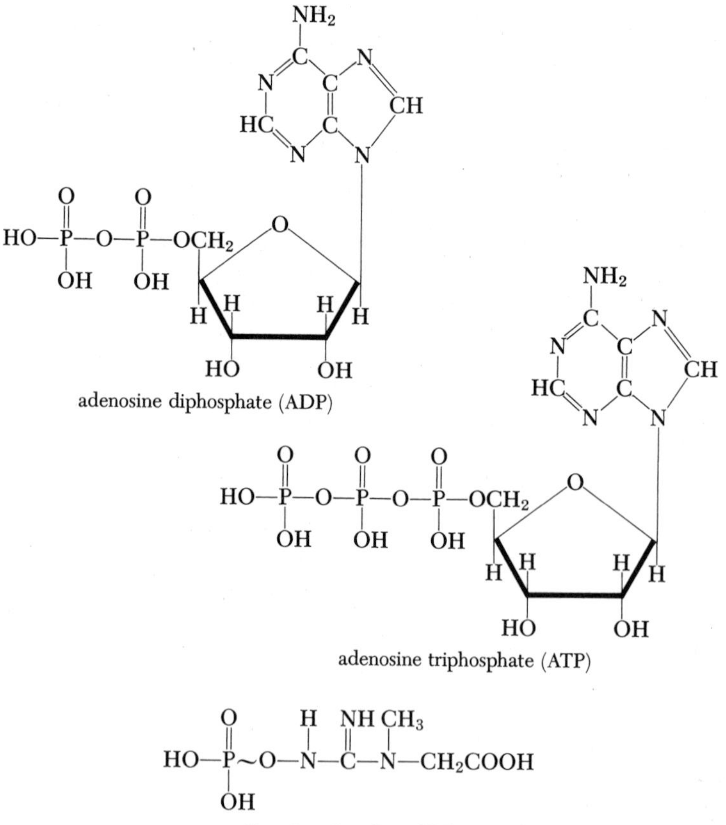

adenosine diphosphate (ADP)

adenosine triphosphate (ATP)

Creatine phosphate (CP)

Fig. 17.3. High energy phosphate compounds. In ADP and ATP the nitrogen-containing ring residue is adenine; it is attached to the pentose which in turn is attached to the phosphate.

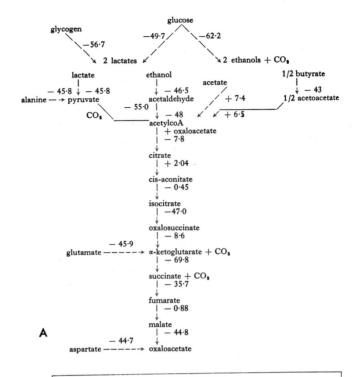

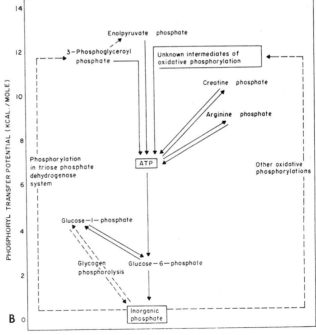

Fig. 17.4. A, changes in free energy ($\triangle F_0$) in kcal. per mole at 25°, pH 7.2, 0.2 atm. O_2, 0.05 atm. CO_2, and the other reactants having a concentration of 0.01M. The free energy changes include changes due to associated reactions notably reactions with molecular oxygen acting as an acceptor for hydrogen removed at various stages. (From Florkin, 1960: Unity and Diversity in Biochemistry. Pergamon Press, London, p. 227.) B, some free energy changes in the biosynthesis of phosphates. (From Atkinson and Morton, Comparative Biochemistry 2:74. Academic Press, New York.)

fer potential of ATP is about 8000 calories per mole (at pH 7.7, 7700 calories per mole), it takes 12,000 calories to produce 1 mole of ATP, as shown in the diagram. The efficiency of the cell in producing high energy phosphates from nutrients therefore should be calculated on this basis.[39, 40] However, the free energy for performing work is considerably less.[56] Consequently an average value of 10,000 calories per mole is used most often in calculating the approximate yield or available energy as well as efficiency.

Dinitrophenol is an inhibitor which prevents the coupling between the carrier molecule ADP and the enzymes transporting the high energy phosphate bonds. Consequently, energy liberated in oxidation is lost to the cell. For this reason, dinitrophenol was tested in a reducing diet for the obese and it was found to stimulate caloric output without causing an increase in synthetic activity. However, because it causes cataract of the eye, its medical use has been banned.

Anaerobic Decomposition of Glucose

In the cell, the initial steps in glucose breakdown up to the formation of pyruvic acid do not require oxygen and are the same regardless of whether or not oxygen is present. Anaerobic oxidation of glucose (called *glycolysis* in animals and *fermentation* in microorganisms and plants) stops at this point.

The various steps in the anaerobic decomposition of glucose are given in Figure 17.5. Glucose must first be phosphorylated at the expense of a high energy phosphate from ATP (Phosphorylation I). Glycogenolysis (which is phosphorolysis catalyzed by phosphorylase), on the other hand, liberates a phosphorylated glucose which already has one high energy phosphate bond (glucose-1-phosphate). In either case a second ATP is needed (Phosphorylation II) before the hexose phosphate shown in the outline is split into two triose phosphates (3-phos-

phoglyceraldehyde and dihydroxyacetone phosphate). It should be noted that the breakdown of the triose phosphate hydrogen is removed by dehydrogenase and after a series of reactions pyruvic acid appears. Some of the liberated energy in the anaerobic process is stored high energy phosphate bonds (Phosphorylations III and IV, right side of Figure 17.5) converting ADP to ATP. Since some ATP is used in phosphorylating glucose, the net gain of ATP is the total stored minus that used. In making a calculation of such an ATP gain, it should be remembered that each glucose gives rise to two trioses and that for each triose decomposed to pyruvic acid, two ADP molecules are converted to two ATP molecules. In terms of energy this means that the anaerobic oxidation of glucose nets about 20,000 calories per mole starting with glucose, or about 30,000 calories per mole starting with glycogen. A large number of the enzymes given in Table 17.2 are involved in the reactions shown, one enzyme usually catalyzing each step.

Under anaerobic conditions, pyruvic acid acts as a hydrogen acceptor, forming lactic acid, as shown in Figure 17.6. Muscle cells, for example, in oxygen debt may accumulate a considerable amount of lactic acid as a consequence. This lactic acid is taken to the liver where part of it is oxidized to carbon dioxide and water, and part of it is reduced to triose which forms hexose phosphate. The latter is stored as glycogen in the cells of the liver. When sugar is needed, the glycogen in the liver undergoes phosphorolysis and the sugar is released into the blood stream.[2]

In yeast still another path is followed. The pyruvic acid is decarboxylated and the acetaldehyde thus formed is reduced to alcohol, as shown in Figure 17.6 in which the enzymes required for the reactions are also indicated. Alcohol dehydrogenase is sensitive to iodoacetate, addition of which interferes with fermentation.

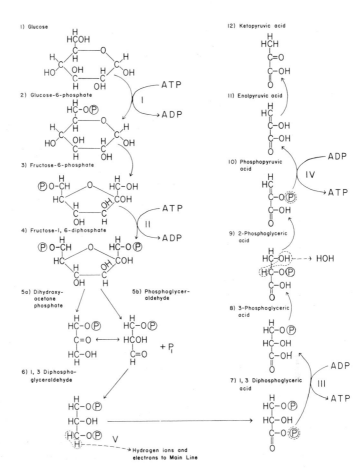

g. 17.5. Anaerobic decom-
)sition of glucose. The termi-
l reactions are given in Figure
‧.6. The enzymes concerned
the reactions given here are
own in Table 17.2.

TABLE 17.2. *Enzymes of Glycolysis*

REACTION*	ENZYME	COENZYME	INHIBITED BY
1 – 2	Glucokinase	ATP, Mg^{++}	dialysis
2 – 3	Phosphoglucoisomerase	—	—
3 – 4	6-Phosphofructo-1-kinase	ATP, Mg^{++}	dialysis
4 – 5	Fructoaldolase	—	—
5a– 5b	Trioseisomerase	—	—
5b– 6	Spontaneous?	—	—
6 – 7	Glyceraldehyde-3-phosphate dehydrogenase	DPN$^+$, HOPO$_3$=	iodoacetate, dialysis
7 – 8	3-Phosphoglycerate-1-kinase	ADP, Mg^{++}	dialysis
8 – 9	2-3 Phosphoglyceric mutase	Mg^{++}	—
9 –10	Enolase	Mg^{++}	NaF
10 –11	Pyruvic kinase	ADP, Mg^{++}	dialysis
11 –12	Spontaneous?	—	—

After Sallach and McGilvery, 1960: Gilson Medical Electronic Chart on Intermediary Metabolism, and Baldwin.[2]

 * Refer to Fig. 17.5.

aerobic - Krebs cycle - releases most of the energy for cells

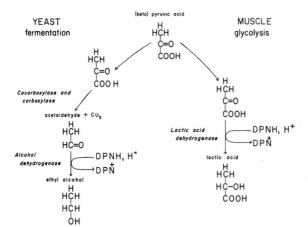

Fig. 17.6. Terminal reactions in yeast fermentation and muscle glycolysis. These reactions follow directly after those in Figure 17.5.

Bisulfite ($NaHSO_3$), when added to trap the acetaldehyde, permits the development of glycerol by reduction of the dihydroxyacetone.[47]

Neither the reduction of pyruvic acid to lactic acid nor the decarboxylation of pyruvic acid to acetaldehyde liberates energy; this can be seen from the heat of combustion of each of these compounds given in Table 15.1. The heat of combustion of lactic acid is greater than that of pyruvic acid, as one might expect of a more highly reduced compound. The heat of combustion of acetaldehyde is the same as that of pyruvic acid.

Aerobic Decomposition of Glucose

Only a small fraction of the energy in a glucose molecule has been liberated by the time pyruvic acid is formed (Table 17.3). The rest of the energy is liberated during the oxidation of pyruvic acid, the latter being perhaps the most important source of energy in all aerobic cells (see Fig. 17.4A).

The energy of pyruvic acid is liberated after a series of stepwise reactions. Pyruvate combines with coenzyme A (CoA) and is decarboxylated, that is, carbon dioxide is split out of the carboxyl

TABLE 17.3. *Yield of high energy phosphate in aerobic degradation of a mole of glucose*

REACTION	TEXT FIGURE NO.	REACTION ON TEXT FIGURE	NET GAIN
Initial phosphorylations	17.5	I,II	−2
Substrate phosphorylation (x2)	17.5	III,IV	+4
Hydrogen ions and electrons through main line:			
from oxidation of 1,3-diphosphopyruvic aldehyde (x2)	17.5	V	+6
from pyruvic to citric acid (x2)	17.8	VI	+6
from isocitric to oxalosuccinic acid (x2)	17.8	VII	+6
from ketoglutaric to succinic acid (x2)	17.8	VIII	+8
from succinic to fumaric acid (x2)	17.8	IX	+4
from malic to oxaloacetic acid (x2)	17.8	X	+6
		Total	+38

CONVERSIONS OF ENERGY AND MATTER IN THE CELL

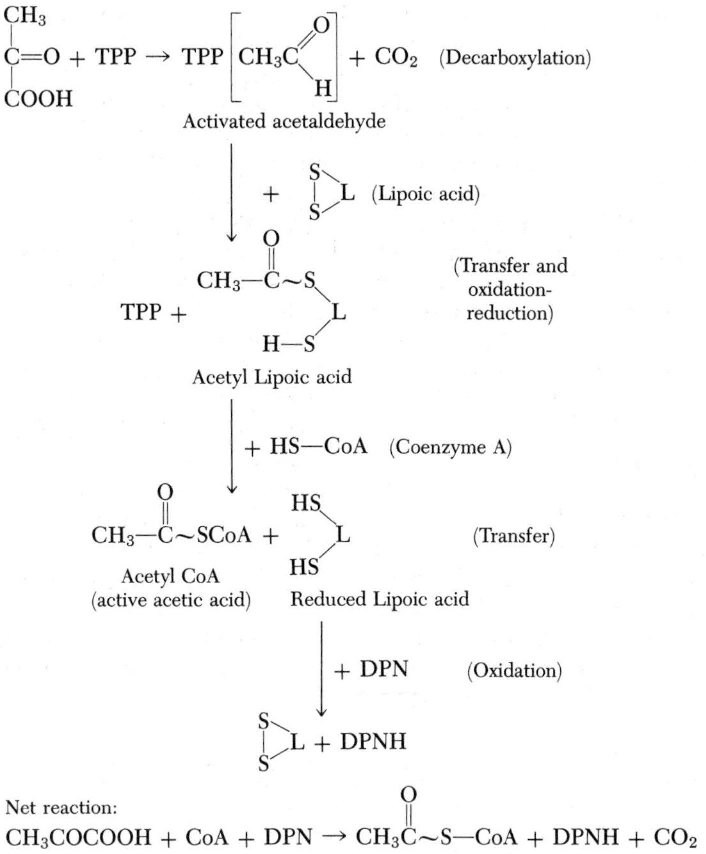

$$\underset{\substack{|\\ \text{COOH}}}{\overset{\substack{CH_3 \\ |}}{C}}=O + TPP \rightarrow TPP \left[CH_3C \overset{O}{\underset{H}{\diagdown}} \right] + CO_2 \quad \text{(Decarboxylation)}$$

Activated acetaldehyde

$+ \quad \overset{S}{\underset{S}{\diagdown}}L \quad \text{(Lipoic acid)}$

$$TPP + \quad \underset{H-S}{\overset{O}{\underset{\diagup}{CH_3-C\sim S}}}L \qquad \begin{array}{l}\text{(Transfer and} \\ \text{oxidation-} \\ \text{reduction)}\end{array}$$

Acetyl Lipoic acid

$+ \text{HS}-\text{CoA} \quad \text{(Coenzyme A)}$

$$\underset{\substack{\text{Acetyl CoA} \\ \text{(active acetic acid)}}}{\overset{O}{\overset{\|}{CH_3-C\sim SCoA}}} + \quad \underset{\substack{HS \\ \diagup \\ HS}}{\overset{HS\diagdown}{L}} \qquad \text{(Transfer)}$$

Reduced Lipoic acid

$+ \text{DPN} \qquad \text{(Oxidation)}$

$\overset{S\diagdown}{\underset{S\diagup}{}}L + \text{DPNH}$

Net reaction:

$$CH_3COCOOH + CoA + DPN \rightarrow CH_3\overset{O}{\overset{\|}{C}}\sim S-CoA + DPNH + CO_2$$

Fig. 17.7. The mechanism of oxidative decarboxylation of pyruvic acid. TPP refers to thiamin pyrophosphate. (From McElroy.[17])

group of the acid. The enzyme catalyzing decarboxylation contains thiamine phosphate (TPP) in its prosthetic group. The reactions resulting in the decarboxylation of pyruvic acid and the formation of acetyl CoA are shown in Figure 17.7. The hydrogen is passed to coenzyme I—diphosphopyridine nucleotide (DPN+). The 2-carbon fragment (acetyl) is now added to a 4-carbon acid (oxaloacetic) to form a 6-carbon acid (citric) as shown in Figure 17.8 (top). Citric acid first undergoes internal rearrangements and then is dehydrogenated. After this it is decarboxylated, giving rise to a 5-carbon acid (α-ketoglutaric). The 5-carbon acid in turn is decarboxylated in the presence of CoA (forming succinyl-CoA), giving rise to a 4-carbon acid (succinic). The 4-carbon acid undergoes a series of dehydrogenations ending with the formation of oxaloacetic acid which again becomes a receptor for an acetyl fragment. A considerable amount of energy, amounting to 40,000 or 50,000 calories per mole, is liberated in each oxidative decarboxylation (see Fig. 17.4). Part of this energy is stored in high energy phosphate bonds (see Table 17.3).

These events, first associated by Krebs,[3, 4] form a cycle which has been called the *Krebs tricarboxylic acid cycle* because several of the acids appearing in it are tricarboxylic. The importance of coenzyme A in the transformation was shown by Lipmann, who elucidated the chemical nature of coenzyme A.[5, 6] The prosthetic group of coenzyme A contains pantothenic acid, one of the vitamins B. For their elucidation of the above reactions Krebs and Lipmann shared the Nobel prize in 1953. These reactions of the Krebs cycle are presented in a simplified way in Figures 17.7 and 17.8. The enzymes concerned in the reactions are given in Table 17.4. The yield of high energy phosphates from the reactions of the Krebs cycle is given in Table 17.3.

The Metabolic Mill

The Krebs tricarboxylic acid cycle has much wider significance in the animal or plant cell than is shown by the degradation of pyruvic acid. It is the means whereby fragments of organic compounds available from various metabolic reactions involving the degradation of pro-

teins, fats and carbohydrates can be utilized effectively. For example, when plant proteins in the food of an animal are digested into their constituent amino acids, the various amino acids appear in proportions different from the proportion needed for the synthesis of animal protein. Most of the amino acids present in excess are then deaminated, and the residues enter the Krebs cycle where, upon being oxidized, they contribute to the formation of high energy phosphate bonds.[50] To illustrate, glutamic acid on deamination forms α-ketoglutaric acid, aspartic acid forms oxaloacetic acid; and alanine forms pyruvic acid. Fatty acid fragments also enter the Krebs cycle. Fatty acids are oxidized by what is called β-oxidation, in the course of which a 2-carbon acid fragment (acetyl) is split from the long chain of the fatty acid.[36,] The acetyl fragment, as described earlier, enters the Krebs cycle. These various relations are shown in Figure 17.9.

TABLE 17.4. *Enzymes Involved in the Krebs Tricarboxylic Acid Cycle*

REACTION	ENZYME*	INHIBITOR
1. Pyruvic acid and acetyl CoA	Oxidative decarboxylation system	—
2. Acetyl CoA and oxaloacetic acid	Condensing enzyme	—
3. Citric to cisaconitic acid	Aconitase	Fluorocitrate
4. Cisaconitic to isocitric acid	Aconitase	—
5. Isocitric to oxalosuccinic acid	Isocitric dehydrogenase; TPN^+	Anaerobiosis
6. Oxalosuccinic to α-keto-glutaric acid	Oxalosuccinic decarboxylase; Mn^{++}	—
7. α-Ketoglutaric to succinic acid	Oxidative decarboxylation system	Arsenite
8. Succinic to fumaric acid	Succinic dehydrogenase	Malonate
9. Fumaric to malic acid	Fumarase	—
10. Malic to oxalosuccinic acid	Malic dehydrogenase; DPN^+	—

* The coenzyme for dehydrogenases of most cells is DPN^+; the coenzyme for isocitric dehydrogenase is TPN^+ although yeast can use both DPN^+ and TPN^+. The only dehydrogenation in the Krebs cycle which does not require a coenzyme is that from succinic to fumaric acid in which the hydrogen acceptor is a cytochrome. Largely after Baldwin.[2]

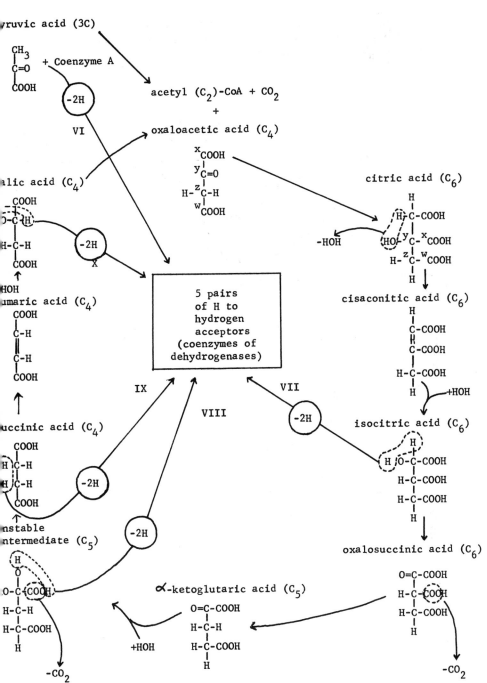

Fig. 17.8. Aerobic breakdown of pyruvic acid. (For anaerobic reactions see Fig. 17.6.) The enzymes involved in the various steps are given in Table 17.4. Decarboxylation of an acid, releasing CO_2 (emphasized in this diagram), can be *reversed* under appropriate conditions in all cells, animal as well as green plant, thus incorporating ("fixing") free CO_2, although in a different way than in photosynthesis (see Chapter 20).

Such cyclic conversion of excess energy from various compounds into the high energy phosphate bonds of creatine phosphate or into the formation of gly- cogen is an effective and efficient meth of storing chemical potential energy. would be infinitely more difficult for th organism to store and use the odd asso

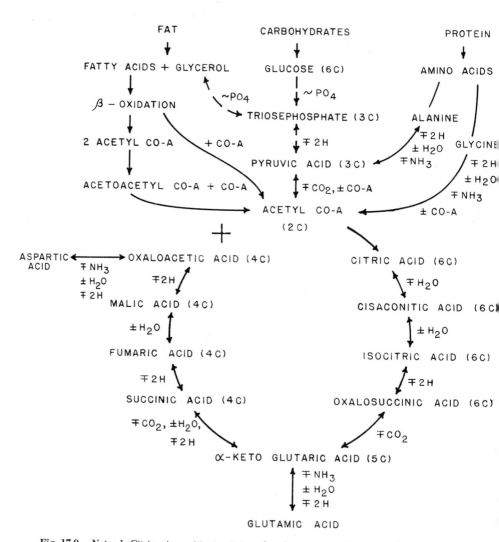

Fig. 17.9. Note: 1. Citric, cisaconitic, isocitric and oxalosuccinic acids are tricarboxylic.

2. Serine, threonine, cysteine and valine go by way of the pathway shown for alanine. Arginine, proline, hydroxyproline, histidine and ornithine go by way of the pathway shown for glutamic acid. Aspartic acid on deamination gives rise to oxaloacetic acid.

3. For high energy phosphate yield see Table 17.3.

4. The upper part of each plus or minus sign indicates the reaction going clockwise; the lower part indicates the converse.

For detailed structures of the acids see Figs. 17.5, 17.6, 17.7 and 17.8, and for a list of the enzymes involved see Tables 17.2 and 17.4. (Modified after Krebs 1948–1949: The Tricarboxylic Acid Cycle. Harvey Lectures, Springfield, Illinois, Charles C. Thomas Company, p. 165.)

CONVERSIONS OF ENERGY AND MATTER IN THE CELL

ent of compounds that enter the Krebs cycle than it is to store high energy phosphates.

This diagram of the metabolic mill also serves to show synthesis in the cell of more complex compounds from fragments, for example, of amino acids from ammonia and the appropriate keto acids[8] (e.g., glutamic acid from ammonia and -ketoglutaric acid). Protein synthesis from phosphorylated amino acids is dealt with elsewhere (Chapter 25). Carbohydrate in excess over that which can be stored in the glycogen depots is converted into fat by way of synthesis of fragments from the Krebs cycle. The synthesis of fatty acids is more indirect than reversal of the degradation of fatty acids (Fig. 17.9). It involves the incorporation of CO_2 into acetyl CoA at the expense of energy from ATP to form a 3-carbon compound. The latter compound is combined with another acetyl CoA to form a 5-carbon compound from which, after reduction and decarboxylation, a 4-carbon fatty acid is produced. Each addition of two carbons to the fatty acid involves a similar round of reactions, details of which may be obtained from a textbook of biochemistry. Fat in animals is stored in fat bodies or adipose tissue. In plants fat is often found in fruit (avocado) or in seeds (nuts). All of these syntheses probably proceed at the expense of high energy phosphate bonds. It is this over-all net of interrelations in the degradation and synthesis of proteins, fat and carbohydrates that is called the *metabolic mill*.

Hydrogen and Electron Transfer in the Main Line of Oxidation-Reduction Reactions

In the major pathway, often called the main line of oxidation-reduction reactions in the cell, hydrogen is removed from a substrate and transferred through a series of enzymes until it is oxidized to water, with an accompanying release of energy.

As stated previously most dehydrogenases (enzymes which catalyze hydrogen transfer) are formed by association of one of the coenzymes—coenzyme I (DPN) or coenzyme II (TPN) with a protein molecule specific to a particular substrate. Hydrogen is usually picked up from the substrate by the coenzyme part of the dehydrogenase and carried to the next enzymes in the chain of events: the flavoproteins, which act as hydrogen carriers.[14] From the flavoprotein each hydrogen is discharged into the cell fluid as a hydrogen ion, and the electrons are passed on to cell pigments known as cytochromes. From the cytochromes electrons are passed to the enzyme *cytochrome oxidase*, which ultimately discharges the electrons to oxygen. The oxygen, thus excited, unites with the hydrogen ions, forming water. The whole series of reactions is shown in Figure 17.10 with the transfer of hydrogens and of electrons indicated in each of the steps.[39, 40]

Dehydrogenases in cells can be most easily detected by observing the color change of methylene blue when the dye is mixed with the tissue extract. In the presence of active hydrogen liberated from a substrate by a dehydrogenase, the methylene blue, acting as a carrier like flavoprotein, is reduced to colorless leucomethylene blue. If the solution containing leucomethylene blue is shaken up with air, the colorless dye is again oxidized, and the blue color reappears— the hydrogen having been passed directly to the oxygen of the air to form water.

The relative dehydrogenase content or dehydrogenase activity of cells may be estimated by the rate of decolorization of methylene blue mixed with tissue mash or *brei* in a Thunberg tube (see Fig. 17.11) from which oxygen has been withdrawn.[15] The presence and activity of the dehydrogenases specific to each of a series of substrates may be studied if various substrates are placed in the tube one at a time.

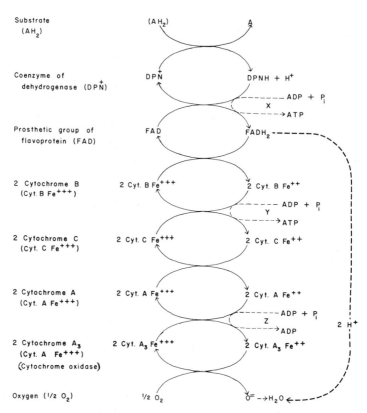

Fig. 17.10. The main line of electron transfers and the probable reactions in ATP synthesis from ADP and inorganic phosphorus (Pi). X, Y and Z denote coupling enzymes, the exact nature of which is still unknown. (After Lehninger, 1960: Fed. Proc., *19*:952.)

The *cytochromes* (Fig. 17.12A) are cell pigments universally present in aerobic cells.[16, 17] They receive electrons from the flavoproteins or other carrier enzymes and pass them to cytochrome oxidase which activates oxygen. At least four cytochromes, A, A_3, B and C, are usually found in cells. In bacteria several new ones have also been described.[57] In plant cells nine cytochromes have been identified.[56] The cytochromes are distinguishable by their absorption spectra; in all, 23 different cytochromes have been studied.[58] A cytochrome has a prosthetic group like the heme portion of hemoglobin (see Fig. 17.12A and B).

The cytochromes were first seen by MacMunn in 1886 in spectroscopic stud-

ies of various cells, but their role in th[e] cell was not understood until 1926 wh[en] Keilin showed that the state of oxidati[on] or reduction of the cytochromes may [be] determined by their absorption spectr[a.] Keilin thus surmised their importance [in] cellular oxidation.

Cytochrome oxidase is an enzyme th[at] has as its porphyrin prosthetic group cyt[o]chrome A_3 (see Fig. 17.10). On recei[v]ing an electron from cytochrome A, th[e] iron in the molecule becomes reduce[d] and when the electron is passed to ox[y]gen the iron is again oxidized. It is poss[i]ble to demonstrate the presence of cyt[o]chrome oxidase by a simple color reactio[n] called the "nadi reaction" devised b[y] Warburg.[18] For this reaction, *p*-pheny[l]

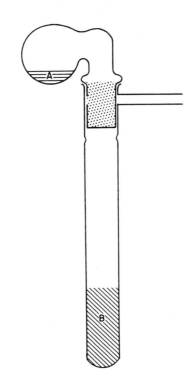

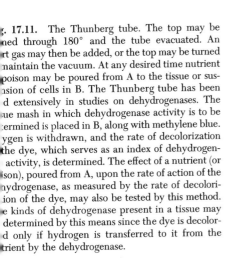

17.11. The Thunberg tube. The top may be
~~ned~~ through 180° and the tube evacuated. An
~~rt~~ gas may then be added, or the top may be turned
~~m~~aintain the vacuum. At any desired time nutrient
~~p~~oison may be poured from A to the tissue or sus-
~~n~~sion of cells in B. The Thunberg tube has been
~~d~~ extensively in studies on dehydrogenases. The
~~su~~e mash in which dehydrogenase activity is to be
~~d~~ermined is placed in B, along with methylene blue.
~~x~~ygen is withdrawn, and the rate of decolorization
~~of~~ the dye, which serves as an index of dehydrogen-
~~~ activity, is determined. The effect of a nutrient (or
~~p~~ison), poured from A, upon the rate of action of the
~~~~hydrogenase, as measured by the rate of decolori-
~~t~~ion of the dye, may also be tested by this method.
~~~e kinds of dehydrogenase present in a tissue may
~~~ determined by this means since the dye is decolor-
~~~d only if hydrogen is transferred to it from the
~~~trient by the dehydrogenase.

~~~ediamine and α-naphthol are mixed
~~~th a tissue or tissue extract, and if cyto-
~~~rome oxidase is present in the tissue a
~~~uish color soon appears. The color is
~~~e result of the formation of the dye,
~~~dophenol. By the intensity of the color
~~~e can determine roughly the amount of
~~~zyme present and demonstrate a con-
~~~ntration gradient of cytochrome oxidase
~~~ cells and tissues. For example, the ani-
~~~al pole of a marine egg has more cyto-
~~~rome oxidase than the vegetal pole,
~~~d the anterior end of the embryo has
~~~ore than the posterior end.[19]

~~A~~lternate Pathways of Glucose Decomposition

The Pentose Shunt. For most aerobic
~~ce~~lls glucose degradation follows the ser-
~~ie~~s of reactions of the Krebs cycle
~~d~~escribed above. However, alternate
~~p~~athways exist, one of the most impor-
~~ta~~nt of these being the *pentose* or *oxida-*

tive shunt which may account for as
much as 10 per cent of the glucose metabolism, and even more under some circumstances.[2, 5, 37, 39]

The first reaction in the pentose shunt
(Fig. 17.13) is the oxidation of glucose-6-
phosphate, in the presence of the enzyme glucose-6-phosphate dehydrogenase,
to form 6-phosphogluconic acid by way
of 6-phosphogluconolactone. The 6-phos-
phogluconic acid is then oxidized, in the
presence of coenzyme TPN, to form
TPNH (the reduced form of the coenzyme), H$^+$ and 3-keto-6-phosphogluconic
acid which, in the presence of the enzyme 3-keto-6-phosphogluconic acid
decarboxylase, is decarboxylated to form
ribulose-5-phosphate and carbon dioxide.
The TPNH and H$^+$ can then reduce
some compound or be oxidized through
the flavin-cytochrome system in the
main line, in which case water is formed.

Ribulose-5-phosphate can be converted
into pentoses, either ribose-5-phosphate

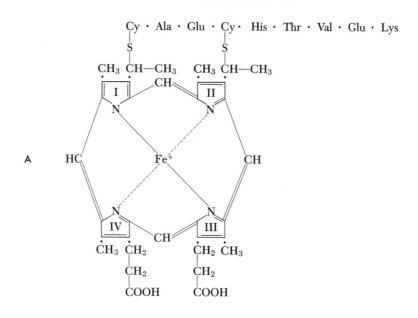

Fig. 17.12. *A*, shows the possible structure of the cytochrome C—peptide. *B*, illustrates the structure of a metalloporphyrin, hemin (the chloride of heme). A porphin is a cyclic tetrapyrrole with no substituent side chains. When substituent side chains are present, the compound is called a porphyrin. Various porphyrins have different side chains. When a metal is present in the center of the ring, the compound is called a metalloporphyrin. (From Anfinsen, 1959: The Molecular Basis of Evolution. Wiley, New York, p. 156. After Tuppy and Bodo.)

or xylulose-5-phosphate, by phosphoribo-isomerase and phosphoketopentose epi-merase, respectively. All three pentoses can enter into a series of reactions catalyzed by the enzyme transketolase (steps 5 and 7 below), transaldolase (step 6) and aldolase (step 8), but the details of the reactions are not fully determined. However, triose phosphate is formed, pos-sibly by a pathway which is the revers of that in photosynthesis (see Chapter 20 In this way, 3 molecules of ribulose-5 phosphate give rise to 5 molecules c triosephosphate. Some of the trioses ma again form hexoses. The major reaction are given below:

1. 6 hexose phosphate $+ 3 O_2 \rightarrow$
   6 gluconic acid phosphate   (17.5

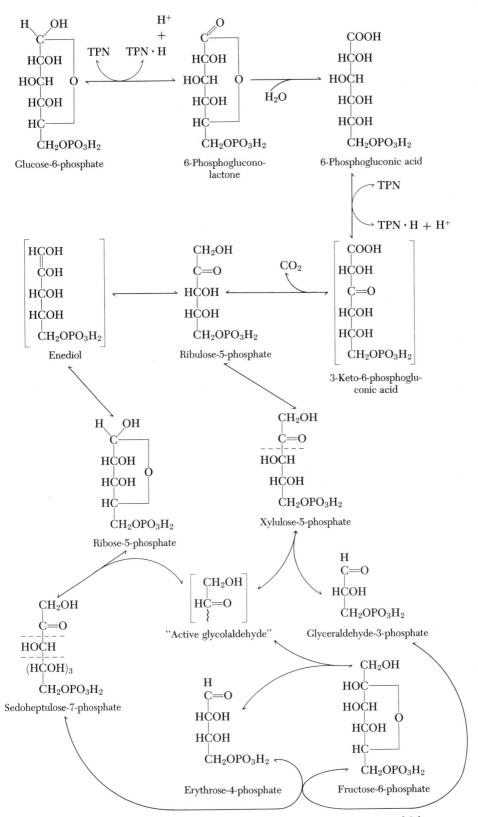

Fig. 17.13. The Pentose Shunt Pathway in Heterotrophic Cells. (From Cantarow and Schepartz, 1962: Biochemistry, Saunders, Philadelphia, p. 432.)

2. 6 gluconic acid phosphate $- 12H \rightarrow$
$\qquad$ 6 phospho-3-ketogluconic acid (17.6)

3. 3-keto-6 phospho-gluconic acid $\rightarrow$
$\qquad 6\,CO_2 + 6$ ribulose phosphate (17.7)

4. 6 xylulose phosphate $\rightleftharpoons 6$ ribulose
$\qquad$ phosphate $\rightleftharpoons 6$ ribose phosphate (17.8)

5. 2 ribose phosphate $+ 2$ xylulose
phosphate $\rightarrow 2$ sedoheptulose phosphate $+$
$\qquad$ 2 triose phosphate (17.9)

6. 2 sedoheptulose phosphate $+ 2$ triose
phosphate $\rightarrow 2$ hexose phosphate $+$
$\qquad$ 2 erythrose (tetrose) phosphate (17.10)

7. 2 erythrose phosphate $+ 2$ xylulose
phosphate $\rightarrow 2$ hexose phosphate $+$
$\qquad$ 2 triose phosphate (17.11)

8. 2 triose phosphate $\rightarrow$ hexose phosphate $+$
$\qquad$ inorganic phosphate (17.12)

Thus, if the course of the cycle as shown above[2] is assumed to occur, the net effect is as if one of the six molecules of glucose had been completely decomposed, the other five (in reactions 6, 7 and 8) being reconstituted.

The enzymes necessary for these reactions occur in all cells tested.[35] High energy phosphates are formed as in the reactions previously considered (38 ATP molecules per hexose decomposed). As some of these compounds are involved in photosynthesis it is not surprising that this pathway also exists in plant cells. It is also found in some microorganisms. Cells of some tumors carry on much more oxidation by way of the oxidative pentose shunt than do normal cells.

Alternate pathways in Microorganisms. Microorganisms, perhaps the most versatile chemists among cells, have explored various pathways for decomposition of organic compounds.[47] Some bacteria— the *chemoautotrophs*—employ oxidation of inorganic compounds such as sulfur or iron as a source of the energy for the synthesis of their organic material from carbon dioxide, water and salts. Some autotrophic bacteria are photosynthetic (see

Chapter 20). The majority of mic organisms are *heterotrophic*, that is, th depend upon organic materials as th sources of energy. Peculiar fermentatio with production of methane, hydrog sulfide and various products of anaero carbohydrate and nitrogen metaboli foreign to animal and plant cells are fou among the microbes. Many compou are attacked, and it has been stated th a microbe can probably be found to compose any organic compound, even c resulting from the skill of the orga chemist and not known to occur in natu When the microbe lacks the enzyme a substance, a new enzyme may induced in it after it has had contact w the substrate for a time. If the micro fails to develop a new enzyme but grown for several generations in the pr ence of the strange substrate, muta may appear which are capable of usi the substrate as a source of energy. T is true even of substances toxic to ma cells. This subject, though fascinating its implications, is too large for conside tion here (see references 47 and 51).

In spite of the many kinds of ferme tations and oxidative processes carried by microorganisms, a degree of un prevails in their biochemistry, and early review[52] comparing these reactio was entitled "The Unity in Biochemistry All the series of reactions depend up certain key reactions common to m life, and some similar enzymes and c enzymes, as well as phosphorylating a high energy storage compounds, a found in all of them.[47, 51]

Pathways in Poisoned Cells. Sin cyanide binds the iron in the prosthe group of cytochrome oxidase, making incapable of transferring electrons, t iron remains in the oxidized state and t cytochromes are unable to discharge th electrons to the enzyme.[31, 34] Becau the absorption spectra of reduced a oxidized cytochromes are different, t effect of cyanide on the respiratory co dition of the cell can be detected spectr opically, cyanide causing the absorption spectrum of the reduced cytochromes to appear.

Although 0.001 molar cyanide blocks the main line of oxidation, a residual respiration, constituting about 5 to 15 per cent of the total and called the cyanide-stable respiration, continues—presumably by pathways other than through cytochrome oxidase. For example, flavoproteins have been found to pass electrons slowly to oxygen, and a few oxidases specific to amino acids remove hydrogen from corresponding amino acids and pass it directly to oxygen, even in the presence of cyanide. The experiments with cyanide, therefore, demonstrate the presence of oxidative pathways other than the main line pathway of oxidation through cytochrome oxidase.[53]

A poison such as urethan which affects many enzymes in a rather unspecific manner is not as useful in demonstrating alternate pathways. Urethan has a certain degree of selectivity for dehydrogenases, and in its presence the oxidized absorption spectrum of the cytochromes appears.

Poisons have been useful in many cases because when they are used to block a specific pathway, alternate pathways show up more clearly. In this way it has been possible to identify and characterize some of the subsidiary pathways which play a role in normal metabolism as well.[21]

Pathways in Tumor Cells. Warburg has emphasized the glycolytic nature of tumor metabolism. Regardless of whether this is a cause or an effect of the derangement of growth which is cancer, it is interesting that there is greater emphasis in many cases, though not all, upon the anaerobic metabolism. Since tumors are often rapidly dividing cells without too much organization, glycolysis could be favored because the supply of oxygen is probably inadequate. No special kind of metabolism unique to tumor cells has been found, the difference in reactions and enzymes being quantitative.[18, 54, 61]

Hydrogen Peroxide Formation as an End Product in Cellular Oxidation

When enzymes carry the hydrogen, removed from a substrate, directly to atmospheric oxygen, hydrogen peroxide rather than water is formed. An example of such a reaction is shown by D-amino oxidase, which catalyzes the oxidative deamination of its substrates to the corresponding keto acids. The hydrogen peroxide, which is known to be an inhibitor of many enzymes and thus acts as a cell poison, is withdrawn as soon as it is formed through the action of some specific enzymes. The most generally distributed enzyme of this type, *catalase*, decomposes hydrogen peroxide to water and oxygen. Catalase, which contains iron in a porphyrin nucleus, has some peroxidase action and is inhibited by cyanide. In many plant cells *peroxidases*, the enzymes that serve to oxidize substrates by using peroxide as a hydrogen acceptor, dispose of the hydrogen peroxide.[2]

Methods for Investigating Intermediary Metabolism

The concepts summarized in the preceding pages were developed only after prolonged research by diverse techniques.[2] The history of their development is involved and cannot be considered here. However, discussion of an interesting controversy illustrates the devious routes taken in making some of the discoveries.

In analyzing cell respiration, Warburg considered activation of oxygen to be the important step. The activated oxygen, he said, would combine with the substrate. At the time, many investigators sought to analyze problems of the cell by making simple analogues, or models, and Warburg found that activated blood charcoal catalyzed oxidation of many of the metabolites present in the cell by activating oxygen. The active agent in blood charcoal is iron, which is subject to poisons like cyanide and carbon monoxide. Warburg therefore searched for an iron-containing agent in the cell that activated oxygen. He obtained evidence for such an agent by the effective use of respiratory inhibitors. He found that this cellular catalyst is inhibited by cyanide and carbon monoxide. The carbon monoxide poisoning proved reversible with visible light, and from the action spectrum of this reversal Warburg determined that the respiratory enzyme was a porphyrin.[27] He called this enzyme the "atmungsferment" or respiratory enzyme. Later, isolation of the enzyme verified his deductions.[2]

On the other hand, Wieland, Warburg's contemporary, emphasized the importance of activation of hydrogen, and as a model of the cell enzymes[28] he used palladium black, which is known to adsorb hydrogen. He found that the palladium black catalyzes the oxidation of some of the organic compounds of the cell, and he postulated the presence of dehydrogenase action in the cell, with activation and removal of hydrogen. Thunberg[15] later gathered evidence for this type of enzyme, using the method shown in Figure 17.11. By using different substrates with tissue preparations he was able to identify a large number of dehydrogenases and to measure their relative concentrations.

It was finally realized that Wieland and Warburg were both correct, that many enzymes were involved in cell respiration and that both hydrogen and oxygen had to be activated. Many of the respiratory enzymes have since been obtained in relatively pure form and their properties have been investigated. Some enzymes seem to be inseparable from granules in the cell. However, when enough is known about each enzyme, it is probable that each will be separated and purified. At the present time the few purified oxidation-reduction enzymes of this type require cofactors (metals and coenzymes) in concentrations higher than those present in the living cell. This might imply that the structural and functional relations between the enzymes and cofactors are optimal in the cell, or perhaps that the have been altered in some way during the purification procedure.[2, 44]

For a study of the steps in the break down or synthesis of an organic compound in the cell of an organism (a field of great interest at the present time), the organism is fed various diets or given nutrients by injection. Its urine is the examined for metabolic intermediate (i.e., intermediate stages in the breakdown of a nutrient).[30] Many nutrients can now be labeled with "tagged" nitrogen, carbon, phosphorus, sulfur, etc., and therefore can be much more readily traced in metabolism than was previously possible.[25] In addition, it has been found possible to determine pathways of break down and synthesis by studying organisms possessing genetic metabolic abnormalities, which would make them incapable of completely decomposing some compounds. As a result intermediates accumulate in their urine in quantities sufficient for identification.[32] Mutants lacking some enzymatic constituent have also been produced in the bread mold Neurospora[29] and in other organisms (see Chapter 25). Such mutants accumulate some of the metabolic intermediates in large quantities, making identification easier.

In vitro studies of intermediary metabolism have been made with cells in tissue cultures, perfused organs (liver, kidney etc.) and slices of tissues. Sometimes the cells are ground to a brei for biochemical studies. Manometric studies of gaseous exchanges in cells in tissue slices have added to the knowledge of intermediary metabolism (see Chapter 19), because comparisons can be made between respiration of normal and of pathological cells or of tissue cells from animals grown on diets omitting certain essential requirements.[32]

It is also important that, as each enzyme is separated and purified, the reaction it catalyzes be studied in vitro. Only when the various thermodynamic and kinetic properties of the isolated system ave been studied under controlled conditions can the part it plays in the whole sequence of reactions in the cell be established with any certainty.

As mentioned previously, enzymes can be separated from extraneous proteins by salting out or by adsorption on resins and, they may be purified by electrophoretic procedures. Even when purification is not possible, considerable information may be obtained by use of a partially purified enzyme, provided the extraneous material does not interfere with the reaction under study. Much has been learned even by the use of heterogeneous suspensions containing many enzymes, such as entire mitochondria, fragmented mitochondria or partially purified enzyme systems from mitochondria.

The rate of an enzymatic reaction is often measured spectrophotometrically because accurate measurements can be made quickly and continuously during the course of the reaction. Fortunately many of the enzymes important in the reactions discussed in this chapter have markedly different absorption spectra in their oxidized and reduced states. Consequently the relative amount of the enzyme system in each state can readily be determined and the course of the reaction can be followed by the change in proportion of each. An example[9] is given in Figure 17.14. Methods for studying enzymatic reactions are considered in treatises on enzymes.[11, 13]

Enzymes in the Organelles of the Cell

The enzymes involved in the anaerobic phase of sugar decomposition are apparently present in the cytoplasmic matrix and not localized on any known particulates. On the other hand, all of the enzymes of the Krebs tricarboxylic acid cycle are localized in the mitochondria. Most of the energy for the metabolism of the cell, therefore, appears to be released and transferred in the mitochondria.[46] Since the various enzymes which participate in the formation and transfer of high energy phosphate bonds are also localized there, the main role of the mitochondria appears to be the formation and liberation of compounds containing high energy phosphate bonds which can be used elsewhere in the cell.[22, 23, 44, 45, 49]

As already described, the mitochondrion has a complex structure, usually with lamellate cristae protruding into the central lumen, providing a large surface area. The problem is to localize and isolate each enzyme, to identify the individual reactions catalyzed by the enzyme and, finally, to reconstruct the enzyme system *in vitro*. However, the association of the enzymes of electron transport and phosphorylation in solid state lipoprotein arrays in the mitochondrial membranes presents formidable experimental problems. Attempts to separate many of the enzymes have failed, although some success has been achieved in submitochondrial systems obtained by fragmenting the mitochondria, the whole series of reactions now being obtained in pieces equal to $\frac{1}{40}$ of a mitochondrion. The difficulties suggest that there may be a biological necessity for structural organization of these catalysts in a moderately rigid, geometrically organized constellation in the membrane to minimize the path distance between slowly diffusing large molecules and to increase the probability of interaction.[40] One conception of the sequence of organization is shown in Figure 17.15, but other data suggest instead that the enzymes may be in solution.[60]

Some evidence indicates that each mitochondrion has about 5000 to 10,000 complete sets of such enzymes. The assemblies are probably distributed equally over the cristae.[40] It will be recalled that a cell has many mitochondria—about 500 being present in many kinds of cells (a liver cell has about 2500); therefore there is ample room to accommodate numerous sets of enzymes.

Corresponding to their role in energy transfer, mitochondria are numerous in active cells and, in general, concentrate in regions of greatest activity. During cell

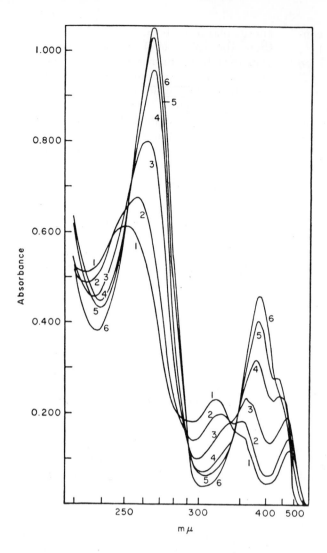

Fig. 17.14. Absorption spectra of flavin mononucleotide (6.4×10^{-5}M in 1 N HCl) at successive oxidation states from about 7 per cent reduction (curve 1) to full oxidation (curve 6); light path 0.5 cm., temperature 28° C.; reduced with metallic Zn. (From Beinert.[9])

division they may be seen actively moving about the spindle.

Enzymes participating in the synthesis of proteins are present in the ribosomes that adhere to the outer surfaces of the walls of the endoplasmic reticulum of the cell. When cells are mechanically crushed the endoplasmic reticulum breaks up into vacuoles, on the outer surface of which are the ribosomes. Treatment with a detergent separates the ribosomes from the lipoprotein membranes of the vacuoles. The ribosomes thus separated are concentrated by centrifugation and are found

to incorporate labeled amino acids into proteins very readily when provided with the proper conditions. It is here then that the major part of protein synthesis of the cell is performed (see Chapter 25).[22]

The nucleus contains enzymes for anaerobic metabolism and for some oxidative phosphorylation as well. The nucleus also contains enzymes for synthesis of DNA, RNA and some proteins. The coenzyme is synthesized in the nucleus and nuclear control of cytoplasmic metabolism is in part the result of the control the nucleus has over the production

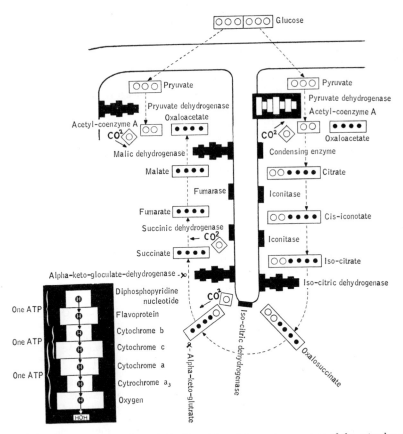

Fig. 17.15. Diagram showing the orderly disposition of the main enzymes of the mitochondria. The piles of disks represent the system of transference of hydrogen. The rectangles indicate the other enzymes. *Right,* Glucose with six carbons which splits into two molecules of pyruvate within the hyaloplasm. Pyruvate penetrates into the mitochondria and after decarboxylation combines with the oxalacetate left from the previous Krebs cycle. The changes of the citrate continue until complete oxidation of the pyruvate. Finally, a molecule of oxalacetate is left to initiate a new cycle.

Lower left, Oxidative system or hydrogen transfer system. The first element of the chain is the diphosphopyridine nucleotide, a coenzyme that removes hydrogen from the metabolite and becomes reduced. Then the hydrogen is transformed into a series of intermediary elements until the oxygen is reached. Each one of these passages generates about three molecules of ATP which are essential sources of energy for vital needs. It can be seen that oxidation is coupled to the phophorylation of ADP to form the ATP. (Modified after *The Cell.* The Upjohn Co., 1958.)

f this substance that passes through the uclear membrane into the cytoplasm (see Chapter 6).

Dynamic Nature of Cell Constituents

Through the use of nutrients containing isotopes of nitrogen (N^{15}) and carbon (C^{14}) it is possible to "label" cell proteins.

The decrease of the labeled nitrogen and carbon may then be measured. By this means it has been possible to demonstrate that cells of all tissues lose some of their labeled material and replace it anew periodically. Even the protein in cells and deposits of connective tissue is replaced, although less rapidly than in cells of more active tissue. Replacement is very rapid in cells of some tissues like the liver.[24]

The results have been generally taken to indicate that the cellular protein is continually breaking down and being replaced. On the other hand, another interpretation of the results is also possible— it may be that individual cells are dying and are being replaced, rather than that part of the protein in all of the cells is being replaced. Studies with bacteria show that nitrogen is being incorporated into the cell at a steady rate so long as the cell is growing. There appears to be no breakdown of protein except when the cells are starved for nitrogen.[55] It thus appears necessary to test the "dynamic state" hypothesis with a variety of animal and plant cells, perhaps in tissue culture, and by a variety of methods before the conclusion can be accepted that the proteins and other cell constituents are in a dynamic state, being continuously broken down and replaced. It may be that the increases occur only with growth (or storage) and that losses of protein attend nitrogen starvation. "Basal" metabolic loss of nitrogen in various organisms may turn out to be only the nitrogen needed to replace the dying cells, since cells are continually shed by the digestive tract, blood and epidermis, and perhaps other tissues of the organism. Bacteria do not appear to replace cellular material, but they add to it in growth. Some tests on tissue cultures suggest that cells which have stopped dividing do replace their cellular materials slowly.[59]

GENERAL REFERENCES

Aisenberg, A. C., 1961: The Glycolysis and Respiration of Tumors. Academic Press, New York.

Albritten, E. C., 1954: Standard Values in Nutrition and Metabolism. Saunders, Philadelphia.

Augenstine, L. (ed.), 1960: Bioenergetics: Consideration of Processes of Absorption, Stabilization, Transfer and Utilization. Academic Press, New York.

Baldwin, E., 1957: Dynamic Aspects of Biochemistry. 3rd Ed. Cambridge Univ. Press, London.

Barker, H. A., 1956: Bacterial Fermentations. Wiley, New York.

Burk, D., 1953: Cell Chemistry. Elsevier, Houst. Papers dedicated to Warburg on his 70th birthd.

Dorfman, R. I., and Goldsmith, E. D., 1951: Influence of Hormones on Enzymes. Ann. N York Acad. Sci. 54:531.

Ennor, A. H., and Morrison, J. F., 1958: Biochemis of Phosphagens and Related Guanidines. Physi Rev. 38:631.

Florkin, M., 1960: Unity and Diversity in Bioche istry. Pergamon Press, London.

George, P., and Rutman, R. J., 1960: The Hi Energy Bond Concept. Progr. Biophys. 10:2.

Goddard, D. R., and Bonner, W. D., 1960: Cell Respiration in Plant Physiology, a Treatise, (Steward, F. C., ed.), Academic Press, New Yo p. 209.

Green, D. E., 1960: Structure and Function in Mitochondrial Electron-Transport System. R Res. suppl. 2:504.

Greenberg, D. M., 1961: Metabolic Pathways, 2 vc Academic Press, New York.

Hsia, D., 1959: Inborn Errors of Metabolism. Ye Book, Chicago.

Hunnekins, F. M., and Whitely, H. R., 1960: Ph phoric Anhydrides and Other Energy-Rich Co pounds. Comp. Biochem. 1:107.

Klotz, I. M., 1957. Some Principles of Energetics Biochemical Reactions. Academic Press, New Yo

Krebs, H. A., 1948–49: The Tricarboxylic Acid Cyc Harvey Lect. 44:165.

Lehninger, A. L., Sept. 1961: How Cells Transfor Energy. Sci. Am. 205:62.

Lipmann, F., 1953: On the Chemistry and Functi of Coenzyme A. Bact. Rev. 17:1.

McElroy, W. D., 1961: Cellular Physiology and Bi chemistry. Prentice Hall, Englewood Cliffs, Ne Jersey.

Ochoa, S., 1951: Biological Mechanisms of Carboxy ation and Decarboxylation. Physiol. Rev. 31:56.

Racker, E. (ed.), 1954: Cellular Metabolism and I fections. Academic Press, New York.

Racker, E., 1961: Mechanism of Synthesis of AT Adv. Enzymol. 23:323.

Stumpf, P. K., and Barber, G. A., 1960: Comparativ Mechanisms for Fatty Acid Oxidation. Com Biochem. 1:75.

Wagner, R., and Mitchell, H. K., 1955: Genetics an Metabolism. Wiley, New York.

Webb, J. L., 1961: Enzymes and Metabolic Inhibitor Academic Press, New York.

Wood, H. G., 1955: Significance of Alternate Pat ways in the Metabolism of Glucose. Physiol. Re 35:841.

LITERATURE CITED

1. In accordance with recommendations of the En zyme Commission of the International Unio of Biochemistry (Nature 1960: 188:466, an

Science, 1960: *132*:1548), the abbreviations DPN, DPNH, TPN and TPNH are to be replaced by NAD (nicotinamide-adenine dinucleotide), NADH₂ (reduced form of nicotinamide-adenine dinucleotide), NADP (nicotinamide-adenine dinucleotide phosphate), and NADPH₂ (reduced form of nicotinamide-adenine dinucleotide phosphate) respectively. However, the old terminology is retained here because all the references cited are given in the old form.

1. Baldwin, E., 1957: Dynamic Aspects of Biochemistry. 3rd Ed. Cambridge Univ. Press, London.
2. Krebs, H. A., 1948–49: Harvey Lect. *44*:165.
3. Krebs, H. A., 1954: Symp. Sec. Microbiol. New York Acad. Med. *8*:35.
4. Cheldelin, V. H., Wang, C. H., and Wang, T. E., 1962: Comp. Biochem. *3*:1.
5. Lipmann, F., Jones, M. E., Black, S., and Flynn, R. M., 1953: J. Cell. Comp. Physiol. (suppl. *1*) *41*:109.
6. Lipmann, F., 1948–49. Harvey Lect. *44*:99; 1954: Science *120*:855.
7. Meister, A., 1955: Adv. Enzymol. *16*:185.
8. Beinert, H., 1956: J. Am. Chem. Soc. *78*:5323.
9. Ochoa, S., 1951: Physiol. Rev. *31*:56.
10. Colowick, S. P., and Kaplan, M. D., 1955–59: Methods in Enzymology. Academic Press, New York, 6 volumes.
11. Atkinson, M. R., and Morton, R. K., 1960: Comp. Biochem. *2*:1.
12. Gaebler, O. E. (ed.), 1950: Enzymes: Units of Biological Structure and Function. Academic Press, New York.
13. Warburg, O., and Christian, W., 1933: Biochem. Ztschr. *266*:375.
14. Thunberg, T., 1930: Quart. Rev. Biol. *5*:318.
15. Keilin, D., 1925: Proc. Roy. Soc. London, Series B. *98*:312.
16. McElroy, W. D., 1961: Cellular Physiology and Biochemistry. Prentice-Hall, Englewood Cliffs, New Jersey.
17. Warburg, O., 1930: The Metabolism of Tumours. Constable, London.
18. Child, C. M., 1953: Biol. Bull. *104*:12.
19. Webb, J. L., 1961: Enzymes and Metabolic Inhibitors. Academic Press, New York.
20. Wooley, D. W., 1953: A Study of Antimetabolites. Wiley, New York; Science *129*:615.
21. Lindberg, O., and Ernster, L., 1954: Protoplasmatologia 3, A, 4. Springer-Verlag, Berlin.
22. Palade, G. E., 1953: J. Histochem. & Cytochem. *1*:188.
23. Schoenheimer, R., 1942: The Dynamic State of Body Constituents. Cambridge Univ. Press, London.
24. Kamen, M. D., 1957: Isotopic Tracers in Biology. Academic Press, New York.
25. Rittenberg, D., 1948–49: Harvey Lect. *44*:200.
26. Warburg, O., and Negelein, E., 1928: Biochem. Ztschr. *193*:339.
27. Wieland, H., 1932: On the Mechanism of Oxidation. Yale Univ. Press, New Haven.
28. Beadle, G. W., 1949: Science in Progress (Baitsell, ed.) *6*:184.
29. Wagner, R. P., and Mitchell, H. K., 1955: Genetics and Metabolism. Wiley, New York.
30. Theorell, H., 1956: Science *124*:467.
31. Duncan, G. G., 1959: Diseases of Metabolism. 4th Ed. Saunders, Philadelphia.
32. Racker, E., 1954: Adv. Enzymol. *15*:141.
33. Sizer, I. W., 1957: Science *125*:54.
34. Wood, H. G., 1955: Physiol. Rev. *35*:841.
35. Krebs, H. A., 1957: Endeavour *16*:125.
36. Racker, E., 1957: Harvey Lect. *51*:143.
37. Lipmann, F., 1955: Am. Scient. *43*:37.
38. Lehninger, A. L., May 1960: Sci. Am. *202*:102.
39. Lehninger, A. L., 1960: Fed. Proc. *19*:952.
40. Kamen, M. D., Aug. 1958: Sci. Am. *197*:77.
41. Green, D. E., July 1958: Sci. Am. *199*:56.
42. Frieden, E., Aug. 1958: Sci. Am. *201*:119.
43. Green, D. E. and Hatefi, Y., 1961: Science *133*:13.
44. Palade, G. E., 1950: *in* Enzymes: Units of Biological Structure and Function (Gaebler, O. E., ed.). Academic Press, New York, p. 185.
45. Siekevitz, P., July 1957: Sci. Am. *197*:131.
46. Kluyver, A. J., and van Niel, C. B., 1956: The Microbe's Contribution to Biology. Harvard Univ. Press, Cambridge, Mass.
47. Green, D. E., Feb. 1960: Sci. Am. *202*:46.
48. Green, D. E., 1957: Symp. Soc. Exp. Biol. *10*:30.
49. Krebs, H. A., and Kornberg, H. L., 1957: Erg. der Physiol. *49*:212.
50. Florkin, M., 1960: Unity and Diversity in Biochemistry. Pergamon, London.
51. Kluyver, A. J., and Donker, H. J. L., 1926: Die Einheit in der Biochemie. Chemie der Zelle und Gewebe *13*:134.
52. Chance, B., 1954: Science *120*:767.
53. Greenstein, J. P., 1954: Biochemistry of Cancer. Academic Press, New York.
54. Spiegelman, S., 1957: *in* The Chemical Basis of Heredity (McElroy, W. D. and Glass, B., eds.). Johns Hopkins Univ. Press, Baltimore.
55. James, W. O., and Leech, R. M., 1960: Endeavour *19*:108.
56. Wood, W. A., 1957. Ann. Rev. Microbiol. *11*:253.
57. Goddard, D. R., and Bonner, W. D., 1960: *in* Plant Physiology, a Treatise (Steward, F. C., ed.), Academic Press, New York, IA, 209.
58. Mazia, D., 1961: *in* The Cell. (Brachet, J., and Mirsky, A. E., eds.), Academic Press, New York, *3*:77.
59. Lehninger, A. L., Sept. 1961: Sci. Am. *205*:62.
60. Boxer, G. E., and Devlin, T. M., 1961: Science *134*:1495.

OXIDATION-REDUCTION POTENTIALS IN CELLULAR OXIDATION

In the main line of oxidation in the cell the hydrogen and electrons removed from a substance are passed to oxygen by a series of enzymes (Figure 17.10). The particular sequence of transfers from one enzyme to another is determined by the oxidation-reduction (redox*) potential, e.g., its tendency to give up or take on electrons of each enzyme. Transfer is along a potential gradient. The mechanical analogue of this is a staircase down which a load is dropped.

Redox Potentials at Electrodes Immersed in Electrolytes

An electrode is a device for conducting electrons. It may conduct them to or from an electrolyte solution, an electric arc or a vacuum tube. It is usually made of metal, or of a metal and one of its salts; but a gas, like hydrogen, may serve as an electrode if the gas is adsorbed on the surface of an inert metal like spongy platinum. The calomel electrode is a metal electrode which is widely used because of its independence of pH and its stability. Another metal electrode used in oxidation-reduction studies is the platinum electrode, which is useful because it is inert and does not react with a solution in which it is immersed.

Members of one class of elements (like hydrogen) give up electrons readily forming ions in solution, while those of another class (like oxygen) take up electrons instead. The redox potential of an element—its tendency to give up or take on electrons—is a characteristic property of the element, and depends upon the nuclear and electronic constitution of the element. In order to measure the electrode potential of an element, it is necessary to immerse the electrode into a solution of one of its salts, to connect the electrodes to a potentiometer and to measure the potential difference between it and some standard electrode as a base line. Thus zinc, which like hydrogen

* Redox is an abbreviation of the term oxidation reduction. It is used especially in connection with oxidation-reduction potential (redox potential) and oxidation-reduction system (redox system).

ives up its electrons readily, dissolves when immersed as an electrode in a solution of one of its salts. As it dissolves it forms ions in the solution:

$$Zn \underset{\text{reduction}}{\overset{\text{oxidation}}{\rightleftarrows}} Zn^{++} + 2e \qquad (18.1)$$

or, in more general terms:

$$Metal \underset{\text{reduction}}{\overset{\text{oxidation}}{\rightleftarrows}} ion + electron \qquad (18.2)$$

An electrode made of zinc in contact with one of its salts is therefore negatively charged. This is always true of a metal if its "specific solution tension," or tendency to dissolve, is greater than the "osmotic pressure" of its ions already in solution. The greater its solution tension, other things being equal, the greater will be the potential developed between the solution and the electrode. On the other hand, copper, a metal of the second class, like oxygen, does not dissolve when immersed as an electrode in one of its salts. Instead, it takes up electrons from the cupric ions in the salt solution, and the cupric ions plate out on the metal. An electrode made up of such a metal in contact with one of its salts is always positive. All metals, on the basis of simi-

lar experimental data, can be arranged in an *electromotive series* which measures their relative potentials (see Table 18.1 and Fig. 18.1).

A potential is a relative concept. Just as altitude and depth are measured with reference to sea level the potential of an electrode is measured by taking the potential difference between the electrode in question and some arbitrary reference electrode used as a standard. The potential of the "normal" hydrogen electrode (see Fig. 18.2) is arbitrarily taken as zero and serves as a reference point for potentials of all electrodes, as shown in Figure 18.1. In the normal hydrogen electrode, gaseous hydrogen at 1 atmosphere pressure is continuously bubbled past a spongy platinum electrode which is kept in a solution 1 normal with respect to hydrogen ions.

To measure the potential, at a given temperature, of a metal electrode immersed in a solution of one of its salts 1 normal in activity, one must connect the electrode through a potentiometer with a hydrogen electrode. For example, it is found by this means that at 25° C. the normal magnesium electrode, measured

TABLE 18.1. *Normal Electrode Potentials at 25° C.*

ELECTRODE	ELECTRODE REACTION	NORMAL* ELECTRODE POTENTIAL (VOLTS) AGAINST HYDROGEN ELECTRODE
Li^+, Li	$Li = Li^+ + e$	-2.9595
Na^+, Na	$Na = Na^+ + e$	-2.7146
Zn^{++}, Zn	$Zn = Zn^{++} + 2e$	-0.7618
Fe^{++}, Fe	$Fe = Fe^{++} + 2e$	-0.441
Pb^{++}, Pb	$Pb = Pb^{++} + 2e$	-0.122
H^+, H_2 (1 atm.)	$\frac{1}{2}H_2 = H^+ + e$	$0.0000\dagger$
Cu^{++}, Cu	$Cu = Cu^{++} + 2e$	$+0.3441$
Ag^+, Ag	$Ag = Ag^+ + e$	$+0.7978$
Au^{+++}, Au	$Au = Au^{+++} + 3e$	$+1.36$

Data from West: Physical Chemistry for Students of Biochemistry and Medicine. The electrode potential is the reduction potential; its sign is arbitrary and follows Clark.[7] When the opposite sign is used for the above electrode potentials the values represent the oxidation potentials or their readiness to be oxidized. (e.g., Lewis and Randall, 1961: Thermodynamics. 2nd Ed. (Pitzer and Brewer, eds.), McGraw-Hill, N. Y.)

* All salts 1 normal in activity.

† At pH 0.0 (1 normal H^+).

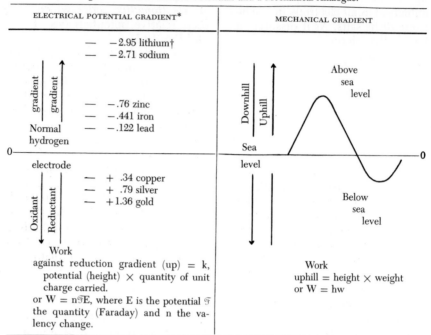

Fig. 18.1. Electromotive Potentials and a Mechanical Analogue.

ELECTRICAL POTENTIAL GRADIENT*	MECHANICAL GRADIENT

ELECTRICAL POTENTIAL GRADIENT side:

— −2.95 lithium†
— −2.71 sodium

gradient / gradient

— −.76 zinc
— −.441 iron
Normal — −.122 lead
hydrogen

0 ——————————————

electrode

— + .34 copper
— + .79 silver
— +1.36 gold

Oxidant / Reductant

Work

against reduction gradient (up) = k, potential (height) × quantity of unit charge carried.
or W = n𝔉E, where E is the potential 𝔉 the quantity (Faraday) and n the valency change.

MECHANICAL GRADIENT side:

Downhill / Uphill

Above
sea
level

Sea
level

Below
sea
level

Work
uphill = height × weight
or W = hw

* Potentials at pH 0.0. Note that the sign of the charge is not that of the ion but of the electrode in contact with a solution of ions.

† The sign of the potential represents the reduction potential (see Table 18.1). Oxidant means oxidizing agent and reductant, reducing agent.

against the normal hydrogen electrode, registers a potential of −1.55 volts. A saturated calomel electrode, containing mercury in contact with mercurous chloride, which in turn is in contact with KCl (Fig. 18.2), registers a potential of +0.2458 volts against the normal hydrogen electrode.

It should be emphasized that biological convention places the strongest reducing agents at the tops of tables and graphs (see Table 18.1 and Fig. 18.1) instead of at the bottom. Such an arrangement makes possible an analogy between the work done during oxidation-reduction reactions through the release of potential electrical-chemical energy when electrons are passed in response to an oxidation gradient (downward in Fig. 18.1) and the work done at the expense of potential mechanical energy as an object goes

downhill in response to gravity. Conversely, when electrons move along a reduction gradient (upward in Fig. 18.1), energy must be put into the system, just as with the mechanical analogue energy is required to carry an object uphill. The amount of energy required to move an electron against a potential gradient is proportional to the potential difference across which the electron moves and to the number of electrons being transported, just as the amount of energy required to move an object uphill is proportional to the distance through which the object moves and to the weight of the object.

In order to emphasize the reducing capacity of a substance, that is, its capacity to donate electrons, the biological convention followed here assigns a negative sign to electrode potentials on the

CONVERSIONS OF ENERGY AND MATTER IN THE CELL

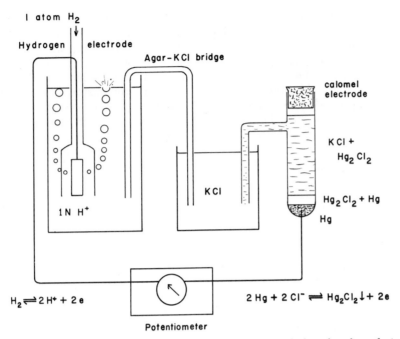

I atom H₂

Hydrogen electrode

Agar–KCl bridge

calomel electrode

$KCl + Hg_2Cl_2$

KCl

$Hg_2Cl_2 + Hg$

Hg

$1N H^+$

$H_2 \rightleftharpoons 2H^+ + 2e$

$2Hg + 2Cl^- \rightleftharpoons Hg_2Cl_2\downarrow + 2e$

Potentiometer

Fig. 18.2.   The hydrogen electrode as used to determine the potential of another electrode, in this case the calomel electrode. The normal hydrogen electrode is taken as 0.0, and against it the calomel electrode has a potential of +0.2458 volts. The potentials of other electrodes can be determined by substituting the electrodes, one at a time, for the calomel electrode. The potential difference between the two electrodes is measured by a potentiometer in which an unknown emf is matched against a known emf (divided as desired by passing it through a slide wire resistance) from a battery. The matching is registered by a null point on a galvanometer. In this way the data in Table 18.1 and in Figure 18.1 were determined.

reducing side of the normal hydrogen electrode. Chemical convention,[2, 3] emphasizing the tendency of an element to be oxidized, assigns the opposite sign to the electrode. It is regrettable that such an arbitrary and confusing difference in usage exists but each is consistent with its own emphasis.[6, 7]

An atom which gives up electrons and becomes a positively charged ion is a reducing agent (reductant), and the greater its tendency to give up electrons, the greater is its reducing potential. The greater the negative electrode potential, the greater is the reducing tendency of the element. Elements (or ions) with highly negative electrode potentials reduce those less negative, and, on the other side of the hydrogen electrode po-

tential, the elements with less positive electrode potentials reduce the more positive ones.

Conversely, anything which takes on electrons, like an oxygen molecule or a copper ion, is an oxidizing agent (oxidant). The greater the tendency of a substance to take on electrons, the greater is its oxidizing potential. Therefore, the more positive the electrode potential, the greater is the oxidizing potential of the element. Elements or ions with highly positive potentials oxidize those less positive, and on the other side of the hydrogen electrode potential the less negative elements oxidize the more negative ones.

To summarize, then, in the electromotive series as listed in Table 18.1, any element is capable of oxidizing the one above it and of reducing the one below it. Each element is therefore an oxidizing agent to those above it in the electromotive series and a reducing agent to those below it. Therefore, the electromotive series represents an *oxidation-reduction series*, and the electrode potential of each element is a measure of the oxidation and reduction capacity of the element.[1, 2]

Measurement of Redox Potentials of Organic Compounds

Organic materials cannot be made to serve as electrodes for measurement of oxidation-reduction potentials, yet in the cell there are oxidation-reduction systems similar to those discussed. For example, in biological oxidation-reduction reactions one often encounters changes in the valencies of iron in iron-prophyrin enzymes, such as cytochrome and cytochrome oxidase:

$$Fe^{++} \underset{\text{reduction}}{\overset{\text{oxidation}}{\rightleftharpoons}} Fe^{+++} + e \quad (18.3)$$

Reductant ────── Oxidant

One also encounters organic systems in which hydrogen and electrons are transferred (in pairs) in oxidation-reduction reactions:

$$H_2Q \underset{\text{reduction}}{\overset{\text{oxidation}}{\rightleftharpoons}} Q + 2H^+ + 2e$$

hydroquinone ────── quinone   (18.4)

Fortunately, however, such redox potentials can be measured indirectly by the use of the platinum electrode. Platinum, an inert metal, does not dissolve when placed in contact with a solution and does not form an oxidation-reduction system with it.[1, 2] Although chemically inert, platinum is a good conductor of electrons, which it transfers from the solution to the potentiometer. The redox potential of an organic system, like the inorganic system, is always measured against the normal hydrogen electrode as a reference standard.

The apparatus for such a determination is illustrated in Figure 18.3. The reductant must be kept reduced by gassing with nitrogen free of oxygen. Aliquots of oxidant are added to the reductant (titrated), the mixture is stirred after each addition and the potential of the mixture is measured with the potentiometer. Redox potentials for different ratios of oxidant to reductant are plotted in Figure 18.4, giving a curve for each redox system. The curves resemble titration curves for weak acids.[6, 7] It is interesting to note that near the middle of the curves, addition of either oxidant or reductant has little effect on the redox potential, a phenomenon resembling the buffer action of a weak acid.

While such measurements are made without too much difficulty, it is more convenient to determine the redox potential (E) of a particular mixture indirectly through the use of Peter's equation (for derivation see Appendix 18.1). For a temperature of 30° C. and a valency change of 2, the equation is:

$$E = E_0 + 0.030 \log_{10} \frac{[\text{oxidant}]}{[\text{reductant}]} \quad (18.5)$$

Here [oxidant] and [reductant] are the given concentrations of the particular oxidant and reductant studied, and E_0, which is experimentally determined, is the redox potential of a mixture containing an equimolal concentration of the given oxidant and reductant. The factor 0.030 includes a term for the absolute temperature; therefore, it is always necessary to specify the temperature when any data on redox potentials are presented (see Appendix 18.1).

It is clear, therefore, that once the E_0 for any given redox system (e.g., ferrous to ferric, or hydroquinone to quinone) is found, the redox potential at any other ratio of concentrations for the same redox system can be quickly calculated.[7]

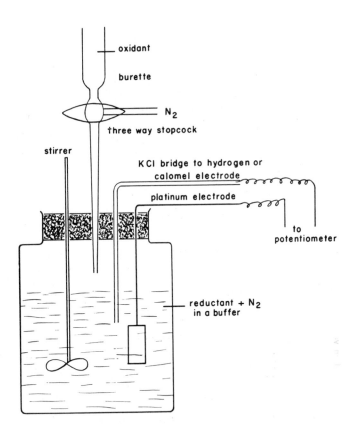

Fig. 18.3. Apparatus for measuring oxidation-reduction potentials. Although a redox potential is always given as between a platinum and a hydrogen electrode (the latter being the standard of reference), a calomel electrode is found in practice to be more convenient than the hydrogen electrode for a laboratory determination. The potential of the calomel electrode against the hydrogen electrode must be taken into account.

The Effect of pH on Redox Potentials

When an oxidation-reduction reaction involves a hydrogen atom of an organic molecule, the hydrogen ion concentration of the solution becomes of great importance. For example, in the oxidation of hydroquinone mentioned above (see equation 18.4) a change in hydrogen ion concentration is found to influence the equilibrium between hydroquinone and quinone (law of mass action). This influences the redox potential by a definite factor (see Appendix 18.2). This fact is of great importance to the cell since many oxidation-reduction reactions in the cell involve not merely electron transfer but also hydrogen transfer. It should be noted that decreasing the hydrogen ion concentration increases the reducing powers of

most of the redox systems, as shown in Figure 18.5. This is to be expected since the hydrogen ion itself is an oxidant:

$$\frac{1}{2}H_2 \underset{\text{reduction}}{\overset{\text{oxidation}}{\rightleftharpoons}} H^+ + e \qquad (18.6)$$

Reductant   Oxidant

Furthermore, it must be emphasized that it is important to know the pH of a redox system because the redox potential of enzyme systems cannot be measured at the pH of the normal hydrogen electrode (pH 0.0 or 1 normal in respect to hydrogen ions). At such a pH, enzymes would be denatured and the results would not have biological significance. Cellular reactions are carried on at pH 7 (or near it) as was shown in Chapter 17. The redox potentials of biological systems, like the redox potentials of metallic

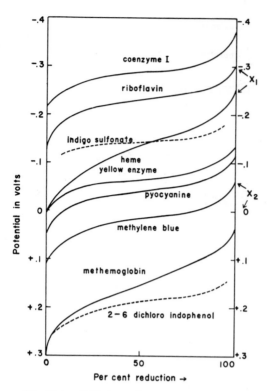

Fig. 18.4. Oxidation-reduction titration curves for dyes and cellular constituents. X_1 indicates the state of an ameba in nitrogen; X_2 represents its state in air.

Note: The convention of placing the potential of greater reduction capacity at the top is followed here and in succeeding graphs. (Data at pH 7.0 from Clark, 1938: J. App. Physics 9:102. Data on indigo sulfonate and indophenol at pH 7.4 from Clark, 1928: U. S. Hygienic Lab. Bul. *151*:308.

systems, are, however, always referred to the normal hydrogen electrode as a standard. A hydrogen electrode at pH 7.0 and at 30° C. has a potential of -0.42 volt against the normal hydrogen electrode.

When comparisons of redox potentials are made at a pH other than 0.0, the pH and the temperature should be indicated. The redox potential of a substance under such conditions is designated E' rather than E, and the potential of an equimolal mixture of reductant and oxidant under such conditions is designated E'_0 rather than E_0.

Potentials Developed by Biological Redox Systems

The study of redox potentials of biological systems is of great significance because these potentials determine the particular sequence of reactions occurring in a cell. For example, why does a dehydrogenase pass the electrons it has removed from a substrate to flavoproteins? Why in turn, do the flavoproteins pass the electrons to each of a number of cytochromes which donate them to cytochrome oxidase, from which they pass to oxygen? On the basis of the principles developed in this chapter, and on the basis of the redox potential measurements, it is now possible to give a reasonable explanation for such sequences. Values (at the indicated temperatures) of redox potentials for sample extracted systems are given in Table 18.2, along with reference values for the hydrogen and the oxygen electrode potentials. These values are E'_0 and were determined at or near pH 7.0. It will be seen from this table that each enzyme system develops a characteristic redox potential, the entire range of values lying between the value of the hydrogen electrode at one end and the value of the oxygen electrode at the other. The enzyme systems and substrates in a cell therefore form a "biological electromotive series" in which each system is theoretically capable of reducing the one below it and oxidizing the one above it.

It has been found that the most rapid pathway for the oxidation-reduction reactions in the cell is that which makes use of the entire sequence of steps from dehydrogenases to cytochrome oxidase. When this pathway is abridged—for example, when flavoprotein passes electrons to oxygen directly, instead of by way of cytochrome and cytochrome oxidase—the pathway is slow.[9, 10] This is demonstrated when a respiring cell is poisoned with a low concentration of cyanide,

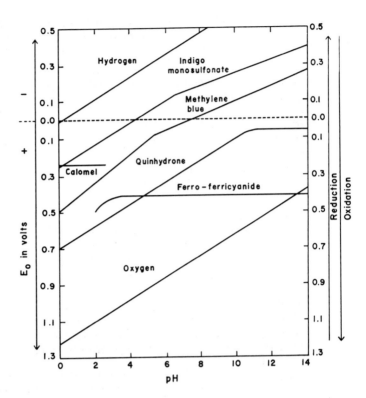

Fig. 18.5. The effect of pH on oxidation-reduction potential when concentration of oxidant equals concentration of reductant. Data from Gortner: Outlines of Biochemistry, 1949: 3rd Ed. John Wiley and Sons. New York, p. 97.)

which inactivates the cytochrome oxidase. Respiration continues but only at a small fraction of its former rate.

Such a series of reactions, in which each reaction involves a small amount of energy exchange and a small difference in redox potential, has great thermodynamic advantage. The larger the number of steps in each of which the energy exchange is small, the closer the system comes to being reversible, and the greater will be the thermodynamic efficiency. However, it is also to be noted that the steps in decomposition more or less correspond to the free energy required to make 1 ATP, hence the steps are correlated with the number of ATP molecules formed from ADP and inorganic phosphate. Consider, for example, the decomposition of one molecule of glucose by way of glycolysis and the Krebs cycle. This process may yield 38 high energy phosphate bonds (in ATP

and CP, see Chapter 17). If for purposes of calculation we take the yield of 1 gram mole of high energy phosphate bonds roughly as 10,000 calories,* the yield per gram mole of glucose decomposed will be 380,000 calories. The heat of combustion of glucose is 673,000 calories per mole. The efficiency of the process on this basis is therefore 56 per cent, a testimonial to the success of a cell in solving its thermodynamic problem, as compared with a heat engine, in which the maximum possible efficiency is 23 per cent.

The presence of at least four cytochromes, b, c, a and a_3, the redox potential of each being successively closer to

---

*See Chapter 17 for the value of a high energy phosphate bond. It takes about 12,000 calories per mole to make the bonds, and the yield is about 8000 calories per mole (free energy). For calculations, the average value, 10,000 calories per mole, is often taken as a rough approximation.

TABLE 18.2. *Normal Oxidation-Reduction Potentials of Some Biologically Important Systems at pH 7.0*

SYSTEM	E'_0	T IN °C.
Ketoglutarate $\rightleftharpoons$ succinate + CO_2 + $2H^+$ + 2e	−0.68	—‡
Formate $\rightleftharpoons CO_2$ + H_2	−0.420	38
$H_2 \rightleftharpoons 2H^+$ + 2e	−0.414	25
DPNH + $H^+ \rightleftharpoons DPN^+$ + $2H^+$ + 2e	−0.317	30†
TPNH + $H^+ \rightleftharpoons TPN^+$ + $2H^+$ + 2e	−0.316	30†
Horseradish oxidase	−0.27	—†
$FADH_2 \rightleftharpoons$ FAD + $2H^+$ + 2e	−0.219	30†
$FMNH_2 \rightleftharpoons$ FMM + $2H^+$ + 2e	−0.219	30†
Lactate $\rightleftharpoons$ pyruvate + $2H^+$ + 2e	−0.180	35
Malate $\rightleftharpoons$ oxaloacetate + $2H^+$ + 2e	−0.102	37
Reduced flavin enzyme $\rightleftharpoons$ flavin enzyme + $2H^+$ + 2e	−0.063	38
Luciferin* $\rightleftharpoons$ oxyluciferin + $2H^+$ + 2e	−0.050	?*
Ferrocytochrome b $\rightleftharpoons$ ferricytochrome b + e	−0.04	25
Succinate $\rightleftharpoons$ fumarate + $2H^+$ + 2e	−0.015	30
Decarboxylase	+0.19	—†
Ferrocytochrome c $\rightleftharpoons$ ferricytochrome c + e	+0.26	25
Ferrocytochrome a $\rightleftharpoons$ ferricytochrome a + e	+0.29	25
Ferrocytochrome $a_3 \rightleftharpoons$ ferricytochrome a_3 + e	?	—‡
Ferrocytochrome oxidase $\rightleftharpoons$ ferricytochrome oxidase + e	?	25
$H_2O \rightleftharpoons \frac{1}{2}O_2$ + $2H^+$ + 2e	+0.815	25

Data from Goddard.[9] Potentials in all cases are at or near neutrality.
* From McElroy and Strehler, 1954: Bact. Rev. *18*.
† From Clark.[1]
‡ From Goddard and Bonner, 1960: *in* Plant Physiology, a Treatise (Steward, ed.). Goddard and Bonner give the TPNH/TPN$^+$ system as −0.324, and DPNH/DPN$^+$ as −0.320.

the redox potential of oxygen in the order given, is probably interpretable on the above grounds. Since the cytochromes have the same prosthetic group, an iron-porphyrin compound, the specificity of each cytochrome probably depends upon the protein to which the prosthetic group is attached. It is the nature of the protein and its union to the prosthetic group which gives each of these protein-porphyrin complexes a characteristic E'_0 value.

Altogether about fifteen biological redox systems with metabolic function have been studied. However, few if any of them are amenable to exact theoretical treatment, since the derivation of the oxidation-reduction equation (Appendix 18.1) depends upon a system in equilibrium,[11] and living systems develop steady states approaching, but never reaching equilibrium.

Coupling of Univalent and Divalent Enzymatic Redox Systems

During an oxidation-reduction reaction the flavoprotein molecule transfers two electrons. Originally it was thought necessary for the flavoprotein molecule to transfer both electrons at once, one to each of two cytochrome b molecules, since the iron in the ferricytochrome b is capable of receiving only one electron. But the reaction of one flavoprotein molecule with two cytochrome b molecules at one time requires a triple collision. Such

CONVERSIONS OF ENERGY AND MATTER IN THE CELL

occurrence is much less probable than
e reaction of one flavoprotein molecule
ith two cytochrome b molecules, one at
time. As a two-step reaction, each step
ould require a collision between only
o molecules.

The problem, whether oxidation-reduc-
on reactions involving the exchange of
o electrons occur in one or two steps,
rmed the basis of a series of brilliant
udies by Michaelis.[4, 5] His solution of
e problem can best be illustrated by his
udy of the oxidation of hydroquinone.
lichaelis demonstrated that curves (see
ig. 18.6) obtained for the redox poten-
als when increments of oxidizing mate-
al are added to hydroquinone indicate
rst the loss of one electron, then another,
successive stages.[4, 5] The loss of the
rst electron is thought to correspond to
e formation of a semiquinone, which is
type of *free radical*. (The hydroquinone
ee radical is highly stable, existing as an
soluble substance called quinhydrone,
hich separates from the solution in the
rm of dark green crystals.) The second
lectron is lost from the semiquinone, and
e semiquinone becomes quinone, the
lly oxidized form, as shown in Figure
8.7. Perhaps semiquinones, or free radi-
als, are always formed whenever two
ydrogens and two electrons are trans-
rred in such oxidation-reduction reac-
ons, but they are too short lived to be
emonstrable by these methods (see para-
agnetic methods, p. 362).[8]

Another example, perhaps of greater
iological interest, is the formation of a
emiquinone during the oxidation-reduc-
ion of riboflavin (vitamin B_2). In this re-
ction, two hydrogen ions and two elec-
rons are transferred stepwise. Riboflavin
s colorless when reduced in acid solution
y a reducing agent, but when it is ex-
osed to air by shaking, it turns a bright
range color until it is fully oxidized, at
which stage it becomes yellow. In this
example, loss of a single electron results
n the formation of an orange colored
emiquinone; loss of the second electron

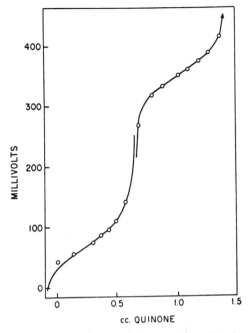

Fig. 18.6. Potentiometric demonstration of single
electron transfer in an oxidation-reduction. Potential
values in millivolts (ordinate) are plotted for increasing amounts of oxidant (quinone) added to the reductant (α-oxyphenazine in 1 normal HCl, pH 0.08). The
temperature is 30° C. Note that for each of the two
electrons transferred from reductant to oxidant a
separate curve (inflection) is obtained, indicating the
transfer of a single electron at a time. (From Michaelis,
1931: J. Biol. Chem., 92:221.)

results in the yellow color of the quinone
form of riboflavin (see Fig. 18.8). It is
evident in this case that the electrons are
transferred one at a time from a riboflavin

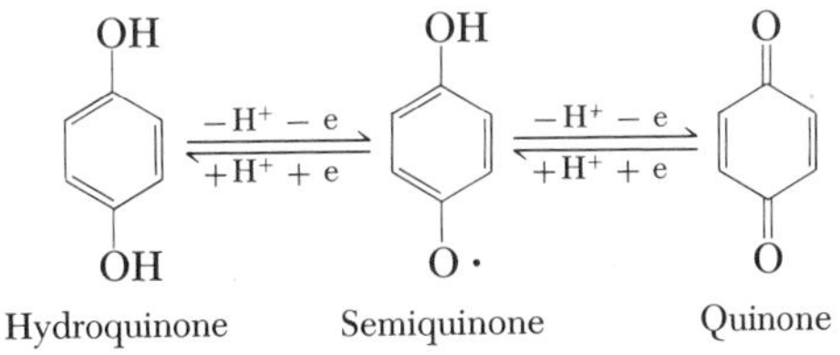

OH $\quad$ OH $\quad$ O

$$\xrightleftharpoons[+H^+ + e]{-H^+ - e} \qquad \xrightleftharpoons[+H^+ + e]{-H^+ - e}$$

OH $\quad$ O· $\quad$ O

Hydroquinone $\quad$ Semiquinone $\quad$ Quinone

Fig. 18.7. Free radical formation (semiquinone) in
the oxidation of hydroquinone to quinone. The oxidation occurs in two steps, one hydrogen ion and electron coming off at a time, the semiquinone having an
unpaired electron which is paired after the second
hydrogen ion and electron are removed.

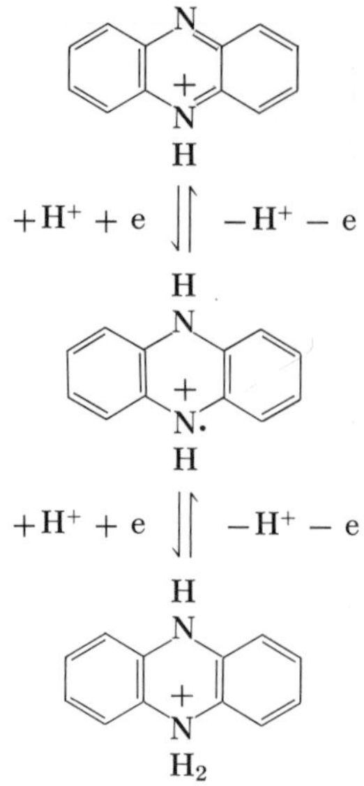

Fig. 18.8. Free radical formation with single electron and hydrogen ion transfer in riboflavin. Note the change in double bonds in the middle ring as electrons and hydrogen ions are transferred. *A*, is the quinone; *B*, the sequinone; and *C*, the hydroquinone. (After Leach, 1954: Adv. Enzymol., *15*:1.)

molecule to an electron acceptor. The color changes can be followed spectrophotometrically and the concentration of the free radical ascertained by this means.[32]

A similar oxidation-reduction reaction occurs in the prosthetic group of the flavoprotein enzyme. This enzyme is colorless in the reduced form and yellow when oxidized. Here too it is suggested that electrons need be transferred one at a time from flavoprotein enzymes to an electron acceptor (cytochrome b). Since proteins stabilize free radicals of compounds attached to them,[10] flavoprotein is particularly favorable as an electron transporting and coupling mechanism.

No problem is posed by transfers among cytochromes b, c, a and a_3 (cytochrome oxidase), because in each case a single electron is passed and only two molecules need collide. The activation of oxygen, however, involves two electrons, but at a given time only one oxygen is

coupled with cytochrome oxidase (s Chapter 17 and Fig. 17.10). If the orga ized systems of enzymes on the crist of the mitochondria serve as semicondu tors, it is unnecessary to postulate quential collisions between enzymes a substrate molecules.[16]

Detection of Free Radicals by Their Magnetic Properties

A spinning electron generates a ma netic field. In atoms, molecules or io the electrons are paired and spinning opposite directions; therefore their ma netic fields cancel out. A free radic having an unpaired electron, is par magnetic, that is, it has a magnetic m ment because of the unpaired electr spin. Application of a magnetic field appropriate strength to such a substan aligns its magnetic axes in the directi of the field at the expense of energy fro the magnetic field. By measuring the a sorption of energy from the magnet field, information can be obtained abo the kinds of free radicals present a their relative concentrations.

Thus, in 1938, Michaelis[33] brought reaction mixture suspected of having fr radicals between the poles of an electr magnet (Fig. 18.9), and after bringing to a balance point on a sensitive balanc he turned on the current to the electr magnet. The balance point was displace The degree of displacement of the ba ance point, as measured by the change weight of the reaction mixture befor and after application of the magneti field, is proportional to the concentratio of free radicals present.[33] This method suitable only when free radicals are pr duced in slow reactions and in relativel high concentrations.[26] However, it possible to refine the method for use i rapid reactions and the method, so mod fied, is still in use.[27, 29]

A more sensitive and rapid method fo detecting the magnetic moments of un paired electrons of free radicals is the elec

CONVERSIONS OF ENERGY AND MATTER IN THE CE

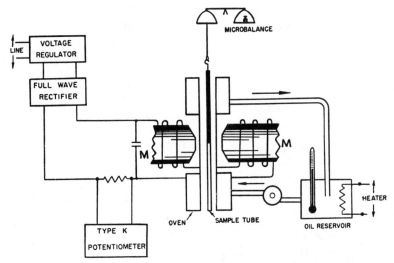

Fig. 18.9. Balance method for measurement of paramagnetism of free radicals. The Gouy apparatus has a thermostat for the sample and means for control and measurement of the magnetizing current. (M) refers to the electromagnet. (From Blois, 1956: Physical Techniques in Biol. Res. 2:423.)

on paramagnetic resonance (EPR) or ectron spin resonance (ESR) method. ere detection of free radicals depends oon the fact that the two orientations of a ee electron in a magnetic field, with or gainst the field, differ by a significant and easurable amount of energy. The elec- on, spinning as it does continually, gener- es a magnetic field. Application of an xternal magnet causes the electron to pre- ess, just as tipping from the vertical causes gyroscope (or a top) to process rather an tip over. The precession of the elec- on is in the microwave frequency range bout 3 cm or 10,000 megacycles per

second). When microwaves travel down a rectangular waveguide (the tube used to guide such waves) they produce a rotating magnetic field at any fixed point. The material to be tested is placed in a side wall of the waveguide (Fig. 18.10), the radio waves are turned on and the external magnetic field is applied to make the electrons precess. When the precession rate reaches the resonance value and the electrons flip to align their fields with the applied magnetic field, they extract energy from the radio waves and the reading on a receiver at the end of the tube dips accordingly (Fig. 18.11).

g. 18.10. Typical experimen- l arrangement used to observe ectron paramagnetic resonance microwave frequencies. The ystron is the source of the waves. he sample holder is in the side all of the wave guide. (From lois, 1956: in Physical Tech- ques in Biol. Res. (Oster, G., and ollister, A., eds.). Academic Press, ew York. 2:432.)

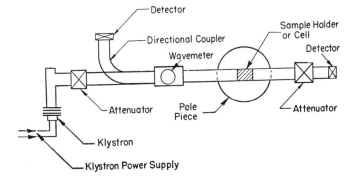

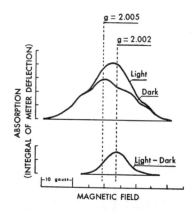

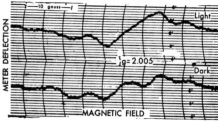

Fig. 18.11. Electron spin resonance from spinach chloroplasts washed twice with 0.5 M sucrose solution. The lower curves represent the actual spectrometer records, and the upper curves represent the integral curves derived from them. (From Commoner, 1957: Science, 126:4.)

The energy involved in causing the flip is given by the following equation:

$$h\nu = g\beta H \tag{18.7}$$

where $h\nu$ is the quantum of electromagnetic energy

h is Planck's constant (6.624×10^{-27} erg seconds)

ν is the frequency per second

g is the spectroscopic splitting factor which is 2.0023 for an electron exhibiting pure "spin only" paramagnetism.

β is the Bohr magneton = 0.927×10^{-20} erg/gauss

H is the magnetic field strength in gauss.

In most organic free radicals a small interaction between the electron spin and the electron orbit causes the g-value to deviate from the spin-only value of 2.0023. The g-value varies in the narrow range of 2.000 to 2.0070 for the materials of greatest importance to the cell. Each

type of free radical shows a characteris-- g-value within this range.

The main pattern traced on the reco-- of ESR on the receiver is from the u-- paired electron in the free radical, b-- the fine structure is the result of the i-- teraction of its field with the fields -- certain surrounding atomic nuclei. Loc-- fields produced by the nuclei may -- strong enough to "split" the electr-- resonance. In the early studies it w-- hoped that this "hyperfine" structu-- would "fingerprint" free radicals in bi-- logical systems and permit their identi-- cation. The hyperfine structure is som-- what more nearly unique than the g-valu-- but really well-resolved patterns ha-- not, thus far, characterized biologic-- systems.[28]

Free radicals have been found mu-- more widespread in chemical and biolo-- ical systems than had previously bee-- realized. Free radicals have been d-- tected, not only in oxidation-reductio-- but also in a large number of other rea-- tions of biological interest such as phot-- chemical and radiological reaction-- thermal cleavage of molecules in chem-- cal systems, photosynthesis, bioluminc-- cence, enzymatic reactions of cells an-- as a result of action of radiations upo-- cells.[19-23, 31]

Biological studies initially had to -- made with lyophilized (low temperatur-- vacuum-dried) cells because water al-- sorbs so strongly the microwaves used f-- detection of free radicals. However, -- has proved possible to make the measur-- ments with frozen biological material-- thus enabling determination of the fre-- radicals present within the materials -- the moment of freezing. Free radicals ar-- usually short lived, but in a frozen syste-- they last for a long time.[22, 24] With sens-- tive methods, concentrations of fre-- radicals of the order of 10^{-6} to 10^{-7} M-- can be detected, even in intact froze-- cells. Recent improvements in physic-- methods have made possible the detec-- tion of free radicals in unfrozen, undrie--

CONVERSIONS OF ENERGY AND MATTER IN THE CEL--

logical systems, opening the possibility
gathering data during the course of
logical reactions, rather than only at
e moment of freezing.[28, 29]

An example of results obtained with
SR analysis is shown in Figure 18.11 for
loroplasts (from spinach leaves) carry-
g on photosynthesis. It seems that
citation of the photosynthetic system in
loroplasts by absorption of light results
the appearance of free radicals which
teract with the magnetic field to give
e resultant curve (light deflections minus
rk deflections).

etermination of Redox Potentials
in the Living Cell

Cell activities greatly influence the
dox potentials of the environment genally by reducing the oxygen tension
d shifting the potential toward a more
egative value.[11, 34] Changes in redox po-
ntials, whether naturally or artificially
oduced, profoundly influence growth
d differentiation of some cells.[25]

It is of some interest to measure the
dox potential at which a whole cell, or
me part of it, is poised when subjected
various environmental conditions. A
mber of approaches have been used to
easure intracellular redox potentials.
me investigators, for instance, have in-
rted microelectrodes into a cell, but
tisfactory electrodes are not easy to
ake, and it is necessary to make sure
at the cell remains in healthy condition.[34]
Another method used for measuring
dox potentials of cells is to inject into a
ving cell some dye which might act as
oxidation-reduction indicator, and to
termine from the color change whether
e dye is reduced or oxidized. By inject-
g, in succession, dyes covering a range
E'₀ values, the likely E'₀ value of the
ll may be determined.[9] Of course, the
, E'₀ and titration curves must first be
termined separately for the various
idizable dyes used. For example, at pH
0 methylene blue has an E'_0 of $+ 0.011$

volt, pyocyanin of -0.034 volt and indophenol just below the E'_0 of cytochrome
c (-0.26 volt). As might be expected, in
the absence of oxygen the over-all redox
potential of a cell was found to be more
negative than in the presence of oxygen.[12]

Since the cytoplasm of the cell is a
polyphasic colloid and has many particles,
organelles and surfaces upon or within
which many enzymatic reactions may occur independently at the same time, it
would be of interest to study the potentials of such isolated fragments. A few
such studies have been made particularly
with mitochondria, which are active centers of aerobic processes.[34]

In summary, oxidation-reduction studies
on biological systems indicate that the
sequence of reactions in the cell occurs
along a most probable biological electromotive series. Not only enzyme kinetics
but also enzyme thermodynamics appear
to be in accord with physical-chemical
principles. The fundamental basis of enzymatic action is therefore well established, although much remains to be
learned about the manner in which enzymes carry out their functions.[13, 14]

It is instructive at this point to calculate the work done by an electron dropping from a reducing potential to the
level of oxygen. The work (W) in volt-
coulombs, or joules, is given by the
equation:

$$W = n\mathcal{F}E \qquad (18.8)$$

where n is the valency change, which is 1 for a
single electron,

$\mathcal{F}$ is the Faraday: 96,500 coulombs. This
constant is Avogadro's number (6.024×10^{23}, the number of molecules in a
gram molecular weight) times the
charge on an electron (1.5921×10^{-19}
coulombs) and therefore represents
the charge on "a mole number of
electrons."

E is the voltage drop in volts.

Since a calorie is equal to 4.185 joules, it
is necessary to divide by 4.185 to convert
the work in joules to calories.

When an electron falls from a highly reducing potential, such as that of TPNH (-0.324 volt) to the level of oxygen (the oxygen electrode, $+0.815$ at pH 7), the voltage drop (E) is 1.14. The calorie equivalent of this voltage drop for a mole number of electrons is:

$$W \text{ (in calories per mole)} = \frac{(1)\,(96{,}500)\,(1.14)}{4.185} = 26{,}300$$

The energy in calories (a more familiar measure of energy and work than volt-coulombs) for any voltage change in the series of enzymes and carriers in the cell may be determined in the same manner. Since efficiency of energy transfer is seldom 100 per cent (see Equation 15.9), more energy may be necessary to reverse a reaction or perform a specific synthesis than the amount so calculated.

APPENDIX

18.1 Derivation of Peter's Equation for Oxidation-Reduction Potentials[6]

To derive Peter's equation (18.5) it is necessary to equate the mechanical work to the electrical work done in reducing 1 gram mole of metal:

$$\text{Metal} \rightleftharpoons e_{solution} + \text{ion} \qquad (18.2)$$

If for purposes of argument the electron e is considered to act as a gas particle, the formulation of laws applying to gases will apply to electrons which are at pressure e_{metal} in the metal and $e_{solution}$ in the solution.

If a gas is allowed to expand slowly a cylinder by pushing a piston over t distance l (an isothermal, reversible, ide expansion), an equilibrium existing all t time, the work done (W) is the force times the distance (l):

$$W = Fl \qquad (18$$

If the piston moves only the distance (the work done (dW) equals:

$$dW = Fdl. \qquad (18.$$

Since

$$P = F/\text{area}, \qquad (18.$$

then

$$F = P \cdot \text{area}. \qquad (18.$$

Substituting this value of F into equati 18.10:

$$dW = P \cdot \text{area} \cdot dl = PdV, \qquad (18.$$

since area $\times$ distance = volume.

According to the gas law,

$$PV = RT \text{ or } P = RT/V. \qquad (18.$$

Substituting this value of P into equati 18.13 gives:

$$dW = \frac{RT}{V}\,dV, \text{ or } RT\,\frac{dV}{V} \qquad (18.$$

Integrating the equation between V_1 a V_2 gives:

$$W = RT \ln \frac{V_2}{V_1} \qquad (18.$$

Here R is the gas constant (8.315 joul per degree), T the absolute temperatur and ln the natural logarithm (2.302 $\log_{10}$).

But,

$$V_2 = \frac{RT}{P_2} \text{ and } V_1 = \frac{RT}{P_1} \qquad (18.$$

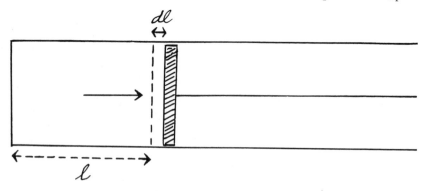

bstituting these values of V_2 and V_1 in
uation 18.15,

$$W = RT \ln \frac{RT/P_2}{RT/P_1} = RT \ln \frac{P_1}{P_2} \quad (18.18)$$

Since for purposes of the derivation
e electrons are considered to act as gas
rticles, they should exert pressure. If
e pressure of the electrons in the metal,
etal, is taken as equal to P_1 and $e_{solution}$
equal to P_2, substitution of these values
equation 18.18 gives:

$$W = RT \ln \frac{e_{metal}}{e_{solution}} \quad (18.19)$$

e electrical work (W) done in the same
ocess is a product of the valency of the
etal, the Faraday or quantity of elec-
city transferred, and the potential
ainst which the work is done:

$$W = n\mathcal{F}E \quad (18.20)$$

ere n is the valency of the metal, $\mathcal{F}$ the
araday (96,000 coulombs) and E the po-
ntial in volts. Since the work for reduc-
on of a gram mole of metal is the same
hichever way it is calculated, then:

$$n\mathcal{F}E = RT\ln \frac{e_{metal}}{e_{solution}} \quad (18.21)$$

$$E = \frac{RT}{n\mathcal{F}} \ln \frac{e_{metal}}{e_{solution}} \quad (18.22)$$

$$E = \frac{RT}{n\mathcal{F}} \ln e_{metal} - \frac{RT}{n\mathcal{F}} \ln e_{solution} \quad (18.23)$$

$RT/n\mathcal{F} \ln e_{metal}$ is set at C', since it is
property characteristic of each metal,
en:

$$E = C' - \frac{RT}{n\mathcal{F}} \ln e_{solution} \quad (18.24)$$

owever, since metal $= e_{solution} + $ ion,
, in more general terms:

$$\text{Reductant} = e_{solution} + \text{oxidant} \quad (18.25)$$

en by the law of mass action:

$$\frac{[e_{sol.}] [ox.]}{[red.]} = K \quad (18.26)$$

$$[e_{sol.}] = K \frac{[red.]}{[ox.]} \quad (18.27)$$

Substituting 18.27 into 18.24,

$$E = C' - \frac{RT}{n\mathcal{F}} \ln \frac{[red.]}{[ox.]} - \frac{RT}{n\mathcal{F}} \ln K$$

$$(18.28)$$

Since $C' - (RT/n\mathcal{F}) \ln K$ is a constant
for any metal (or oxidation-reduction system) it may be set equal to E_0:

$$E_0 = C' - \frac{RT}{n\mathcal{F}} \ln K \quad (18.29)$$

Then substituting this value of E_0 in
equation 18.28 gives:

$$E = E_0 - \frac{RT}{n\mathcal{F}} \ln \frac{[red.]}{[ox.]} \quad (18.30)$$

or, $$E = E_0 + \frac{RT}{n\mathcal{F}} \ln \frac{[ox.]}{[red.]} \quad (18.31)$$

Peter's equation may be simplified if it
is applied under a special set of conditions, for example, at 30° C., or 303° absolute, and with n equal to 2, as was done
in equation 18.5,

$$E = E_0 + 0.030 \log_{10} \frac{[oxidant]}{[reductant]} \quad (18.5)$$

Also, by setting,

$$[oxidant] = [reductant],$$

in which case,

$$\log_{10} \frac{[oxidant]}{[reductant]} = O,$$

then: $$E = E_0$$

E_0 values for various oxidation systems
are given in Table 18.2. Comparisons of
the redox potentials of compounds are
most frequently made on this basis.

18.2 Equation for the Effect of pH on Oxidation-Reduction Potentials

If hydrogen ions are produced in the
course of an oxidation-reduction reaction,
a second term must be added to Peter's
equation. Thus:

$$H_2Q \rightleftharpoons Q + 2H^+ + 2e \quad (18.32)$$

| Reductant in solution | Oxidant in solution | On electrode |

The equation corresponding to this reaction is:

$$E = E_0 + \frac{RT}{n\mathscr{F}} \ln \frac{[\text{oxidant}]}{[\text{reductant}]} + \frac{RT}{\mathscr{F}} \ln [H^+]$$

$$(18.33)$$

If we substitute numerical values for R, n (the valency change, taken as 2 for organic redox systems since two electrons are generally involved, and as 1 for hydrogen since only one electron is involved), $\mathscr{F}$ and T (take T as 30° C., or 303° absolute) and give the equation in terms of $\log_{10}$, the equation becomes:

$$E = E_0 + 0.03 \log_{10} \frac{[\text{oxidant}]}{[\text{reductant}]} - 0.06 \, (\text{pH})$$

$$(18.34)$$

18.3 Measurement of pH by the Quinhydrone Electrode

Because of the relation between E and pH in equation 18.34, it is possible to use some oxidation-reduction systems to measure the pH. In practice this is seldom done since the glass electrode is so much more convenient. However, it is instructive to discuss the use of the quinhydrone electrode for this purpose because it illustrates the linear response of the oxidation-reduction potential to pH. Quinhydrone, an equimolar mixture of hydroquinone and quinone, is added to the solution of unknown pH to be tested, and the potential, E, between the platinum electrode and the calomel electrode is determined. E_0 for quinhydrone is known, and the second term in equation 18.34 is zero because the concentration of oxidant equals the concentration of reductant; therefore the pH is readily calculated:

$$E = E_0 - 0.06 \, (\text{pH}) \qquad (18.35)$$

It is even more convenient to read the pH from a chart relating pH to E values for quinhydrone, as shown in Figure 18.5.

18.4 Use of a Calomel Electrode Instead of a Hydrogen Electrode

The hydrogen electrode is always the base line against which all potentials are measured whether at pH 0.0 for meta or at pH 7 for systems of biological or gin. In practice in the laboratory, however, a calomel electrode, with a known potential against the hydrogen electrode is used instead of a hydrogen electrode because the latter is so inconvenient. The saturated calomel electrode, is nonpolarizable* and has a potential of $+0.245$ volt against the normal hydrogen electrode at pH 7.0. When the potential of biological oxidation-reduction system (X is determined against a calomel electrode the reading obtained for X must be corrected by adding algebraically to it the potential difference of the calomel electrode against the hydrogen electrode. For example, if the potential of X against the calomel electrode is -0.1742 volt, its true potential against the hydrogen electrode is $+0.2458$ volt plus -0.1742, or $+0.0716$ volt.

GENERAL REFERENCES

Anfinsen, C. B., and Kielley, W. W., 1954: Biologic Oxidations. Ann. Rev. Biochem., 23: 17–34.

Barron, E. S. G., 1952: The Mechanism of Enzymatic Oxidation-Reductions, in Trends in Physiology and Biochemistry (Barron, E. G. S., ed.). Academic Press, New York, pp. 1–24.

Bass, A. N., and Broida, H. P., 1960: Formation and Trapping of Free Radicals. Academic Press, New York.

Blois, M. S., Jr., (ed.), 1961: Free Radicals in Biological Systems. Academic Press, New York.

Blois, M. S., Jr., 1956: Magnetic Methods in Physical Techniques in Biological Research (Oster, G., and Pollister, A. eds.). Academic Press, New York, vol 2, pp. 393–440.

Carrington, A., 1962: The Principles of Electron-spin Resonance. Endeavour, 21: 51.

Cater, D. B., 1960: Oxygen Tension and Oxidation Reduction Potentials in Living Systems. Prog Biophys. 10: 103–194.

* No gases are formed during its operation.

CONVERSIONS OF ENERGY AND MATTER IN THE CELL

rk, W. M., Cohen, B., Gibbs, H. D., and Cannan,
R., 1928: Studies on Oxidation-Reduction. I-X Hygienic Laboratory Bul. No. 151.

rk, W. M., 1952: Topics in Physical Chemistry.
Williams & Wilkins, Baltimore.

rk, W. M., 1960: Oxidation-Reduction Potentials
of Organic Systems. Williams & Wilkins, Baltimore.

witt, L. F., 1950: Oxidation-Reduction Potentials
in Bacteriology and Biochemistry. 6th. Ed. Williams & Wilkins, Baltimore.

dwig, G. W., 1962: Electron-Spin Resonance. Science, 135:899.

chaelis, L., 1930: Oxidation-Reduction Potentials.
Lippincott, Philadelphia.

chaelis, L., 1935: Semiquinones, the Intermediate
Steps of Reversible Organic Oxidation-Reduction.
Chem. Rev., 16:243.

utman-Dickenson, A. F., 1959: Free Radicals.
Methuen, London.

LITERATURE CITED

Clark, W. M., 1960: Oxidation-Reduction Potentials of Organic Systems. Williams & Wilkins,
Baltimore.

Glasstone, S., 1960: Elements of Physical Chemistry. 2nd Ed. Van Nostrand, New York.

Lewis, G. N., and Randall, M., 1961. Thermodynamics. 2nd Ed. McGraw-Hill, New York.

Michaelis, L., 1935: Chem. Rev. 16:243.

Michaelis, L., 1940: Ann. New York. Acad. Sci.
40:39.

Clark, W., M., et al., 1928: Studies on Oxidation-
Reduction. Hygienic Lab. Bul. No. 151.

Clark, W. M., 1952: Topics in Physical Chemistry. Williams & Wilkins, Baltimore.

Michaelis, L., 1930: Oxidation-Reduction Potentials. Lippincott, Philadelphia.

Goddard, D., 1945: in Physical Chemistry of
Cells and Tissues (Höber, R., ed.). Blakiston,
New York, Ch. 26.

Barron, E. S. G., 1952: in Trends in Physiology
and Biochemistry. (Barron, E. G. S., ed.) Academic Press, New York, pp. 1–24.

Bull, H. B., 1951: Physical Biochemistry. 2nd
Ed. Wiley, New York.

Hewitt, L. F., 1950: Oxidation-Reduction Potentials in Bacteriology and Biochemistry. 6th Ed.
Williams & Wilkins, Baltimore.

13. Anfinsen, C. B., and Kielley, W. W., 1954: Ann.
Rev. Biochem. 23:17.

14. Green, D. E., and Beinert, H., 1955: Ann. Rev.
Biochem. 24:1.

15. Podolsky, R. J., and Morales, M. F., 1956: J. Biol.
Chem. 218:945.

16. Leach, S. J., 1956: Adv. Enzymol. 15:1.

17. Szent-Györgyi, A., 1956: Bioenergetics. Science
124:873. 1957: Bioenergetics. Academic Press,
New York.

18. Willard, H. H., Furman, N. H., and Bacon, E. K.,
1957: A Short Course in Quantitative Analysis.
2nd. Ed. Van Nostrand, Princeton, N. J.

19. Commoner, B., et al., 1957: Science 126:57.

20. Ehrenberg, A., and Ludwig, G. D., 1958: Science
127:1177.

21. Hollocher, T. C., Jr., and Commoner, B., 1960:
Proc. Nat. Acad. Sci. U. S. 46:416.

22. Commoner, B., and Hollocher, T. C., Jr., 1960:
Proc. Nat. Acad. Sci. U. S. 46:405.

23. Gutowsky, H. S., and Nachod, F. C., (eds.),
1958: Nuclear Magnetic Resonance. Ann. New
York Acad. Sci. 70, Art. 4:764–930.

24. Herzfeld, C. M., and Bass, A. M., March 1957:
Sci. Am. 196:90.

25. Brooks, M. M., 1956: Protoplasma 46:104.

26. Chance, B., 1961: in Free Radicals in Biological
Systems (Blois, M. S., ed.). Academic Press,
New York, p. 1.

27. Brill, A., 1961: in Free Radicals in Biological
Systems (Blois, M. S., ed.). Academic Press,
New York, p. 53.

28. Pake, G. E., 1961: in Free Radicals in Biological
Systems (Blois, M. S., ed.). Academic Press,
New York, p. 91.

29. Chance, B., Bicking, L., and Legallois, V., 1961:
in Free Radicals in Biological Systems (Blois,
M. S., ed.). Academic Press, New York, p. 101.

30. Blois, H., Brown, H. W., and Maling, J., 1961: in
Free Radicals in Biological Systems (Blois, M.
S., ed.). Academic Press, New York, p. 117.

31. Beinert, H., and Sands, R., 1961: in Free Radicals
in Biological Systems (Blois, M. S., ed.). Academic Press, New York, p. 17.

32. Blois, M. S., Jr., (ed.), 1961: Free Radicals in
Biological Systems. Academic Press, New York.

33. Blois, M. S., Jr., 1956: Magnetic Methods in
Physical Techniques in Biological Research
(Oster, G., and Pollister, A. W., eds.), vol. 2,
p. 393. Academic Press, New York.

34. Cater, D. B., 1960: Progr. Biophys. 10:153.

CHAPTER 19

CELLULAR RESPIRATION, FERMENTATION AND LUMINESCENCE

Cellular respiration is the aerobic oxidation of nutrients in the cell with the help of atmospheric oxygen, in the course of which energy is liberated and carbon dioxide is given off. In glycolysis and fermentation, nutrients are oxidized in the absence of atmospheric oxygen, that is, anaerobically. Organisms which live in the presence of oxygen are aerobes; those that live in its absence are anaerobes.

Aerobic Metabolism: Oxygen Consumption of Cells

The oxygen consumption of cells is measured by the volume of oxygen consumed (at standard temperature and pressure, STP) per unit weight of organism per unit of time. This is called the Q_{O_2} or rate of respiration. The units of measurement used are microliters (μl.) per milligram per hour for small samples or milliliters per gram per hour for larger samples. Data could be cited either for wet or dry weight; the latter is approximately one fourth of the former (see Table 19.1).

While many methods have been us for measurement of respiration, only on will be described here because it is simple in principle (see Fig. 19.1). Fo description of others see Appendix 19 A suspension of cells is placed in ves A, the center well of which contains p tassium hydroxide. Vessel B contains cells and serves as a compensator. T two vessels are connected to each oth through a manometer, which is set at t zero position (level) at the start of experiment. As oxygen is consumed, t pressure in the closed system falls and t level on the right side of the manomet (as shown in the figure) rises becau carbon dioxide, given off during the re piration, is absorbed by the potassiu hydroxide. The volume of oxygen co sumed can be determined by addi enough air from the calibrated syringe just compensate for the change in lev of the manometer. To insure equilibriu the vessels should be shaken, preferab in a constant temperature bath.

Unicellular organisms, such as bacter yeast, some molds, unicellular algae, sm

TABLE 19.1. *Respiration Rates of Various Organisms and Tissues.*
(Q_{O_2} *is Given in Milliliters per Gram of Wet Weight per Hour.*)

GROUP	ORGANISM	°C.	Q_{O_2}	REMARKS
Microorganisms	Bacillus mesentericus vulgatus*	16	12.1	
	Azotobacter chroococcum†	28	500–1000	
	Bacillus fluorescens non liquefaciens‡		4100	
	Neurospora crassa§	26	6.4	
	Saccharomyces cereviseae‖	26	8–14.5	
	Paramecium¶	20	0.5	
Plants	Verbascum thapsus*	23	0.093	leaf
			0.204	pistil
			0.190	stamen
	Papaver rhoeas*	22	0.803	leaf
			0.172	pistil
			0.280	stamen
Invertebrates	Anemonia sulcata‡	18	0.0134	
	Asterias rubens‡	15	0.03	
	Nereis virens‡	15	0.026	
	Mytilus¶ (mussel)	20	0.02	
	Astacus¶ (crayfish)	20	0.047	
	Vanessa¶ (butterfly)	20	0.6	at rest
			100.0	in flight
Vertebrate	carp¶	20	0.1	
	mouse¶	37	2.5	at rest
			20.0	running
	man¶	37	0.2	at rest
			4.0	maximal work
Animal tissues	rat liver†	37.5	2.2–3.3	
	rat kidney cortex†	37.5	5.2–9.0	
	rat brain cortex†	37.5	2.7	
	rat voluntary muscle#	37	1.5	at rest
		37	10.0	active
	frog nerve#	15	0.02	at rest
		15	0.75	active
	rabbit nerve#	37	0.29	at rest

All Q_{O_2} values given as volume of oxygen per gram of dry weight per hour have been divided by 4 to give the value for wet weight.

* Stiles and Leach, 1952: Respiration in Plants.

† Tabulae Biologicae, 1934: 9.

‡ Heilbrunn, 1952: An Outline of General Physiology. 3rd Ed.

§ Giese and Tatum, 1946: Arch. Biochem. 9.

‖ Giese and Swanson, 1947: J. Cell. Comp. Physiol. 30.

¶ Krogh.[6]

Holmes.[5]

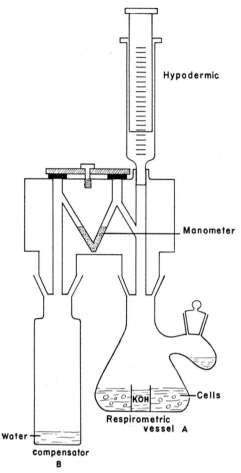

Labels on figure:
Hypodermic
Manometer
Cells
Respirometric vessel A
KOH
Water
compensator B

Fig. 19.1. The Scholander-Wennesland modification of the Fenn-Winterstein respirometer. Usually a calibrated screw plunger is used instead of a hypodermic syringe.

colonial algae, protozoans, marine eggs, sperm and red blood cells, lend themselves especially well to such studies since suspensions of them are readily prepared and handled. Compact tissues, however, must be sliced thinly before the respiration of the cells can be studied in respirometric flasks. In this manner liver and brain slices have been extensively studied, and to a lesser extent sections of leaf, stem and root.

When data gathered in this manner

are compared, it becomes immediately apparent that the Q_{O_2} of diverse organisms and tissues (Table 19.1) varies widely. Some microbes, like *Azotobacter* and *Bacillus fluorescens*, respire more actively than any of the others listed, and yeast and mold respire more actively than protozoans and cells from animal tissues.[2]

It is of interest to find out what connection exists between rates of respiration and sizes of various organisms. If we compare the respiratory rates of the unicellular organisms in Table 19.1, we will see that the rate of respiration varies with the ratio of surface to volume of the cell. Microbes, being of small linear dimensions, have a larger surface in relation to volume than do the larger cells. When cell size increases, the Q_{O_2} declines.[3] The range of size among protozoans is ample to illustrate this point clearly (see Fig. 19.2). Thus the increase in the respiratory rate of the large multinucleate ameba *Pelomyxa carolinensis* (*Chaos chaos*) over that of the small ameba *Amoeba proteus* is only about half the increase in bulk. Probably *Pelomyxa* represents the limit of effective increase in size of a single cell. In the course of evolution the increase in mass brought about by the aggregation of small cells proved more effective in maintaining a sufficiently high respiratory rate than could a corresponding increase in the mass of a single cell.[3]

When the Q_{O_2} of larger animals and plants[4] is compared with that of microbes the contrast is even more striking (Table 19.1). One probable reason for this difference is the method used for comparison. To illustrate, respiration of microorganisms is generally measured in the presence of nutrient favorable for maximal activity. On the other hand, respiration of cells of a larger organism is usually measured during a relatively inactive state. When such organisms are aroused to maximal activity, their metabolic rates increase

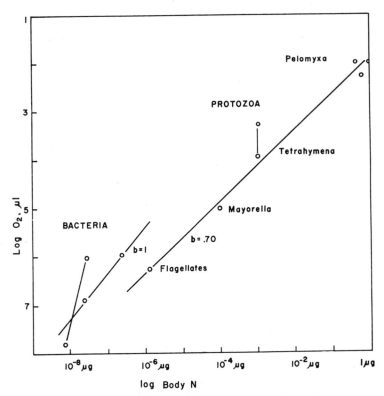

Fig. 19.2. The relation between size, as measured by the logarithm of the nitrogen content (N) of the body, and respiration, as measured by the logarithm of the volume of oxygen consumed by single celled organisms. Note that the points of protozoans fall along a straight line, the slope of which (b, the exponent in equation 19.1) is 0.70. This slope tells us that the rate of respiration increases much more slowly than the mass (size) of the protozoan. For bacteria, on the other hand, the slope (b) of the line is 1.0, indicating that over the small size range covered by the experiments the respiration increases proportionally with size. The higher value for b indicated in the far left line has questionable significance. (After Zeuthen, 1953: Quart. Rev. Biol., 28:3.)

entyfold to a hundredfold (Table 19.1), which time their oxygen consumption mes within the range of the oxygen nsumption shown by active microornisms.[4, 6]

If respiratory rates are plotted against e sizes of various organisms, it will be en that respiratory rate falls with increase in size. Even when an individual a species increases in size during its velopment, its rate of respiration (Q_{O_2}) lls (see Fig. 19.3). In warm-blooded imals it is clear that the greater the tio of surface area to volume, the eater are the heat loss and the rate of

respiration. For example, the shrew loses so much heat because of its large surface to volume ratio that it must eat continually to get enough food to keep warm.[9] The humming bird has solved this problem by becoming torpid during sleep, its temperature falling almost to that of the environment.[10] Consequently, a higher metabolic rate is expected in small mammals or birds than in larger ones. A limit is thus set to the minimal size of a warm-blooded form. Whether loss of heat is also the cause of the greater respiratory rates found in small invertebrates is not certain at the present time.

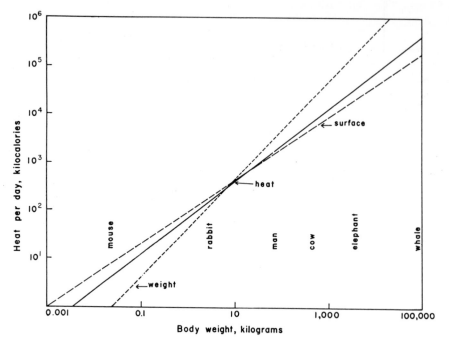

Fig. 19.3. Relation between respiratory rate (measured as heat per day) and size. Heat is shown by the solid line; surface is shown by the broken line with longer segments; weight is shown by the broken line with shorter segments. Note that respiratory rate is more closely correlated with surface than with weight. (After Kleiber, 1947: Physiol. Rev., 27:530.)

The oxygen consumed by an animal per unit time can be related to its surface and volume by means of an empirical equation:

$$O_v = KW^b \qquad (19.1)$$

In this equation O_v is the volume of oxygen consumed per unit time, K is a constant, W the weight of the organism and b is an exponent.[8] For most animals tested, b = 0.73. Since O_v is the Q_{O_2} times the weight of the animal, equation 19.1 indicates that the Q_{O_2} is related to the 0.73 power of W.

One reason for the decrease in Q_{O_2} with increase in size is perhaps the corresponding increase in the larger organism's content of inert materials. According to the principle of similitude,[11] the volume of an animal increases as the cube of its linear dimensions, while the

strength of bones and other connect tissue, etc., increases only as the squ of the animal's linear dimensions. Con quently, the mass of bone, cartilage a fibrous connective tissue increases proportionally as the animal increases size. Such tissue is, metabolically spe ing, relatively inert and contributes lit to the Q_{O_2}, which is primarily a functi of the active tissues.[3] Similarly, in plan cell walls and supporting tissue and v cular tubes ("dead wood") add bulk wi out contributing metabolizing tissue.

If the cells could be removed from tissues of animals (or plants), individ cells would probably respire at mu more nearly the same rate than do t tissues of animals (and plants) of differ sizes. This is apparent from studies respiration of cell suspensions growi actively in tissue culture.[30]

CONVERSIONS OF ENERGY AND MATTER IN THE C

e Effect of Temperature on Respiratory Rate

The respiratory rate of a suspension of ls increases with a rise of environmen- temperature within the limits of the okinetic zone (see Chapter 10). The nperature coefficient (Q_{10}) of respira- n is generally found to be in the range 2 to 4, indicating that a 10° C. rise in nperature increases the rate of the iction twofold to fourfold (see Fig. 4). However, exposure to temperatures her than the optimum in the biokinetic ie may result in injury, after which the piration declines.

The respiratory rates of multicellular nts and cold-blooded multicellular ani- ls increase in a characteristic way when the temperature of the environment rises within the limits of the biokinetic zone. The respiratory rates of young mammals, in which the "thermostatic" mechanism is not yet in operation, vary with temperature in the same way as the respiratory rates of cold-blooded organ- isms[6] (see Fig. 19.5). The cells in the tis- sues therefore appear to respond to tem- perature in much the same way as suspensions of cells. However, the rates of respiration of mature warm-blooded ani- mals do not vary with temperature in the same manner because their body temper- ature tends to remain constant, and a fall in environmental temperature may even lead to increased respiration releasing the extra heat needed to maintain a constant temperature.

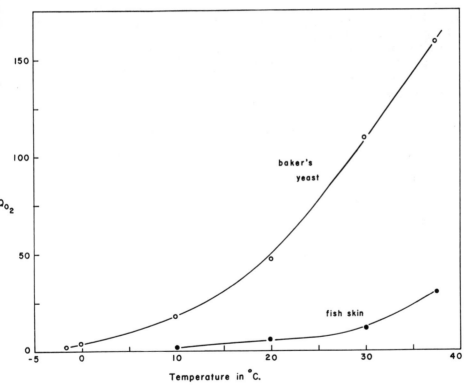

Fig. 19.4.   Relation between temperature and respiratory rate in fish skin and yeast. (Data from Tabulae Biologicae, 1934, 9:223.)

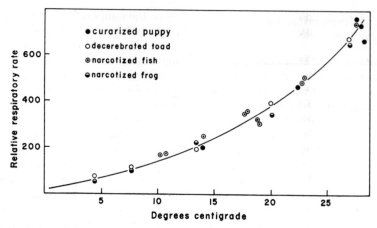

Fig. 19.5.   Relation between temperature and respiratory rates of entire animals. Immobilized animals were used because motility causes large variations in respiratory rate. (Data from Krogh, 1914: Int. Ztschr. Phys. Chem. Biol., *1*:491.)

The Effect of Oxygen Tension
on Respiration

The relation between oxygen tension (see Chapter 7) and cellular respiration is of considerable interest, since oxygen must enter all living cells in dissolved state. For example, when the oxygen tension of a liquid containing luminous bacteria in suspension falls to 3 per ce of that in the atmosphere the respirato rate of the bacteria begins to fall. It clines rapidly to one-half the normal ra when the oxygen tension has fallen 0.25 per cent of atmospheric oxygen, shown by the data in Figure 19.6. T curve plotting the relation between resp atory rate and oxygen tension is similar

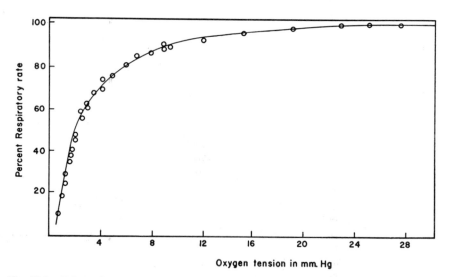

Fig. 19.6.   Relation between oxygen tension and the respiratory rate of luminous bacteria. Dimming occurs when the respiratory rate falls to 50 per cent. (From Shoup, 1929–1930: J. Gen. Physiol., *13*:41.)

CONVERSIONS OF ENERGY AND MATTER IN THE CE

curve relating the amount of oxygen
sorbed by charcoal at different gas
essures. This suggests that adsorption of
ygen underlies the relation between
l respiration and oxygen tension. It is
ggested that, for maximal respiration,
ygen sufficient to saturate the active
rfaces of the cytochrome oxidase must
present.[12]

spiratory Inhibitors

Many substances inhibit respiration (see
g. 19.7). Compounds with relatively
nspecific action are likely to be effec-
e in proportion to the degree to which
ey penetrate the cell. Some data on
ch narcotics have already been dis-
ssed in connection with permeability
idies (see Chapter 12), and the data in
ble 12.5 correlate the lipoid solubility
a number of narcotics with their
ects on the respiration of cells. The ex-
llent correlation suggests that a narcotic
ist penetrate the cell to exert its
tion.[13]

Some substances that have been studied
their effects on respiration are cya-
de, azide and ethyl urethan. Cyanide
ıds the iron group in cytochrome
idase, preventing transfer of electrons
oxygen, thereby preventing activation
oxygen. Consequently, it depresses
spiration even when present in rela-
ely low concentrations (about 0.001
olar). Azide resembles cyanide in its ac-
on. Ethyl urethan is much less specific
d interferes with a large number of en-
mes in the cell; consequently, a rela-
ely high concentration (from 0.1 to 0.5
olar) is necessary to reduce respiration.
me enzymes, e.g., dehydrogenases and
ciferases, are more sensitive than other
ızymes to urethan.

he Effect of Water on Respiration

Dehydration depresses respiration, and
is difficult to demonstrate oxygen con-
mption in dormant dehydrated stages

of organisms such as cysts, spores or seeds.
The decline in the respiratory rate of a
single protozoan undergoing encystment,
and presumably dehydration, has been
studied[14] in a microrespirometer (see Fig.
19.8). Conversely, it has been found that
the respiratory rate increases as water is
absorbed during excystment. Similar experiments with wheat seeds show that as
the percentage of water content in the
wheat kernels increases above 14.75 per
cent, the respiratory rate rapidly increases. This suggests that perhaps below
this value all the water is bound, whereas
above it, free water is present in appreciable amounts for the resumption of cell
activities.[15] Experiments with cells of
lichens demonstrate that the metabolically
inert dried cells can be activated to a
high rate of respiration (and photosynthesis in the light) about 30 minutes after
wetting[45, 46] (Fig. 19.9). These and other
experiments indicate the importance of
adequate free water for maintenance of
cellular reactions. The water present in
dormant stages of organisms is largely
bound water, not free to participate in
chemical reactions. Neither hydrolyses
nor oxidations, both of which are required
for maintenance of active existence, occur in the absence of water.

**Respiratory Quotient (R.Q.) and
Reduction Level (R.L.)**

The *respiratory quotient* (R.Q.) is the
ratio of the carbon dioxide produced to
the oxygen consumed by an organism:

$$R.Q. = \frac{CO_2}{O_2} \qquad (19.2)$$

From this ratio considerable information
can be gathered about the nutrients being
metabolized.

The respiratory quotient for cells metabolizing carbohydrates with a general
formula $(CH_2O)_n$ is 1, because a molecule
of carbon dioxide is produced for every
molecule of oxygen that is consumed during the complete combustion of a carbo-

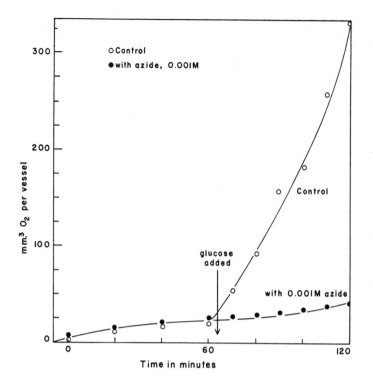

Fig. 19.7. The effect of a spiratory poison on the resp tion of yeast. The azide, wh resembles cyanide in its ac on respiration, was added one group of cultures (bl circles) but not to the com (open circles). Note that the dogenous respiration (before addition of glucose) is little fected by azide, since expe mental and control points side by side, but note also t exogenous respiration (after addition of glucose) is virtu abolished. In the same exp ment 0.3 molar urethan little effect on endogenou exogenous respiration, altho it strongly inhibited fermen tion. (Data from classro experiment.)

hydrate. For example, experiments with various microorganisms fed on carbohydrates show a respiratory quotient of 1.

$$CH_2O + O_2 \rightarrow CO_2 + H_2O; \ R.Q. = \frac{CO_2}{O_2} = \frac{1}{1} = 1$$

The respiratory quotient of cells metabolizing fats is less than 1, because oxygen consumption is greater than carbon dioxide production. A calculation of the oxygen required for complete combustion of a fat molecule such as tripalmitin, $(C_{15}H_{31}COO)_3C_3H_5$, makes this clear:

$$(C_{15}H_{31}COO)_3C_3H_5 + 72.5 \ O_2 \rightarrow$$
$$51 \ CO_2 + 49 \ H_2O$$

$$R.Q. = \frac{CO_2}{O_2} = \frac{51}{72.5} = 0.70$$

The respiratory quotient varies with the nature of the fat metabolized. For instance, for tributyrin, a fat with short-chain fatty acid, it is 0.8.

The respiratory quotient for cells metabolizing protein is also less than 1, be-

cause proteins are made up of ami acids, which require more oxygen complete combustion than carbohydra do. Since the amino acids have a sh chain, an R.Q. of 0.8 is generally assign to proteins.

If an organism is fed a mixed diet, t R.Q. depends upon the relative prop tion of the types of nutrients used. F example, the R.Q. for man on an avera diet of carbohydrates, fats and protein 0.825.[50]

Occasionally the R.Q. of respiring ce is greater than 1. For example, wh some of the oxygen released by the ca bohydrate during its synthesis into fat used as a hydrogen acceptor instead atmospheric oxygen, less atmosphe oxygen is consumed. For quite a differe reason, the R.Q. of cells going into ox gen debt may be temporarily great than 1 (until the debt is paid), becau more carbon dioxide is being produc by fermentative processes than can

counted for by the cellular uptake of
oxygen.[6] The R.Q. of plant cells in the
dark varies as much as the R.Q. of animal
cells, depending upon the nutrient being
consumed.[4]

Another very useful concept is the *reduction level* (R.L.). The reduction level
of a compound that is being oxidized is
the reciprocal of the respiratory quotient
and is usually expressed in the following
way:

$$R.L. = \frac{1}{R.Q.} = \frac{2\,n_C + \frac{1}{2}\,n_H - n_O}{2\,n_C} \quad (19.3)$$

In this equation n_C, n_H and n_O are, respectively, the numbers of carbon, hydrogen
and oxygen atoms in the molecule being
oxidized.[17]

For a carbohydrate (CH_2O) the value
of R.L. is 1:

$$R.L. = \frac{2(1) + \frac{1}{2}(2) - 1}{2(1)} = 1$$

Since the R.Q. is the reciprocal of the
R.L., an R.Q. value gives information on
the level of reduction of the compounds
considered. When the R.Q. is low (e.g.,
when fats or proteins are used) the reduction level is high. A high R.Q. indicates
low reduction level of the combusted
compounds, e.g., carbohydrates or partly oxidized substances of lower reduction level.

The higher the reduction level of a compound, the greater are its chemical energy content and its metabolic usefulness.
An approximation of the heat of combustion in kilocalories per mole can be calculated from the reduction level by
multiplying the R.L. by 110 and the
number of carbons in the compound.*
Values calculated in this manner for a
number of compounds are given in Table
19.2 alongside data determined experimentally with a calorimeter.

Because fats have a high reduction
level they serve as valuable storage materials in some animal and plant cells. In a
gram of fat there is almost double the energy available in a gram of protein or
carbohydrate.

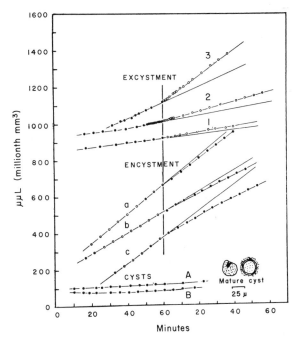

Fig. 19.8. Respiration of a single ciliate protozoan
(*Bresslaua*) in a microrespirometer during encystment
and excystment. Note that during encystment respiration progressively falls (*a, b, c*). Cysts (A, B) show
little respiration. During excystment respiration gradually rises (1, 2, 3). (After Scholander, *et. al.*, 1952:
Biol. Bull., *102*:182.)

Heat Evolved during Respiration

Considerable heat is developed as a byproduct of cellular respiration, aerobic
and anaerobic. This is readily measured
with a thermometer during the activities
of microorganisms in a manure pile. Heat
produced by plant cells is more difficult
to detect because it is so readily lost, but
a temperature rise is demonstrable under

---

* This figure stems from the fact that approximately
110 kilocalories of energy are required to reduce 1
gram mole of CO_2 to the carbohydrate level. This
level lies between the more highly reduced fats and
the less reduced organic acids.

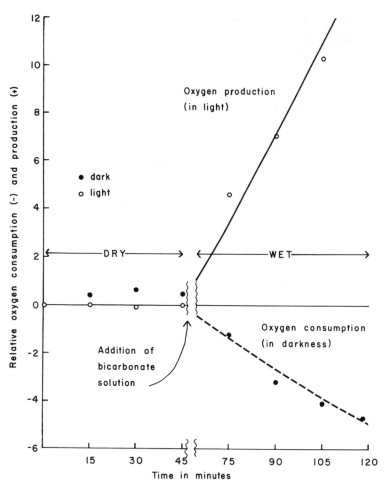

Fig. 19.9. Effect of hydration on respiration and photosynthesis in a lichen. About 0.5 gm. of foliose lichen freshly collected was added to each of two flasks, one of which was tightly sealed with tinfoil to exclude light, the other illuminated. The dark flask had KOH in the side well, the other none. After addition of bicarbonate buffer as a source of CO_2 for photosynthesis, the vessels were kept open to the atmosphere for about 20 minutes. No readings were taken during this time, because desorption of gases attached to the dry lichen occurs in both cases. Readings were resumed when desorption was about complete. (Classroom experiment.)

controlled conditions. For example, considerable heat is produced by a germinating seed, and the cells of a spadix of an arum lily are said to become warm enough to attract insects.

Movement and exertion of all animals is accompanied by a marked increase in the rate of respiration which increases with their temperature. For example, the temperature in the muscle cells of a fish may be several degrees higher than the

temperature at the surface of the bod The temperature of warm-blooded a mals also rises upon exertion, an expe ence familiar to everyone. Maximal ex tion in man may be accompanied by t development of a fever temperature high as 103° F. which, after exertion h ended, falls rapidly through evaporati of water from the skin. Shivering, t rhythmic reflex contraction of muscles a means of raising the body temperatu

CONVERSIONS OF ENERGY AND MATTER IN THE C

TABLE 19.2. *Reduction Levels of Some Carbon Compounds*

COMPOUND	FORMULA	REDUCTION LEVEL	HEAT OF COMBUSTION (MEASURED) IN KCAL./MOLE	HEAT OF COMBUSTION (CALCULATED) IN KCAL./MOLE	NUMBER OF CARBONS	HEAT OF COMBUSTION PER CARBON IN KCAL./MOLE
ethane	CH_4	2.0	210.8	220.0	1	220
ayl alcohol	C_2H_5OH	1.5	327.0	330.0	2	115
rbohydrate	$(CH_2O)_n$					
e.g., glucose	$(CH_2O)_6$	1.0	673.0	660.0	6	110
ctic acid	$C_3H_6O_3$	1.0	326.0	330.0	3	110
ccinic acid	$C_4H_6O_4$	0.88	357.1	387.2	4	94.5
ruvic acid	$C_3H_4O_3$	0.83	279.1	273.9	3	91.3
lic acid	$C_4H_6O_5$	0.75	320.1	330.0	4	82.2
rmic acid	CH_2O_2	0.5	62.8	55.0	1	55
alic acid	$C_2H_2O_4$	0.25	60.2	55.0	2	27.5
rbon dioxide	CO_2	0.0	0.0	0.0	1	0.0

Data on the heat of combustion of pyruvic acid is from International Critical Tables, V. Data on heats of combustion of all other compounds is from Handbook of Chemistry and Physics. 35th Ed.

en necessary. An increase in temperature, however achieved (e.g., fever), increases the cellular respiration.

The temperature of cells of land plants es when they are exposed to intense nlight, and the cells are cooled by the aporation of water from the surfaces of e plant. This cooling reduces the piratory rates of the cells.

direct Calorimetry

Energy exchanges in organisms may be termined directly with a calorimeter e Chapter 15) or indirectly by a measement of the gaseous exchanges, since e energy spent by the cells of an organn is ultimately derived from the oxidan of foodstuffs. Because of its convenice, the latter method is now used most exclusively in medicine for tests of sal and of activity metabolism.

As already seen, when 1 gram molecu-weight of glucose is oxidized in mebolism, 6×22.4 liters, or a total of 4.4 liters of oxygen is consumed, and 3,000 calories of heat are released:

$$H_{12}O_6 + 6O_2 \rightarrow$$
$$6CO_2 + 6H_2O + 673,000 \text{ calories} \quad (19.4)$$

r liter of oxygen used, then, 673,000/

134.4 or 5007 calories of heat are liberated. Per liter of oxygen used for the combustion of fat, 4686 calories are liberated; and per liter of oxygen used for the combustion of proteins, 4500 calories are liberated. When these foodstuffs are oxidized in the proportions present in the average mixed diet of man, one liter of oxygen releases 4825 calories. Therefore, if in an experiment a man consumes 5 liters of oxygen in 20 minutes, he will liberate approximately 24,125 calories of heat. This rate of respiration continued for a day liberates approximately 2×10^6 calories or 2000 kilocalories (Kcal. or Cal.) per day. This is equivalent to the heat required to raise 20 liters of water from the freezing point to the boiling point.

On the basis of the principles outlined above, and on the basis of the Q_{O_2}, it is possible to make calculations of the food requirements of cells or organisms. An interesting example of such calculations is provided by the hummingbird, which, while hovering, uses 80 milliliters of oxygen per gram of its weight per hour. Since its total weight is about 4 grams, it uses about 320 milliliters of oxygen per hour. Assuming, as for an animal using carbohydrate, that one liter of oxygen corresponds to 5000 calories, and that 1.34 grams of carbohydrate are used in the process, the hummingbird needs 0.320 × 1.34 or 0.428 grams of carbohydrate per hour. If fat is used, only one-half this weight would be required, since the caloric value of fat per unit weight is twice that of carbohydrate.

If, in addition to oxygen consumption, it were possible to measure the carbon dioxide production as well, the R.Q. could be calculated. From the R.Q. and the nitrogenous waste of a suspension of cells or an animal, the energy contribution of carbohydrate, fat and protein can be determined. This has been done in a few cases. For example, the R.Q. of man on a mixed diet is 0.825. One gram of urea represents the utilization of 3 grams of protein. For each gram of protein 0.95 liters of oxygen have been consumed and 0.76 liters of carbon dioxide produced. The fraction of oxygen used in combustion of the protein portion may be determined and subtracted from the total oxygen used.

The fraction of carbon dioxide produced by protein may similarly be subtracted from the total carbon dioxide produced. The remainder represents that produced by a combination of fat and carbohydrate. From these values for oxygen and carbon dioxide it is possible to obtain an R.Q. for the nonprotein component of the food utilized. By use of Figure 19.10, relating the nonprotein R.Q. to oxygen used in carbohydrate consumption, it is possible to determine the fraction of carbohydrate used in the diet, the remainder constituting the fat component.[50] From such studies it is evident that the main source of energy in cells is carbohydrate.

However, the cells of some animals (butterflies, hibernators and migrators) utilize fat directly, as indicated by an R.Q. of about 0.7. When a butterfly, for example, is fed sugar, the R.Q. rises to 1.5 or more, indicating that fat is being

formed and deposited in the cells.[51] C of starving animals use fats (and so protein) when reserves of carbohydra are gone and, as expected, the R.Q. then about 0.7.

The R.Q. of respiring plant cells vari A plant using carbohydrate as its m source of nutrient has an R.Q. near un When dependent upon fat, e.g., a ger nating seedling with large fat stores, t R.Q. may be about 0.7. However, some cases the R.Q. may be as low as ((Linum, fourth day after germinatio This is believed to be the result of upta of oxygen during the formation of carl hydrates from fats, the converse of wl happens when plant and animal c make fats from sugar. The carbohydra are then presumably decomposed sir most plant cells show typical anaerol and aerobic pathways like those describ in Chapter 17. The R.Q. of succule plants, which accumulate organic aci may be quite low also.[4]

Anaerobic Metabolism: Glycolysis and Fermentation

The term "glycolysis" refers to ferme tation or anaerobic oxidation as it occu in animal cells; the term "fermentatio is often applied only to anaerobic pr esses of oxidation in other types of ce although it was originally defined Pasteur as "respiration in the absence air." During anaerobic metabolism hyd gen acceptors other than atmosphe oxygen receive the hydrogen, and carb dioxide is usually given off. Equations the reactions in glycolysis and alcoho fermentation are given in Chapter 17.

Anaerobic metabolism releases on about one twentieth of the energy ava able in nutrients and is consequent much less efficient than aerobic meta olism in utilization of a given quantity glucose. However, cells of both anim and plants make use of it in emergenci

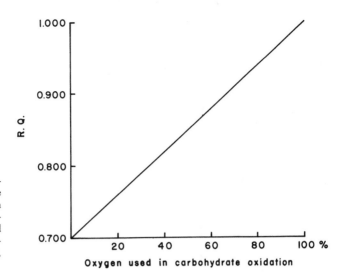

Fig. 19.10. Relation between non-protein R.Q. and percentage of the non-protein oxygen consumption which is used in oxidation of carbohydrate. (After Ruch, T. C., and Fulton, J. F., 1960: Medical Physiology and Biophysics. Saunders, Philadelphia.)

and, under unfavorable conditions, cells of animal parasites and some bacteria located in environments lacking in free oxygen depend entirely upon anaerobic processes.

All cells are capable of temporary anaerobic existence. Many bacteria and protozoans tolerate anaerobiosis for prolonged periods, some indefinitely.[18] The multicellular organisms are relatively less tolerant to anaerobiosis except for limited periods. Even cells in most tissues can tolerate anoxia briefly. However, the cells in the central nervous system of vertebrates suffer very quickly from oxygen lack.[50]

Violent exertion of muscles results in an oxygen debt, that is, energy is liberated largely by glycolytic processes which proceed in the muscle cells in the absence of adequate oxygen. The oxygen debt is paid off when exertion ceases, and the incompletely oxidized products of glycolysis are then completely oxidized or built into glycogen for future use.[6, 50] It is doubtful that many animals are obligate anaerobes, although a few can live under relatively anaerobic conditions, and some, accustomed to such conditions, are even injured at higher oxygen tensions. Some sea animals in the intertidal zone are subjected periodically to low oxygen in the stagnant water of pools or burrows when the tide is out.[6] Some symbiotic protozoans (like those constituting the cellulose digesting fauna of the termite) live under relatively anaerobic conditions[18] and are killed when the oxygen tension is raised.[20] Protozoans in the rumen of a cow are probably under completely anaerobic conditions.[19]

Multicellular plants seem to survive an environment lacking in oxygen better than animals do,[4] although a young maize seedling dies after 14 hours in nitrogen at 40° C. or after 24 hours in nitrogen at 18° C. Because they are actively growing, the cells of seedlings are more sensitive than those of older plants.[4] The nature of the anaerobic processes in plant cells, termed fermentation, has not been fully elucidated, although in many cases alcohol is formed and carbon dioxide is given off.[4]

Many bacteria are capable of anaerobic existence, and some can live only in the complete absence of oxygen. Examples of such obligate anaerobes are certain butyric and lactic acid bacteria and the denitrifying bacteria like *Bacillus denitri-*

ficans. Clostridium botulinum is another obligate anaerobe, which produces a highly toxic poison in foods on which it grows. Many microbes are facultative anaerobes, that is, they can survive a lack of free oxygen if they are given adequate nutrients, but in the presence of free oxygen they need be provided with only the simplest substrates. Other butyric and lactic acid bacteria, as well as various thermophilic bacteria, are facultative anaerobes. Yeast is capable of anaerobic existence, utilizing the energy in sugar from which it makes alcohol and carbon dioxide. When oxygen is available, yeast is capable of oxidizing the alcohol completely to carbon dioxide and water except when the strain is genetically defective and lacks the cytochrome oxidase system.[53]

Microbes have exploited various pathways of fermentation in their struggle for survival. Among these might be mentioned lactic acid, propionic acid, butyric acid, alcoholic fermentations and mixed fermentations.[21, 54] Many of these interesting fermentations have been of industrial importance.

When only carbon dioxide is produced during glycolysis or fermentation, the rate of the process may be determined manometrically. Sometimes, however, gases other than carbon dioxide are formed in addition (e.g., hydrogen in *Escherichia coli* fermentations). When this occurs the carbon dioxide must be absorbed by KOH, and the other gases must then be measured in the manometer and identified by chemical tests.

Speculatively speaking, the fact that all organisms have some capacity for anaerobic existence, at least for a time, may indicate a possible vestige of anaerobic metabolism of early life. If life originated on an earth that lacked free oxygen, as some would have us think, it would have been anaerobic, utilizing for metabolism the stores of organic nutrient which had been formed by photochemical and thermochemical reactions.

According to Oparin, in his book *The Origin of Life*, the original organic substances on the cooling surface of the earth were probably highly reduced compounds like the hydrocarbons and ammonia. The hydrocarbons and their derivatives offer immense chemical possibilities. Using them, the modern organic chemist can reproduce in the laboratory almost all the organic substances present in nature. For example, by oxidation of acetylene with water, aldehyde may be produced. Aldehydes can be polymerized to form sugars. Organic acids may be formed by oxidations, and so may amino acids in the presence of ammonia. By polymerization of amino acids, proteins are probably formed. It must be realized that in an atmosphere lacking in oxygen and on an earth devoid of life, the organic chemicals, formed under the energetic action of electric discharges and the short ultraviolet radiations, were stable and remained for long periods, giving ample opportunity for interaction with one another. Presumably under such circumstances the first life, a system which could duplicate itself, had its origin. Nurtured by the organic compounds which it used to duplicate itself, life so depleted the environment of an available supply of such materials. But inherent in life is the capacity for change, and presumably some forms of life early developed a capacity to utilize the energy of sunlight for the reduction of carbon dioxide. According to Oparin's conception, free oxygen appeared only after forms capable of photosynthesis had developed. When oxygen became available, efficient aerobic reactions were added to the anaerobic processes utilized by organisms.[22, 24] On the other hand, the content of oxygen isotopes in sea water is different from that of the atmosphere, suggesting an origin of the oxygen in the atmosphere by some means other than photosynthesis, since the latter liberates oxygen only from water[55] (see Chapter 20).

CONVERSIONS OF ENERGY AND MATTER IN THE CE

According to Horowitz,[23] the synthe-
sizing capacity of cells increased stepwise
as organic nutrients dwindled one by one
in the environment, because then each
genetic acquisition would have survival
value. Thus, forms capable of photosynthesis appeared only after the organic
nutrient available for life had dwindled
or disappeared, at which time the capacity for photosynthesis had supreme
survival value.

Bioluminescence—Cell Oxidations with Emission of Light

Just as by day the slightest movement
attracts the eye, so by night the slightest
flash of light is immediately noticed. Consequently the flash of the firefly and the
luminous wake of a boat have always attracted attention, even in ancient times.[60]
These phenomena are explained by bioluminescence, the emission of light as a
consequence of the cellular oxidation of
some substrate in the presence of an enzyme.[60-63] Luminous bacteria (Fig. 19.11),
fungi and protozoa (Fig. 19.12), as well
as luminous invertebrates and vertebrates,
are known, and luminescence has been
described in species belonging to forty
different orders in half of the 25 phyla
of animals.[61] Robert Boyle, in 1667,
showed that luminescence of fungi on
rotten wood, like cellular respiration,
ceases when air (later shown to be the
oxygen in air) is withdrawn, and recurs
when air is readmitted. Reamur, in 1723,
demonstrated that jellyfish cease luminescing when dried, but resume luminescing when water is added. DuBois in
1885 demonstrated that luminescence results from the oxidation of a heat-stable
substrate, which he called *luciferin*, in
the presence of a heat-sensitive enzyme,
which he called *luciferase*. He found that
luciferin was present in the luminous extract from a firefly in limited quantities
and was soon exhausted, but that the
enzyme luciferase remained essentially
unchanged.[62]

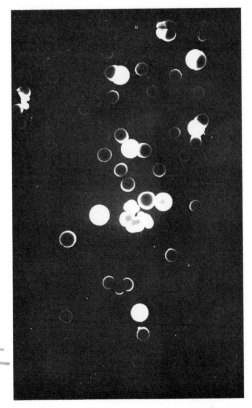

Fig. 19.11. Colonies of the luminous bacteria,
Achromobacter fischeri, photographed using only
their own light. The brilliant strain is a variant which
tolerates the acidity developed in the medium and
remains bright while the other strain turns dim.

Recent investigations with extracts
from luminous bacteria have demonstrated the intimate relationships between
the luminescent systems and the energy-
liberating enzymatic reactions of the
cell.[61] To obtain the extract, the bacteria
(grown on a synthetic medium) are har-
vested by centrifugation and dried in acetone cooled to $-15°$ C. The dried
powder is homogenized in water at room
temperature and centrifuged to remove
debris. The supernatant is luminous, but
the luminescence can be inhibited at
$-20°$ C., a temperature at which the
molecules are unable to attain the necessary energy of activation.[61]

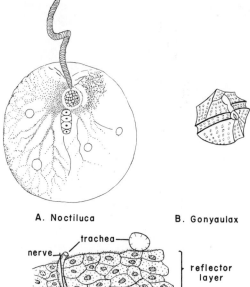

A. Noctiluca   **B. Gonyaulax**

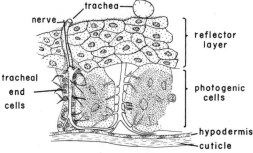

C. Luminous organ of a firefly

Fig. 19.12. *A, Noctiluca* (about 700 μ in diameter) and *B, Gonyaulax* (about 200 μ in diameter), two luminous dinoflagellates found along the Atlantic and Pacific Coasts. The wake of a boat passing through a dense population of such dinoflagellates is luminous because the movement of the water excites the protozoans to give off light. *C,* The luminous organ of a firefly, *Photinus.* (After Williams, 1916: J. Morph. 28:145.)

The characteristics of the luminescence in this extract are much like those of the luminous system in the bacteria. For example, the temperature optimum for both is about 25° C., and the emission spectrum is between 4750 and 5000 Å. There is little doubt that the extract contains the luminous system of the bacteria.

Evidence points to the probable identity of luciferin from bacteria with reduced flavin mononucleotide ($FMNH_2$).[61] $FMNH_2$ has been shown to react with an aldehyde present in the cells to form complex:

$$FMNH_2 + CH_3\ldots\ldots CHO \rightarrow$$
$$FMNH_2-CH_3\ldots\ldots CHO \quad (19$$

The complex is oxidized in the presen of luciferase:

$$FMNH_2-CH_3\ldots\ldots CHO + O_2 \rightarrow$$
$$FMN-CH_3\ldots\ldots COOH^* + H_2O \quad (19$$

$$FMN-CH_3\ldots\ldots COOH^* \rightarrow$$
$$FMN + CH_3\ldots\ldots COOH + h\nu \text{ (light)} \quad (19$$

$$FMN + DPNH + H^+ \rightarrow DPN^+ + FMNH_2$$
$$(19.$$

The DPN^+ is then once again reduced b hydrogen from various dehydrogenatio occurring in the bacterial cells (see Chap ter 17), e.g., the oxidation of malate oxaloacetate. Various aldehydes from C to C_{16} may complex *in vitro* with FMNF to form bacterial luciferin.[64] However, is not known which or how many these aldehydes serve this purpose in th luminous bacteria. It is interesting to no that mutant strains of luminous bacter (*Achromobacter fischeri*) which lack th ability to form aldehydes, and therefor do not luminesce, can be made luminou by adding a solution of any of thes aldehydes.

Since the oxidation of the bacteri luciferin does not yield enough energy t account for the wavelengths of ligl emitted, peroxidation of the luciferi molecule is suggested. In chemilumines cence such peroxidation is known t occur.[64]

The luciferase extracted from bacteri has been purified by fractional precipita tion with ammonium sulfate and by sep aration on starch-column chromatograph The enzyme appears to require a fre sulfhydryl group for its activity and i therefore extremely sensitive to heav metals. Its only function appears to b the luminous reaction, although it wa first believed to be a respiratory enzym

* Indicates excitation of the molecule.

nce it appears in the crude extract with PNH (diphosphopyridine nucleotide) tidase.[64]

The luciferin and luciferase systems of ue East Coast fireflies have also been extacted and studied by McElroy and his ssociates.[64, 65] Firefly luciferin probably ccurs in the lantern in aqueous solution nd, being quite stable, can be purified the presence of air by filter paper iromatography or by use of appropriate esins. At a pH greater than 7.0, pure iciferin, when exposed to ultraviolet ght, gives off a yellow-green fluorescence hich can be seen as a separate band on ie chromatograph. The luciferin lumiesces only in the presence of ATP and ime divalent ion, such as Mn^{++}, Mg^{++} r Co^{++}, in addition to firefly luciferase nd oxygen. The need for ATP links the iciferin-luciferase system to carbohytrate metabolism as the source of energy. ince inorganic phosphate appears as a y-product of firefly luminescence, a detradation of high energy phosphate bonds indicated.

The sequence of reactions in firefly iminescence appears to be as follows:

$$LH_2 \text{ (luciferin)} + ATP \rightarrow$$
$$LH_2\text{-AMP(adenyl-luciferin)} +$$
$$POP\text{(pyrophosphate)} \quad (19.9)$$

denyl-luciferin is regarded as the active iciferin molecule that is peroxidated by eaction with atmospheric oxygen and ibsequently breaks down to adenyloxyiciferin, water and adenylic acid:

$$LH_2\text{-AMP} + \tfrac{1}{2}O_2 \rightarrow L\text{-AMP*} + H_2O \quad (19.10)$$

$$L\text{-AMP*} \rightarrow L + AMP + h\nu \quad (19.11)$$

t is thought that probably adenyloxyluci-erin is the excited molecule which emits s excess energy as a quantum of yellow ght (563 mμ).[64] For each luciferin mole-ule oxidized, 1 quantum of light is mitted (0.73 to 1.03). This extraordinary fficiency of the process suggests an en-rgy-stabilizing role for the luciferase and reat specificity of the enzyme. However,

adenyloxyluciferin readily combines with luciferase, thereby acting as a potent inhibitor of the enzyme. Since coenzyme A combines with adenyloxyluciferin to form oxyluciferyl-CoA and adenylic acid, it has a stimulating effect on luminescence.[66] The pyrophosphate formed in reaction 19.9 is decomposed by the pyrophosphatase available in the cells; therefore it does not affect the reaction.

Some of the compounds, postulated by McElroy and his co-workers for the above reactions, have been isolated. For example, adenyl-luciferin can be formed in vitro from ATP and crystalline luciferin, and this compound can be hydrolyzed anaerobically to form luciferin and adenylic acid (AMP). The oxyluciferin and various phosphate compounds have also been isolated from firefly extracts. Intermediate compounds (peroxides?) are being investigated. They are postulated because, as was previously pointed out, the energy yield (40 to 50 Kcal) from oxidation of one luciferin molecule is insufficient to furnish the energy for the light quanta emitted (52 to 64 Kcal). The energy yield from peroxide formation is more than enough (75 Kcal), thus making this, by analogy with peroxidation in chemiluminescence, a tempting suggestion.[64]

The molecular weight of crystalline firefly luciferin is 308 and its empirical formula is $C_{13}H_{12}N_2S_2O_3$. Oxyluciferin, which usually occurs with luciferin as a contaminant, has a molecular weight just two units less, 306. Luciferin has two pK values, one at pH 3.0 (COOH), another at pH 8.4 (phenolic OH?). The sulfur of luciferin is thought to be present in a ring, not as a thiol group.[64]

The luciferase of fireflies, which has also been purified and crystallized,[67] shows all the general properties of its class of enzymes. Its molecular weight is about 100,000, its isoelectric pH is 6.1 to

* Indicates an excited molecule.

6.2, its pH optimum is 7.8 and its temperature optimum is 23° C.

Bioluminescence has also been studied in the extracts of a number of other organisms, e.g., from *Cypridina* ("water firefly"), a Japanese ostracod crustacean, from the marine dinoflagellate, *Gonyaulax*, and others.[68, 69] By use of pure preparations of luciferin and luciferase of *Cypridina* it has been shown that the dark-adapted eye will perceive a flash from a solution containing 10^{-11} M luciferin and 10^{-15} M luciferase.[36]

From all these data, it is apparent that the word *luciferin* refers not to a chemical entity, but rather to a class of compounds which may differ chemically among themselves, but all are oxidized in the presence of an enzyme and atmospheric oxygen with the emission of light. *Luciferase* is the name given to the class of enzymes which catalyze the bioluminescent reactions. They have all the common properties of enzymes (see Chapter 16). Like all other enzymes, luciferase absorbs ultraviolet light maximally at 2800 Å and at wavelengths shorter than 2500 Å, resembling in this respect various unconjugated proteins. Like other enzymes it is inactivated by ultraviolet light (within the region in which it absorbs), by heat and by various other agents which denature proteins. The luciferases do not appear to contain metal ions and are not sensitive to cyanide, but some of them are markedly sensitive to urethan.[61]

Physical Nature of Bioluminescence

A substance gives off light when the outer shell electrons in virtual orbits of the excited state return once more to their normal positions. When heat furnishes the energy for excitation, as in incandescent bodies, the low efficiency of light production (e.g., 0.42 per cent in the carbon filament lamp and 2.5 per cent the tungsten filament lamp) indicates t low probability of this type of excitatic In fluorescent lamps, electrons, falli through a voltage gradient, collide w gas molecules, transferring kinetic ergy to the gas molecules and there exciting their electrons to virtual orbi The efficiency of conversion in this ca is about five times that in the best inca descent lamps.

Light may also be obtained by exciti electrons mechanically, as is done grinding crystals. Light is also produc by some exothermal chemical reactio called chemiluminescences, during whi sufficient energy is released to raise ele trons of the substrate or its products an excited state. The chemiluminesce oxidation of luminol (3-aminophthalcyc hydrazide) has been studied more exte sively than most of the others.[64] Biolun nescence, then, is chemiluminescen occurring in living cells.[62]

The intensity of light emitted in bi luminescence is very low. It is so striki to us at night because the dark-adapte human eye is extraordinarily sensitive light. Lode has estimated that if the e tire dome of St. Peter's in Rome we covered with a layer of luminous bacteri the intensity of light would be abo equal to that from one standard candle.

Although the intensity of the lumine cence is low, the visual efficiency of tl light is high compared with artifici sources, being 95 per cent for the ligl from the firefly *Photurus pennsylvanic* 45 per cent for the luminous bacteria, per cent for *Cypridina* and 12 to 14 p cent for fluorescent lamps. In these con parisons, account is taken of the visu efficiency of the human eye at the diffe ent wavelengths in the emission spect of the luminous organisms (Fig. 19.13 Neither infrared nor ultraviolet light ha been detected in the emission spectra luminous organisms.[62]

CONVERSIONS OF ENERGY AND MATTER IN THE CE

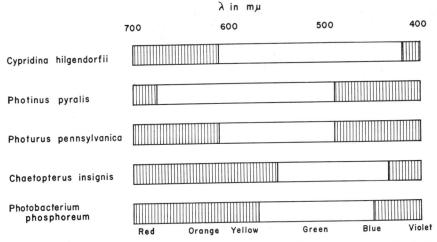

Fig. 19.13. Luminescent spectra from luminous secretions or cells in various species of animals. The uppermost is from the "water firefly" of Japan, a crustacean; the next two are from American fireflies; the fourth is from a luminous, tube-dwelling worm; the last is from a luminous bacterium. To the eye the light of the first appears bluish, the light of the second yellowish, the light of the last three greenish. (Data from Harvey, 1920: The Nature of Animal Light. Lippincott, Philadelphia, p. 47.)

APPENDIX

.1 Methods of Measuring Respiration

Chemical Methods. The oxygen con-nt of a sample of water may be meas-ed by the Winkler method. This proce-ire involves addition of a solution of ,anganous chloride and of a mixture of ɔtassium iodide and potassium hydroxide ʰ the sample of water, which is then ɛntly shaken to mix the reagents. The xygen present in the sample oxidizes ɔme of the manganous ion to manganic ɪn. Strong acid (HCl or H_2SO_4) is added ʰen the precipitate is settled. The iodide then oxidized to iodine in proportion) the manganic ion present, and the ɔdine is titrated with thiosulfate, starch eing used as an indicator.[25] This method ɪay be used to calculate oxygen con-ɪmption (or of oxygen production) of ɛlls.[26]

Carbon dioxide produced during cell espiration may be measured if it is trapped in calcium hydroxide or barium hydroxide which is then titrated with oxalic acid. A considerable amount of error may result unless the carbon dioxide produced during respiration has been completely absorbed by the alkali.

The expired carbon dioxide may also be absorbed by a weighed sample of soda lime which is weighed again after exposure. This method is used in calorim-etry (see Fig. 15.5).

Carbon dioxide production may also be measured by the change in pH, if an in-dicator is used.[27, 28] This is feasible only if buffers are lacking in the solution and if the respiration is not too rapid. The method does not distinguish between car-bon dioxide and any other metabolic acids produced during the experiment.

Volumetric Methods. In the Fenn-Winterstein apparatus (see Fig. 19.14), two flasks are attached to a capillary con-taining a droplet of kerosene. Into one flask, containing a well, filled with hydroxide, are placed respiring cells. The corresponding

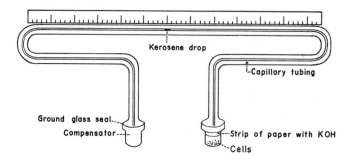

Fig. 19.14. Microadaptation the Fenn-Winterstein manomete (After Swenson, 1950: Proc. N. Acad. Sci. U. S. 36:381.)

flask on the other side serves as a compensator or control. As the oxygen is used, carbon dioxide is formed and is absorbed by the hydroxide. The net effect is a decrease in pressure in the vessel containing the respiring cells, thus causing the kerosene drop to move toward the vessel. If the volume of the capillary is known, the oxygen consumption may be measured directly.[29, 30] Since a temperature change affects both flasks, its effect is canceled out, and since the system is closed to the atmosphere, it is also unaffected by barometric changes. The temperature change, however, does affect the rate of respiration of the cells.

Another direct and convenient volumetric method for determination of oxygen consumption (see Fig. 19.1) is the Scholander-Wennesland modification[1] of the Fenn-Winterstein method. This has already been described (see p. 372).

Manometric Methods. A method developed by Barcroft for blood-gas analysis was later modified by Warburg for measurement of gaseous exchanges such as those which occur in respiration, photosynthesis or various chemical reactions. The essential pieces of equipment, a manometer and an attached vessel, are shown in Figure 19.15. The organism or tissue is placed in the flask and hydroxide is added to the center well. After thermal equilibrium has been achieved, the vessel is closed off from the atmosphere by the stopcock at the top of the manometer. As oxygen is consumed and carbon dioxide is given off, the carbon dioxide is absorbed by the hydroxide in the well, and the

pressure in the system falls, causing th manometric fluid to rise in the arm towar the respiratory flask.

In making readings, the manometr fluid is first set at a fixed point on the righ side of the manometer to keep the vo ume of the system constant. The diffe ence between the heights of the fluid i the two arms of the manometer is the determined after a period of respiratio The Warburg method, as generally use measures the pressure change in a syste of constant volume. By use of the ga laws, the volume of oxygen consume can be determined from the change i pressure.[30-33]

Because changes in temperature an barometric pressure affect the mano meters, which are open to the atmospher on the outer side, it is necessary to hav a control manometer called a *thermobar meter,* similar to the others but withou cells.

The main advantage of manometr methods is their versatility. By prope management, exchanges of oxygen an carbon dioxide, glycolysis or other aci production, and any system yielding ga exchanges may be studied. The need t calibrate the vessels and manometers fc quantitative measurements is a minc disadvantage.

In either volumetric or manometri techniques, it is possible to use vessel with side arms containing nutrients, po sons or other substances of interest. Thes substances may be added independentl of one another and at any time desirec and their effects on respiration may thu

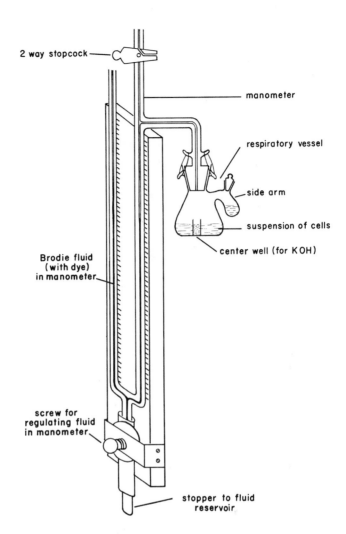

2 way stopcock

manometer

respiratory vessel

side arm

suspension of cells

center well (for KOH)

Brodie fluid
(with dye)
in manometer

screw for
regulating fluid
in manometer

g. 19.15. A vessel and manome-
r for the Barcroft-Warburg respi-
meter. The stopcock is set in
osition for a measurement.

stopper to fluid
reservoir

e determined. Vessels of various designs
re available for special purposes.[30]

Cartesian Diver Methods. For ex-
emely small numbers of cells, the Car-
sian diver method has been used.[34, 35]
ew forms of the Cartesian diver (Fig.
9.16) have been developed for measur-
ig the respiratory rate of a single egg or
single protozoan.[14, 37]

The Cartesian diver is a very small
ibe in which are placed in succession a
rop of fluid containing the cells, a drop
f hydroxide to absorb the carbon dioxide
eleased during respiration and an oil seal
r a little plug. Each of these drops is

separated by a bubble of air (see Fig.
19.17). As oxygen is consumed by the
cells, and as the carbon dioxide released
is absorbed by the hydroxide, the diver
sinks because its buoyancy decreases. The
diver may be refloated if the pressure on
the "diving chamber" is lowered. In practice a definite level in the diving chamber
is taken as the zero position, and the
diver is kept at this level. In this way
errors resulting from solution of gas at
different pressures are avoided.

The Cartesian diver is used most frequently for measurement of the *relative*
rates of oxygen consumption during the

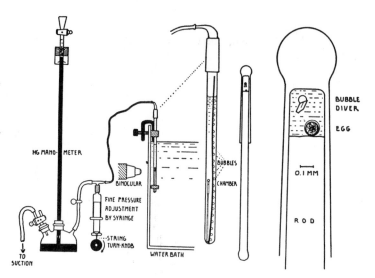

Fig. 19.16. The ultramicro or reference Cartesian diver. In this case the oxygen tension of the sample containing the egg is measured by the buoyancy of the minute bubble diver, itself smaller than the egg. (From Scholander, et al., 1952: Biol. Bul. *102*:159.)

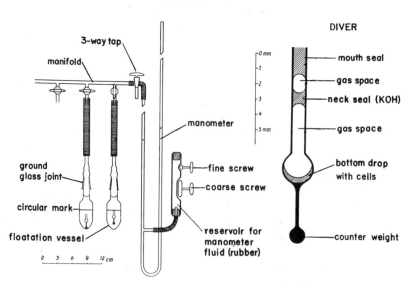

Fig. 19.17. Cartesian diver assembly. A whole series of diver chambers may be attached through a manifold to a single manometer. The floatation vessels containing the divers are attached by way of rubber tubing to the manifold as is the manometer. The reservoir is attached to the manometer by rubber tubing. (After Holter, 1943: Compt. Rend. Lab. Carlsberg Series Chimique, *24*:403.)

CONVERSIONS OF ENERGY AND MATTER IN THE CE

urse of the experiments rather than for ɔsolute measurements, but the latter ɑn be obtained by calculation from the ɔressure changes measured. The disadɑntage of the Cartesian diver method is ɪɑt the techniques are sufficiently deliɑte to require extensive training for sucessful operation.

Polarographic Methods. The dropping ɪercury electrode, originally developed ɜ an analytic chemical technique,[38, 44, 56] ɑas been modified for the determination ɪ the oxygen content of water, provided ɪɑt electrolytes are present in the water, ɑ condition always met in biological exɜeriments since organisms require salts.

In practice, a dropping mercury elecɪode (see Fig. 19.18) is attached to the ɜegative terminal of a battery. The posiɪve terminal of the battery is connected ɪhrough a potentiometer and a galvanoɪeter to the experimental solution by a ɑalomel electrode. The potentiometer is ɜenerally set to deliver 0.5 volt, and the ɪurrent is measured by a galvanometer. ɪydrogen ions combine with oxygen to ɔrm hydrogen peroxide at the electrode ɪurface. At a fixed voltage applied beɪween the two electrodes the rate of disɪharge of hydrogen ions and the rate of ɔrmation of hydrogen peroxide is pro

portional to the oxygen content of the water. The study is conducted at a low voltage because electrolysis of water will occur above 2 volts.

The apparatus is calibrated as follows. First the base line of current for zero oxygen content is determined after the water is gassed with nitrogen for a long time. Next the water is saturated with air, or any desired known mixture containing oxygen, and the oxygen content of the solution is determined by the Winkler method, or the content of oxygen in equilibrium with air is calculated from known data. The current of the solution is then measured to give a starting point for the experiment. Next the organism is placed in the solution, and the subsequent decrease in oxygen content is measured by the decrease in current. Each decrement in current represents a proportional decrease in oxygen content. Knowing the oxygen content at the start, one can calculate the respiratory rate from the rate of change in current.

The main advantage of the polarographic method is the rapidity and accuracy with which measurements can be made. One disadvantage is the necessity of adequate stirring within the reaction vessel to make certain of equalization of

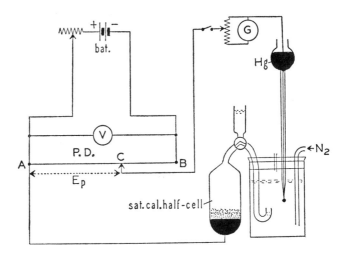

ɪig. 19.18.   Diagram of a manuɑly operated polarograph. A voltɪeter (V) measures the voltage of ɪ battery (bat.), the positive pole of ɪhich is connected to a calomel ɪectrode (sat. cal. half cell) which ɪakes contact with the test soluɪon in a beaker. The negative pole ɪf the battery is connected through ɑ potential divider to the dropping ɪercury electrode. A galvanomeɪer (G) measures the current changes ɑt a fixed voltage as oxygen is ɪonsumed (or produced) during the ɪtay of organisms in the beaker. Niɪrogen (N_2) may be bubbled through ɪhe beaker for a zero oxygen readɪg. (From Clark, W. M. 1952: ɪopics in Physical Chemistry. Wilɪams & Wilkins, Baltimore, p. 521).

conditions throughout its volume. However, shaking is necessary in most respirometric methods to insure equilibrium between the water and air. Shaking is unnecessary when the volume is small, as in a diver, or when the entire water volume is sampled by the Winkler method.

The polarographic method is highly adaptable to a wide range in size of respiring organisms.[56, 58] It has the advantage over all the other methods in that it records the oxygen tension, which is in some cases more important to know than the oxygen content of the water or the oxygen consumed by the organism. Because it records continuously and instantaneously, it is especially valuable in following quick changes in respiration (or oxygen production) and for determining the critical oxygen tension, the tension below which the respiration of cells (or organisms) is proportional to the oxygen tension.[57-59]

To avoid the toxic action of mercury on cells a platinum electrode has been used in place of the dropping mercury electrode[57, 59] (Fig. 19.19). It also is negatively charged and serves as the surface on which the hydrogen ions discharge and peroxide is formed. The platinum electrode has been used extensively in photosynthetic research where layers of algal fronds one cell thick can be placed directly on the surface of the platinum electrode. In closed vessels of solution the dissolved oxygen is continuously consumed by the electrode reaction itself, so that the current drifts slowly downward. If respiring cells are present, the downward drift is faster. Conversely, if oxygen is produced photosynthetically, the current will rise. In the "steady state" modification of the method, the fluid in the vessel caused to flow, is stirred or is aerated. The platinum electrode has recently been used for determination of oxygen tension and consumption in other types of cells as well,[70] an oscillating electrode overcoming some of the objections to its use with animal cells.

Other Methods. Another electrometric method for measuring respiratory rates is determination of the change in electrical resistance of a strip of moist filter paper taking up carbon dioxide from respiring organisms.[41] The speed with which these measurements can be made allows one to study the almost immediate effects of an experimental variable. This method is so sensitive that it enables one to determine the respiratory rate of a single *Nitella* cell.[41]

The carbon dioxide respired by cells in air can also be measured by infrared absorption *spectroscopy*[39] since carbon dioxide absorbs specifically in the infrared (i.e., at 4.2 μ). However, special and expensive equipment that is generally not available in most laboratories is required; therefore the method will not be discussed here.

Respiration of luminous bacteria may be measured by the "dimming" time.[40] In luminous bacteria, oxygen is required for both respiration and luminescence but much less oxygen is used for luminescence than for respiration. When the oxygen tension falls below the limiting value, the bacteria suddenly cease luminescing. They "dim out." The lapse of time between the start of the experiment and the time when luminescence ceases is a measure of the relative rate of respiration. The effects of various drugs, narcotics and poisons upon respiration can be quickly determined by this method, provided they have no selective effect on luminescence.

19.2 Relative Sensitivities of Various Methods

The Warburg method, in which accurate manometer readings can be made to 1 mm., has a sensitivity of about 1 μl. Its sensitivity can be increased by the hydraulic lever principle.[42] The Fenn-Winterstein manometer is more sensitive than the Warburg manometer but less sensitive than Cartesian divers. A variety of Cartean divers have been developed. That of euthen[43] has an air volume of 1 μl. and sensitivity of 2.5 to 5.0 × 10^{-5} μl. Larger ivers[35] have a correspondingly lower nsitivity, while the minute divers used r single eggs[14] are a hundred times ore sensitive. The polarographic method accurate to about 0.1 per cent and aims are made for even greater accuy when all precautions are observed.

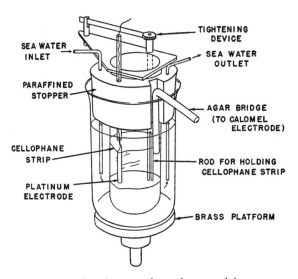

Fig. 19.19. The platinum electrode as used for studies with thin sheets of marine algae. The platinum electrode is cemented to the test tube, and over it is mounted the algal tissue, which is held in place by a permeable cellophane strip (tightened by a slotted rod at the rear). Sea water in the beaker may be made to flow through continuously, or aerated. (From Haxo and Blinks, 1949–50: J. Gen. Physiol. *33*:393.)

GENERAL REFERENCES

lbritton, E. C., 1954: Standard Values in Nutrition and Metabolism. Saunders, Philadelphia.

arcroft, J., 1934: Features in the Architecture of Physiological Function. Cambridge Univ. Press, London.

on Brand, T., 1946: Anaerobiosis in Invertebrates. Biodynamica, Normandy, Mo.

ale, E. F., 1947: The Chemical Activities of Bacteria. Univ. Tutorial Press, London.

arvey, E. N., 1952: Bioluminescence. Academic Press, New York.

olmes, E., 1937: Metabolism of Living Tissues. Cambridge Univ. Press, London.

leiber, M., 1961: The Fire of Life, Wiley, New York.

luyver, A. J., and van Niel, C. B., 1956: The Microbe's Contribution to Biology. Harvard Univ. Press, Cambridge, Mass.

rogh, A., 1941: Comparative Physiology of Respiratory Mechanisms. Univ. of Pennsylvania Press, Philadelphia.

iles, W., and Leach, W., 1952: Respiration in Plants. Wiley, New York.

mbreit, W. W., Burris, R. H., and Stauffer, J. F., 1957: Manometric Techniques and Tissue Metabolism. 3rd Ed. Burgess, Minneapolis.

LITERATURE CITED

1. Wennesland, R., 1951: Science, *114*:100.
2. Heilbrunn, L. V., 1952: An Outline of General Physiology. 3rd Ed. Saunders, Philadelphia, p. 300.
3. Zeuthen, E., 1953: Quart. Rev. Biol. *28*:1.
4. Stiles, W., and Leach, W., 1952: Respiration in Plants. 3rd Ed. Wiley, New York.
5. Holmes, E., 1937: Metabolism of Living Tissues. Cambridge Univ. Press, London.
6. Krogh, A., 1941: The Comparative Physiology of Respiratory Mechanisms. Univ. of Pennsylvania Press, Philadelphia.
7. Brown, F. A., Jr., Bennett, M. F., and Webb, H. M., 1955: J. Cell. Comp. Physiol. *44*:477.
8. Kleiber, M., 1947: Physiol. Rev. *27*:511.
9. Pearson, O. P., Aug., 1954: Sci. Am., *191*:66.
10. Pearson, O. P., Jan., 1953. Sci. Am., *188*:69.
11. Bonner, J., 1952: Morphogenesis. Princeton Univ. Press, Princeton, N. J.
12. Harvey, E. N., 1940: Living Light. Princeton Univ. Press, Princeton, N. J., p. 124.
13. Danielli, J. F., 1950: Cell Physiology and Pharmacology. Elsevier, Houston.
14. Scholander, P. F., Claff, C. L., and Sveinsson, S. L., 1952: Biol. Bull. *102*:57, 178, 185.
15. Bailey, C. H., and Gurjar, A. M., 1910: J. Agr. Res., *12*:685.
16. McElroy, W. D., and Glass, B. (eds.), 1961: Light and Life, Johns Hopkins Univ. Press, Baltimore.
17. Rabinowitch, E. I., 1945: Photosynthesis and Related Problems. I. Interscience, New York, p. 109.
18. von Brand, T., 1945: The Anaerobic Metabolism of Invertebrates, *in* Biodynamica 5:165.
19. Hungate, R. E., 1942–43: Biol. Bull. *83*:303; *84*:157.
20. Cleveland, L. R., 1926: Quart. Rev. Biol. *1*:51.

21. Gale, E. J., 1947: The Chemical Activities of Bacteria. Univ. Tutorial Press, London.
22. Oparin, A. I., 1957: The Origin of Life, 3rd Ed. Oliver and Boyd, London.
23. Horowitz, N. H., 1945: Proc. Nat. Acad. Sci. 31:153.
24. Blum, H. F., 1955: Time's Arrow and Evolution. 2nd Ed. Princeton Univ. Press, Princeton, N. J.
25. Allee, W. C., and Oesting, R., 1934: Physiol. Zool. 7:509.
26. Welch, P. S., 1948: Limnological Methods. Blakiston, New York, pp. 206–213.
27. Blinks, L. R., and Skow, R. K., 1938: Proc. Nat. Acad. Sci. U. S. 24:413.
28. Baumberger, J. P., and Winzler, R. J., 1939: Ind. & Eng. Chem. Anal. Ed. 11:371.
29. Winterstein, H., 1912: Biochem. Ztschr. 46:440.
30. Umbreit, W. W., Burris, R. H. and Stauffer, J. F. 1957: Manometric Techniques and Tissue Metabolism. 3rd Ed. Burgess, Minneapolis.
31. Dixon, M., 1934: Manometric Methods. Cambridge Univ. Press, London.
32. Tobias, J. M., 1949: Physiol. Rev. 23:51.
33. Myers, J., and Matsen, F. A., 1955: Archiv. Biochem. 55:373.
34. Kirk, P., 1950: Quantitative Ultramicroanalysis. Wiley, New York, Ch. 8.
35. Holter, H., and Linderstrom-Lang, K., 1943: Compt. Rend. Lab. Carlsberg 24:333, 399.
36. Johnson, F. H., Shimomura, O., and Saiga, Y., 1961: Science 134:1755.
37. Zeuthen, E., 1953: J. Embryol. Exp. Morph. 1:239.
38. Kolthoff, I. M., and Lingane, J. J., 1952: Polarography. 2nd Ed., 2 vols. Interscience, New York.
39. McAlister, E. D., 1937: Smithsonian Miscel. Coll. 95:1.
40. Harvey, E. N., 1952: Bioluminescence. Academic Press, New York.
41. Skow, R. K., and Blinks, L. R., 1940: Collecting Net, Vol. 15, No. 10.
42. Burk, D., and Hobby, G., 1954: Science 120:640.
43. Zeuthen, E., 1950: Biol. Bull. 98:139.
44. Heyrovsky, J., 1960: Trends in Polarography. Science 132:123.
45. Cuthberts, J. B., 1934: Trans. Roy. Soc. S. Africa 22:35.
46. Butin, H., 1954: Biol. Zentralbl. 73:459.
47. Lamb, I. M., Oct., 1959: Sci. Am. 201:144.
48. Odum, E. P., and Connell, E. E., 1956: Scien 123:892.
49. Lyman, C. P., and Chatfield, P. O., 1955: Physi Rev. 35:463.
50. Ruch, T. C., and Fulton, J. F., 1960: Medic Physiology and Biophysics. Saunders, Phi delphia.
51. Niemierko, W., 1959: Symposium of Proceedin of 4th International Congress of Biochemist (Levelbook, L., ed.). Pergamon, London, p. 18
52. Scholander, P. F., and Iversen, O., 1958: Skan J. Clinical & Lab. Invest. 10:429.
53. Harris, M., 1956: J. Cell. Comp. Physiol. 48:9
54. Barker, H. A., 1956: Bacterial Fermentatior Wiley, New York.
55. Dole, M., 1949: Science 109:77.
56. Barker, G. C., and Milner, G. W. C., 196 Endeavour 20:26.
57. Haxo, F. T., and Blinks, L. R., 1950: J. Ge Physiol. 33:389.
58. Müller, O. H., 1951: The Polarographic Metho of Analysis. 2nd Ed. Chem. Educ. Publ. C Easton, Pa.
59. Blinks, L. R., and Skow, R., 1938: Proc. Na Acad. Sci. U. S. 24:420.
60. Harvey, E. N., 1957: A History of Biolumine cence. Am. Philosoph. Soc., Philadelphia.
61. Harvey, E. N., 1960: Comp. Biochem. 2:545.
62. Harvey, E. N., 1940: Living Light, Princetc Univ. Press, Princeton, N. J.
63. Harvey, E. N., 1952: Bioluminescence. Academ Press, New York.
64. McElroy, W. D., 1960: Fed. Proc. 19, p. 941.
65. Johnson, F. H., (ed.), 1955: Luminescence in Bi logical Systems, A.A.A.S., Washington.
66. Seliger, H. H., and McElroy, W. D., 1960: Arcl Biochem. 88:136.
67. Green, A. A., and McElroy, W. D., 1956: Bi chim. Biophys. Acta 20:170.
68. Chase, A. M., (in press) Photobiology (Gies A. C., ed.). Academic Press, New York, Ch. 2
69. Hastings, J. W., and Sweeney, B. M., 1957: Cell. Comp. Physiol. 49:209.
70. Cater, D. B., 1960: Progr. Biophys. 10:153.

PHOTOSYNTHESIS

)f all the processes in nature, photosynhesis is perhaps the most fundamental. 'ransferring the free energy of sunlight, he green plant combines carbon dioxide nd water—the end products of metablism in all organisms—and from them uilds carbohydrates, which directly or ndirectly serve as the source of free enrgy of all living things. It has been calulated that each carbon dioxide molecule n the atmosphere is incorporated into a ,lant structure once every 200 years and hat all the oxygen in the air is renewed ,y plants every 2000 years. Yet it is only ecently that a thorough, systematic tudy of photosynthesis has been atempted; and botanists, chemists, physiists and physiologists, working together n the photosynthetic process, have nade some of the most dramatic discoveries in cell physiology.[1, 2]

More than 2000 years ago Aristotle oberved that sunlight was necessary for ;reening of plants. The requirement of ght for photosynthesis was next indiated by the experiments of Stephen Iales (1677–1761) and Senebier (1742–809). Then, in 1786, Ingenhousz, inpired by Priestley's work on oxygen, ,rovided proof that in the light, carbon lioxide is absorbed and oxygen is given off, while in the dark, carbon dioxide is given off and oxygen is absorbed by plants. In 1804 de Saussure showed that during photosynthesis, equal volumes of carbon dioxide and oxygen are exchanged and that often equal volumes are exchanged during respiration. His was the first truly quantitative study of photosynthesis.[1, 3, 69]

Warburg[4] was one of the ·first to use *Chlorella vulgaris*, a unicellular green alga (see Fig. 20.1), for studies of photosynthesis. Cultures of pedigreed *Chlorella* and other simple algae grown under light of known quality and intensity, and kept at a constant temperature and in a nutrient of standard composition, are more alike than the cells of a leaf. The population of *Chlorella* can be washed any number of times and suspended in a replenishable medium of known constitution for experimentation. The temperature, the concentration of carbon dioxide in equilibrium with a bicarbonate buffer, the intensity and the quality of the light and the rate of diffusion of the materials from the cells can all be controlled during the course of experimentation.[5, 6]

Such cultures are used in most studies employing manometric techniques. Thin thalli of marine algae are more conven-

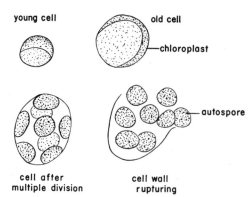

young cell   old cell

—chloroplast

—autospore

cell after
multiple division

cell wall
rupturing

Fig. 20.1. *Chlorella,* an alga used extensively in studies on photosynthesis. Note the cup-shaped chloroplast and the multiple fission. Eight autospores are shown in the figure, but 4, 8 or 16 may be formed. Individual *Chlorella* cells are small (2 to 8 μ in diameter) and lacking in definitive structures, making identification of a species difficult. This may create confusion in experimental work unless subcultures of the same stock are used. (After Smith, 1933: Freshwater Algae of the United States. McGraw-Hill, New York, p. 269; and after Fritsch, 1927: British Freshwater Algae. Cambridge University Press, London, Fig. 118.)

ient when the platinum oxygen electrode is used to measure oxygen production because the tissue can be held directly over the electrode.[7] When photosynthesis has been measured by conductivity change[62] or pH change,[8, 9] single large algal cells have been used. For still other studies photosynthetic sulfur bacteria have been of interest, and for investigation of photophosphorylation and photoreductions occurring during photosynthesis, chloroplasts from spinach leaves and other plants have been most effective.[67, 68]

Photosynthesis as an
Oxidation-Reduction Reaction

The over-all reaction which takes place in photosynthesis might be written as follows:

$$CO_2 + H_2O \xrightarrow{\text{light}} (CH_2O) + O_2 \quad (20.1)$$

Here (CH_2O) represents a carbohydrate. That the ratio of oxygen evolved to car-

bon dioxide consumed is 1 has been veri- fied many times since the early work of de Saussure.[10] In some plant cells, such as diatoms, fats appear as a result of photosynthesis, and some investigators have suggested that perhaps fats might be the first products of photosynthesis. However, the photosynthetic quotient in diatoms has a value of 1 (that of fat syn- thesis is greater than 1), and oil never accumulates except in cells which have ceased growing. In plant cells as in ani- mal cells, fat is a food reserve.

Van Niel[11] suggested that water is a hydrogen donor in the oxidation-reduc- tion process which occurs in photosynthe- sis. He based his argument on the reactions which occur in photosynthetic sulfur bacteria:

$$2H_2S + CO_2 \rightarrow H_2O + 2S + CH_2O \quad (20.)$$

In the green plant cell H_2O appears to be the hydrogen donor, playing a role similar to that of H_2S in the sulfur bac- teria, and, by analogy, the above equation may be written as follows:

$$2H_2O + CO_2 \rightarrow H_2O + O_2 + CH_2O \quad (20.)$$

Convincing proof of the validity of van Niel's argument came from work with iso- topic tracers. Ruben, using water marked with the oxygen isotope O^{18}, showed that when a culture of *Chlorella* is exposed to light, the gaseous oxygen that is liberated —and only the gaseous oxygen—contains the isotopic oxygen.[12, 13] This is taken as clear evidence that all the oxygen liberated comes from water and that water functions as a hydrogen donor in photosynthesis.

On the other hand, bacteria capable of photosynthesis use a variety of hydrogen donors, including H_2S and various or- ganic compounds. Because of this it has been proposed that organisms using or- ganic hydrogen donors are primitive ones. Presumably, as organic donors were ex- hausted in some early geological era, organisms developed that could use water as the hydrogen donor. Oxygen, accord-

398

ng to this view, appeared in the atmosphere only after the photosynthetic pattern of the green plant cells had been stablished. The unity of the mechanism of photosynthesis suggests that the process had a single origin and that photosynthesis, as it occurs in various plant groups now, developed only later.[44-46]

Light (Photochemical) Reactions in Photosynthesis

A primary photochemical reaction in photosynthesis is apparent from the fact that light is necessary. However, several lines of evidence indicate that thermochemical reactions follow the photochemical reaction.

At low light intensity the photochemical reaction is the limiting reaction in photosynthesis. In a *Chlorella* suspension illuminated with low intensities of light, the temperature may be varied over fairly wide limits (15° to 32° C.) without greatly altering the rate of the reaction (see Table 20.1). The temperature coefficient (Q_{10}) of photosynthesis over this range is about 1.06. The rate at which the chlorophyll molecules absorb and transmit the limited number of light quanta is not increased by raising the temperature. The initial portion of the curves in Figure 20.2 brings this out clearly.

If light intensity is increased to the point at which it saturates the system, that is, the point at which each chlorophyll molecule is supplied with all the light it can absorb, and if the temperature is then increased, the rate of photosynthesis increases. At high intensity, then, it is the thermo-

chemical reactions, which follow the photochemical reaction, that are rate limiting. In this case a temperature coefficient as high as 4.3 is found over the range of 10° to 32° C. (see Table 20.1 and Fig. 20.2).

A preparation of *Chlorella* exposed to flashing light performs more photosynthesis per unit dose of light than does a preparation exposed to continuous light. In other words, a given amount of light is more efficiently used if a dark period follows a light period. At low temperature, when the periods of darkness (following the flashes) are varied, the efficiency of a given dose of light increases with the length of the dark period up to a maximum which may be considered as the time required for completion of the dark reactions. Some of the data are shown in Figure 20.3. The lower the temperature, the longer must be the dark period, because the completion of the thermochemical reaction is then slower.[14, 15] Some supporting evidence for light and dark reactions in photosynthesis also comes from studies of the effects of ultraviolet radiations on the process of photosynthesis.[16]

All these experiments demonstrate that at least two types of reactions are involved in photosynthesis: first, a reaction in which light is absorbed and used by chlorophyll and, second, thermochemical dark reactions in which carbon dioxide fixation takes place (the rate of carbon dioxide fixation is determined by the kinetic energy of the molecules). The photochemical reaction has been named the Hill reaction, and the fundamental thermochemical reaction following it has

TABLE **20.1.** *Effect of Temperature and Light Intensity on the Rate of Photosynthesis*

Temp. range	4–10	10–20	20–30	5–10	16–25	15–25	25–32
Q_{10}	4.3	2.1	1.6	4.7	2.0	1.06	1.0
Rel. intensity of light	45	45	45	16	16	1.8	1.0
		High		Medium		Low	

From Warburg, 1919: Biochem. Zeit. *100*.

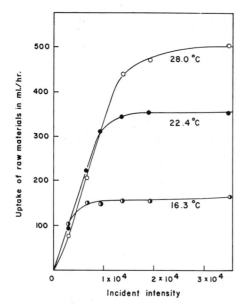

Fig. 20.2. Influence of temperature on rate of photosynthesis of purple sulfur bacteria (Thiorhodaceae) at different intensities of light. Note that at low light intensity, temperature has little effect on the rate of photosynthesis. (From Wassink, et al., 1942: Enzymologia, *10*:304.)

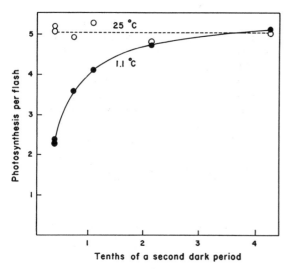

Fig. 20.3. Increase in efficiency of use of light at low temperature with long dark periods between flashes. (After Emerson and Arnold, 1932: J. Gen. Physiol., *15*:403.)

been named the Blackman reaction. T\[\]names are in honor of pioneering inve\[\]tigators.

Robert Hill discovered that fresh leav\[\]ground in water containing suitable h\[\]drogen acceptors give off oxygen whe\[\]exposed to light, even though the ce\[\]are crushed and photosynthesis of carb\[\]hydrate has ceased.[17, 18, 19] A variety \[\]dyes and other compounds, such as ferr\[\]cyanide, are photochemically reduce\[\]For example, quinone is reduced to h\[\]droquinone (see Fig. 18.7). These expe\[\]ments indicate that a reduction pool \[\]hydrogen is produced even when light \[\]absorbed by the chloroplast fragments.

It is interesting to note that the num\[\]ber of quanta of light which must \[\]absorbed by the chlorophyll in disrupte\[\]chloroplasts to liberate one molecule \[\]oxygen is of the same order as the num\[\]ber required in intact green plant cell\[\]This indicates that the process of phot\[\]chemical decomposition of water in di\[\]rupted chloroplasts is probably the sam\[\]as in the intact green cells. The only di\[\]ference is that under these condition\[\]the hydrogen produced is not utilized \[\]doing work useful to the cell.

Van Niel[46], without specifying th\[\]mechanism, postulated that water whic\[\]serves as the hydrogen donor in the phot\[\]synthesis of green plants, is split by th\[\]energy of light in the presence \[\]chlorophyll:

$$HOH + h\nu \rightarrow H\cdot + OH\cdot \quad (20.4)$$

In this equation $h\nu$ represents a quantu\[\]of light and $H\cdot$ and $OH\cdot$ represent fre\[\]radicals. The hydrogen radical so forme\[\]produces a reduction pool which reduce\[\]the dyes and other compounds provide\[\]Recombination of the OH radicals form\[\]water and oxygen:

$$OH\cdot + OH\cdot \rightarrow H_2O + \frac{1}{2}O_2 \quad (20.$$

While the hypothesis proposed by va\[\]Niel was stimulating to research, it wa\[\]not backed by evidence and posed a di\[\]ficult problem. There is insufficient energ\[\]

400

1 quantum of light absorbed by chloroyll to decompose water (Fig. 20.17). It
o appeared improbable that a molecule
chlorophyll could accumulate the en-
gy of several quanta of light necessary to
otolyze the water.

Arnon and his co-workers proposed a
ecific mechanism to explain the way
which the reduction pool is proced.[67, 68] They reasoned that in oxida-
e phosphorylation, as electrons fall
om a large negative potential through
e series of cytochromes to a positive
tential, these electrons give off energy
hich is stored as ATP (see Fig. 17.10).
erefore, if electrons of chlorophyll,
cited to high energy states by light ab-
rption, could be coupled with the cyto-
romes, the light energy might thereby
converted to chemical energy of ATP
r other high energy compounds).
vidence has accumulated that electrons
triplet states[85] and free radicals are
rmed during photosynthesis (Fig. 18.11),
dicating loss of electrons from chloroyll during photic excitation.[78-84] More
rect evidence of such conversion was
esented when Arnon and his co-
orkers showed that the electrons raised
excited states in chlorophyll can in-
eed pass their energy along any one of
ree pathways, as a result of which the
ergy is used to form ATP from ADP or
reduce coenzymes.* Their investiga-
on showed that photosynthetic phos-
horylation occurred also in isolated
loroplasts if appropriate factors and co-
ctors, removed through the isolation
ocedures, were again supplied. Such
hotophosphorylation, requiring no oxy-
en, is independent of oxidative phos-
horylation which, it will be recalled,
ccurs in the mitochondria (see Chapter
7). Mitochondria are not present in the
hloroplast, yet the green plant cell can
rm 30 times as much ATP by photo-
hosphorylation as it can by oxidative
hosphorylation.

It proved possible to separate the pho-

tochemical reaction completely from the
thermochemical reactions. When chloroplasts are ground and centrifuged, three
components are obtained—a green layer,
a supernatant and a lipid layer. This
green portion, consisting of grana of
chlorophyll, can carry out the entire photochemical reaction with the formation,
anaerobically, of ATP from ADP and the
reduction of coenzymes.[70]

When the products of photochemical
phosphorylation and coenzyme reduction
(reduction pool) were added to the other
fractions of the chloroplast, which contains the enzymes for the dark reactions
in photosynthesis, the result was the reduction of carbon dioxide in the solution
to carbohydrate. It was found that cytochromes changed absorption spectra as
these reactions occurred, suggesting that
they were involved. Furthermore, it was
found that photosynthetic plant cells have
unique cytochromes (e.g., cytochrome b_6
and cytochrome f) not found in animal
cells or microorganisms. In addition, in
order to obtain maximal yields it was
found that the system must be supplied
with catalytic amounts of several factors:
among these are vitamin K, FMN (flavin
mononucleotide) and chloride.

All of these facts and others not documented have led to the development of
the scheme shown in Figure 20.4 and in
Table 20.2, which summarizes the infor-

---

* It takes about 12,000 calories to make a mole of
ATP from a mole each of ADP and inorganic phosphate (see Chapter 18). The voltage equivalent for
this amount of energy can be calculated from the
equation:

$$W = n\mathcal{F}E \qquad (18.20)$$

Then: $12,000 \text{ calories} = \dfrac{(1)(96,000)(E)}{4.185}$

$$E = 0.52 \text{ volts}$$

The drop in potential from TPNH to oxygen, according to Table 18.2, is about 1.14 volts—far more than
is necessary for producing 1 ATP from ADP and inorganic phosphate. This allows for the inherent inefficiency of all cellular energy exchanges (see Equation 15.9).

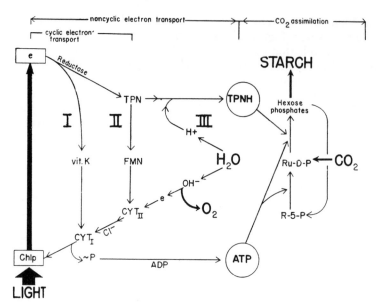

Fig. 20.4. Proposed scheme for the photochemical reaction in photosynthesis. Chlorophyll (Chlp), on absorbing a light quantum (hν) becomes "excited," and as a result, electrons, which are raised to a high energy level by the light, escape. The energy of these photically excited electrons is converted into the pyrophosphate-bond energy of adenosine triphosphate (ATP) during the "downhill" return of the electrons to chlorophyll by either of two cyclic pathways, I and II. Pathway I passes through vitamin K; pathway II passes through riboflavin phosphate (FMN). Both pathways result in the formation of ATP from ADP and inorganic phosphate. (For details, see Table 20.2.)

Pathway III, which is noncyclic, transports high energy electrons from photically excited chlorophyll to triphosphopyridine nucleotide (TPN$^+$), permitting reduction of the latter to TPNH with hydrogen ions (in solution). The electrons supplied to TPN from chlorophyll are replaced by other electrons from OH$^-$ ions (in solution) from which ions they pass to chlorophyll, there to be excited to high energy levels when chlorophyll absorbs light. Evolution of oxygen (and formation of water) accompanies the donation of electrons by hydroxyl ions.

TPNH and ATP, produced by photic excitation of chlorophyll, are used for assimilation of carbon dioxide to the level of sugar and starch in a series of dark reactions involving regeneration of ribose-5-phosphate (R-5-P) and ribulose diphosphate (Ru-D-P). For details of the dark reactions see Figs. 20.5 and 20.6 and Table 20.3. (After Arnon, 1959: Nature *184*:10.)

mation as a series of probable reactions proceeding in the chloroplast. The fall of the electron in the electrical potential gradient from a high work potential to a low work potential liberates the energy which becomes available, in the presence of the appropriate transferases, to be bound as high energy phosphate in ATP or used to reduce coenzyme TPN.

Vitamin K appears to involve the direct cyclic electron circuit through a cytochrome (given as Cyt. I pathway I in Fig. 20.4). The equations for the reactions involved in this cycle are given in Table

20.2. The electron may also pass cyclically through Pathway II by way of the reductase to TPN$^+$, FMN and cytochrome II and thence to cytochrome I (the latter reaction being catalyzed by chloride ion). The photic potential energy of the electron is thus converted to chemical potential energy of the high energy phosphate bond in ATP. The third pathway (III) is usually designated as the noncyclic pathway because the electrons do not complete a cycle as they do in the two other routes, but are continually supplied by hydroxyl ions. Water, which is known to

TABLE **20.2.**   *Photophosphorylation and Photoreduction in Photosynthesis*

Pathway I

2 Chlorophyll ($=$ Chlp) $+$ 2 quanta ($=h\nu$) $\rightarrow$ 2 Chlp* (Chlorophyll excited)
2 Chlp* $\rightarrow$ 2 Chlp$^+$ (Chlorophyll minus electron) $+$ 2 electrons ($=$ e)
Vit K$_{ox}$ $+$ 2 e $\rightarrow$ Vit K$_{red}$
Vit K$_{red}$ $+$ 2 Fe^{3+}Cyt$_I$ $\rightarrow$ Vit K$_{ox}$ $+$ 2 Fe^{2+}Cyt$_I$
2 Fe^{2+}Cyt$_I$ $+$ 2 Chlp$^+$ $+$ ADP $+$ H$_3$PO$_4$ $\rightarrow$ 2 Fe^{3+}Cyt$_I$ $+$ 2 Chlp $+$ ATP

Sum: ADP $+$ H$_3$PO$_4$ $+$ 2hν $\rightarrow$ ATP

Pathway II

2 Chlp $+$ 2 hν $\rightarrow$ 2 Chlp$^+$ $+$ 2 e
TPN$^+$ $+$ 2 H $+$ 2 e $\rightarrow$ TPNH $+$ H$^+$
TPNH $+$ H$^+$ $+$ FMN $\rightarrow$ TPN$^+$ $+$ FMNH$_2$
FMNH$_2$ $+$ 2 Fe^{3+}Cyt$_{II}$ $\rightarrow$ FMN $+$ 2 Fe^{2+}Cyt$_{II}$ $+$ 2 H$^+$
2 Fe^{2+}Cyt$_{II}$ $+$ 2 Fe^{3+}Cyt$_I$ $\xrightarrow{Cl^-}$ 2 Fe^{3+}Cyt$_{II}$ $+$ 2 Fe^{2+}Cyt$_I$
2 Fe^{2+}Cyt$_I^+$ $+$ 2 Chlp$^+$ $+$ ADP $+$ H$_3$PO$_4$ $\rightarrow$ 2 Fe^{3+}Cyt$_I$ $+$ 2 Chlp $+$ ATP

Sum: ADP $+$ H$_3$PO$_4$ $+$ 2 hν $\rightarrow$ ATP

Pathway III

2 Chlp $+$ 2 hν $\rightarrow$ 2 Chlp$^+$ $+$ 2 e
2 H$_2$O $\rightarrow$ 2 H$^+$ $+$ 2 OH$^-$
TPN$^+$ $+$ 2 H$^+$ $+$ 2 e $\rightarrow$ TPNH $+$ H$^+$
2 OH$^-$ $+$ 2 Fe^{3+}Cyt$_{II}$ $\rightarrow$ 2 Fe^{2+}Cyt$_{II}$ $+$ ½ O$_2$ $+$ H$_2$O
2 Fe^{2+}Cyt$_{II}$ $+$ 2 Fe^{3+}Cyt$_I$ $\rightarrow$ 2 Fe^{3+}Cyt$_{II}$ $+$ 2 Fe^{2+}Cyt$_I$
2 Fe^{2+}Cyt$_I$ $+$ 2 Chlp$^+$ $+$ ADP $+$ H$_3$PO$_4$ $\rightarrow$ 2 Fe^{3+}Cyt$_I$ $+$ 2 Chlp $+$ ATP

Sum: TPN$^+$ $+$ 2 H$_2$O $+$ ADP $+$ H$_3$PO$_4$ $+$ 2 hν $\rightarrow$
TPNH $+$ H$^+$ $+$ ½ O$_2$ $+$ ATP $+$ H$_2$O

* After Arnon.[67]

e slightly dissociated into hydrogen and hydroxyl ions, supplies the hydroxyl ions to Pathway III, and oxygen and water are produced as a result. The hydrogen ions, thus made available by the decomposition of water, reduce TPN$^+$ to TPNH.

It is apparent that the reactions which form the reduction pool have been extensively studied. The photochemical reactions, then, constitute the means for reduction of TPN$^+$ and the formation of ATP from ADP. These compounds diffusing into the nongreen portion of the chloroplast can complete the reduction of CO$_2$ to carbohydrate.[88]

It would be of interest at this time to consider a photosynthetic sulfur bacterium called *Chromatium* which has a simpler photosynthetic mechanism than the green plant cell. *Chromatium* lacks chloroplasts, but its chlorophyll and other pigments are contained in chromatophores. *Chromatium*, being an anaerobe, does not use water as a source of hydrogen ions to reduce TPN$^+$, nor does it produce oxygen as do green plant cells; in fact, it does not tolerate oxygen. Experiments have shown that hydrogen can serve in place of water as the source of reductant to convert TPN$^+$ to TPNH (the electron being passed to Cyt$_{II}$). As a matter of fact, if hydrogen and ATP are supplied to the cells, carbohydrates are synthesized in the dark. Apparently the potential of hydrogen is sufficient to reduce TPN$^+$ to TPNH without light energy. In *Chromatium*, therefore, the light energy is necessary only for the production of ATP, which normally occurs along pathways I and II—i.e., the cyclic electron pathways.* This may represent a more primitive photosynthetic system than that in green plants.

The Thermochemical Reactions in Photosynthesis

Several techniques have been largely responsible for the successful analysis of the thermochemical "dark" reactions in photosynthesis. One of these is the use of radioactive carbon, making it possible to tag the carbon dioxide ($C^{14}O_2$) which is incorporated into organic compounds during photosynthesis. Another technique is paper chromatography (see Appendix 20.3), by which the exceedingly small amounts of substances which appear even after a second of illumination can be identified. Each compound containing C^{14} can then be determined quantitatively if sensitized photographic films are exposed to the radioactive spots on the paper chromatogram.† From the relative density of spots on the developed films the relative concentrations of the various compounds containing C^{14} can be determined, and if the film is calibrated by a simultaneous exposure to a compound with a known amount of C^{14}, the actual concentration of each compound can be determined quantitatively. By increasing the length of exposure of cells to light, one can chart the spread of radioactive carbon into a variety of organic compounds. It is also possible to compare the pathway by which plants incorporate C^{14} into compounds in the dark with the pathway taken during illumination.[21] Still another technique which has proved very fruitful in analyzing thermochemical re-

actions is the isolation of the enzymes involved in each of the thermochemical steps in photosynthesis.[22]

Because of the appealing simplicity of the idea, some workers considered the possibility that photosynthesis is a reversal of the Krebs cycle,[23] that the hydrogen made available from water during photosynthesis might be used to reverse each step in the dehydrogenation and decarboxylation occurring in respiration (see Chapter 17). The reactions of the Krebs cycle (Fig. 17.8) are known to be reversible in both plant and animal cells: the reverse of decarboxylation is carbon dioxide fixation; the reverse of dehydrogenation is reduction. In both animal and plant tissues, carbon dioxide is split out of isocitric acid to form α-ketoglutaric acid as one of the steps of the Krebs cycle. Furthermore, carbon dioxide is incorporated into α-ketoglutaric acid (a 5-carbon acid), provided isocitric dehydrogenase, manganous ion and reduced coenzyme II (TPNH), are present. Also, in the dark, carbon dioxide in all cells is combined with pyruvic acid to form oxaloacetic acid.[24] In fact, for reversal of the oxidations and decarboxylations of the Krebs cycle, it is necessary only to reduce the coenzymes of the dehydrogenases and to supply ATP and the appropriate enzymes. In animal cells, the coenzymes of the dehydrogenases are reduced only in the presence of a suitable hydrogen donor from which hydrogen and energy are liberated. In green

---

* In some anaerobic photosynthetic bacteria using hydrogen donors other than hydrogen or water, e.g., succinate, not only is TPN$^+$ reduced to TPNH but atmospheric nitrogen is reduced to ammonia (fixed). Such nitrogen fixation occurs at the expense of photic energy.[67, 68] This fact is of considerable importance in view of the great importance of nitrogen fixation in the economy of nature (see Nitrogen Cycle, Fig. 15.7).

† An alternate method is to cut out the paper containing the radioactive compound and measure its radioactivity directly with a Geiger counter.

lant cells, sunlight absorbed by the
rana of chlorophyll supplies the energy
or production of ATP and for reduction
f coenzymes.[23] However, experimental
ata are not in keeping with this explana-
on. It has been shown that reversal of
ie Krebs cycle occurs in plant cells most
onspicuously in the dark. Furthermore,
hotosynthetic cells have few mitochon-
ria. ATP is produced largely by way of
hotophosphorylation as described above.
ll of the reactions can occur in the
hloroplast, which lacks mitochondria
nd in which no oxidative phosphoryla-
on can occur.[31]

The pathway of the thermochemical
eactions in photosynthesis has been
ffectively studied by tracing the spread
f C^{14} into compounds after illumination.
n most of the experiments, cells which
ave been brought to a steady state of
hotosynthesis in the presence of ade-
uate carbon dioxide are provided with a
olution of bicarbonate containing the
adioactive carbon. At a determined time
he cells are killed and analyzed quanti-
atively by chromatography and sensitized
hotographic film for various compounds
ontaining C^{14} (see Appendix 20.3). In
ells killed immediately after exposure to
ight the C^{14} is found mainly in phospho-
lyceric acid. In cells killed within 5 sec-
nds after illumination, traces of phos-
hoglyceric acid, alanine, asparic acid
nd malic acid containing C^{14} appear. In
ells killed within 15 seconds after illumi-
ation, in addition to the other com-
ounds listed, faint traces of sucrose
ontaining C^{14} may be detected and also
ome pentose, glucose phosphate, and
ructose phosphate, all containing C^{14}.
After a minute of illumination has elapsed
efore the cells are killed, abundant ra-
lioactive glucose phosphate and fructose
hosphate are found. At the end of 5
ninutes of illumination radioactivity ap-
ears even in the lipids of the cell, and
y way of the amino acids such radioac-
ivity may be able to reach the proteins.

It is quite evident that the radioactive
carbon obtained from carbon dioxide is
rapidly spread throughout the various
classes of compounds present in the plant
cell.[25-29]

Since after brief exposure of a plant cell
to illumination, the 3-carbon acid, phosphoglyceric acid, is the first compound to
incorporate radioactive carbon, its genesis
becomes of prime importance. About half
of its radioactivity resides in the carboxyl
group, suggesting that the $C^{14}O_2$ had
been added to a larger molecule from
which the phosphoglyceric acid has been
split off. Since radioactivity accumulates
rapidly in the center of a pentose sugar,
the pentose sugar would appear to be the
molecule which most likely incorporates
the carbon dioxide. The enzymes involved
in this transfer are now known (see Table
20.3). It is thought that after the pentose
combines with carbon dioxide it almost immediately splits to form two molecules of
phosphoglyceric acid. Following the pathway of $C^{14}O_2$, one finds that the molecules of phosphoglyceric acid are further
phosphorylated to form diphosphoglyceric
acid. In the presence of reduced coenzyme I (DPNH), diphosphoglyceric acid
is reduced to form triose phosphate and
inorganic phosphate. Two triose phosphate molecules unite to form the sugar
hexose (fructose) diphosphate, as indicated by the fact that a higher percentage
of the labeling in this molecule appears
in the centrally located carbons 3 or 4.
From hexose (fructose) diphosphate,
hexose phosphate is formed by loss of a
phosphate, and from it glucose phosphate
is formed in the presence of an isomerase.
From these molecules various disaccharides and polysaccharides may then
be synthesized. The acids of the Krebs
cycle containing C^{14} are formed from the
glucose used in respiration (primarily in
the dark, since illumination inhibits these
reactions). C^{14} appears in amino acids
when some of the keto acids are ami-
nated, and it appears in lipids and pro-

TABLE **20.3.** *Photosynthetic Dark Reactions*

Reactions Fixing Carbon Dioxide Into Pentose Forming Hexose

NUMBER REACTANTS	PRODUCTS	ENZYMES
1. Pentose phosphate + ATP	Ribulose diphosphate + ADP	Phosphopentokinase
2. Ribulose diphosphate + CO_2 + H_2O	2 Phosphoglyceric acid	Pentose diphosphate carboxylase
3. 2 Phosphoglyceric acid + 2ATP	2 Diphosphoglyceric acid + 2ADP	Phosphoglyceric acid kinase
4. 2 Diphosphoglyceric acid + 2DPNH + 2H$^+$	2 Triose phosphate + DPN$^+$ + phosphate (inorganic)	Triose phosphate dehydrogenase
5. 2 Triose phosphate	Hexose diphosphate	Aldolase, triose phosphate isomerase

Reactions Regenerating Pentose

6. Hexose diphosphate + H_2O	Hexose monophosphate + phosphate (inorganic)	Hexose diphosphatase (magnesium dependent)
7. Hexose monophosphate + triose phosphate	Pentose phosphate + erythrose (tetrose) phosphate	Transketolase
8. Hexose monophosphate + erythrose phosphate	Sedoheptulose phosphate + triose phosphate	Transaldolase
9. Sedoheptulose phosphate + triose phosphate	2 Pentose phosphate	Transketolase
Sum of (1 to 9) × 3: $3CO_2$ + 9ATP + $5H_2O$ + 6DPNH + 6H$^+$	1 triose phosphate + 9ADP + 6DPN$^+$ + 8 inorganic phosphate	

Reactions Regenerating DPNH, ATP and Providing H$^+$

10. H_2O + DPN$^+$	DPNH + H$^+$ + ½O_2 + 2e	Splitting of water. See Fig. 20.4.
11. DPNH + 3ADP + 3 inorganic phosphate + H$^+$ + ½O_2 + 2e	DPN$^+$ + 3ATP + $4H_2O$	
Sum of (1 to 11) × 3: $3CO_2$ + $2H_2O$ + inorganic phosphate	1 Triose phosphate + 3O_2	

ATP = adenosine triphosphate; ADP = adenosine diphosphate; DPN$^+$ = diphosphopyridine nucleotide oxidized, DPNH, reduced; e = electron. (Data from Racker.[22])

teins when these compounds are built from fragments in the Krebs cycle (see Fig. 17.9).

Pentose, which appears to serve as the carbon dioxide acceptor in the thermochemical reactions of photosynthesis, can be produced by the oxidation of glucose to gluconic acid, which can be oxidatively decarboxylated in small amounts. However, since this would constitute reversal of photosynthetic carbon fixation, another source of pentose seems more likely.

Tracing the pathway of C[14] in compounds suggests the following scheme for the synthesis of pentose. It is similar to the pentose shunt already discussed for eterotropic cells (Fig. 17.13). Hexose phosphate combines with a triose in the presence of transketolase to form a pentose and a tetrose (4-carbon) sugar. The tetrose combines with a hexose under the influence of transaldolase and the compound formed then splits to form a 7-carbon sugar, heptulose, and a triose. The heptulose may then combine with triose in the presence of transketolase to form two molecules of pentose. In this manner continuous supplies of pentose are maintained. These supplies are adequate to fix carbon dioxide in the thermochemical reactions of photosynthesis (see Table 20.3 and Figs. 20.5 and 20.6). This scheme is supported by the fact that pentose is always isolated in illuminated cells along with the 7-carbon sugar, heptulose. The latter contains about half of its radioactivity in the central carbons, indicating that it is formed by the combination of smaller fragments. For elucidating the dark reactions in photosynthesis, Calvin received the Nobel Prize in 1961.[87]

The Chloroplast as a Complete Photosynthetic Unit. Intact chloroplasts are capable of complete photosynthesis outside the cell, provided all the cofactors are supplied.[30] The chloroplast, therefore, constitutes a photosynthetic unit.

The chloroplasts in the cells of green plants contain highly organized units of chlorophyll called *grana* (see Fig. 5.10). Such grana appear to be lacking in algal cells. In photosynthetic bacteria free grana or *chromatophores* are found.[86] These grana can be seen by electron microscopy to be organized into lamellae, as shown in Figures 5.10, 5.11 and 5.12.[34, 35] By chemical analysis grana have been shown to consist of lipids, proteins and other compounds which are thought to be arranged in a characteristic manner[74] as diagramed in Figure 20.7. The organization of a granum is destroyed when chloroplasts are disrupted by grinding or other methods.

Three reactions are observed in intact chloroplasts: (1) the Hill reaction, following light absorption; (2) photosynthetic phosphorylation, during which adenosine diphosphate forms adenosine triphosphate—a reaction occurring in the absence of oxygen and distinct from metabolic phosphorylation; (3) the dark reaction or carbon dioxide fixation. That they are three separate reactions can be demonstrated as follows. Carbon dioxide fixation ceases when iodoacetamide is added, but photosynthetic phosphorylation and the Hill reaction continue; methylene blue inhibits both carbon dioxide fixation and photosynthetic phosphorylation but not the Hill reaction; o-phenanthroline, which inhibits photolysis of water, inhibits all three reactions.[31] Presumably these reactions, in addition to many other reactions, all occur in the chloroplasts inside the living cell, and during the course of these reactions the photosynthetic products are built into other derivatives.

By the use of x-rays, green mutant strains of *Chlorella* have been produced which absorb light and evolve oxygen but are incapable of performing the photosynthesis of carbohydrates.[20] Such mutants can be grown in a solution of glucose and salts, indicating that they are capable of manufacturing their other requirements.

The Function of Pigments in Photosynthesis

Chlorophyll is present in all photosynthetic cells, although it is sometimes masked by the presence of other pigments. While several varieties of chlorophyll have been identified, all have the same essential porphyrin structure, or tetrapyrrole nucleus, shown in Figure 20.8. Magnesium, in nonionic form, is present in this nucleus and is attached to the ends of the pyrroles. In chemical terms, chlorophylls are methyl phytol esters of the parent dicarboxylic acids, the chlorophyllins. Phytol is a long chain

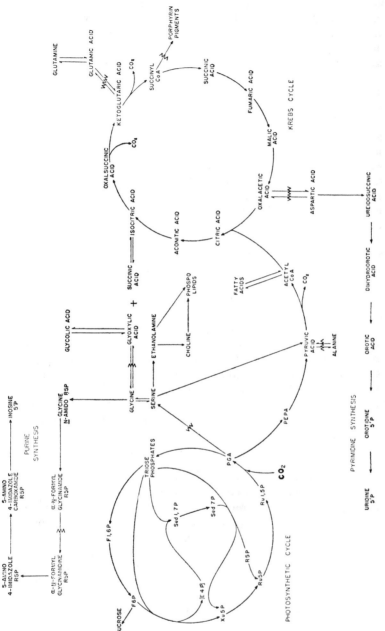

Fig. 20.5. Interrelationships between photosynthesis, respiration and biosyntheses in the green plant cell. The following abbreviations are used in the photosynthetic cycle:

(F6P), fructose 6-phosphate (fructose monophosphate)
(F1, 6P), fructose 1,6-diphosphate
(Sed1, 7P), sedoheptulose 1,7-diphosphate
(Sed7P), sedoheptulose 7-phosphate
(PGA), phosphoglyceric acid

(Ru1, 5P), ribulose 1,5-diphosphate
(Ru5P), ribulose 5-phosphate
(R5P), ribose 5-phosphate
(Xu5P), xylulose 5-phosphate
(E4P), erythrose (tetrose) 4-phosphate

Leading from the photosynthetic cycle towards the Krebs cycle on the lowest arc in the diagram are phosphoenol pyruvic acid (PEPA) and coenzyme A (CoA). (From Bassham, J. A., and Calvin, M., 1957: The Path of Carbon in Photosynthesis. Prentice-Hall, Englewood Cliffs,

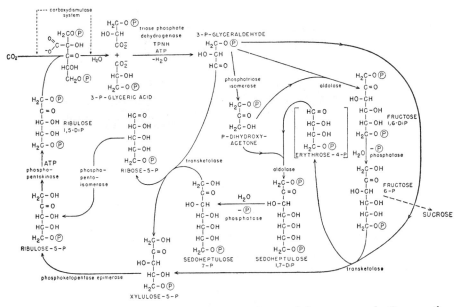

Fig. 20.6. Details of the dark reactions of photosynthesis and the pentose cycle. Compare the pentose cycle in photosynthetic plants to the pentose shunt in cells of heterotrophic microorganisms and animals (Fig. 17.13 and Equations 17.5 to 17.12). (From Bassham, J. A., and Calvin, M., 1957: The Path of Carbon in Photosynthesis. Prentice-Hall, Englewood Cliffs, N. J.)

cohol, containing one double bond. It can be thought of as derivable from vitamin A by hydrogenation. The various chlorophylls differ from one another only the side chains attached to the outer ds of the tetrapyrrole nucleus.[36, 37] een plant cells have chlorophylls a and brown algal cells and diatoms have chlorophylls a and c and red algal cells ve chlorophylls a and d. The purple cteria have a chlorophyll called bacriochlorophyll, which resembles chloroyll a. The green sulfur bacteria have a lorophyll-like compound called bacrio-viridin, the exact structure of which s not been determined.[38] Cells of iolated green plants (sprouted in the rk) contain protochlorophyll which is ickly reduced to chlorophyll when the af is illuminated.[36] Evidence exists that e chlorophylls in chloroplasts are atched to proteins in the grana. Most of e chlorophylls absorb in the red and lue-violet parts of the spectrum (see Fig.

20.9), except for bacteriochlorophyll, which absorbs in the infrared and the blue violet.[66] When illuminated, chlorophyll shows a brilliant fluorescent band in the red. This is one of its most characteristic properties. It also shows a weaker band in the far red. In addition, after illumination, chlorophyll emits light in the dark for as long as 2 minutes, a property which is inhibited when agents such as cyanide or azide are present. Since these agents also inhibit photosynthesis, light emission by chlorophyll is thought to be the result of a reversal of some step in photosynthesis.[39, 40, 83]

In all plant cells and in the purple sulfur bacteria (which are capable of photosynthesis), carotenoids (yellowish pigments) are present. There is some question, however, that carotenoids are present in the green sulfur bacteria (also capable of photosynthesis). The carotenoids are essentially hydrocarbons (see Fig. 20.10) and fall into two main groups,

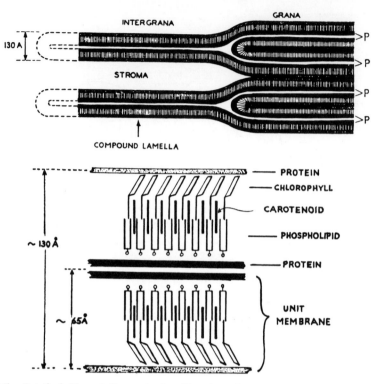

Fig. 20.7. Detail of chlorophyll organization. Hypothetical representation of lamellation in the mesophyll chloroplast of corn (*Zea mays*). At the top is a diagram of the density observed in sections of osmium-fixed material under the electron microscope; at the bottom, an interpretation of this in terms of protein, lipid and chlorophyll. (After Hodge, McLean, and Mercer, 1955: J. Biophys. Biochem. Cytol., *1*:605.)

the carotenes and the xanthophylls, the latter being hydroxy compounds otherwise similar to carotenes. A large number of carotenes and xanthophylls exist, but they will not be enumerated here. The carotenoids absorb strongly in the blue-violet and ultraviolet ends of the spectrum (Fig. 20.9). In each plant group, characteristic carotenoids are found. A few of the main ones are listed in Table 20.4. The carotenoids, like the chlorophylls, seem to be attached to proteins in the chloroplasts of cells. In some anaerobic photosynthetic bacteria, they appear to protect chlorophyll from photo-oxidation.[77]

The action spectrum for photosynthesis in many green plants shows highest efficiency in the red end of the spectrum, somewhat lower efficiency in the blue end and least efficiency in the green portion of the spectrum (see Fig. 20.1). Chlorophyll shows maximum absorption in the red end with somewhat lower absorption in the blue end of the spectrum and virtually none in the green, while carotenoids absorb little, if at all, in the red end but absorb strongly in the blue end of the spectrum. This suggests that light absorbed by carotenoids in many green plant cells is, perhaps, not useful in photosynthesis.[41, 42] However, the carotenoids of brown algae do participate in the process of photosynthesis, since the action spectrum of photosynthesis here corresponds to the absorption spectrum

CONVERSIONS OF ENERGY AND MATTER IN THE CE

a mixture of extracted chlorophyll and carotenoid fucoxanthin (see Fig. 20.12). The phycoerythrin (red pigment) and ycocyanin (blue pigment) found in the and blue-green algae are protein pigments (phycobilins), readily destroyed by it. The prosthetic group in each of se pigments is related to the bile pigents, being in each case an open tetrarrole (see Fig. 20.13). This prosthetic up differs from that of chlorophyll in t the pyrroles are not joined to form a g, and magnesium is lacking. Proof has en presented that the pigments in red l blue-green algae take an active part photosynthesis, and the highest effincy for photosynthesis in the red algae n the green part of the spectrum (see . 20.14), where the red pigment abbs strongly (see Fig. 20.15) and where orophyll absorbs least.[41, 65, 82]

Although in the cell, pigments other n chlorophyll, such as the phycobilins

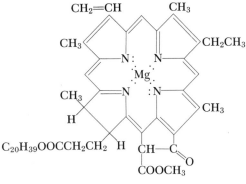

Chlorophyll a

Fig. 20.8. The **chlorophylls** are magnesium complexes of porphyrins esterified with the long-chain alcohol phytol, $C_{20}H_{39}OH$. Chlorophyll b differs from chlorophyll a in that it has an aldehyde group replacing the methyl group in the 3 position. Chlorophyll a is present in cells of all photosynthetic forms except the photosynthetic bacteria which have a closely related form of chlorophyll.

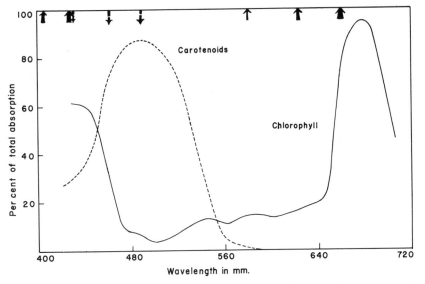

Fig. 20.9. Absorption spectra of chlorophyll and carotenoids. Only the overall absorption regions for each class of pigments are given. Individual pigments of each group have some sharp peaks and usually narrower ranges. For example, major peaks for chlorophyll a are shown by upward arrows at the top of the graph, with the relative thickness of the arrow indicating the relative amount of absorption. Main absorption peaks of β-carotene are shown by downward arrows at the top of the graph. For details of absorption by members of these classes of pigments, see references 61 and 75. (After Emerson and Lewis, 1942: J. Gen. Physiol., 25:587.)

TABLE **20.4.** *Pigments in Photosynthetic Bacteria and Plants*

GROUP OF PLANTS	CHLOROPHYLLS	CAROTENOIDS*	OTHER PIGMEN
Green plants	a and b	several, e.g., β-caro-tene and lutein	anthocyans (no photosynthet
Green sulfur bacteria	bacterioviridin	several	—
Purple sulfur bacteria	bacterio-chlorophyll	several, e.g., spirilloxanthin	—
Brown algae	a and c	several, e.g., fuco-xanthin	—
Diatoms	a and c	several, e.g., fuco-xanthin	—
Yellow-green algae	a and e	several	—
Red algae	a and d	several, e.g., β-caro-tene and lutein	phycobilins (ph coerythrin, p cocyanin)
Blue-green algae	a	several	phycobilins

After Strain, H. H., 1951: Manual of Phycology. (Smith, G. M., ed.) Chronica Botanica Company, pp. 243–262.

* All plants and bacteria contain both carotenes and xanthophylls; several kinds of each are often present. β-carotene is found in all plants.

and some carotenoids (e.g., fucoxanthin), absorb light used in photosynthesis, the fluorescence spectrum obtained on illumination is always that of chlorophyll a, even when plants are illuminated with wavelengths which are little absorbed by chlorophyll.[42, 43] Absorption of light by chlorophylls b, c and d also excites chlorophyll a to fluorescence. This suggests that light absorbed by all the other

pigments is transferred to chlorophyll which perhaps alone uses the energy excite electrons as discussed above. How ever, some evidence given below mak this conclusion seem unlikely.

The enhancement of the photosynth tic effectiveness of a long wavelength light by simultaneous exposure of pho synthetic plant cells to shorter wav lengths of light (called the Emers

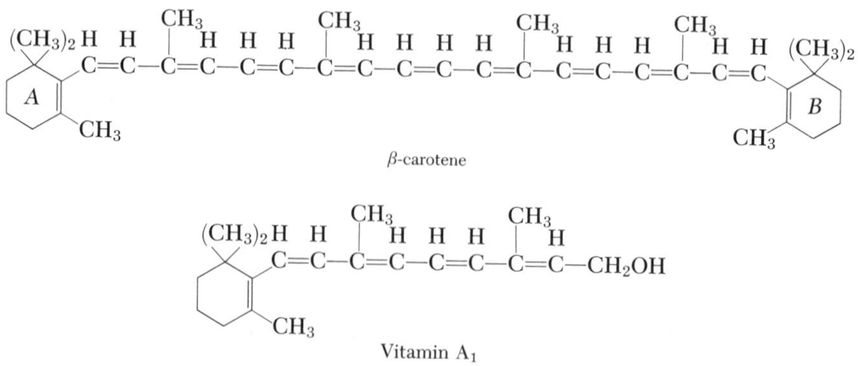

β-carotene

Vitamin A$_1$

Fig. 20.10. β-Carotene and vitamin A$_1$. Note that vitamin A is essentially one-half of a β-carotene molecule in which units A and B are mirror images of each other.

CONVERSIONS OF ENERGY AND MATTER IN THE CE

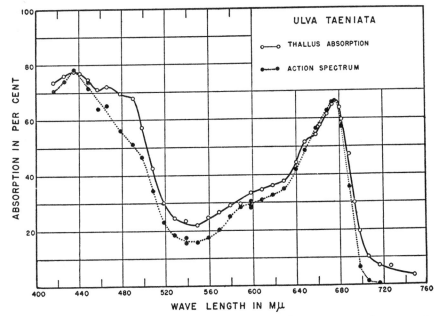

Fig. 20.11. Correspondence between absorption spectrum and action spectrum for a green alga, *Ulva taeniata.* Note that in this plant the efficiency in blue light is very high. (From Haxo and Blinks, 1950: J. Gen. Physiol., *33*:408.)

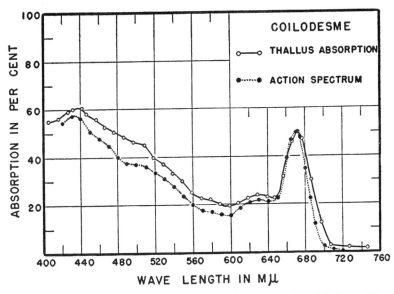

Fig. 20.12. Absorption spectrum and action spectrum for a brown alga, *Coilodesme.* (From Haxo and Blinks, 1950: J. Gen. Physiol., *33*:408.)

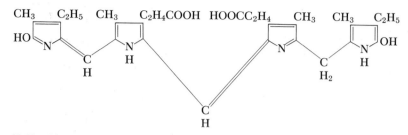

Fig. 20.13. The structure of the prosthetic group of phycocyanin, a pigment found in red and blue-green algae. Note that it is an open pyrrole instead of a closed one like chlorophyll, and it resembles the bile pigments resulting from a breakdown of heme in hemoglobin. Phycocyanin has the chemical name mesobiliviolin. Phycoerythrin, the red pigment of red algae, is similar in general structure to phycocyanin and is called mesobilierythrin. These prosthetic groups are attached to proteins.

effect) might be explained in the following manner.[71] If *Chlorella* cells are being illuminated with light at 700 mμ, additional illumination with light at shorter wavelengths increases photosynthesis over the sum of the photosynthesis occurring with the same light exposure but at each wavelength separately. It has also been found that the transient or brief enhancement in photosynthesis (called the Blinks effect) follows shifts from a long wavelength (700 mμ) to a shorter wavelength.[72] In both of these cases the acti spectrum (Fig. 20.16) resembles the a sorption spectrum of chlorophyll b, as the simultaneous illumination with short and a long wavelength broug chlorophyll b, in addition to chloroph a, into photosynthetic activity, thus creasing the effectiveness of the pho synthetic process.[76, 80]

It has also been found that if the lo wavelength is followed after several s onds of darkness by the short wavelengt

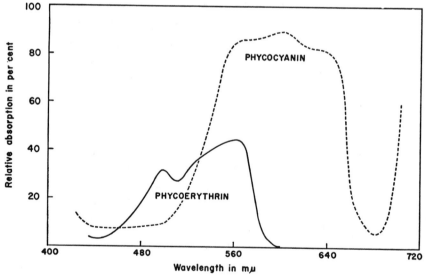

Fig. 20.14. Absorption spectra of phycocyanin and phycoerythrin. (Modified respectively after Emerson and Lewis, 1942: J. Gen. Physiol., 25:579, and from Haxo and Blinks, 1950: J. Gen. Physiol., 33:389.)

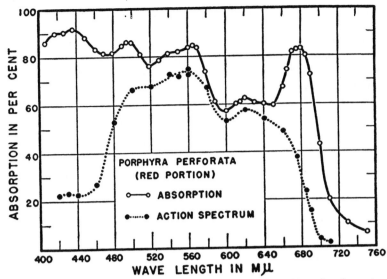

Fig. 20.15. Action and absorption spectra of a red alga, *Porphyra*. Note that the region of the spectrum absorbed most by the phycoerythrin (compare with Fig. 20.14) is most effective in photosynthesis. (From Haxo and Blinks, 1950: J. Gen. Physiol., 33:414.)

momentary increase in rate of photo-nthesis (transient enhancement) is still ident. Also, when the order of longer d shorter wavelengths is reversed, hancement still occurs.[76] These and

other lines of data now make it appear likely that the two pigments involved in photosynthesis may play different roles, one perhaps being primarily concerned with photophosphorylation, the other

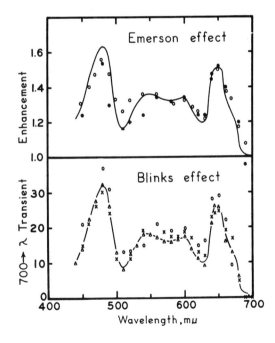

g. 20.16. The action spectrum for the enhance-ent effect (Emerson effect) was obtained by illu-inating a plant exposed to 700 mμ with each of a mber of shorter wavelengths. The action spectrum r the Blinks effect was obtained by recording the ansient increase in photosynthesis following the ift from 700 mμ to each of a number of shorter avelengths of light. Each wavelength (λ) was ad-sted in intensity to give a rate of photosynthesis jual to that obtained with 700 mμ alone. Then, the vo wavelengths were used simultaneously and the hancement of the transient was determined. (From rench.[76])

with reduction of TPN$^+$ to TPNH. The enhancement produced by simultaneous excitation of both pigments probably results from the greater likelihood of reduction of carbon dioxide when both TPNH and ATP are supplied in optimal amounts.*

The action spectra for the Emerson and Blinks effects obtained with plants possessing phycobilins (red and blue-green algae) and those with fucoxanthins (diatoms) suggest that these accessory pigments are also involved in photosynthetic enhancement. All these observations offer still more opportunities for a further analysis of the photosynthetic process.

APPENDIX

20.1 Quantum Efficiency of Photosynthesis

Formation of 1 gram mole of glucose requires 709,000 calories (free energy change), that is, this amount of energy is required to reduce 6 gram moles of carbon dioxide. To reduce a gram mole of carbon dioxide requires one sixth of this energy or 118,00 calories. A mole quantum at 6600 Å (red light) is equivalent to 43,000 calories (see Chapter 9). Theoretically, therefore, at least 3 quanta of red light are necessary to bring about the reduction of one molecule of carbon dioxide.

Warburg, in an early study, determined the amount of light required by *Chlorella* to bring about the reduction of one carbon dioxide molecule.[4] He used a dense suspension of *Chlorella* in a manometric vessel, the sides and top of which were silvered to reflect the light. From his experimental data Warburg found that about 4 quanta were necessary (Table 20.5).

Subsequent investigators have found 8 to 12 quanta necessary to reduce a molecule of carbon dioxide in a variety of green, brown and red algae, and in photosynthetic sulfur bacteria.[47-49] Furthermore, the same values have been obtained

by manometric, electrometric or polarographic, and calorimetric techniques (s Table 20.5). The types of errors characteristic of each of these techniques a quite different; therefore, it seems u likely that because of systematic errc they would all deviate consistently in tl same direction.

Warburg and his co-workers in view this redetermined the quantum requir ments for reduction of a carbon dioxic molecule, using a number of plants, ar they reaffirmed their previous value.[50] these studies, respiration is usually cor pensated for by white light. Once tl compensation point is found, the suspe sion of cells is illuminated with an exper mental source of light of any desired ar known wavelength or intensity.

It is difficult to assign reasons for tl differences between the results of tl two groups of workers. The followir possibilities have been suggested: (1) ph tosynthesis cannot be completely diser tangled from other concomitant reaction especially those of respiration;[52-54] (the exact end product of photosynthes is not known—if different workers alt conditions to vary the end metabol product, their results will differ; (3) mo of the measurements require that tl available instruments be pushed to tl very limits of their sensitivity. The diffi culty will be resolved only when worke from the opposite camps pool their r sources and attack the problem jointly.

Even if the exact number of quant required for the reduction of a molecul of carbon dioxide cannot be given wit certainty at the present time, significar findings have emerged from the quantur efficiency studies. Investigators have cor sistently found the same quantum r quirement (within the limits of error) fc the reduction of one molecule of carbo

* However some evidence indicates that ATP pr duction, which probably occurs at both long ar short wavelengths, is itself enhanced by illuminatic with long and short wavelengths.[76]

TABLE 20.5. *Quantum Efficiency of Photosynthesis in Representative Plants*

GROUP	ORGANISM	Number of quanta required to reduce one molecule of CO_2	
		DATA	ORDER OF MAGNITUDE
Green sulfur bacteria	*Chlorobium thiosulfa-tophilum*[*]	White light: 7.8 to 11.8	8–12
Purple sulfur bacteria	Chromatium strain D[†]	Band: 540 to 600 mμ: 8.5 to 11.8 (on thiosulfate) 8.5 to 16 (on hydrogen)	8–12
Green algae	*Chlorella pyreno-dosa*[‡]	Green (546 mμ): Wisconsin strain: 8.8 to 9.1 Emerson strain: 7.3 to 9.3 Burk strain: 8.1 to 9.7	8–10
	Chlorella[§]	Blue (436 mμ): 5.7 to 5.1 Yellow (578 mμ): 3.8 to 4.3 Red (660 mμ): 4.1 to 4.4	4–6

Number of quanta required to reduce one molecule of CO_2

GROUP	ORGANISM	WAVELENGTH IN mμ					ORDER OF MAGNITUDE
		436	500	560	620	675	
	Ulva lobata[‖]	14.3	18.1	20.0	16.6	12.5	12–20
Brown algae	*Coiladesme californica*[‖]	14.5	13.7	14.3	13.2	13.3	13–14
Red algae	*Porphyra naiadum*[‖]	35.6	17.2	13.3	14.5	23.2	14–36
	Delesseria decipiens[‖]	29.4	15.8	15.8	19.2	32.2	16–32
Flowering plants	*Phyllospadix scouleri*[‖]	17.0	20.8	17.9	14.7	13.3	14–21

[*] Larsen, et al.[51]

[†] Wassink, et al., 1942: Enzymologia *10*.

[‡] Yuan, et al., 1955: Biochim. et Biophys. Acta *17*. This article summarizes many of the experiments performed on quantum efficiency in Chlorella.

[§] Warburg and Negelein, 1923: Ztschr. f. Physik. Chemie *106*. See also Burk, et al., 1949: Science *110*, and Burk, 1955: Science *121*, reaffirming these low values.

[‖] Yocum and Blinks, 1954: J. Gen. Physiol. *38*. Quoted in detail because it covers such a variety of forms; 436 mμ is absorbed by both chlorophyll and carotenoids, 500 by carotenoids, 560 especially by phycoerythirin, 620 especially by phycocyanin, and 675 especially by chlorophyll a. The lowest quantum values are given in the table.

dioxide, regardless of the type of cells studied—whether from green plants; blue-green, red or brown algae; purple or green sulfur bacteria.[51] The photosynthetic sulfur bacteria, some of which use hydrogen sulfide as a hydrogen donor, are perhaps especially interesting since on thermodynamic grounds a lesser energy requirement might be expected, hydrogen sulfide being a highly reduced compound. However, experiments show that the same number of quanta are necessary. The same is true for strains of algae or bacteria which are adapted to use hydrogen gas. In certain purple bacteria various organic compounds containing potential chemical energy can be utilized as hydrogen donors, but the quantum requirement is still 8 to 12. Apparently, hydrogen, organic compounds and hydrogen sulfide serve (like water) only as hydrogen donors. This points again to the similarity of the photosynthetic mechanism wherever it is present.

If the efficiency of the photosynthetic conversion of light energy to chemical energy is calculated on the basis that 8 to 12 quanta (43,000 calories per mole quantum) of red light (6600 Å) are required to reduce 1 gram mole of carbon dioxide, the theoretical requirement being 118,000 calories per mole, a value of 23 to 43 per cent is obtained. The efficiency is 118,000 calories, divided by the product of the number of quanta required to reduce one carbon dioxide molecule, times the mole quantum at the particular wavelength. Considering the number of steps in the process of photosynthesis, the value of 23 to 43 per cent is a relatively high order of efficiency.

20.2 Energy Available for Photosynthesis and Energy Requirements for Photochemical Action

The energy available for photosynthesis lies between the red and blue wavelengths of sunlight. As shown in Figu[re] 20.17, this is equivalent to about 40,00[0] to 66,000 calories per mole quantu[m] (Avogadro's number times the energy [of] a quantum). The equivalent values [in] electron volts/mole are also shown opp[o]site the values in calories. This amount [of] energy is insufficient to dissociate th[e] water molecule.

The amount of energy per mole qua[n]tum in the ultraviolet is sufficient to di[s]sociate a number of compounds and [to] induce synthesis of carbohydrate an[d] other compounds. These "photosynthe[e]ses" are of special interest in the study [of] the evolution of organic compounds an[d] the origin of life (see Chapter 25).

20.3 Paper Chromatography

In the general chromatographic metho[d] as introduced into biology by Tswett[63] i[n] 1906, various adsorbants—starch, alum[i]num oxide, etc.—are poured as a slur[ry] into a tube (see Fig. 20.18a). An unknow[n] is poured on the widened top of the tub[e] and then "developed" by the slow trickl[e] of an appropriate solvent through th[e] column. The rate at which any compoun[d] migrates through the column depend[s] upon the balance between its affinity fo[r] the solvent and its adsorption on the pa[r]ticles of the column. This method of sep[a]rating compounds is spoken of a[s] adsorption chromatography.

Another chromatographic method de[-]pends upon partition of a solute betwee[n] two solvents in which the solute has dif[-]ferential solubility. The use of a separa[-]tory funnel in separating organi[c] compounds is sufficiently familiar to illus[-]trate the principle involved. If a solut[e] has a greater solubility in one solven[t] than in another, the two solvents bein[g] immiscible, shaking the solute in a sep[-]aratory funnel containing the two solvent[s] will make possible removal and concen[-]tration of the solute in the solvent in whic[h] it has greater solubility, especially if

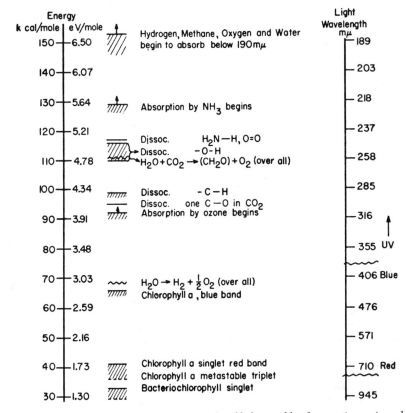

Energy				Light Wavelength
k cal/mole	e V/mole			mμ

Hydrogen, Methane, Oxygen and Water begin to absorb below 190mμ

$$H_2O + CO_2 \rightarrow (CH_2O) + O_2 \text{ (over all)}$$

Dissoc. H_2N-H, $O=O$
Dissoc. $-O-H$

Absorption by NH_3 begins

Dissoc. $-C-H$
Dissoc. one $C-O$ in CO_2
Absorption by ozone begins

$$H_2O \rightarrow H_2 + \tfrac{1}{2}O_2 \text{ (over all)}$$
Chlorophyll a , blue band

Chlorophyll a singlet red band
Chlorophyll a metastable triplet
Bacteriochlorophyll singlet

Energy scale values: 150 — 6.50, 140 — 6.07, 130 — 5.64, 120 — 5.21, 110 — 4.78, 100 — 4.34, 90 — 3.91, 80 — 3.48, 70 — 3.03, 60 — 2.59, 50 — 2.16, 40 — 1.73, 30 — 1.30

Light wavelength scale: 189, 203, 218, 237, 258, 285, 316, 355 UV, 406 Blue, 476, 571, 710 Red, 945

Fig. 20.17. Energy available at various wavelengths of light capable of promoting various photochemical reactions.

eries of such extractions are performed. omething like this separation can be chieved on a column of some powdered naterial if one of the solvents wets the owder. The solvent wetting the powder vill form a stationary solvent phase, and he powder will, in this case, have only he function of holding the solvent which vets it. In practice, the solute in the ppropriate organic solvent is added to he top of the wet column and developed ›y washing with additional aliquots of the olvent. As the second solvent, immiscible vith the first, moves through the column, he solute is partitioned between the two olvents, as if an infinite number of sepratory funnels were being used in series o extract the solute. The solute moves as

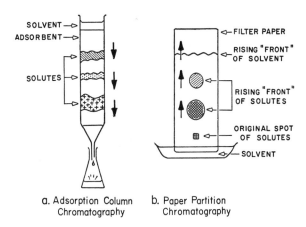

a. Adsorption Column Chromatography

b. Paper Partition Chromatography

Fig. 20.18. Column and paper chromatography. (From Cantarow and Schepartz: Biochemistry.)

a band on the column. If instead of one solute, several have been dissolved in the solution poured on the top of the column, they will be separated as several bands on the column because of their differences in partition between the two solvents.[61]

Paper chromatography, as developed in 1941 by Martin and Synge,[59] is a variation of Tswett's partition chromatographic method. It is a method based also on the differential solubility of compounds in solvents, and it achieves separation by partition of the solute between the two solvents. The paper acts as a support for one of the solvents (in theory at least). The solution to be tested is placed as a spot on a large sheet of filter paper. When the spot is dry the paper is placed with one edge dipping into a tray containing the mixture of solvents, the choice of solvents depending upon the solubility of the solutes to be chromatographed. After the solvent front has moved the desired distance beyond the sample spot, the solvent front is marked, and the paper is dried and sprayed with some agent to "develop" the spots of materials which have migrated from the original sample spot. As an example, a mixture of amino acids is spotted on filter paper, and the paper is dipped into a butyl alcohol-water mixture. Diverse amino acids are differentially soluble in these two solvents, some being more soluble in water, others more soluble in butyl alcohol. The alcohol-water mixture migrates along the filter paper fibers upward through the sample spot, and the various substances with differential solubility migrate to different distances from the original spot, those most soluble in butyl alcohol moving farthest. After the solvent front has advanced past the spot to a distance considered from experience to be adequate, the line of the solvent front is marked and the paper is dried. For detection of amino acids the paper is then sprayed with ninhydrin, which forms a

purplish color on reacting with an amir acid. Control chromatograms, made fro known mixtures of amino acids, are ru in parallel with the unknown. From th positions of known amino acids the ur known acids can be determined (see Fi 20.18b). From the depth of the colc reaction quantitative data may b gathered.[60]

The ratio of the distance traveled b any particular substance to the distanc covered by the solvent is known as th ratio of the fronts or R_f. This ratio usually constant for a given substance i a particular solvent and under given con ditions (e.g., temperature). The R_f value determined from controls of know amino acids under similar conditions ma be used as standards for identification c unknown amino acids.

When a "one dimensional" chromatc gram does not adequately separate th components of a mixture, the once-deve oped paper is placed, after it has dried, i a pan of another mixture of solvents i such a way that the movement of th second mixture of solvents occurs a right angles to the movement of the firs producing a "two dimensional" chroma togram.[60]

When the substances separated b paper chromatography are radioactive they can be visualized by photography The filter paper is pressed against a sen sitive photographic film. The ionizin radiations from the radioactive materia will so affect the film that on develop ment the film will show darkening in pro portion to the radiation, the amount o radiation depending upon the concentra tion of the radioactive substance. From the R_f values of controls and from th density of the darkened areas on film ex posed to known concentrations of radio active material, identification and quanti tative analysis of an unknown materia are possible, even when the unknown i present only in traces, as, for example after a few seconds of photosynthesis.

GENERAL REFERENCES

ınual Reviews. Annual Review of Plant Physiology, Stanford, California. Contains yearly reviews of some phase of photosynthesis.

non, D. I., Nov. 1960: The Role of Light in Photosynthesis. Sci. Am. 203:104–118.

non, D. I., 1961: Changing Concepts of Photosynthesis. Bull. Torrey Bot. Club 88:215–259.

non, D. I., 1961: Cell-free Photosynthesis and the Energy Conversion Process, in Life and Light (McElroy, W. D., and Glass, B., eds.). Johns Hopkins Press, Baltimore, pp. 489–566.

ssham, J. A., and Calvin, M., 1957: The Path of Carbon in Photosynthesis. Prentice-Hall, Englewood Cliffs, N. J.

ssham, J. A., June, 1962: The Path of Carbon in Photosynthesis. Sci. Am. 206:89–100.

inks, L. R., 1954: The Photosynthetic Function of Pigments Other Than Chlorophyll. Ann. Rev. Plant Physiol. 5:93–114.

inks, L. R., 1960: Action Spectra of Chromatic Transients and the Emerson Effect in Marine Algae. Proc. Nat. Acad. Sci. U. S. 46:327–332.

alvin, M., 1962: Path of Carbon in Photosynthesis. Science 135:879–889.

merson, R., Chalmers, R., and Cederstrand, C., 1957: Some Factors Influencing the Long Wavelength Limit of Photosynthesis. Proc. Nat. Acad. Sci. U. S. 43:133–143.

ranck, J., and Loomis, W., eds., 1949: Photosynthesis in Plants. Iowa State Coll. Press, Ames.

rench, C. S., 1960: The Chlorophylls in Vivo and in Vitro. Encyclopedia of Plant Physiology (Ruhland, W., ed.) Springer-Verlag, Berlin, pp. 252–297.

affron, H. 1957: Photosynthesis and the Origin of Life. Symposium 15, Soc. Study of Dev. and Growth, pp. 127–154.

affron, H., 1960: Energy Storage: Photosynthesis in Plant Physiology, a Treatise (Steward, F. C., ed.), Academic Press, New York, vol. IB, pp. 3–277.

ill, R., and Whittingham, C. P., 1955: Photosynthesis. Wiley, New York. A good brief account.

agendorf, A. T., 1962: Biochemistry of Energy Transformations During Photosynthesis, in Survey of Biological Progress (Glass, B. ed.). Academic Press, New York, 4:181–344.

ın Niel, C. B., 1949: The Comparative Biochemistry of Photosynthesis, in Photosynthesis in Plants (Franck, J., and Loomis, W., eds.). Iowa State Coll. Press, Ames.

abinowitch, E. I., 1945: Photosynthesis and Related Processes. Interscience, New York, vol. I, Chemistry of Photosynthesis. 1951: vol. II, Part I. Problems of Spectroscopy and Fluorescence of Photosynthetic Pigments; Kinetics of Photosynthesis. 1956: vol. II, Part II. Kinetics of Photosynthesis.

acker, E., 1955: Synthesis of Carbohydrates from Carbon Dioxide and Hydrogen in a Cell Free System. Nature, 175:249–251.

Reid, C., 1957: Excited States in Chemistry and Biology. Academic Press, New York.

LITERATURE CITED

1. Hill, R., and Whittingham, C. P., 1955: Photosynthesis. Wiley, New York.
2. Rabinowitch, E. I., 1945 to 1956: Photosynthesis and Related Processes, vols. I and II. Interscience, New York.
3. Spoehr, H. A., 1926: Photosynthesis. Chemical Monograph Co., New York.
4. Warburg, O., and Negelein, N., 1923: Ztschr. f. Physik. Chemie. 106:191.
5. Myers, J., 1951: Ann. Rev. Microbiol. 5:157.
6. Myers, J., 1951: Plant Physiol. 25:539.
7. Haxo, F. T., and Blinks, L. R., 1950: J. Gen. Physiol. 33:389.
8. Rosenberg, J. L., 1954: J. Gen. Physiol. 37:753.
9. Blinks, L. R., and Skow, R. K., 1938: Proc. Nat. Acad. Sci. U. S. 24:420.
10. Smith, J. H. C., 1949: in Photosynthesis in Plants (Franck and Loomis, eds.). Iowa State Coll. Press, Ames, p. 53.
11. van Niel, C. B., 1931: Arch. Mikrobiol. 3:1. 1936: Arch. Mikrobiol. 7:323.
12. Ruben, S., Randall, M., Kamen, M., and Hyde, J. L., 1941: J. Am. Chem. Soc., 63:877.
13. Dorough, G. D., and Calvin, M., 1951: J. Am. Chem. Soc. 73:2362.
14. Emerson, R., and Arnold, W., 1932: J. Gen. Physiol. 15:391.
15. Clendening, K. A., and Ehrmantrout, H. C., 1950: Arch. Biochem. 29:387.
16. Arnold, W., 1933: J. Gen. Physiol. 17:135.
17. Hill, R., 1939: Proc. Roy. Soc. B127:192.
18. Lumry, R., Spikes, J. D., and Eyring, H., 1954: Ann. Rev. Plant Physiol. 5:271.
19. French, C. S., Holt, A. S., Powell, R. D., and Anson, M. L., 1946: Science 103:505.
20. Davis, E. A., 1948: Science 108:110. 1952: Am. J. Bot., 39:535. See also Bendix, S., and Allen, M. B., 1962: Arch. Mikrobiol. 41:115.
21. Calvin, M., 1949: J. Chem. Ed. 26:639.
22. Racker, E., 1955: Nature 175:249.
23. Ochoa, S., and Vishniac, W., 1952: Science 115:297.
24. Whittingham, C. P., 1955: Biol. Rev. 30:40.
25. Calvin, M., and Massini, P., 1952: Experimentia 8:445.
26. Calvin, M., 1950–51: Harvey Lect. 46:218.
27. Bassham, J. A., Benson, A. A., and Calvin, M., 1953: J. Chem. Ed. 30:274.
28. Bassham, J. A., Benson, A. A., and Calvin, M., 1953: J. Am. Chem. Soc. 76:1760.
29. Bassham, J. A., June, 1962: Sci. Am. 206:89.

30. Arnon, D. I., 1955: Biochem. Biophys. Acta *16*:607.
31. Arnon, D. I., 1955: Science *122*:9.
32. Duysens, L. N. M., 1954: Science *120*:353.
33. Davenport, H. E., 1952: Nature *170*:1112.
34. Steinman, E., and Sjostrand, F. S., 1955: Exp. Cell. Res. *8*:15.
35. Sponsler, O. L., and Bath, J. D., 1955: Protoplasma *44*:332.
36. Smith, J. H. C., 1949: J. Chem. Ed. *26*:631.
37. Granick, S., 1953: Chem. Eng. News *31*:748.
38. Strain, H. H., 1949: *in* Photosynthesis in Plants (Franck, J. and Loomis, W. eds.). Iowa State Coll. Press, Ames, p. 133.
39. Strehler, B. L., and Arnold, W., 1951: J. Gen. Physiol. *34*:809.
40. Arnold, W., and Davidson, J. B., 1954: J. Gen. Physiol. *37*:677.
41. Blinks, L. R., 1954: Ann. Rev. Plant Physiol. *5*:93.
42. Duysens, L. N. M., 1951: Nature *168*:548.
43. Franck, J., French, C. S., and Puck, T. T., 1941: J. Phys. Chem. *45*:1268.
44. Oparin, A. I., 1957: The Origin of Life on Earth. 3rd Ed. Oliver and Boyd, London.
45. Horowitz, N. H., 1945: Proc. Nat. Acad. Sci. U. S. *31*:153.
46. van Niel, C. B., 1949: *in* Photosynthesis in Plants (Franck, J. and Loomis, W., eds.). Iowa State Coll. Press, Ames, p. 437.
47. Wassink, E. C., 1948: Ann. Rev. Biochem. *17*:559.
48. Franck, J., 1951: Ann. Rev. Plant Physiol. *2*:53.
49. Nishimura, M. S., Whittingham, M. S., and Emerson, R., 1951: Symp. Soc. Exp. Biol. *5*:176.
50. Burk, D., Hendricks, S., Korzenovsky, M., Shocken, V., and Warburg, O., 1949: Science *110*:225.
51. Larsen, H., Yocum, C. S., and van Niel, C. B., 1952: J. Gen. Physiol. *36*:161.
52. Brown, A. H., 1953: Am. J. Bot. *40*:719.
53. Calvin, M., 1955: Science *121*:620.
54. Bassham, J. A., Shibata, K., and Calvin, M., 1955: Biochim. Biophys. Acta *17*:332.
55. Franck, J., 1953: Arch. Biochem. Biophys. *45*:190.
56. Burk, D., 1953: Fed. Proc. *12*:611.
57. Calvin, M., and Barltrop, J. A., 1952: J. Am. Chem. Soc. *74*:6153.
58. Warburg, O., 1952: Naturwiss. *39*:439.
59. Martin, A. J. P., and Synge, R. L. M., 1941: Biochem. J. *35*:1358.
60. Block, R. J., Durrum, E. L., and Zweig, G., 1955: Paper Chromatography and Paper Electrophoresis. Academic Press, New York.
61. Strain, H. H., 1958: Chloroplast Pigments and Chromatographic Analysis. Penn. State Univ. Press, University Park, Penn.
62. Skow, R. K., and Blinks, L. R., 1940: Collecting Net, vol. 15, no. 10.

63. Tswett, M., 1906: Ber. Deutsch. Botan. G *24*:316.
64. Bassham, J. A., and Calvin, M., 1956: *in* Curre in Biochemical Research (Green, D. E., e Interscience, New York, p. 29.
65. Emerson, R., and Lewis, C., 1942: J. G Physiol. *25*:579.
66. French, C. S., and Young, V. M. K., 1956: *in* diation Biology (Hollaender, A., ed.). *3*:3 McGraw Hill, New York.
67. Arnon, D. I., 1959: Nature *184*:10.
68. Arnon, D. I., Nov. 1960: Sci. Am. *203*:104.
69. Arnon, D. I., 1961: Bull. Torrey Bot. Club *88*:2
70. Trebst, A. V., Tsujimoto, H. Y., and Arnon, D. 1958: Nature *182*:351.
71. Emerson, R., Chalmers, R., and Cederstrand, 1957: Proc. Nat. Acad. Sci. U. S. *43*:133.
72. Blinks, L. R., 1950: Proc. Nat. Acad. Sci. U *46*:327.
73. Allen, M. B., (ed.), 1960: Comparative Bioche istry of Photoreactive Processes. Academ Press, New York.
74. Hodge, A. J., McLean, J. D., and Mercer, F. 1955: J. Biophys. Biochem. Cytol. *1*:605.
75. French, C. S., 1960: *in* Encyclopedia of Pl Physiology (Ruhland, W., ed.). Springer-Verl Vienna, vol. 5, p. 252.
76. French, C. S., 1961: *in* Life and Light (McElr W. D., and Glass, B., eds.), Johns Hopkins Pre Baltimore, p. 447, and personal communic tion.
77. Sistrom, W. R., Griffin, M., and Stanier, R. 1956: J. Cell. Comp. Physiol. *48*:473.
78. Arnold, W., and Clayton, R. K., 1960: Proc. N Acad. Sci. U. S. *46*:769.
79. Arnold, W., and Sherwood, H. K., 1957: Pr Nat. Acad. Sci. U. S. *43*:105.
80. Myers, J., and French, C. S., 1960: J. G Physiol. *43*:723.
81. Sogo, P. B., Carter, L. A., and Calvin, M., 196 *in* Free Radicals in Biological Systems (Blo M. S., ed.), Academic Press, New York, p. 3
82. Krasnovskii, A. A., 1955: Izv. Akad. Nauk SSS Ser. Biol. *2*:122.
83. Krasnovskii, A. A., 1959: Biophysika *4*:1.
84. Tollin, G., Sogo, P. B., and Calvin, M., 195 Ann. New York Acad. Sci. *74*:310.
85. Reid, C., 1957: Excited States in Chemistry a Biology. Academic Press, New York.
86. Gaffron, H., 1960: *in* Plant Physiology, a Treat (Steward, F. C., ed.). Academic Press, N York, vol. IB, p. 3.
87. Calvin, M., 1962: Science *135*:879.
88. For a criticism of this scheme and presentation alternate schemes, see Clayton, R. (in pres *in* Photobiology (Giese, A. C., ed.), Academ Press, New York.

IRRITABILITY AND CONTRACTILITY

All life is continually challenged by the demands of the environment. If an organism is to survive it must obtain nutrients, resist inimical attacks and at all costs reproduce its own kind. Chance plays a large part in the struggle for existence but those organisms that survive must respond in an adaptive way.

The responses of all living things to their environment ultimately depend upon cellular *irritability*, one of the fundamental properties of life. Perhaps more than anyone else, Francis Glisson (1587–1677) of Cambridge was the first to consider that irritability, manifesting itself in the appearance of alteration of movement, is a general property of life and a result of the organism's possession of energy. Another early figure of note was John Brown (1735–1788), who said that living things are stimulated by external factors, such as heat, food, foreign matter and poisons, as well as by interactions of internal organs. Brown's is a commonplace conception today but one that was quite novel at the time. Irritability, as defined today, is the capacity to react to the environment, internal and external. Energy is continuously expended by the cell in its efforts to keep itself in a condition of readiness to react.

The living organism appears to respond to the environment as a whole, rather than to a single factor of the environment at a time. However, for experimental purposes it is more convenient to vary each factor of the environment singly and to study its effect. If the change in quantity or quality of an environmental factor is large enough to be detected by an organism, it constitutes a *stimulus*. The stimulus evokes in the living organism a change which constitutes the *response*. The cytoplasmic change evoked by a particular stimulus is probably fundamentally alike in all cells, but the mechanisms it sets into action, culminating in the response of the organism as a whole, depends upon the type of organism under consideration. The response generally involves movement dependent upon *contractility*, a property as distinctive of all life as irritability.

Unicellular organisms incorporate in a single cell all they need for an adaptive response to stimuli. Some of them have no specialized sensitive structures (*receptors*) or special motile structures (*effectors*) and can respond, so far as can be seen, mainly by growth—a response evidently adequate. However, some microorganisms have a receptor, e.g., the eyespot of *Chlamydomonas* (Fig. 2.1), but more often the entire cell is sensitive to light (*Amoeba*). Some protozoans even have a complex system for coordinating the effectors (Fig. 23.5).[46, 47] Special effectors may also be present, such as pseudopodia in ameboid cells and cilia (or flagella) in ciliated and flagellated protozoans, various bacteria, plant zoospores and gametes of multicellular organisms.

The main adaptive response of multicellular plants to most stimuli is by *growth movements*. Some plants, however, respond also to some stimuli by *turgor movements*. In each case, the cellular change is transmitted to the effector cells and the plant reacts in a particular adaptive manner.

Turgor movements are strikingly shown by the sensitive plant *Mimosa* which may be stimulated in a variety of ways (e.g., by touch). The change in turgor of some cells in the *pulvinus*, as the effector at the base of each leaflet (and petiole) is called, accounts for the response.[48, 49] When the electrical impulse generated by the stimulus reaches the cells of the pulvini, turgor is lost from cells on one side, causing the leaflets to close together. As turgor is gradually reestablished in the cells of the pulvinus the leaflets recover their original position. Turgor movements are also found in floral organs of some plants and in insect-trapping (carnivorous) plants.[1]

Growth movements, in response to a stimulus, also called growth curvature or *tropisms*, are too slow to be detected under uninterrupted observation by the human eye but are clearly visible in time-lapse photographic records. Differential growth underlies responses to gravity, temperature, light, water, chemicals and touch, and the tropisms are designated geotropism, thermotropism, phototropism, hydrotropism, chemotropism and thigmotropism, respectively.

The concept of tropism was introduced in 1832 by the botanist Augustin de Candolle (1778–1841) and has been vigorously studied since. Phototropism might be taken as an example to illustrate the general features of a tropistic response. Some time after a plant is exposed to light, more active growth (in the region of undifferentiated cells) on

IRRITABILITY AND CONTRACTILITY

the side away from the light, turns the plant toward the light. Darwin, long ago, showed that when a tinfoil cap is placed over the tip of an oat coleoptile, the plant fails to respond to light. A receptor for light, present in the growing tip, can be demonstrated in other plants as well. The action spectrum of a response to light indicates activity of a pigment absorbing strongly in the blue-violet end of the visible spectrum, presumably a carotenoid.[2]

It can be demonstrated that a *growth hormone*, called *auxin*, is produced at the growing tip. Auxins are relatively small molecules (the main one, indole acetic acid, has a molecular weight of 175.18); therefore, they presumably diffuse readily. Auxin is known to be transported downward away from the tip and it is found to accumulate on the side away from the light. Only cells which have not yet differentiated, such as those in the region of elongation of the stem, respond to auxin by lengthening. Hormones are the basis of many interesting and stimulating studies. Asymmetric distribution of auxins is thought to account for many other plant responses, e.g., tip dominance, setting of fruit, shedding of leaves and, along with other hormones (e.g., phytochrome, Chapter 9), for coordination of plant activities.[51] They are dealt with in textbooks of plant physiology.[2] The effect of auxin can be counteracted by specific growth inhibitors (e.g., maleic anhydride).

Specialized sensitive structures, complex motile organs and hormones function in the responses of multicellular animals which, on the whole, also respond adaptively to the environment. Some of the cells involved in these specialized activities are greatly modified in accordance with their functions and grouped in organs of complex structure.

Multicellular animals respond to a stimulus chiefly by muscular movement, which may be very rapid compared to the slow responses that characterize plants. However, animals may also respond to stimuli by secretion from glands, e.g., when a hungry dog is confronted with food, saliva will flow freely. Some animals will respond in other ways. Thus, those with luminous organs (Fig. 19.12) may give off light upon stimulation, while electric fish stun their prey by an electric shock.

The simplest response pattern in animals is the *reflex arc*, which is the automatic response of an effector (or a group of effectors) to a stimulus (Fig. 22.8). In a reflex arc the excitation resulting from the action of the stimulus on the receptor cells generates a disturbance called the nerve impulse, which is passed by nerve cells (neurons) called *afferent* (sensory) *neurons* to the central nervous system where it is relayed by *interneurons* to *efferent* (motor) *neurons* connecting with the effectors (generally muscles). The response of an animal as a whole may consist of a series of such reflexes in a chain, the first reflex tripping the second, the second the third, and so on, or it may also respond by complex reactions which originate in the higher centers of the nervous system. However, some effectors are independent of neuronal connections. For example, ameboid cells such as leucocytes, which are widespread in the blood or body fluid of animals, and most ciliated epithelial cells[50] respond directly to chemicals and not through nervous control.

Ductless glands of internal secretion (endocrine glands) secrete hormones into the blood which aid in coordinating responses, as well as growth and metabolic processes of the animals. Such glands are called into action sometimes by the nervous system—at other times, by chemical changes in the body. The central nervous system plays a major role in coordination of immediate responses. Coordinative action of endocrines and nerves is considered in textbooks of animal physiology.[45]

A brief discussion of cellular irritability as manifested by the electrical changes induced in cells by stimulation is given in Chapters 21 and 22. Contractility manifested in cells as a consequence of stimulation is considered in Chapter 23 and the chemistry of contractile processes of cells in Chapter 24.

21

ACTION POTENTIALS OF CELLS

n *action potential* is usually defined as the temporary change in electric potential between stimulated and resting portions of a cell. It follows stimulation and passes from one end of the cell to the other. Because it moves as a wave of excitation, it is also spoken of as a propagated potential. Action potentials are especially prominent on nerve and muscle cells,[38] but they are also found to occur in many other excitable plant and animal cells[28, 56] and during fertilization of an egg.[31] Since an action potential is best developed on a nerve cell, where it is called a *nerve impulse*, it will be discussed in greater detail below.

The Nature of the Nerve Impulse

Neurons, as nerve cells are usually called, are fundamentally similar to other cells in that they have a cell body with cytoplasm, a nucleus and a cell membrane. Therefore, they are subject to the same principles that govern the behavior of all living cells. But by adaptation to their specialized function, they possess structures admirably fitting them for the conduction of nerve impulses. *Dendrites,* short outgrowths from the cell body, carry impulses to the cell body, and *axons,* long outgrowths, carry the impulses to the next neuron. An axon is often referred to as a nerve fiber, but, in a loose way, nerve fiber may also refer to a neuron.

As seen in Figure 21.1, the *axon* of the vertebrate myelinated neuron is wrapped in a *myelin sheath* consisting of multiple membranes of the Schwann cells, the nuclei of which are shown along the sheath (see also Figs. 14.10 and 14.11). The myelin sheath varies, being thinner on invertebrate neurons where it may consist of a single layer of sheath cells, and possibly being practically absent in the finer fibers, called non-myelinated fibers, in the vertebrate autonomic nervous system. The myelin sheath does not enclose the dendrites, the cell body or the terminations of the axon. Myelin seems to act as an insulator, and myelinated neurons transmit the nerve impulse more rapidly than nonmyelinated ones of the same diameter (see Tables 21.1 and 21.2).

Neurons vary in size and form.[55] The largest nerve fibers in a mammalian nerve

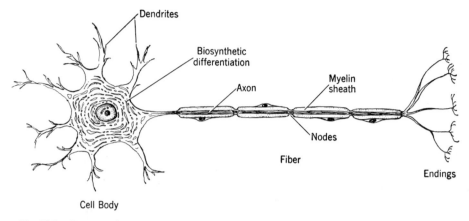

Fig. 21.1. Diagram of a myelinated neuron. The nuclei along the axon are in Schwann cells which form the myelin sheath. Such cells cover the axon except at the Nodes of Ranvier and at the terminal branching portion. The terminal endings make synaptic connections with peripheral tissue. [From Schmitt, F. O., 1959: Biophysical Science. A Study Program (Oncley, J. L., ed.). Wiley, New York, p. 456.]

are designated the A fibers, those of intermediate size, the B fibers, and the small ones, the C fibers (see Table 21.1). These are further classified into subgroups which are given Greek letter designations.[38] Fibers of different size vary considerably in their properties.

A nerve is usually made up of a bundle of many neurons. However, single fibers can be dissected out of a bundle and studied individually, and much of the information of action potentials has been obtained in this manner.[7]

The twitching of the muscles in the leg of a frog when the sciatic nerve is cut is a common observation; twitching can be induced also by pinching the nerve, b heating it or by applying a chemical to i Pioneer investigators used the muscl twitch as evidence of a nerve impuls traveling along the nerve from the poin of stimulation to the muscle, and th nerve-muscle preparation became a clas sic tool in the study of nerve transmission Direct measurements of nerve activity however, were initiated in 1786 b Galvani, who obtained evidence for th presence of electric currents in nerve a well as in muscle, even when stimul other than electricity (e.g., pinching were used, and in 1848 Emil Du Bois Reymond published a book calle

TABLE 21.1. *Properties of Neurons of Different Sizes*
(Cat and Rabbit Saphenous Nerves)

PROPERTIES	GROUP		
	A	B	C
Diameter of fiber (μ)	20–1	3	—
Conduction velocity (m./sec.)	100–5	14–3	2
Duration of action potential (msec.)	0.4–0.5	1.2	2.0
Absolute refractory period (msec.)	0.4–1.0	1.2	2.0

After Grundfest, 1940: Ann. Rev. Physiol. 2.

IRRITABILITY AND CONTRACTILITY

esearches on Animal Electricity. However, ready means for detecting electric currents in excited nerve cells were not available until much later. The introduction of the cathode ray oscillograph by Gasser and Erlanger in 1922 provided an instrument which stimulated tremendous progress in studies of the electrical properties of nerve cells.[29, 38]

The cathode ray oscilloscope is generally used to measure action potentials and other electrical manifestations of living things, because the electron beam, having very slight inertia, responds to an imposed potential with practically no delay. In the oscilloscope the stream of electrons coming from the hot filament of the tube impinges upon a fluorescent screen covered with a transparent plastic marked like graph paper (see Fig. 21.2). Activated by an oscillating circuit, the beam sweeps at any desired frequency across the screen from side to side between two vertical plates in the tube. An action potential from a nerve fiber can be passed through an amplifier and imposed upon two horizontal plates, causing the beam to move upward or downward according to the potential. The screen of the oscilloscope may be calibrated for time, by imposing a known sweep frequency upon the electron beam, and for voltage, by means of a standard cell. Because the image has afterglow

(phosphorescence), it can be readily photographed for a permanent record. The zero position may be altered at will so that the entire screen may be used to measure negative or positive variations only, as dictated by the experiment at hand, and the electrical connections may be made in such a way as to have upward movement of the beam indicate either positive or negative deflection.

A neuron excited by pinching, by chemical irritation or by other stimuli becomes negative to the unexcited portion, as shown by recording the electrical changes (see Fig. 21.3). If two pickup electrodes are applied at some distance from the point of excitation, the electrode nearer to the stimulated part of the neuron at first becomes negative to the other electrode; then, after a brief time, it becomes positive to the other electrode. The brief negativity can be interpreted as the arrival of a moving wave of excitation (action potential) on the nerve cell at the position of the first electrode, and the subsequent positivity can be interpreted as the neuron's recovery from the excitation at the first electrode as the wave of excitation passes to the second electrode, and the latter is rendered negative to the first. Because the electrode proximal to the stimulus is first negative and then positive, the action potential, or the nerve impulse, is said to

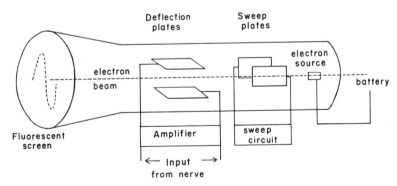

Deflection plates   Sweep plates

electron source

electron beam

battery

Fluorescent screen

Amplifier

sweep circuit

← Input →
from nerve

Fig. 21.2. Diagram of a cathode ray oscilloscope showing a trace of a diphasic spike on the fluorescent screen.

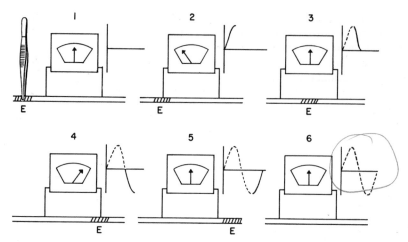

Fig. 21.3.   The diphasic nature of the action potential on a nerve. A pinch of the forceps stimulates the nerve, and a wave of excitation (E) passes the left pickup electrode (that is, the one nearest the point of stimulation) making it temporarily negative to the right one. Later, when the impulse reaches it, the right pickup electrode becomes temporarily negative to the left one. Finally, after the wave of excitation has passed both pickup electrodes, the hand on the dial returns to zero. If the movement of the hand on the dial is plotted, a graph similar to those at the upper right of these diagrams is obtained.

be *diphasic* in character. A whole series of electrodes, laid along the nerve fiber, will necessarily show the same phenomenon as the impulse travels to the end of the fiber.

Once an impulse has been initiated, it passes to the end of the neuron. Regardless of the intensity of stimulation beyond the threshold, the magnitude of the nerve impulse on a single neuron under the same conditions is always the same. This characteristic of the nerve impulse is referred to as the *all or none* principle of nerve action. The nerve impulse has been likened to a trail of gunpowder, along which each bit is set off by the fire next to it, regardless of whether a match or a blowtorch was first used to ignite it. The neuron appears to be ready to discharge, needing only to be triggered.[40] The magnitude of the action potential on a single neuron is the same, under the same conditions, whether measured near the stimulus or far from it (see Fig. 21.4). Cold and anesthetics decrease excitability of a neuron, but the action potential is measured in front of and behind a anesthetized (or chilled) portion of a neuron, its magnitude remaining the same provided the nerve impulse is able t pass. Transmission therefore occurs *without decrement.*[40]

Once a nerve impulse has passed ove any point of a neuron, a *refractory perio* ensues, a sort of "busy signal" perio during which the neuron is recovering i capacity to react. At first no stimulus regardless of its strength, will evoke response at the point of stimulation; the a response may be elicited but only by stimulus much stronger than is normall needed; gradually the neuron recovers it normal sensitivity. If the neuron has bee excited to carry a train or volley of im pulses, its recovery is slower than after single impulse.

These changes in excitability of a neu ron are correlated with the phases of th action potential as illustrated in Figure 21.5 and 21.6. The data for these curve are the potentials between the two re cording electrodes as described earlier

...e *spike* is the peak, or the maximal, ...tion potential. For any neuron the ...ike is of constant magnitude and seems ...pass unaltered along the length of the ...uron. No additional activity can be ...duced by a shock of any strength until ...e spike at the point of stimulation has ...en completed. It is thought that the ...bsolute refractory period corresponds to ...e time during which the spike appears ...the particular point on a neuron. For ...e short period during the tail of the ...ike, a stimulus much stronger than nor...al is needed to excite the neuron. This ...riod is called the *relative refractory ...riod.* * This is followed by the *negative ...fter-potential,* which is the broad base ...the end of the tail of the spike and is a ...riod of increased excitability (lowered ...reshold) resulting, presumably, from ...e negative after-potential. This in turn ...followed by the *positive after-potential,* ...hich is seen below the zero line of the ...raph (Fig. 21.5); this is a period of ...creased excitability (higher threshold), ...resumably, a consequence of the excess ...ositive charge.[38] Finally, the neuron ...sumes normal sensitivity.

...The after-potentials are not always the ...me in all nerve fibers. Sometimes only ...ositive after-potentials appear, as in ...mall mammalian C fibers. The after...otentials also depend in part upon the ...eatment to which the neuron has been ...ubjected.[38] The voltages and the time ...or the spike and the various stages of the ...efractory period are different for differ...nt types of neurons (Table 21.2). In ...arge mammalian fibers (A fibers) the ...ike reaches a magnitude of a few hun...redths of a volt, while the negative ...fter-potential reaches about one twen...eth this voltage, and the positive after...otential about one five-hundredth. The ...ike lasts about 1 millisecond, the nega...ve after-potential about 15 milliseconds, ...nd the positive after-potential as long as ...0 millisecond. As Gasser[40] has put it: ...If the spikes may be called the message

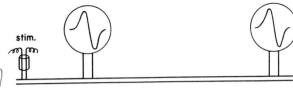

Fig. 21.4. Conduction without a decrement. On the oscilloscope screen the diphasic spike for a given fiber is equal in height at short and long distances from the point of stimulation.

carriers of the nervous system, the after-potentials in contrast may be called the indicators of the readiness with which messages will be accepted."

Figure 21.6 shows an actual oscilloscopic record of a nerve action spike. It will be noticed that the two arms of the diphasic spike are not symmetrical. The first one is larger because, when the excitation reaches the first electrode, the potential suddenly changes from zero to the maximal value. However, when the excitation reaches the second electrode, the first electrode has not yet fallen to zero but is still negative. The second spike can arise only after the second electrode has become more negative than the first, the time required for it to do this being usually taken as a measure of the time it takes the nerve impulse to travel from the first electrode to the second. Also, the second spike never reaches the magnitude of the first one because, by the time the nerve excitation has reached its maximum at the second electrode, the region of the nerve at the first electrode will not yet have fallen to zero, and the electrodes can measure only potential differences, not absolute values. The area of excitation (negativity) on the nerve at any one time may occupy a space of several millimeters to many centimeters.

It is also noteworthy that after-potentials are not recorded because they are too small to register with the amplifica-

* Sometimes the after-potentials are included in the relative refractory period, but present usage is against this.

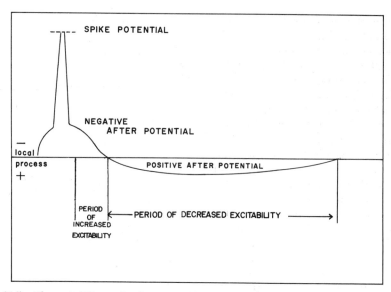

Fig. 21.5. The excitability cycle of a neuron. Excitation leads to a brief local change which fires into a spike if the threshold has been passed. The spike is followed by negative after-potential, and the negative after-potential is followed by a slow positive after-potential. If the spike were drawn in proportion to the local potential and the after-potentials, it would extend beyond the page edge by several feet. The prepotentials which precede the spike are not shown adequately on this diagram. See also Figure 21.10. (After Morgan, 1943: Physiological Psychology. McGraw-Hill Book Company, New York.)

tion (gain) used. The small pip which precedes the spike is a *stimulus artifact* and is a record of the electric wave passing along the nerve fibers in purely physical fashion. A piece of string soaked in balanced salt solution will serve as well as the nerve fiber for propagation of this artifact.

The Rate of Conduction of the Nerve Impulse

Although the nerve impulse travels so fast that one prominent physiologist (J. Müller, 1801–1858) despaired of its ever being measured, its speed was recorded later by one of his students, Hermann von Helmholtz (1821–1894), who used a smoked drum, a coil and a pendulum, but whose crude method nonetheless gave values close to those accepted today. The speed of the nerve impulse on large mammalian nerve fibers has since

been shown to be seldom over 100 mete per second. This shows that the impul: is not a simple electrical wave (whic would travel at an extremely high velo ity) but rather some reaction in the nerv cell which is accompanied by an electr cal wave.

The rate of conduction of the nerv impulse increases with an increase i cross sectional diameter of the neuro and with increasing thickness of the my lin sheath. The thickness of the myeli sheath may be measured by its birefring ence. When the product of the birefring ence multiplied by the diameter is near constant, the rate of propagation is th same even for neurons of diverse origin as shown in the last column of Tabl 21.2. For myelinated nerve fibers o mammals, the rate of conduction of th nerve impulse varies with the cross sec tion diameter, as illustrated in Figur 21.7. The rate of transmission for a give

IRRITABILITY AND CONTRACTILIT

TABLE 21.2. *Velocity of Propagation of the Nerve Impulse as Affected by Axon Diameter and Sheath Thickness**

NERVE CELL	FIBER DIAM. (FD) IN μ	AXON DIAM. (AD) IN μ	$\dfrac{AD}{FD}$	BIREFRINGENCE (B)	VELOCITY (CA) (M./SEC.)	B × FD
Squid, giant	650	637	.98	−.0001	25	—
Earthworm, giant	100	90	.90	.0010	25	.10
Shrimp, giant	50	43	.87	.0024	25	.12
Frog, sciatic	10	7.5	.75	.0105	25	.105
Cat, saphenous (20° C.)	8.7	6.6	.76	.014	25	.12
Catfish	8.8	5.8	.58	.012	25	.105

* Sheath thickness is determined by birefringence. Birefringence is measured in terms of the degree of rotation of the analyzer prism in a polarizing microscope required to extinguish the polarized light from the nerve. The thicker the layer of myelin, the greater the birefringence, as seen in the vertebrate nerves compared with the invertebrate nerves. For use of a polarizing microscope see Chapter 14. (Modified from Taylor, 1942: J. Cell. Comp. Physiol. *20.*)

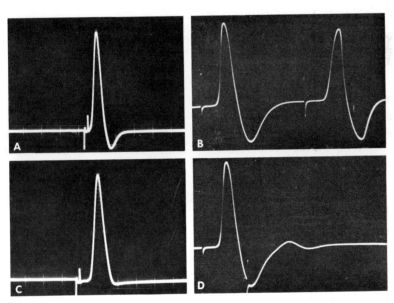

Fig. 21.6. Action potentials (spikes) on a frog sciatic nerve. *A*, compound diphasic action potential from the fastest (alpha) fibers of the frog sciatic nerve, recorded by a pair of electrodes 1 cm. apart, located 1 cm. from the stimulating electrode. *B*, two stimuli applied to the frog nerve in rapid succession 0.007 second apart. Two diphasic spikes appear. *C*, compound monophasic action potential recorded from the nerve in *A*, at a pair of electrodes 1 cm. apart located 2 cm. from the stimulating electrodes. The nerve has been crushed between the recording electrodes. Note that the first phase of the action potential is now broader than in *A*, because of the elimination of the second electrode response, which in *A* hastens the falling phase. Markers for *A* and *C* indicate 1 millisecond. *D*, two stimuli given 0.003 second apart. The nerve is unable to respond to the second stimulus because it is still in the refractory phase. In all the records the small break in the record is the stimulus artifact. (*A* and *C* by courtesy of Dr. D. Kennedy. *B* and *D* from Katz[54].)

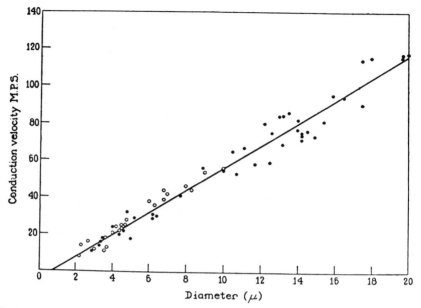

Fig. 21.7. The linear relation between diameter and conduction velocity of mammalian myelinated nerve fibers. Each point represents a determination of the maximum conduction velocity of a given nerve, plotted against the diameter of the largest fiber in that nerve. Dots represent adult nerves; circles represent immature nerves. (After Hursh, from Gasser, 1941: Ohio J. Sci., *41*:145.)

neuron is a constant; it may be slowed at a partial block, but beyond the block it continues at its characteristic rate. The rate of conduction of the nerve impulse at a specified temperature in nerve cells of a wide variety of animals is shown in Table 21.3.

The Strength-Duration Relationship

Although pressure, heat, chemicals, etc., may also evoke a nerve impulse, these stimuli cannot be conveniently applied without damaging the nerve cell, nor can they be readily measured. Ever since the pioneer studies of Galvani, electrical stimulation has been used almost exclusively for studies of the nerve impulse. For this purpose an inductorium (see Fig. 21.8) is employed, and high voltage shocks at low currents are given as stimuli or, better still, an electronic stimulator can be used which develops the desired voltage almost instantly and

in which the duration of current flow can be precisely controlled.[37, 40]

When a neuron is stimulated, the cathode rather than the anode of the stimulating electrode is placed toward the pickup electrodes of the recording instrument, since at the anode the threshold required for stimulation rises even to the point of blocking the nerve impulse arising at the cathode.[40] In the absence of an anodal block, a nerve cell will transmit impulses in both directions from a spot stimulated electrically.

When electric current is used as a stimulus, a minimum or *threshold current* is necessary to stimulate neurons. Below threshold current there is no response because the neuron recovers as rapidly as it is affected and no nerve impulse can be initiated, even after continuous or repeated stimulation. The threshold current, which after operating for a long period is just able to stimulate the neuron, is called the *rheobase*. The time

TABLE 21.3. *Comparison of Conduction Rates of Nerve Impulses in Vertebrate and Invertebrate Nerves*

TYPE OF NERVOUS STRUCTURE	GROUP OF ANIMALS	GENUS AND TYPE OF NERVE	TEMPERATURE IN °C.	VELOCITY IN METERS/SECOND
nerve net:	Coelenterate	Anemone (*Metridium*)	21	0.121–0.146
		Calliactis, net	—	0.04–0.15
		Calliactis, through tracts	—	1.2
ganglionic cord:	Annelid	Earthworm (*Lumbricus*)	—	0.6
	Arthropod	Myriapod (*Scolopendra*)	—	2.5
		Crayfish (*Cambarus*)	—	1.2
nerve fibers:	Mollusk	Snail (*Helix*), < 1 μ diam.	15–18	0.4–0.05
		Mytilus, pedal nerve	—	0.64
		Sepia, < 50 μ diam.	—	3.5, 2.26
	Arthropod	*Limulus*, leg nerve	—	4.6, 1.3
		Lobster, leg nerve	—	9.2, 1.8
	Vertebrate	Turtle, vagus, n.m.	—	0.8, 0.3
		Frog, nonmyelinated	21.5	0.5–0.4
		Frog, dorsal root	21.5	42.0
		Rabbit, depressor, 2–4 μ	38	5.0
		Dog, saphenous, 17 μ	38	83.3
giant fibers:	Mollusk	*Loligo*, 718 μ diam.	—	22.3
	Annelid	Earthworm (*Lumbricus*),		
		lateral	10–12	7–12
		median	10–12	17–25
	Arthropod	*Leander*, 35 μ diam.	17	18–23
	Vertebrate	*Ameirus*, 22–43 μ	10–15	50–60

After Prosser, 1946: Physiol. Rev. *26*.

required to stimulate a neuron with a current of rheobasic strength is called the *utilization time*. (The strength-duration relationship is usually described in terms of the current rather than in terms of the voltage, and this convention is followed here.*)

If a current stronger than rheobase is used to stimulate a nerve fiber, it need not be applied for as long a time as the utilization time. This is most clearly illustrated in a curve relating the strength of current and the duration of time it must act in order to initiate a nerve impulse. Such a curve is called the *strength-duration curve* (see Fig. 21.9). As will be seen, provided the product of the current and the square root of the time is maintained constant, the neuron is always stimulated. This product is referred to as *threshold stimulation*. Any product less than this constitutes a *subthreshold stimulation*. Though the quantitative values may be quite different for diverse excitable systems, the general shape of the strength-duration curve is usually similar.[32, 33]

A current above rheobase but applied for a time less than that "required" on the basis of the strength-duration curve, fails to evoke a response in a neuron. However, if the same stimulus is repeated

* Since by Ohm's law the current in a circuit is directly proportional to the electromotive force and inversely proportional to the resistance of the circuit, the current in amperes is directly proportional to the voltage in volts.

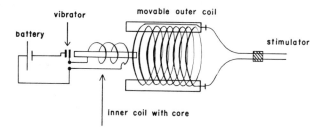

Fig. 21.8. A diagram of an induct
ium. A high voltage, low ampera
current is induced in the outer c
when current flows in the inner c
The magnetic effect of the current
the inner coil breaks the current in t
outer coil by attracting the vibrator
the core of the inner coil. When t
current stops and the magnetic for
falls, the vibrator is released from t
core and again completes the circuit.

rapidly enough (e.g., every 0.15 milliseconds) for a sufficient number of times,
stimulation occurs by *summation*, provided the sum of all the applications of
the stimulus is greater than the minimum
demanded by the strength-duration
curve. Stimulation under such conditions
therefore does not violate the strength-
duration principle. Summation, even
when adequate, will fail to stimulate if
the time elapsed between stimuli is increased beyond a certain limit, because

the system recovers from each stimul
To trigger the excitatory process, bo
the strength of the current and its app
cation time must be sufficient to ove
come the tendency of the neuron
recover.[41]

In the special case where the voltag
is steadily applied and gradually increase
up to, and kept at, a value which wou
normally stimulate a nerve fiber if appli
suddenly, it is found that the nerve fib
will not respond. For this experiment a

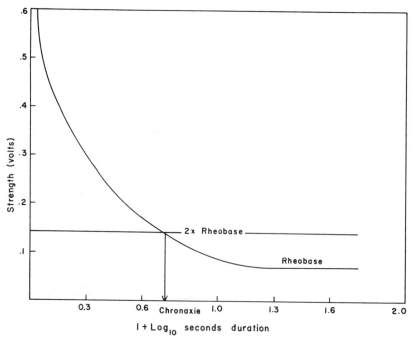

Fig. 21.9. Strength-duration curve for a nerve from the crab *Cancer productus*. Similar curves are
obtained for any excitable system although absolute values vary. The chronaxie is the time required
to stimulate when the current is twice rheobase. It is marked at the base of the arrow on the time
scale.

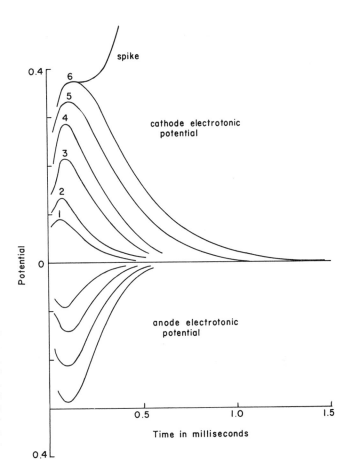

spike

0.4

6
5
4
3
2
1

cathode electrotonic
potential

Potential

0

anode electrotonic
potential

0.5   1.0   1.5

Time in milliseconds

0.4

Fig. 21.10. Local excitatory state in a crab nerve following shocks of increasing intensity at the stimulating electrodes. The local excitation rises at both anode and cathode and decays in a millisecond. When cathodal local excitation passes threshold, the neuron suddenly fires and the excitation is then propagated the full length of the fiber. (After Hodgkin, 1938: Proc. Roy. Soc., B126:95.)

instrument called a rheochord is used. Although seemingly violating the strength-duration principle, this failure of the nerve fiber to respond is explainable, presumably, on the basis that the nerve fiber is capable of recovery during the time of the slow rate of change in voltage. A rapid rate of voltage change is therefore still another factor necessary to bring about a response, even when the strength-duration relationships are satisfied.[29, 40]

Defining excitation of a nerve cell has been likened to "defining quantitatively the effort needed to bring a leaky vessel to overflowing."[41] Perhaps this is best seen in studies of subthreshold stimulation. While a subthreshold stimulus is incapable of evoking a propagated spike potential, it does alter the neuron, and a measurable, local, nonpropagated potential appears, indicating a mild state of excitation (see Fig. 21.10). This excitation declines exponentially since a recovery process always counters excitation.[41] Both excitation and recovery processes have been formulated mathematically, but the subject is too complex for discussion here.[45]

Usually a current greater than rheobase is found more convenient for a comparison of the excitability of diverse excitable cells, e.g., the *chronaxie*, which is the time required for a current twice the rheobase to just stimulate an excitable cell. By this means, the excitability of nerve cells, muscle cells, protozoans and plant cells has been compared.[32] While the chronaxie is used less today, determination of the strength-duration curves is valuable because it illustrates most clearly the quantitative relations between excitation and stimulus.

Accommodation

According to the strength-duration principle, a neuron responds by a propagated action spike potential only if an adequate current is applied for a sufficient time, that is, if *threshold stimulation* is given. This is true only at the cathode; at the anode no propagated response occurs even if stimuli of much larger magnitude are applied.[40] That the nerve fiber is affected by anodal stimulation, but is able to accommodate to it as it does to all stimulation, is shown by the state of electrotonus induced by anodic shocks of any magnitude (a state of *anelectrotonus*). For example, after any anodal shock, the subsequent cathodal threshold required for stimulation is always greater than normal, demonstrating that a partial block has been established by the anelectrotonus. The block is greater the larger the anodal shock and the shorter the time intervening before application of cathodal stimulation, as if the anelectrotonus induced by anodal stimulation must first be overcome before stimulation can occur. On the other hand, after subthreshold cathodal shock which induces a state of *catelectrotonus*, the threshold at the cathode is lowered to the extent that a subsequent stimulus of less than normal threshold stimulation is adequate if applied soon afterward (in a fraction of a millisecond), as if the cathodal shock were being added (summation) to a partially excited neuron in a state of *catelectrotonus*.

Reaction of a nerve fiber, therefore, depends upon its preceding experience. The threshold of a neuron is altered, not only by subthreshold stimuli but also by the after-potentials following passage a nerve impulse. Furthermore, after-p tentials are much more persistent aft repetitive stimulation of a neuron. Th are also prolonged by some drugs such veratrine.

Core Conductor Theory of the Nerve Impulse

On applying electrodes to the surfa of a nerve fiber, electrotonic potentia develop on the fiber at the electrodes a in their vicinity. These potentials indica that current is flowing along specific lin as shown in Figure 21.11. The potenti change is greatest immediately unde neath the electrodes and falls off exp nentially at points progressively farth away. It is proposed that the develo ment of these potentials and their ass ciated currents can be best accounted f if the nerve fiber is considered to act a *core conductor*, that is, as a cylinder conducting fluid material (axoplasm, th cytoplasm of the axon) with a sheath (ce membrane) of high electrical resistanc surrounded by a layer of conductir medium (balanced salt solution). Th cell membrane which becomes polarize is thus presumed to impose a capaci on the system such that the nerve fib may be viewed as a condenser capable being charged on application of a pote tial difference across it. Such an electric model of a nerve fiber may be co structed and studied. However, und steady state conditions in the living ner fiber during application of a difference potential, a slow flow of current is foun to occur. To allow for this slow leak current in the electrical model it is nece sary to couple a resistance with the co denser through which such slow leakag could take place.

A measurable time is usually require for the electrotonic potential to develo both at the electrodes applied to a ner fiber and in their immediate neighbo

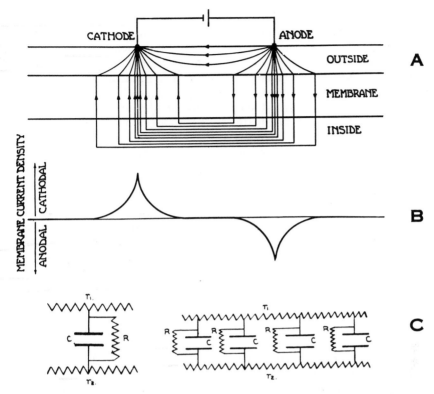

Fig. 21.11. Core conductor theory of nerve fiber excitation. *A* shows the current distribution in a nerve fiber during passage of a constant current. Current lines represent spatial spread and direction of current flow outside, through, and inside the membrane of the nerve fiber. *B*, lateral spread of current shown by plotting the density of penetrating current (membrane current) against the length of the nerve fiber. The current falls off in an approximately exponential manner with distance from the electrode. *C*, electrical models of a nerve fiber. (*C*) represents the capacitance, (*R*) the transverse resistance and (r_1) and (r_2) represent the longitudinal resistances. The model to the left is the simplest electrical circuit having some of the properties of a nerve fiber. The series of such models shown to the right also account for the time characteristics in the build-up of electrotonic potential. (After Ruch and Fulton, 1960: Medical Physiology and Biophysics. Saunders, Philadelphia.)

od. To account for this time requirement, it is necessary to consider the nerve fiber as being made up of a series of such condenser-resistance units (Fig. 21.11C), each one like the one described above. When a potential is applied through a pair of electrodes on the nerve fiber, its structures, acting like a condenser, are charged, with the result that the potential at and near the electrodes builds up and tends to oppose the further flow of current.

Provided the resistance and capacitance of the nerve fiber membrane and the resistance of its cell membrane sheath and core (axoplasm) are known (and these can be calculated from experimentally determinable properties of nerve fibers), it is possible to predict quantitatively the development of electrotonus, with time as a factor, in a nerve fiber, if the nerve fiber is considered to act like the electrical model described above. When the steady state condition has been attained, the distribution of electrotonic potentials around the electrodes can also be computed. The predictions made on the basis of such a model of the nerve fiber are well in agreement with the facts, and the core conductor formulation has been useful in planning experimental studies, especially in defining more clearly the properties of parts of the nerve fiber.

For passive conduction, such as occurs in an electric wire, a cable made like a nerve fiber would be of little use because its losses are great: the surface leakage and the resistivity of its core are 10^8 greater and its sheath capacity 10^6 greater than commercial cables. In it a weak signal (just sufficient to produce a spike) fades out within a few millimeters. The "cable" model would fail to conduct an impulse were it not for the regenerative processes on a nerve fiber that reamplify a signal above threshold along each point of the line.[53]

The peculiar cable properties of a nerve cell are, however, of importance in permitting subthreshold stimulation to remain sufficiently long for summation. Especially in the dendrites of a neuron is this of importance since here the excitability is local, graded and decremental. Succeeding increments of depolarization may therefore summate to the threshold required to initiate the propagated all-or-none spike on the axon.

Saltatory Conduction of the Nerve Impulse

Conduction in myelinated nerve fibers is exceedingly rapid compared with that in nonmyelinated nerve fibers of similar size. The myelin sheath is interrupted periodically by the *nodes of Ranvier* (Fig. 21.1), at which the membrane of a neuron makes contact with the bathing fluid. The nodes are further apart in neurons of large diameter than in neurons of small diameter. For example, the distance between nodes is about 0.2 mm. for a bullfrog neuron of 4 μ diameter, about 1.5

mm. for a neuron of 12 μ diameter and 2 mm. for one of 15 μ diameter.[7] It h been suggested that perhaps conducti in myelinated neurons is so rapid becau the action potential skips from node node rather than having to travel aloi the membrane. Such skipping from noc to node is called *saltatory conductic* (see Fig. 22.7D).

Nodal threshold for stimulation much lower than the internodal thre hold[7] (see Fig. 21.12). Since upon stim lation of a nerve cell with any kind stimulus an electric field is formed whic operates from the point of excitation ov a span of about two nodes, this electr field is much more likely to evoke change in a region of low thresho (node) than in a region of high thresho (internode). When a node is cathodal stimulated and the two nodes on eith side of it are anesthetized, conduction the impulse is still achieved across tl neighboring nodes, but the same stimul fails if applied to the internode. Also, tl impulse does not pass across two ane thetized neighboring nodes even if stim lation is nodal, because in this case tl third node is beyond the operation of tl electric field. A squid giant axon fails conduct the impulse across a dead se tion unless a metal wire is laid across th section. The electric field is not stroi enough in air but is adequate in the be ter conductor furnished by the wire.

One objection to the theory of salt tory conduction is that nodes have n generally been seen in the central ner ous system, yet conduction in the bra and cord equals that in the peripher nerve fibers. However, improved tecl niques have revealed nodes in prepar tions of the central nervous system, ar most workers appear to be convinced the generality of saltatory conduction.

It is interesting to note that Lillie pr dicted saltatory conduction in nerv fibers on the basis of an iron wire an logue to the neuron.[36] An iron wir when placed in a solution of concei

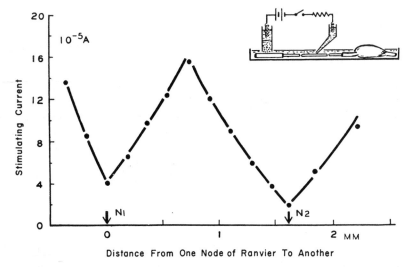

Fig. 21.12. A graph demonstrating that nodal stimulation is lower than internodal stimulation. (After Tasaki, 1953: Nervous Transmission. Charles C Thomas Company, Springfield, Illinois, p. 6.)

ated nitric acid, becomes coated with ide. When the coated wire is placed in ore dilute nitric acid, nothing happens iless it is stimulated by heat or elec- city, or mechanically by a scratch. imulation sets off a wave of oxidation- duction which runs the length of the ire (all-or-none), followed by formation a new coating. After a "refractory riod," stimulation sets off another wave oxidation-reduction. When the wire is cased in sections of glass tubing, the ave of oxidation-reduction passes from posed "node" to "node" in saltatory shion.

sting Metabolism of Nerve Cells

Nerve cells at rest respire at about the me rate per unit of mass as resting uscle cells. Improvements in respiro- etry and especially the development of icrorespirometers have made possible e measurement of gaseous exchange d a respiratory quotient of approxi- ately 0.8 has been found for the neu- n, indicating that several nutrients are ing oxidized.[9-12] While sugar is be- ved to be the main source of energy,

because it is lost rapidly in the respiring nerve cells, presence of creatine, am- monia and phosphate as metabolic wastes produced in respiration indicates that protein and lipid are also being consumed. When nerve cells are subjected to anaero- biosis, lactic acid accumulates, indicating that during anaerobic metabolism the source of energy for maintaining excitabil- ity is mainly glycogen. The tolerance of anaerobic conditions, in fact, depends partly upon the amount of glycogen reserve available. For example, crab nerve fibers, which naturally have much glycogen, conduct without oxygen for 5 hours, while mammalian nerve fibers, with little glycogen, stop in 20 minutes.

The resting metabolism of nerve cells resembles the endogenous metabolism of microorganisms in that it is not suscepti- ble to the metabolic poison azide, even in concentrations which block the activity metabolism in nerve cells. Many of the enzymes participating in aerobic and anaerobic metabolism in other cells, also enzymes required for phosphorylations, have been identified in nerve cells,[13] but, partly because the material is limited and so much supporting connective tissues surround a nerve fiber, enzymatic studies on nerve cells have not been extensive.

Activity Metabolism of Nerve Cells

On stimulation, the metabolic rate of myelinated nerve cells increases from 1.3 to 4.0 times the resting rate. The respiratory quotient of stimulated nerve cells is 1.0, suggesting carbohydrate utilization.[10] Biochemical evidence indicates that sugar is oxidized in neurons of the central nervous system and in nonmyelinated nerve fibers. However, the nutrients used in myelinated nerve cells have not been identified, although decreases in ribonucleic acid content have been noticed after extensive nerve activity[44] (see Chapter 6). The RNA may, however, act as a mediator in the manufacture of other materials.[53]

It is thought that the immediate source of energy for conduction of the nerve impulse in vertebrate nerve cells in all cases is probably creatine phosphate. Creatine and inorganic phosphate, in addition to ammonia, are among the metabolic products which appear in greater amounts in a perfusate of tetanized nerve fibers.[12] The breakdown of creatine phosphate is more rapid during nerve activity than when the neurons are at rest, and presumably the high energy of the phosphate bond is in some way involved in the transmission of the nerve impulse. In invertebrate nerve cells other phosphates have been shown to be utilized.[12]

Another metabolic change observed in active nerve cells is the breakdown of acetylcholine:

$$[(CH_3)_3\overset{+}{N}CH_2CH_2OCOCH_3]OH^- \xrightarrow[\substack{\text{acetylcholine} \\ \text{esterase}}]{HOH}$$

acetylcholine

$$[(CH_3)_3\overset{+}{N}CH_2CH_2OH]OH^- +$$

choline

$$[CH_3COO^-]H^+ \quad (21.1)$$

acetic acid

Acetylcholine is widespread in the nervous system, and cut ends of stimulated nerve cells leak acetylcholine into the perfusate. This ester is synthesized in the presence of the enzyme choline acetylase, which is also widespread in nerve cells. Acetylcholine is spontaneously hydrolyzed into the inactive compounds choline and acetic acid, a reaction greatly speeded by the enzyme acetylcholine esterase, found in all nerve cells, as well as many other kinds of cells. Acetylcholine occurs in highest concentration on the surface of neurons.[14] Its action is inhibited by the drug eserine. Nachmansohn[14] has suggested that acetylcholine is the trigger which initiates the nerve impulse.

A clear picture of the rapid sequence of metabolic events in the nerve fiber is not yet available. However, instruments exist for measuring the evolution of heat and the physical changes in electric charge, resistance and capacitance (i.e. function as a condenser) during and after passage of the nervous impulse. No methods of comparable speed have been developed to measure the chemical changes preceding or concomitant with the nervous impulse.

Heat Production during Nerve Activity

The changes in evolution of heat during activity metabolism of nerve cells have been measured (with a thermopile). The data provide a clue to the relative order of some of the reactions that take place in nerve cells.

Even with refined equipment it is difficult to measure directly the heat evolved during the passage of a single nerve impulse. When the preparation is treated with veratrine, which exaggerates after potentials,[12, 22] the volley of nerve impulses resulting from tetanic stimulation produces measureable heat. From the measurement of the total amount of heat produced by a volley of nerve impulses, the heat evolved in a single impulse

442

timated to be 10^{-7} small calories per am of nerve fiber.[16] Only a small fraction (about ⅓₀) of the heat is apparently ven off during the initial action potential; the remainder of the heat develops uring the recovery process. It is thought at the initial spike of the action potential may correspond to the period of eakdown of high energy phosphate onds. The recovery period may thus be e time during which glucose and other ompounds are decomposed and the high ergy phosphate bonds are rebuilt.

The more frequently the nerve cell is imulated, the smaller is the increment heat production and oxygen consumption per nerve impulse. This is an adaptive response, and the greater efficiency the frequently stimulated neuron is robably a result of the better physical-hemical state of the excited cell.

In an atmosphere of pure nitrogen the te of heat production of resting nerve ells declines over a period of 2 hours, ut even after this time heat continues to e evolved, though at about one-fifth the te in air. Metabolism continues anaerobically, accumulating lactic acid.[10, 21] Vhen, on return to air, the nerve cells ecover from the oxygen debt, they volve extra heat before resuming normal eat production (see Fig. 21.13).

ffects of Various Factors on the Action Potential of Nerve Cells

Fatigue. Because the refractory period ermits neurons to recover their normal xcitability, it is practically impossible to atigue nerve cells in the presence of an dequate supply of oxygen and nutrients. xperimentally it is possible to obtain 000 full-sized responses per second from nerve fiber (A fibers from a frog), and, ith stronger shock, up to 2000 have een obtained for a short time.[8, 17] With ormal stimulation of receptor cells *in ivo*, volleys up to 160 impulses per second are found, e.g., the pad of the foot of a cat sends in 9 to 100 impulses per second in response to tactile stimulation. Such a relatively low frequency of impulses allows for ready recovery. If stimulated to discharge at abnormally rapid rates, a nerve fiber conducts more slowly, its refractory period becomes longer, the initial potential declines and the threshold rises—all signs of a failure to return completely to normal. To this extent a nerve fiber many be fatigued.

Anoxia. Lack of oxygen ultimately blocks transmission of impulses in a nerve cell. For example, the action potential of a nerve fiber so stimulated that the nerve impulse has to travel through a section kept in pure nitrogen shows progressively smaller spikes in that section for about an hour (i.e., for a frog nerve fiber in nitrogen, a 3 per cent loss in spike size occurred in 15 minutes, 13 per cent in 30 and 49 per cent in 40 minutes). At the same time the rate of transmission of the nerve impulse declines.[18-20] Beyond the section in nitrogen, the spikes are of normal size, as expected on the basis of the all-or-none principle. After an hour, transmission of the nerve impulse in the section kept in nitrogen ceases, indicating that a block has been established. The higher the temperature, within the limits of viability of the nerve fiber, the more rapidly the block appears.

A nerve fiber kept anoxic for a time accumulates an oxygen debt. When it is returned to air the nerve fiber takes up oxygen more rapidly for a while until it has paid its debt. Presumably, anaerobic processes are unable to bring the nerve cell into complete recovery.[19, 20]

If a nerve in a state of anoxia is poisoned by iodoacetate so that glycolysis also ceases, conduction ceases much sooner than in an anoxic but unpoisoned control. Such an experiment indicates that in the absence of oxygen, glycolysis, at least in part, supplies the energy required to synthesize the compounds that maintain the nerve cell in a condition of

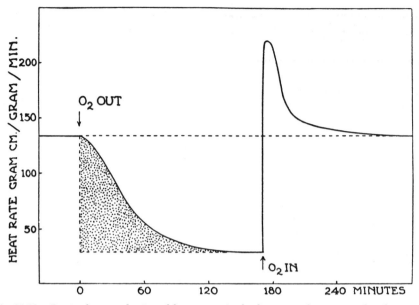

Fig. 21.13. Resting heat production of frog nerve. At the first arrow the nerve is placed in nitrogen, with resulting slow fall in heat rate. At the second arrow the nerve is replaced in oxygen. (After Beresina, modified from Feng, 1936: Ergbn. Physiol., 38:73.)

readiness to respond.[35] This is suggested also by the heat changes during anaerobic metabolism, as seen above.

Respiration in the presence of oxygen is necessary for continued maintenance of the readiness of the nerve cell to respond to stimulation, indicating a continuous expenditure of energy to maintain irritability.

Effect of Anesthetics on the Nerve Impulse. Many anesthetics and narcotics block conduction of the nerve impulse. The time required to block conduction is dependent upon the concentration of anesthetic; the higher the concentration, the shorter will be the time required. The span or area of the nerve fiber to which anesthetic is applied also affects the speed with which the anesthetic acts, conduction being blocked more rapidly the larger the area treated. Some anesthetics (e.g., cocaine) produce a definite effect which is reversible; others, like chloral hydrate, produce an effect that becomes progressively more injurious and

less reversible the longer the time action.[22]

Application of an anesthetic raises t threshold for stimulation of a nerve fib and larger stimuli are then required evoke a spike. There are other changes properties of the nerve fibers as an thesia progresses, e.g., the sensitivity a chemical stimulus such as citrate is duced, the velocity of conduction of action potential decreases and the size the spike evoked by a stimulating sho successively declines, while the refracto period increases in length. Anesthes therefore, induces a progressive decrea in the excitability of neurons.[7, 22]

Action Potentials in Muscle Fibers

Action potentials, as indicated prev ously, are not confined to nerve ce alone. Similar changes in potential occ also in various muscle fibers. Thus t excited portion of the muscle fiber al becomes negative to the resting portio

d an action potential as high as 100
illivolts may be recorded on a muscle
er. Many years ago Galvani demon-
ated the electrical nature and similarity
 muscle and nerve excitation by con-
cting two sciatic nerve-gastrocnemius
uscle preparations in series (see Fig.
.14). When the first muscle was excited
 contraction, for example, by pinching
e nerve connected to it, it excited the
iatic nerve of the second muscle, which
ntracted soon after the contraction of
e first.[29]

Action potentials are demonstrable in
uscle cells of the gut, the heart, the ovi-
ict, the uterus, etc.[40] The tracing of the
tion potential of the heart is called an
ctrocardiogram (Fig. 21.15). The re-
arkable feature of the electrocardiogram
 a large mammal is the fact that the con-
icting heart has a large enough action
itential to be picked up on the surface
 the body in spite of the activities of an
iormous amount of intervening tissues.
The most unique action potentials are

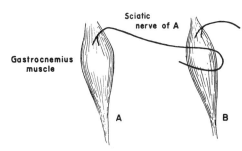

Fig. 21.14. Excitation of a nerve by a muscle.
When the sciatic nerve which makes its ending on
muscle B is pinched, muscle B is excited. Action currents on the surface of muscle B then excite the
sciatic nerve leading to muscle A.

those which appear in the electric fish. In
electric fishes a considerable number of
muscle fibers have become modified to
form the electric organs, which are composed of a series of electric units. Each
such electric unit, known as an *electroplax*, begins during early embryonic development as a normal skeletal muscle
fiber, but later develops into what looks
like a flat plate attached to a myoneural

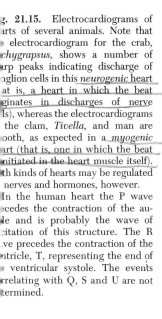

3. 21.15. Electrocardiograms of
arts of several animals. Note that
 electrocardiogram for the crab,
chygrapsus, shows a number of
irp peaks indicating discharge of
iglion cells in this *neurogenic* heart
at is, a heart in which the beat
ginates in discharges of nerve
ls), whereas the electrocardiograms
 the clam, *Tivella*, and man are
ooth, as expected in a *myogenic*
art (that is, one in which the beat
nitiated in the heart muscle itself).
th kinds of hearts may be regulated
 nerves and hormones, however.
In the human heart the P wave
ecedes the contraction of the au-
le and is probably the wave of
citation of this structure. The R
ve precedes the contraction of the
ntricle, T, representing the end of
 ventricular systole. The events
rrelating with Q, S and U are not
termined.

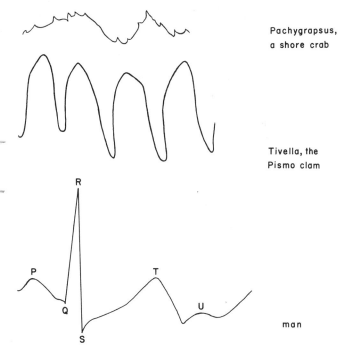

Pachygrapsus,
a shore crab

Tivella, the
Pismo clam

man

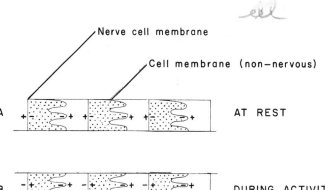

electric eel

Nerve cell membrane

Cell membrane (non–nervous)

A   AT REST

B   DURING ACTIVITY

Fig. 21.16. Diagrammatic repsentation of the changes in t electroplaxes (single units) of electric organ of a fish. At r (A) both the nerve cell membra and the ordinary cell membra have a positive charge, the insi of the cell being negative. Wh excited the nerve cell membra is not only depolarized, but k comes negatively charged (Under such conditions, becau of the structure of the electi organ, the voltages of the seri of electroplaxes add up, like t voltages in a series of little b teries. (After Gerebtzoff a Schoffeniels, 1960: Comp. B chem. 2:519.)

junction (see Fig. 21.16). Like a myoneural junction, the electroplax fatigues rapidly and is susceptible to the drug curare, which readily blocks the passage of the nerve impulse to the electric organ. A single electroplax gives off a peak voltage of 50 to 150 millivolts. The large voltage measured in electric fishes is made possible by the arrangement of the electroplaxes in an organ as a series of batteries, summing the voltages of the individual electroplaxes. By parallel connections between series of electroplaxes, large currents can be obtained. The electric eel *Electrophorus electricus,* for example, has been found to produce electric shocks of several hundred volts.[23, 24]

It is interesting to point out that Alessandro Volta (1745–1827) designed the first voltaic cell, using the electric organ of the electric fish as a model.[30] Just as many electroplaxes in series give off a high voltage, so did his "pile" of copper and zinc disks in which the voltage was summated as in a series of batteries. The example illustrates a case where physics received a great impetus from investigation of a biological phenomenon.

Action Potentials in Excitable
Plant Cells

Excitable plant cells also develop action potentials when stimulated. For

example, in the sensitive plant *Mimo* or in the carnivorous plant Venus's ft trap, the action potentials that develo immediately after stimulation of the se sitive cells (see Fig. 21.17) and pass the pulvini may be recorded by a galv nometer.[34] The action potentials are fo lowed by the turgor movement.

Even more remarkable are the actio potentials in *Nitella,* a fresh water al with very large multinucleate cells.[25-28, When a *Nitella* cell is stimulated by pre sure, heat, light, chemicals or electricit an action potential is evoked whic reaches a value of about a tenth of a vo

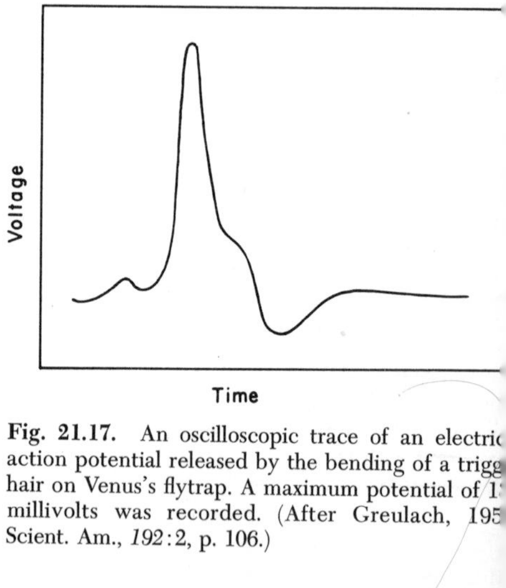

Voltage

Time

Fig. 21.17. An oscilloscopic trace of an electri action potential released by the bending of a trigg hair on Venus's flytrap. A maximum potential of 1 millivolts was recorded. (After Greulach, 195 Scient. Am., 192:2, p. 106.)

d is propagated at the rate of about a
ntimeter per second. Like the nerve
tion potential, it is diphasic. The ac-
n potential usually passes to the ends
the cell; however, it may die out after
ving traversed only a part of it, a be-
vior contrary to the all-or-none princi-
e characteristic of the nerve impulse.
ke nerve cells, however, *Nitella* cells
ow summation of stimuli. After excita-
n a *Nitella* cell becomes refractory
 incapable of being stimulated for a
ief time. The refractory period may last
 seconds to several minutes, or after
ugh handling, as during isolation of an
ternode cell for an experiment, *Nitella*
ay be refractory for hours.

The action potential of a *Nitella* cell is
t just an electrical wave, since it trav-
s more slowly than electricity, but it is
parently a change in the cell membrane
companied by an electrical disturbance.
at the electrical wave is important for
opagation of the membrane change is
monstrated experimentally. Thus when
portion of a *Nitella* cell is blocked by
ld or anesthetic, the action potential
es not pass the block, yet if a U-shaped
ece of filter paper, or string, moistened
th balanced salt solution bridges the
ock, the action potential is conducted
rough the bridge (see Fig. 21.18).

Passage of an action potential in *Nitella*
pt in the dark is accompanied by in-
eased oxygen consumption and carbon
oxide production. Heat is also given off.
hese metabolic accompaniments of the
tion potential are thought to be the
sult of reactions involved in regenerat-
g the cellular membrane altered by
citation.

onophasic Action Potentials

When a nerve fiber or a *Nitella* cell is
ushed between one of the pickup elec-
odes, the action potential becomes
onophasic (see Fig. 21.19 and 21.20),
nce only when the action potential
sses one of the electrodes will a change
 potential be recorded, the crushed part

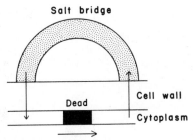

Fig. 21.18. Diagram of a by-pass for a block in
a *Nitella* cell. Part of the cytoplasm has been killed
with chloroform. The salt bridge, consisting of filter
paper or string soaked in salt solution, completes the
circuit and makes transmission possible (After Osterhout and Hill, 1929–30: J. Gen. Physiol., *13*:548.)

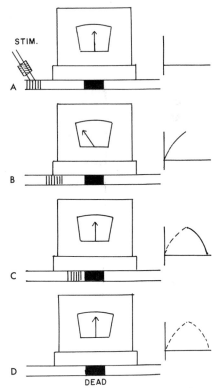

Fig. 21.19. Monophasic action potentials in an
excitable cell with a dead section (shown in black)
between the electrodes. *A*, Stimulation (stim.) excites
the cell. *B*, When the excitation (shown by cross
hatching) reaches the electrode, the needle of the
galvanometer is deflected because the excited area is
negative to the unexcited one. *C*, When the excitation passes the electrode the needle falls to zero,
since both electrodes are then on unexcited areas at
the same potential. *D*, Because the excitation cannot
pass the dead region, the needle is not deflected
again and the spike is said to be monophasic.

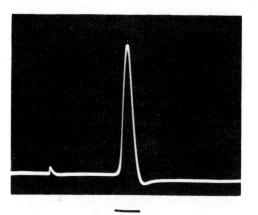

Fig. 21.20. Single fiber (central interneuron) isolated from the crayfish ventral nerve cord and recorded in oil. Monophasic recording leads. Time mark (below spike), 1 msec. Preceding the spike is seen the stimulus artifact. (By courtesy of Dr. D. Kennedy.)

being incapable of propagating the potential. This arrangement is convenient for some types of study and is most generally used.

By placing the pickup electrodes far apart on an uninjured nerve fiber it is possible to record what are essentially monophasic action potentials. However, the electrodes must be so far apart as to make this procedure impractical when recording from the surface of the nerve fiber.

GENERAL REFERENCES

Arshavski, Y. I., 1960: The Role of Metabolism in the Production of Bioelectric Potentials. Russian Rev. of Biol. 50:55–68.

Audus, L., 1959: Plant Growth Substances. Hill, London.

Blinks, L. R., 1955: Some Electrical Properties of Large Plant Cells, in Electrochemistry in Biology and Medicine (Shedlovsky, T., ed.). Wiley, New York, pp. 187–212.

Brazier, M. A. B., 1960: The Electrical Activity of the Nervous System. 2nd Ed. Macmillan, New York.

Davson, H., 1959: A Textbook of General Physiology. 2nd Ed. Little, Brown, Boston. Ch. 4.

Erlanger, J., and Gasser, H. S., 1937: Electrical Si of Nervous Activity. Univ. of Pennsylvania Pr Philadelphia.

Hamburger, V., 1957: The Life History of a Ne Cell. Am. Sci. 45:263–277.

Hyden, H., 1960: The Neuron, in The Cell (Brach J., and Mirsky, A. E., eds.). Academic Press, N York, vol. 4, Ch. 8, pp. 215–323.

Hyden, H., Dec. 1961: Satellite Cells in the Nerv System. Sci. Am. 205:62–70.

Keynes, R. D., 1957: Electric Organs, in Physiolc of Fishes (Brown, M., ed.). Academic Press, N York, vol. 2, pp. 323–340.

Ruch, T. C., and Fulton, J. F., 1960: Medical Ph iology and Biophysics. Saunders, Philadelphia, C 1–4.

Shrank, A. R., 1957: Bioelectric Implications in Pl Tropisms. Symp. Soc. Exp. Biol. 11:95.

Suckling, E. E., 1961: Bioelectricity. McGraw-H New York.

Tasaki, I., 1953: Nervous Transmission. Thom Springfield, Ill.

LITERATURE CITED

1. Lloyd, F. E., 1942: The Carnivorous Plan Chronica Botanica, Waltham, Mass.

2. Bonner, J., and Galston, A., 1952: Plant Ph iology. Freeman, San Francisco.

3. Pantin, C. F. A., 1950: Symp. Soc. Exp. Bi 4:175.

4. Prosser, C. L., and Brown, F., Jr., 1961: Comp ative Animal Physiology. 2nd Ed. Saunde Philadelphia.

5. Turner, G., 1960: General Endocrinology. 3rd F Saunders, Philadelphia.

6. Therman, P. O., 1952: Cold Spring Harbor Syn 17:103.

7. Tasaki, I., 1953: Nervous Transmission. Thom Springfield, Ill.

8. Bodian, D., 1950: The Nerve Impulse. Tra First Conference, Josiah Macy, Jr., Foundatic (Nachmansohn, D., ed.) New York, p. 108.

9. Fenn, W. O., 1929: Harvey Lect., 23:115.

10. Gerard, R. W., 1932: Physiol. Rev. 12:469.

11. Gerard, R. W., 1936: Cold Spring Harbor Syn 4:194.

12. Brink, F., Jr., Bronk, D. W., Carlson, F. D., a Connelly, C., 1952: Cold Spring Harbor Syn 17:53.

13. Abood, L. G., and Gerard, R. W., 1954: J. Ce Comp. Physiol. 43:379.

14. Nachmansohn, D. (ed.), 1950: The Nerve Impul Trans. First Conference, Josiah Macy, J Foundation, New York.

15. Gerard, R. W., 1931: Quart. Rev. Biol. 6:59.

16. Hill, A. V., 1933: Proc. Roy. Soc., London, s 113:345.

IRRITABILITY AND CONTRACTILI

7. Adrian, E. D., 1950: Symp. Soc. Exp. Biol., *4*:85.
8. Schmitt, F. O., and Cori, C. F., 1937: Am. J. Physiol. *106*:339.
9. Fenn, W. O., and Gerschman, R., 1950: J. Gen. Physiol. *33*:195.
0. Lundberg, A., and Oscarsson, O., 1953: Acta Physiol. Skand. *30* (suppl. 111) 99.
1. Schallek, W., 1949: Biol. Bull. *97*:252.
2. Brink, F., Jr., 1951: The Nerve Impulse. Trans. Second Conference, Josiah Macy, Jr., Foundation, New York, p. 124.
3. Cox, R. T., 1943: Am. J. Physics *11*:13.
4. Keynes, R. D., and Martins-Ferreria, H., 1953: J. Physiol. *119*:315.
5. Osterhout, W. J. V., 1936: Physiol. Rev. *16*:216.
6. Blinks, L. R., 1949: Proc. Nat. Acad. Sci. U. S. *35*:566.
7. Umrath, K., 1954: Protoplasma *43*:237.
8. Blinks, L. R., 1955: *in* Electrochemistry in Biology and Medicine (Shedlovsky, T., ed.). Wiley, New York, p. 187.
9. Amberson, W. R., and Smith, D. C., 1948: Outline of Physiology. 2nd Ed. Appleton, New York, p. 113.
0. Watson, E. C., 1945: Am. J. Physics *13*:397.
1. Tyler, A., Monroy, A., Kao, C. Y., and Grundfest, H., 1955: Biol Bull. *109*:352.
2. Lapicque, L., 1926: L'excitabilité en Function du Temps, Univ. de France, Paris.
3. Heilbrunn, L. V., 1952: An Outline of General Physiology. 3rd Ed. Saunders, Philadelphia.
4. Greulach, V. A., Feb. 1955: Sci. Am., *192*:106.
5. Gerard, R., 1946: Ann. New York Acad. Sci. *47*:575.
6. Lillie, R. S., 1922: Physiol. Rev. *2*:1.
7. Gerebtzoff, M. A., and Schoffeniels, E., 1960: Comp. Biochem. *2*:519.

38. Erlanger, J., and Gasser, H. S., 1937: Electrical Signs of Nervous Activity. Univ. of Pennsylvania Press, Philadelphia.
39. Adrian, E. D., 1921: J. Physiol. *55*:193.
40. Brazier, M. A. B., 1960: The Electrical Activity of the Nervous System. 2nd Ed. Macmillan, New York.
41. Johnson, F. H., Eyring, H., and Pollisar, M. J., 1954: The Kinetic Basis of Molecular Biology. Wiley, New York, p. 611.
42. Hodgkin, A. L., 1951: Biol. Bull. *26*:339.
43. Hakansson, C. H., 1957: Arch. Physiol. Skand. *41*:199.
44. Hydén, H., 1960: *in* The Cell (Brachet, J., and Mirsky, A. E., eds.). Academic Press, New York, vol. 4, p. 215.
45. Ruch, T. C., and Fulton, J. F., 1960: Medical Physiology and Biophysics. Saunders, Philadelphia, Ch. 1–4.
46. Roth, L. E., 1958: Exp. Cell Res. 5 (suppl.):573.
47. Taylor, C. V., 1920. Univ. of California Publ. Zool. *19*:403.
48. Datta, M., and Dutt, A. K., 1957: Nature *179*:253.
49. Gernand, K., and Ebrig, H., 1957: Biol. Zentralbl. *76*:181.
50. Bone, Q., 1958: Nature *181*:193.
51. Audus, L., 1959: Plant Growth Hormones. Hill, London.
52. Kishimoto, U., 1957: J. Gen. Physiol. *40*:663.
53. Katz, B., 1959: *in* Biophysical Science, a Study Program (Oncley, J. L., ed.). Wiley, New York, p. 466.
54. Katz, B., Nov. 1952: Sci. Am. *187*:55.
55. Bodian, D., 1952: Cold Spring Harbor Symp. *17*:1.
56. Hisada, M., 1957: J. Cell. Comp. Physiol. *50* (suppl. 1):57.

DEVELOPMENT, PROPAGATION
AND TRANSMISSION OF THE
ACTION POTENTIAL

Since the action potential is apparently the "language" by which excitable cells communicate information and in this manner evoke response, its nature, its origin and the mechanism of its propagation and its transmission are of profound interest. In this connection several additional questions arise for consideration: Does a potential difference already exist between the outside and the inside of a cell not undergoing stimulation? If so, what causes this resting potential, and how is it altered during the development and propagation of an action potential following stimulation of the cell?

Resting Potentials across the
Cell Membrane

It has been clearly demonstrated experimentally that a potential difference, called the *resting potential*, exists at all times between the outside and inside of all normal cells at rest (that is, not stimulated). The experiment is performed by inserting one electrode inside a cell and placing another on its surface (see Fig.

22.1). Cells such as the squid giant axon, large muscle fibers or large plant cells like *Valonia, Halicystis* or *Nitella* are best fo this purpose because of their size. However, for small cells minute transverse electrodes are being employed with success.[3] A resting potential of approximately 10 to 100 millivolts (mv.) is registered in most cells. In the squid giant axon and frog muscle fiber the potential is about 50 to 75 mv.; in *Halicystis*, 70 to 80 mv.; in a *Nitella* cell, 100 to 200 mv.[1-3] In all cases the outside is positive to the inside,[4-6] except in one species of *Valonia*, on which the outside is 10 to 20 mv. negative to the inside. However, this is not a contradiction and has been satisfactorily explained.[4]

An approximation of the potential difference between the outside and the inside of a cell may be obtained by injuring or crushing one part of the cell to "gain entry" to the inside. One electrode is placed on the injured portion, the other on an intact portion and an *injury potential* is measured. Its magnitude is 50 mv. or less for most cells tested, the outside

ways being positive to the injured
·gion (inside).

It is probable that the true potential
fference between the outside and the
side of the cells is larger than measured
y all these methods, because the cells
e injured during penetration of the
ectrode into the cell and because
nances for shorting are considerable.

In attempting to explain the resting
otential of a cell it is of importance to
onsider in some detail an inanimate sys-
em as an analogy. It is shown that a po-
ential difference arises when a membrane
selectively permeable to either anions
r cations, and a difference in concentra-
on of some nondiffusible ion exists
etween the inside and the outside of the
membrane. Such a difference in potential
; called a *concentration chain potential.*
. potential difference also arises when
ations (or anions) of different diffusibili-
es are present on opposite sides of a
membrane, even if they are at the same
oncentration; it is called a *chemical*
hain potential.

*Concentration Chain Potentials across
n Artificial Membrane.* When an arti-
cial membrane separates solutions con-
aining different concentrations of the same
lectrolyte, the nature of the potential

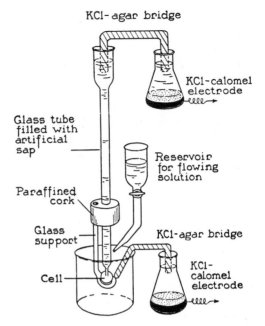

Fig. 22.1. Method of determining the resting potential on a plant cell. One electrode is placed inside
a *Halicystis* cell and another electrode, on its surface. (From Blinks, 1933: J. Gen. Physiol., *17*:111.)

depends upon the permeability of the
membrane to the cations and anions of
this electrolyte.[8] Four different cases are
described below and in Figure 22.2 (see
also Appendix 22.1).

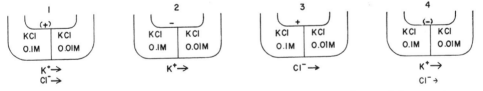

Fig. 22.2. Concentration chain potentials. Potentials developed when solutions of the same electrolyte are present in different concentrations on opposite sides of a membrane. The arrows show
only the over-all movement, since the movement of a given ion is not restricted entirely to passage
through the membrane in one direction. The charge on the membrane may be temporary (as indicated by parentheses) or continued, depending upon the conditions. When the membrane is permeable to both ions, as in case 1, the potential is fleeting. When it is permeable only to cations, the
solution of higher concentration becomes negative (case 2). When it is permeable only to anions,
the solution of higher concentration becomes positive to the other solution (case 3). When the membrane is a mosaic of areas, some permeable to cations and some permeable to anions, the charge
depends upon the ratio of the two kinds of areas. If the areas permeable to cations predominate
(case 4), the solution of higher concentration becomes negative to the other solution, but only briefly
since the concentrations of the two solutions eventually become equalized by the movement of cations and anions from the solution of higher concentration to the solution of lower concentration.

1. If the membrane is equally permeable to both the ions, e.g., K^+ and Cl^-, the potential is transitory, since the ions ultimately distribute themselves equally between the two solutions. The mobility of the ions determines how long the potential will last; K^+ and Cl^- have almost equal mobilities; therefore the potential would be slight and would fall much sooner than if NaCl were used on each side of the membrane. Na^+ is less mobile than Cl^-; therefore the side of the membrane with a higher concentration of NaCl would remain positive to the other for a brief but finite time. The greater the difference in mobilities the longer would the temporary potential last.

2. If the membrane is permeable to cations but not to anions, e.g., to K^+, but not to Cl^-, then a potential develops between the two sides, and the solution of higher concentration becomes negative to the one of lower concentration. The magnitude of the potential can be calculated from the Nernst equation:

$$E = \frac{RT}{n\mathfrak{F}} \ln \frac{C_1}{C_2} \qquad (22.1)$$

In this equation E is the potential in volts, R the gas constant (taken as 8.312 joules per degree per mole), T the absolute temperature in degrees, n the valency change, $\mathfrak{F}$ the Faraday (96,500 coulombs per gram equivalent), ln the natural logarithm ($2.3 \times \log_{10}$), C_1 the higher concentration and C_2 the lower concentration (molal) of the electrolyte.

The equation can be simplified by combining the constants R, n and $\mathfrak{F}$ and converting ln to $\log_{10}$. Then setting up the equation for room temperature, 27° C. (300° absolute), and converting to millivolts:

$$E = 59.5 \log_{10} \frac{C_1}{C_2} \qquad (22.2)$$

For a tenfold difference in concentration, $\log_{10} C_1/C_2$ equals 1; therefore, E is 59.5 mv.

An example of such a membrane one made of celloidin (cellulose nitrate which bears a negative charge. A potential is established across such a membrane separating two solutions of $K($ because K^+ penetrates to some extent whereas Cl^- does not.[9] The tendency of K^+ to penetrate is expressed by the magnitude of the potential developed.

In general, whenever an indiffusible ion is present on one side of the membrane only, and diffusible ions are present on both sides, the situation is much like the Donnan equilibrium previously formulated for proteins (see Chapter 12).

3. If the membrane is permeable to anions but not to cations, e.g., to Cl but not to K^+, a potential develops, but the solution of higher concentration in this case becomes positive to the one of lower concentration because of the movement of the anions. The tendency for the anions to diffuse is expressed in the potential developed. A celloidin membrane made up with the dye rhodamine B, or coated with protamine, is positively charged and permeable to anions only.

4. A mosaic membrane, made up partly of celloidin and partly of rhodamine B–celloidin, separating solutions of different concentrations, will permit anions to penetrate the rhodamine B-containing portion and cations to penetrate the celloidin portion. The magnitude and sign of the potential developed depend upon the ratio of the cation-permeable portion of the membrane to the anion-permeable portion of the membrane and upon the rate of penetration of the two ions. The greater the mobility of the ions and the greater their penetration of the membrane, the more transitory will be the charge. The solution of high concentration will be positive to the one of low concentration if the total membrane area permeable to anions is large, and negative if the area permeable to cations is large. The potential will be less than the calculated concentration chain potential be

ween the two solutions, because both ions pass from the higher to the lower concentration, reducing the concentration difference. Furthermore, the potential will fall to zero when the two solutions become equalized in concentration.

Origin of Resting Potential across the Cell Membrane.[60] The resting potential is presumably maintained as long as the cell is alive and active. For example, when the potential is tested periodically or over a week on an impaled living *Halicystis*, it is found to be repeatable day after day.[4] This indicates that the source of the potential is also persistent.[10, 11] It is postulated that such a potential could result from a sustained difference in either cation or anion concentration between inside and outside of cells, as discussed above (cases 2 and 3), but not when both ions penetrate the membrane, because then the potential would decline as equilibrium is reached. If the potential across the cell membrane is due to such a concentration chain, some persistent concentration difference in either anions or cations should be demonstrable. Furthermore, if the concentration of the ion responsible for the resting potential is equalized on the two sides of the membrane, either by leaching the cell free of it or by matching the concentration of the ion inside the cell with a solution applied to the outside, the potential should fall to zero. Such tests were tried with a number of cells.

The concentration of various ions inside cells and in their bathing medium is given in Table 22.1. It will be noted that K^+ is present in a much higher concentration inside the cells than outside (e.g., a *Nitella* cell contains K^+ in the central sap vacuole in a concentration 1065 times as great as in the pond water in which it grows). Although it has been claimed that the potassium in cells may be bound and not exchangeable with that outside, the high conductivity of the cells (in which potassium is the main cation) and the ready diffusion of labeled potassium from one end of the cell to the other indicate that, in cells tested, most of the potassium is in ionic form.[12, 38]

In *Nitella* Na^+ and Cl^- are also present in much higher concentration in the central sap vacuole than in pond water, but in the frog nerve fiber, the squid giant axon and in most cells both of these ions are

TABLE 22.1. *Concentration of Some Ions in Cells and Bathing Media**

CELL	K^+	Na^+	Cl^-	ORGANIC ANIONS
Nitella[1]	54.3	10.0	90.7	—
Pond water[1]	0.05	0.2	0.9	—
Squid giant axon[2]	400	50	40	381.4
Squid blood[2]	20	440	560	—
Sea water[2]	10	460	540	traces
Crab nerve[3] fiber	112	54	52	—
Crab blood[3]	12.1	469	524	—
Frog muscle fiber[4]	124	10.4	1.5	70
Frog plasma[4]	2.25	109	77.5	12.9†

* Data are in mM per liter (1), mM per kg. water (2, 3, 4).
† Accounting incomplete.
[1] Hoagland and Davis, 1922–23: J. Gen. Physiol. 5:629.
[2] Hodgkin.[42] Slicks of sea water may contain considerable organic matter.
[3] Shaw, J. Exp. Biol. 32.
[4] Conway, 1957: Metabolic Aspects of Transport Across Membranes (Murphy, ed.).

present in much lower concentration than in the bathing medium.

Whenever indiffusible anions (or indiffusible cations) are present inside the cell and diffusible anions (or cations) are outside, a steady state develops which resembles the Donnan equilibrium for proteins. The Donnan formulation has been applied to predict the movements of Na^+, K^+ and Cl^- into and out of living cells. Since several ions are present in different concentrations on the two sides of the cell membrane, in theory, all of the diffusible ions present in the cell and in the bathing fluid to which the cell is exposed should be considered in any equation purporting to relate the concentration differences of ions outside and inside the cell to its membrane potential. However, the equation below (derived by Hodgkin and Katz[50] from the Goldman constant field equation[49]) is a version of the Nernst equation (22.1) modified to take into consideration the development of the resting potential of the excitable cell in terms of only the three ions present in highest concentration in the cell and the bathing medium:[12] (See equation at bottom of page.)

Where E is the potential across the cell membrane, P_{K^+}, P_{Na^+} and P_{Cl^-} refer to the permeability coefficients of K^+, Na^+ and Cl^- respectively, and "in" and "out" refer to the inside and outside of the cell, respectively.

This formulation assumes that the structure of the membrane is stable and that changes in the ionic environment in no way affect the permeability characteristics of the membrane. It is therefore an approximation, since it is known that increase in outside K^+ concentration results in a small decrease in the resistance of the cell membrane while increase in Ca^+ has the reverse effect.[51]

Equation 22.3 may be simplified by

dropping out the term for Na^+ since it i[s] shown that in the resting state most cel[l] have only about one per cent permeabilit[y] for Na^+ that they do for K^+. Furthermore when the Na^+ concentration of the bathing medium is varied over a wide range the resting potential of the cell is no[t] affected, indicating that the Na^+ gradien[t] across the cell membrane plays little i[n] any role in establishment and mainte nance of the resting potential.[38] Further more, if the permeability of the cel[l] membrane to K^+ and Cl^- is assumed t[o] be about equal in both directions,* th[e] permeability constants in the equatio[n] cancel out, leaving only the terms fo[r] concentrations of K^+ and Cl^- inside an[d] outside the cell, the ones for K^+ bein[g] of greater importance in most cells.[56]

Increasing the concentrations of K^+ i[n] the medium of *Nitella* causes a progres sive decline in its resting potential whic[h] is abolished when the K^+ concentratio[n] outside the cell equals that inside. It i[s] even possible to reverse the resting po tential if the concentration of K^+ be comes greater on the outside than inside[1] the cell. The effects are completel[y] reversible, indicating that the cells re main healthy during the tests (see Fig 22.3).

Since K^+ is present in most cells in a concentration much higher than in the medium bathing them, it is tempting t[o] postulate that it acts in other cells as i[n] *Nitella*. In fact, experiments have show[n] that increasing concentrations of K^+ ap plied to the outside of the squid gian[t] axon or frog sartorius muscle fiber or fro[g] myelinated nerve fiber[12] reduce the rest ing potentials in these cells as in *Nitella*, but the experimental results, especially for muscle fibers, are in best agreement with theory if the Cl^- concentrations are

* Under certain conditions it is not.

$$E = \frac{RT}{\mathfrak{F}} \ln \left(\frac{P_{K^+}(K^+)\text{ in } + P_{Na^+}(Na^+)\text{ in } + P_{Cl^-}(Cl^-)\text{ out}}{P_{K^+}(K^+)\text{ out} + P_{Na^+}(Na^+)\text{ out} + P_{Cl^-}(Cl^-)\text{ in}} \right) \quad (22.3)$$

454

IRRITABILITY AND CONTRACTILITY

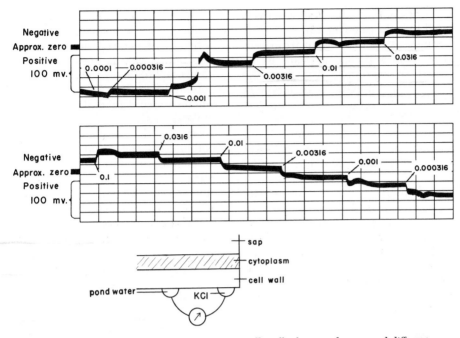

Fig. 22.3. Changes in potential produced in a *Nitella* cell when pond water and different concentrations of KCl are applied to the cell wall in the manner shown in the diagram beneath the graphs. The figures on the graphs indicate the molal concentrations of KCl applied. In the upper graph the potential is progressively decreased as the concentration of KCl is progressively increased, until at 0.0316 M the potential is reversed. The lower graph shows the reverse effect as the concentration of KCl on the outside is lowered. (After Hill and Osterhout.[59])

also taken into account. This indicates that the Cl⁻ contributes to the net potential, even though its share in most cells is small.

That the gradient of K⁺ across the cell membrane determines the resting potential is shown by replacing the axoplasm of a squid giant axon with a solution containing K⁺ and anions. When the gradient of K⁺ between the inside and the outside of the axon approximated that between axoplasm and blood, the resting potential was only slightly less than that of an isolated but unaltered axon. Reduction of the K⁺ gradient, however achieved, caused a proportional decline in resting potential as predicted by the Nernst equation, and the potential could even be reversed by making the K⁺ concentration outside greater than that inside the axon.

Variations in anions on the other hand, had little effect.[56]

K⁺ and Cl⁻ appear to be very nearly in electrochemical equilibrium, the large concentration difference between the inside and the outside of the cell for each of these ions being very nearly balanced by the charge on the cell membrane. However, for Na⁺, both the concentration gradient and electrochemical gradient tend to bring the ion into the cell. Unless the cell membrane is infinitely impermeable to Na⁺, a mechanism other than the one based on these factors is necessary to keep Na⁺ at a steady low level inside the cell. It will be recalled that both K⁺ and Na⁺ enter the cell membrane, and that entry of the Na⁺, while slow, is nonetheless measurable. Yet only K⁺ accumulates inside the cell.

It is evident therefore that Na⁺ is actively extruded by cells (see Ch. 13).

In many cases Na⁺ extrusion from cells (by the sodium pump) appears to be linked with active uptake of K⁺ from the medium by what appears to be a type of cation-exchange process. For example, extrusion of Na⁺ becomes reduced greatly when K⁺ content is reduced, and in general, the rates of both processes change simultaneously and in a parallel manner.[37]

It is of interest to note that in one species of *Halicystis* the concentration of potassium in the sap is about the same as that in sea water, yet the outside of the cell is 70 millivolts positive to the inside, and the potential persists even if the vacuolar content is removed and sea water is substituted. It is evident that resting potentials in such cells must be explained on some basis other than by analogy with the potassium concentration chain potential.

To determine whether anion gradients explain the resting potential of such cells, tests have been made with diverse anions. The anions inside a living cell are largely the organic ions resulting from metabolism—such as, acetate, pyruvate, lactate and amino acids—plus some inorganic ions, like sulfate, all of which pass through the cell membranes very slowly. These ions, collectively called X⁻, are absent from the natural bathing medium or present there in negligible quantities. Instead, the bathing medium is rich in chloride ion, which penetrates through cell membranes relatively readily but is always present inside cells in low concentration. A greater concentration of chloride ion outside rather than inside the cell favors inward penetration of chloride ion from the medium, leaving the outside of the cell positively charged. If the reasoning is correct, substitution of chloride ion in the bathing medium with a very slowly diffusing or nondiffusing anion should reduce or abolish the potential. This is verified in experiments on *Halicystis*[11] (see Fig. 22.4).

Relation of the Resting Potential Metabolism. Maintenance of the resting potential of the cell depends upon the presence of oxygen. Thus, when free oxygen is lacking in *Halicystis*, the resting potential falls (Fig. 22.4), but rises again when oxygen is readmitted, or the plant is illuminated.[10, 11] Lack of oxygen reduces, but does not abolish, the resting potential of the squid giant axon and other neurons, and the reduction is accompanied by a loss of potassium.[14-1] Since glycolytic metabolism occurs in the absence of oxygen (see Chapter 17), the nerve cell continues to liberate energy but does so at a reduced rate as indicated by the decrease in liberation of heat. Inhibition of glycolysis by poisons specific to glycolytic processes (e.g., iodoacetic acid, fluoride or phlorhizin),* should reduce the resting potential even more. Experiments verify this prediction, although in no case is the resting potential abolished completely so long as the nerve cell remains alive. The residual potential probably depends upon physical phenomena such as the Donnan equilibrium of the proteins. On the other hand, in an anoxic muscle fiber poisoned with iodoacetic acid, the potential falls to zero in 2 to 3 hours.[12]

The very gradual decline in the membrane potential of cells in which metabolic poisons have eliminated energy sources for the sodium pump indicate how slow transmembrane leakage really is. The decrease in potential is attributable to the gradual diminution of the ionic gradients.[35]

To sum up, some cells apparently maintain across the cell membrane a resting potential between the inside and the outside of the cell on the basis of differences in concentration of some cations, while others do so on the basis of differences in concentration of some anions. Since

* These poisons act in very different ways. Iodoacetic acid inactivates sulfhydryl groups—specifically, in this case, triosephosphate dehydrogenase (see Table 17.2). Fluoride inhibits enolase. Phlorizin inhibits glucose uptake.

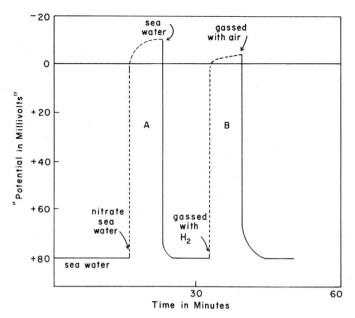

Fig. 22.4. *A*, the potential of *Halicystis* as affected by the replacement of the chloride of sea water with nitrate. *B*, the potential of *Halicystis* as affected by the removal of oxygen. The dotted line in *A* shows the fall in potential when *Halicystis* is placed in nitrate sea water. The dotted line in *B* shows the fall in potential when *Halicystis* is freed of oxygen by being gassed with hydrogen. The solid vertical line in *A* shows the return of the potential to the original resting value when the cell is returned to sea water. The solid vertical line in *B* shows the return of the potential when the cell is supplied with oxygen by being gassed with air. In each case the cell was set up as illustrated in Fig. 22.1. (After Blinks, 1940: Cold Spring Harbor Symposia, 8:204.)

metabolism appears necessary to maintain the resting potential of a cell, it is inferred that metabolic energy is needed to maintain the difference in concentration of ions between the outside and the inside of the cell. Inasmuch as the polarized state is necessary for irritability, the cell must pay for maintaining its state of irritability by continuously expending energy.

The cost of maintaining an irritable state is suggested by the following calculation, based on the Nernst equation (22.1). The energy (W) required to move 1 mole of Na^+ from inside (in) to outside (out) of a two compartment system, and 1 mole of K^+ in the opposite direction is:

$$W = \frac{RT}{\mathfrak{F}} \left(\ln \frac{Na^+_{out}}{Na^+_{in}} + \ln \frac{K^+_{in}}{K^+_{out}} \right), \quad (22.4)$$

where Na^+_{out}, Na^+_{in}, K^+_{out} and K^+_{in} are ion concentrations (or activities, strictly speaking). It is found that about 3000 calories per mole are required to move a mole of Na^+ and K^+ for the concentration gradient of Na^+ and K^+ found in the nerve fiber.[35] If about 7000 to 12,000 calories per mole are available from the hydrolysis of 1 mole of ATP to ADP, it should be possible to move several Na^+ for each ADP formed. For frog nerve fibers at rest, the oxygen uptake is 1.5 μmole/gram(wet)/hour, and the Na^+ flux is about 6.6 μmole/gram(wet)/hour. Thus, the ratio of Na:O is 2.2. The ratio of ADP converted to ATP per oxygen atom reduced (P:O) in mitochondria is about 3. It would thus appear that only about 30 per cent of the resting metabolism is available for work other than ion transport.[35]

A similar calculation for nerve fibers stimulated to produce action potentials for an hour at 50 volleys per second shows that even with the severalfold increase in respiratory metabolism, more than two thirds of the energy made available (as high energy phosphate) from oxygen consumption is probably devoted to ion transport.[35]

Origin of the Propagated Action Potential

An excitable cell, e.g., a neuron, a muscle fiber or a *Nitella* cell, like all other cells, has a resting potential at all times between the inside and outside of the cell, across the cell membrane. But, in addition, it can develop and propagate an action potential upon stimulation.[60]

How, then, is the resting potential of an excitable cell altered during the development of an action potential? The positive charge on the outer surface of the cell membrane, because of the presence of positively charged ions, is delicately balanced by the negatively charged anions of salts, organic acids, etc., inside the cell. Application of an electrode as a stimulus disturbs the resting arrangement and distribution of these ions. If the membrane is slightly disturbed, only a local potential develops, the disturbed area becoming negative to the surrounding more positive region on the cell membrane as sodium ions enter the cell in small numbers.[17] A local potential remains near the point of stimulation, but only briefly, since the ions soon redistribute themselves to the steady-state pattern of a resting cell. The stronger the stimulus, the larger is the local potential and the greater the area of disturbance on the cell membrane. It is estimated that about 6×10^9 electrons are needed to stimulate a nerve cell.[18] If a local potential on a neuron reaches one-fifth to one-third the height of a spike, it develops into a spike which passes the full length of the axon in the all-or-none manner of a propagated action potential (see Fig. 22.5). The neuron (or other excitable cell) is then said to have been stimulated. This in essence is a statement of the Bernstein membrane theory, which is a development of ideas first introduced by Du Bois-Reymond.[38]

That stimulation of an excitable cell produces a profound change is seen by the altered electrical properties of the cell's membrane. Thus, upon stimulation the electrical resistance[12] in a *Nitella* cell falls from 100,000 to 500 ohms per square cm., and in the squid giant axon it falls from 1000 to 25 ohms per square cm. Furthermore, potassium is lost in measurable quantities from squid giant axons and *Nitella*. Both lines of evidence indicate that on stimulation the cell membranes of these excitable cells have become much more freely permeable to certain ions. A free interchange of ions between the outside and the inside of a cell at the point of stimulation would depolarize and abolish the resting potential in that portion of the cell. Recording with electrodes inside some excitable cells has demonstrated that the point of stimulation on the membrane of the excited cell not only loses its charge (depolarizes) but changes charge and becomes negative to the inside (Fig. 22.6). Measurements on the squid giant axon[19, 51] indicate that the stimulated portion of the nerve fiber becomes almost as negative as it was previously positive. This has been verified on many animal cells but does not occur in cells of *Nitella* where only depolarization occurs.[12]

By use of radioactive tracers the movements of sodium and potassium ions across the membrane of the nerve fiber have been followed during stimulation and recovery of the axon.[21-23] At the point of stimulation the permeability to Na^+ is suddenly increased several hundredfold and reaches its peak in 100 microseconds. The potential gradient across the cell membrane is thus temporarily abolished at the point of stimulation, which becomes first depolarized and then develops a negative charge by entry of Na^+ into the cell. At the close of this period (the rise of the spike) the mem

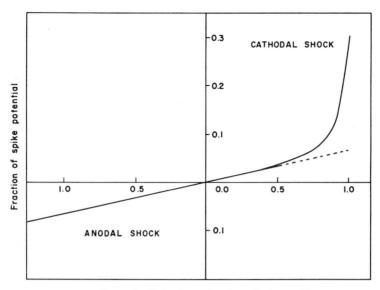

Fig. 22.5. Relations between local potentials and spike potentials on a nerve cell. The spike does not arise from anodal shock even when the shock is very large, but it does arise from cathodal shock when a given fraction (about 0.3) of the spike potential has been reached. Each potential was measured 0.29 millisecond after the shock. The dotted line in the cathodal shock quadrant is an extrapolation showing the potential that would be developed if a spike did not arise. (After Hodgkin, 1938: Proc. Roy. Soc., *B126*:96.)

brane again becomes essentially impermeable to sodium, but its K⁺ permeability increases and, at the fall of the spike potential, K⁺ leaks out from the point of stimulation and repolarizes the cell. Since K⁺ leaks out at a slower rate than Na⁺ moves inward, the repolarization of the membrane to resting potential is slower than its depolarization. Presumably, at the end of the spike, the sodium pump once more comes into operation, as does the coupled active transport of K⁺ into the cell, and the membrane begins to recover its normal permeability to ions at this point.

The spike cannot be explained by temporary suspension of the sodium pump because, when the latter is suspended by metabolic poisons, the action potential of the cell does change but only very slowly and gradually. The events which transpire during spike development involve large numbers of ions and are extremely rapid. However, neither the nature of the changes in the cell membrane resulting in increased permeability nor the nature of the restorative processes is fully understood.[38, 43]

However, it should not be inferred that sodium ions which have entered the cell will at once be expelled or that potassium ions which have left the cell will have to be regained by the nerve fiber before it can recover. The quantity of ions lost (about 10^{-12} M) during a single impulse is but a small fraction (about 0.0001 per cent in the squid giant axon) of that present in the nerve fiber. Even if the sodium pump did not become active again, the squid giant axon could be stimulated thousands of times before the ion store would become exhausted.[38] But to recover its sensitivity, the membrane of the nerve fiber must first shut off the sodium influx as

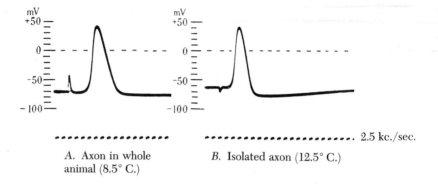

mV
+50
0
-50
-100

mV
+50
0
-50
-100

.... 2.5 kc./sec.

A. Axon in whole
animal (8.5° C.)

B. Isolated axon (12.5° C.)

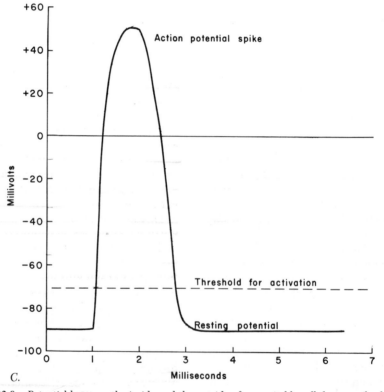

+60

+40

+20

0

Millivolts

-20

-40

-60

-80

-100

Action potential spike

Threshold for activation

Resting potential

0   1   2   3   4   5   6   7

Milliseconds

C.

Fig. 22.6. Potential between the inside and the outside of an excitable cell during spike formation. *A* is from an intact giant axon of the squid (*Loligo forbesi*), *B* is from an isolated squid giant
axon and *C* is from a single isolated electroplax of the electric fish (*Electrophorus electricus*). (*A* and
B from Hodgkin, 1958: Proc. Roy. Soc., London *B148*:1; *C* from Gerebtzoff and Schoffeniels,
1960: Comp. Biochem. *2*:525.)

the potassium efflux repolarizes it. If the nerve fiber is not stimulated again, the sodium pump presumably resumes operation and the accumulated Na^+ is voided while the lost K^+ is simultaneously regained.

In contrast to ionic movements that occur at the nerve axon, both Na^+ entry and K^+ loss occur simultaneously in nerve cell dendrites, which generally show local, nonpropagating, decremental potentials. The degree of response is determined by the number of channels open for Na^+ and K^+ and the duration and extent of each channel opening. In areas of the cell where a sharp difference between Na^+ influx and K^+ efflux does not occur, propagated impulses do not arise. Such graded, nonpropagating potentials are of importance in receptor-sensory neuron systems as well as in synapses, making possible the effective passage of information as well as integration of the information.

That sodium is the conductor of current during the rise of the action potential is demonstrated by substituting for it a cation that does not penetrate the cell as readily as Na^+. The decrease in height of the spike is proportional to the decrease of Na^+ in the bathing fluid. The sodium ion is as vital to the height of the spike in most cells as is the potassium ion to the resting potential of cells. However, Na^+ is apparently not always the ion that carries the current. In some algae (e.g., *Chara*) it appears that leakage of Cl^- from the cell serves the same purpose. In some crustacean muscle fibers there is evidence for influx of divalent ions instead of sodium ions.[38]

Theory of the Propagation of the Action Potential

It is to be expected that local circuits will flow from the unstimulated, positively charged areas of the cell membrane to the stimulated, depolarized or negative portion, and as each new area becomes depolarized or negative, it in turn acts as the sink toward which the current flows from the adjacent area (see Fig. 22.7). Progressive depolarization, or reversal of charge, of the entire length of the neuron therefore follows from the point of stimulation outwardly as if an electrode were traveling along the nerve fiber at the rate of conduction characteristic of the fiber.[24] It has been demonstrated that the source of the current is the flow of sodium ions into the cell.[23] This, briefly, is the so-called *local circuit theory* of propagation of action potential.

Repolarization of the surface of an excited fiber with a positive charge sets in as soon as the absolute refractory period is over, and progresses so rapidly that never more than a fraction of a nerve fiber is depolarized at a time. However, this may be a region of a few millimeters to a few centimeters, depending upon the duration of the spike and its speed of propagation. Recovery occurs most likely at the expense of high energy phosphate bonds, since the concentration of creatine phosphate declines after stimulation. Because a nerve can continue to discharge for some time in the absence of free oxygen, even when glycolysis is inhibited by a poison, a store of high energy phosphate bonds must be available for the purpose. These are presumably rebuilt at the expense of the metabolic activities of the neuron—slowly in the complete absence of oxygen and much more rapidly in the presence of oxygen. Experiments with tracers indicate that, during recovery, sodium ions leave the cell and potassium ions re-enter.[25] That work, requiring metabolic energy, must be done during recovery of a stimulated cell is indicated by the evolution of heat.

It is quite evident that various properties of the propagated action potential (nerve impulse) may be interpreted on the basis of the local circuit theory of

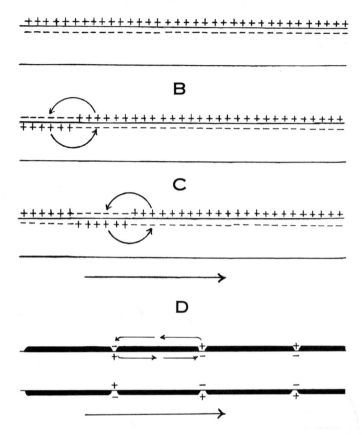

Fig. 22.7. Diagram to illustrate the local circuit theory of propagation of the action potential (*A, B, C*) in unmyelinated neurons and muscle fibers as compared to the saltatory conduction in myelinated neurons (*D*). *A* is the membrane of an unexcited nerve (or muscle) fiber; *B* shows the cell membrane excited at one end; *C* shows the movement of the action potential, followed by recovery; *D* shows node-to-node saltatory conduction. In large nerve fibers less than one hundredth as much ionic exchange occurs during an impulse in saltatory conduction as compared to conduction in an unmyelinated nerve fiber. The arrows in *C* and *D* show the direction of impulse propagation. (After Hodgkin, 1957: Proc. Roy. Soc., *B148*:1.)

propagation. Thus, when either a stimulus below rheobase is used or a stimulus above rheobase is applied for too short a time, the membrane is not altered enough to produce a sink, and the ions soon redistribute themselves into the normal pattern for the resting potential of the unstimulated cell. All-or-none response and conduction without a decrement are to be expected of a nerve fiber if the membrane of the entire fiber is initially equally polarized (charged). The reaction is self-generating if the same amount of electrical change occurs along the entire length of the nerve fiber. The absolute refractory period represents the time during which the membrane is no longer selectively permeable, or, as is often stated, the "sodium gate is wide open."

Sodium enters the nerve fiber during this period, and the neuron is therefore inexcitable. The initial state of polarization is presumably regained during the relative refractory period when the cell membrane once again becomes impermeable to sodium, and potassium leaks out in response to the concentration gradient. The states of increased and, later, of decreased excitability (in vertebrate A fibers at least) occur probably because the membrane has not fully regained normal permeability. Consequently, a response may be elicited, but a different threshold of stimulation is required. A quantitative formulation of the theory in terms of the distribution of specific ions is not yet possible.

The neuron cell membrane register

many events, and its exact state and response are largely dependent upon its history. For example, in A fibers, during tetanic stimulation, the after-potentials become more prominent if the stimuli arrive before the neuron has recovered entirely. If they should arrive when the neuron displays a negative after-potential, the spike appears to be higher by the amount of the negative after-potential. The positive after-potential is also gradually augmented by tetanic stimulation and the neuron becomes less excitable because a greater stimulus is required for depolarization.[26] Furthermore, subthreshold stimulation by a steady cathodal current lowers the excitability because it leads to accommodation when the rate of displacement of ions is equaled by that of recovery. When a neuron is depolarized by asphyxia, it is rendered incapable of response, yet it can be repolarized by a battery current and induced to respond at least once.[32] A state of polarization is seemingly necessary for maintaining excitability.

Saltatory conduction, as discussed previously for myelinated nerve fibers (see Fig. 21.12 and 22.7), is thought to be the result of local circuits occurring only from node to node. The amount of naked axon is very slight even at the nodes, perhaps a few hundred angstrom units at most, because, according to electron micrograph studies, the Schwann cells of the myelin sheath send finger-like growths along the axon. The amount of sodium and potassium ion exchange is thus greatly reduced and the net work required of the cell for response is thereby much lowered.[52]

Sensory Fiber Action Potentials

Receptor cells are much more sensitive to certain stimuli than are other cells, e.g., a pressure receptor is much more sensitive to pressure than neurons in a nerve trunk. Sometimes the distal branches of the afferent neuron are modified to serve as receptors, e.g., muscle sense organs and pain receptors.

Receptor cells when stimulated excite adjacent afferent (sensory) neurons which inform the central nervous system about the strength of the stimulus (Fig. 22.8). Since Adrian's classic experiments 30 years ago it has been recognized that varying the strength of a stimulus (e.g., pressure on a pressure receptor) affects only the frequency of discharge, not the size of the impulses sent into the central nervous system. The code, then, appears to be frequency modulation of a single type of message for a given neuron.[36, 45]

In 1950 Katz demonstrated that stretching a muscle mechanoreceptor, which is a modified part of the fibers of an afferent neuron, generates in the sensitive fibers a local, graded, decremental potential, the magnitude and duration of which depends upon the intensity and duration of stimulation. The local potential, if above threshold, sets off on the axon of the afferent neuron a volley of propagated action potentials. Discharges continue on the afferent axon as long as the depolarization of the receptor fibers remains above threshold. It was soon demonstrated that upon stimulation similar changes (generator potentials) occur in other types of receptors as well.[57, 61]

By removing parts of the receptor, an attempt has been made to determine the sensitive region of a pressure receptor, which consists of a structure enclosing the distal fibers of an afferent neuron. Even when only a core of the receptor remains about the nerve fiber, stretching or deforming the core induces volleys of impulses along the attached fiber. When the enclosed nerve fiber ending itself is damaged, discharge stops.[43] It would appear that the *biological transducer* which transforms the mechanical energy into electrical energy is possibly the terminal portion of the neuron.

There is evidence that following stimulation of such a receptor neuron, the electrical membrane resistance of its dis-

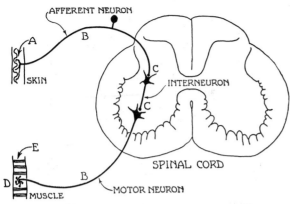

Fig. 22.8. Diagram of a simple reflex arc. *A* shows the receptor at which excitation of afferent neurons occurs. The impulses generated at *A* are conducted by the axons (*B*) to the central nervous system by the afferent neuron, in the cord by interneurons and out to the effector (muscle) (*E*) by the motor neuron (efferent). Synaptic transmission occurs at *C* and neuromuscular transmission at *D*. (From Ruch and Fulton, 1960: Medical Physiology and Biophysics. Saunders, Philadelphia, p. 33.)

tal portion is reduced, permitting ions to enter, partially depolarizing its membrane. When depolarization has reached threshold, propagated action potentials are initiated on the nerve fiber (axon). The local depolarization characteristic of a receptor is spoken of as a *generator potential*, because it generates the propagated action potential on the axon.[43]

The excitation of an afferent axon does not differ significantly from excitation of any nerve fiber or excitable cell. However, a fundamental difference apparently exists between electrical stimulation of a nerve fiber and stimulation through receptor cells. A single electrical stimulation above threshold of an afferent nerve fiber results in a single spike, while even a brief stimulation of a receptor almost invariably results in a volley of impulses along the afferent nerve fiber (Fig. 22.9). For a given kind of receptor, the frequency and duration of the volley depend upon the intensity of receptor stimulation because these factors largely determine how long the generator potential is maintained at a sufficient level to continue to excite the afferent fiber. If the stimulation has been weak and brief, then the subsequent generator potential on the fine terminations of the afferent fiber will be small and will decay rapidly. Consequently, only a few spikes will be induced in the volley. If stimulation is intense, the corresponding generator potential will be greater both in electrical charge and in the area of the neuron altered, and decay will be slower. As a consequence, the resultant volley of impulses will be more prolonged.[34, 36, 43]

It is everyday experience that our sense receptors "get used" to a given stimulus continuously applied, unless it is increased in intensity. The probable basis for such change in sensitivity of receptor cells is the failure of the receptor to induce discharges along the afferent neuron. It can readily be demonstrated, by electrical stimulation, that the afferent neuron is not fatigued, but rather that the stimulus fails to maintain a generator potential sufficient to produce discharge. When this happens, *accommodation* has been achieved. Accommodation occur at different rates in diverse receptor

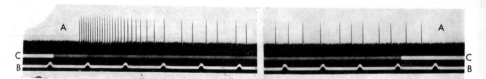

Fig. 22.9. Volley of impulses (*A*) on an afferent neuron. Single nerve fiber from an ommatidium of *Limulus*. The lower notched markings (*B*) are fifths of a second. The line above the time signal (*C*) shows when the light went on and off. The vertical break represents a time lapse of 2.4 seconds. (From Hartline and Graham, 1932: J. Cell. Comp. Physiol., *1*:285.)

(Fig. 22.10). For example, touch receptors accommodate fairly readily while pressure receptors in the carotid artery show almost no accommodation and continue to discharge as long as pressure is applied.[17] In a receptor, accommodated to a given intensity of stimulation, impulses can again be induced by sufficiently increasing the strength of the stimulus. In this case a generator potential has again been induced, but the accommodation will occur again at a rate characteristic for the receptor.[34, 45]

Ultimately a receptor cell may react feebly or fail to respond when it becomes fatigued. This suggests that some material is necessary for action of receptors and when it is temporarily exhausted, the receptor is less responsive. This and other interesting problems of receptor physiology and their part in the behavior patterns of animals are considered in textbooks of animal physiology.[47]

Synaptic Transmission of Action Potentials

The synapse is defined as the functional connection between two neurons. It was so named in 1898 by Sherrington who considered the synapse to be a region of contact, not confluence, of two excitable cells. Electron microscopy has since demonstrated that the cells at a synapse are indeed separate—not only are presynaptic and postsynaptic cell membranes present, but between them exists a synaptic cleft several hundred angstrom units wide[33] (see Fig. 22.8 and 22.11).

Synaptic contacts vary in structure. For example, a crossing of cells with similar fiber membranes lying alongside one another (en passant synapses) is found in coelenterates. A more prolonged contact of fiber membranes in the loop synapses (neuropile connections) is found in many invertebrates. The most highly differentiated contacts between neurons occur in vertebrates where the modified ends of the nerve fibers are applied to dendrites

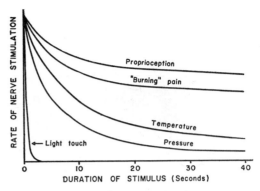

Fig. 22.10. Accomodation in various receptors as measured by frequency of impulse discharge after continuous application of a stimulus of the same intensity. (From Guyton, 1956: Textbook of Medical Physiology. Saunders, Philadelphia.)

or to the nerve cell body. Many of the sensory nerve connections are of this type, and the nerve fiber endings may be cup-like, club-like or basket-like. End feet synapses (bouton termineaux) are found ending on the motor neurons (see Fig. 22.11). It is interesting that in the vertebrate central nervous system, however, the synapses of complex cells (e.g., Purkinje cells) are of a rather simple type, nerve fiber abutting against nerve fiber (en passant). The myoneural junction (muscle end plate) is the synapse between a motor neuron and a muscle fiber, and is an area of considerable contact between nerve fiber and muscle cell (Fig. 22.12). These varied types of synapses have functional significance and are discussed in textbooks of neurophysiology.[53]

When the surface of contact between two neurons is similar (e.g., in the en passant synapses of coelenterates), the synapse may transmit in both directions. When neurons interconnect in a complex manner at a synapse, the synapse transmits in one direction only, that is, it is polarized.[29] Polarization probably results from differentiation in neurosecretory activity at presynaptic and postsynaptic membranes and it may occur even where the contacts between these membranes are apparently structurally undifferen-

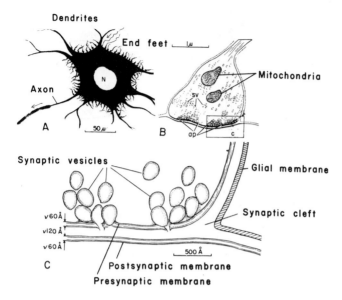

Dendrites

End feet

Mitochondria

Axon

N

A

50μ

B

sv

ap

c

Synaptic vesicles

Glial membrane

Synaptic cleft

∨60Å

∨120Å

∨60Å

500 Å

C

Postsynaptic membrane

Presynaptic membrane

Fig. 22.11. Diagram showing a synaptic junction at various magnifications. *A*, a motor neuron under medium power of a light microscope. Note the numerous end feet—the terminations of axons of interneurons. (*N*) represents the nucleus of the motor neuron. *B*, one end foot under an electron microscope, magnified 60 times over *A*. In addition to the mitochondria, note the synaptic vesicles (sv) and the active points (ap) where the synaptic vesicles appear to aggregate and open onto the synapse. The dotted line represents the glial membrane. *C*, one sector of *B* as seen using high resolution electron microscopy. Note that some of the synaptic vesicles are rupturing into the synaptic cleft through the presynaptic membrane. Observe that the membranes bordering the cleft are much like any other cell membranes. The synaptic cleft is a real separation between the cells enclosed by the membrane of a supporting or glial cell. (DeRobertis, 1959.)

tiated, e.g., in the central nervous system of the vertebrate.

Two theories have been proposed to explain synaptic transmission and are discussed below. Both have had their proponents, and the problem is not fully resolved.[37, 43]

Electrical Theory of Synaptic Transmission. Synaptic transmission by electrotonic spread from the presynaptic to the postsynaptic membrane has been demonstrated in the crayfish giant motor synapse. Here the synaptic delay is very short—0.1 millisecond (ms.) from beginning of prespike (local potential) to beginning of the excitatory postsynaptic potential. Presynaptic depolarization actually spreads across the synapse and is measurable as an appreciable potential difference in the postsynaptic membrane. The postsynaptic depolarization does not in turn cause appreciable hyperpolarization of the presynaptic fiber, indicating a unidirectional action (rectifier action) of the spread of polarization. It is proposed[41]

that the synaptic membrane acts as a rectifier of positive current from the presynaptic to the postsynaptic fiber, with high resistance to flow in the opposite direction. The synaptic rectifier is oriented in the right direction to allow the presynaptic action current to stimulate the postfiber. The electrotonic current resulting from the spike on the presynaptic fiber is sufficient to account for normal transmission. It seems unlikely that this type of transmission is limited to neurons in the crayfish abdomen, but this is the only documented case.[37, 41]

Chemical Theory of Synaptic Transmission. In all other cases studied the synaptic delay is much greater than in the crayfish giant motor synapse, and varies between about 0.3 to 10 milliseconds. Consequently it is thought unlikely that electrotonic spread occurs from presynaptic to postsynaptic fibers because the field on the presynaptic fiber is disappearing or gone before the postsynaptic local potential develops. Internal electrodes fai

466

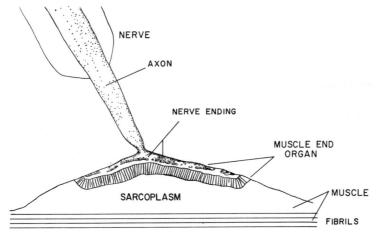

Fig. 22.12. Diagram of a vertebrate muscle end organ. Note that the organ is made up partly of nervous and partly of muscular elements. Sarcoplasm is the cytoplasm of a muscle fiber. (Adapted from Acheson, 1948: Fed. Proc., 7:447.)

to indicate induction of electrotonus at the time of maximal electric field on the presynaptic fiber.[54] It is suggested that the presynaptic potential on reaching the synapse activates a chain of events which results in the secretion of a *transmitter substance,* which, when released, attaches itself to special receptor molecules in the surface of the contacting postsynaptic excitable cell.[39] This chemical combination leads to a membrane change which depolarizes the postsynaptic cell locally. When depolarization exceeds the threshold level, a propagated action potential is initiated.[37]

The neuromuscular junction is an example of a synapse at which chemical transmission is well supported by experimental data.[58] It has been possible to demonstrate that a transmitter substance (acetylcholine) is produced at the presynaptic nerve fibers which, when applied to the end plate of the muscle fiber, causes a local depolarization of the cell membrane and sets up action potentials followed by contraction of the muscle fiber. The chemical effect is localized to the synaptic area of the muscle fiber. In this junction there is an irreducible synaptic delay of 0.5 to 1 millisecond be-

tween the arrival of the nerve impulse and the start of the local (end plate) potential, part of this time being necessary for secretion of the acetylcholine. Histochemical studies have demonstrated a localization at this junction of the enzyme *acetylcholine esterase,* the function of which is the decomposition of the acetylcholine to choline and acetic acid, thus preventing a prolonged depolarized state. When this enzyme is poisoned (e.g., by the drug *eserine*), stimulation of the motor nerve is followed by multiple contractions.[37]

Stimulation of the motor neuron produces no measurable potentials at the end plate at the time the spike reaches its terminal portion. When potential changes of either polarity are imposed on the terminal portion of the motor nerve fiber, they do not spread beyond the nerve terminal, but they increase the rate of acetylcholine discharge. There is thus no evidence of cable transfer of electric current from motor fiber to muscle fiber, but there is adequate evidence of chemical changes leading to action potentials and contractions. It has been possible to apply acetylcholine solutions directly to the motor end plate (to reach the surface of the receptor areas) and under these conditions as little as 10^{-16} gram equivalents of acetylcholine give rise to an effective depolarization of the muscle fiber followed by a spike and contraction. Application of acetylcholine inside the muscle fiber at the postsynaptic membrane has no effect. The muscle end organ thus acts much like a chemoreceptor, a small quantity of the substance sufficing to depolarize the cell.[37]

The way in which the transmitter substance causes depolarization is not entirely understood, but the most likely mechanism is the opening of some ionic channel in the cell membrane. There is evidence that acetylcholine simultaneously increases the membrane permeability of the motor end plate to several monovalent ions (e.g., sodium, potassium, ammonium) and possibly opens up an ionic channel to all small ions on both sides of the membrane. The result is a partial depolarization to a level of about 10 to 20 mv. (negative inside) which corresponds to a free diffusion (liquid junction) potential between the cytoplasm and the external fluid. This local nonpropagated depolarization sets off the propagated spike potential.[37]

When potentials are recorded on the end plate (postsynaptic) during rest, minute potential changes of about 0.5 millivolt are observed on oscillographic records, with a rapid rise (1 millisecond) and a slower decay (about 20 milliseconds), indicating momentary depolarizations of the end plate. This "miniature" end plate potential appears to indicate spontaneous release of "packets" of acetylcholine by the motorneuron, since gradual application of a very low concentration of acetylcholine gives a smooth change, not the sudden changes seen in the records. The miniature end plate potentials are reduced in size by curare, and their amplitude and duration increase when the action of the acetylcholine esterase at the end plate is blocked with a poison, preventing local hydrolysis of

the acetylcholine. All these experiments suggest that acetylcholine is continuously manufactured and expelled from the nerve cell endings, but the spontaneous release inducing the small potentials occurs not continuously but in packets. Presumably an impulse reaching the synapse causes a much larger number of such packets to be released at once and is accompanied by a much larger potential change which serves to depolarize the cell.[37] It is interesting that in the crustacean myoneural junction where another chemical transmitter is active, miniature potentials are also recorded.[27]

Electron microscopy has shown that the synaptic vesicles are almost always seen at synapses, groups of them moving to active spots (Fig. 22.11B) where they appear to rupture into the synaptic cleft. While confirming evidence connecting secretion from these vesicles to transmission has not yet been presented, the suggestion is an appealing one.[33]

Acetylcholine probably plays a role other than myoneural in synapses. For example, in autonomic ganglia where nerve fibers (preganglionic) from the central nervous system synapse with other (postganglionic) nerve fibers passing directly to effectors in the viscera, experiments show that when the preganglionic nerve fibers are stimulated, and their synapses are perfused with balanced salt solution during the excitation, the ester acetylcholine appears in the perfusate. This perfusate has been found to produce electrical changes leading to excitation when applied at other autonomic synapses. However, experimental application of acetylcholine is usually ineffective in exciting synapses of the central nervous system.[37, 47]

Other transmitter substances also play a part in synaptic transmission. For example, sympathin (norepinephrine) is important in the postganglionic fibers of the sympathetic nervous system. A "sensory" substance of unknown chemical nature s been postulated for the synapses of ferent nerve fibers.[37,39] Transmitter bstances are found in the central nervus system and have been isolated and sted but not identified chemically with rtainty. The potential changes that they oduce, however, have been measured d correlated with the existing ionic adients. At the synapses between interurons and motor neurons, for example, e application of transmitter substance creases the permeability of the postnaptic region to all ions, resulting in polarization.[37]

Transmitter substances have been demstrated in synapses of invertebrates, it the biochemical identity of these subances is uncertain. There is suggestive idence that 5-hydroxytryptamine is one ch transmitter. Acetylcholine probably nctions in a few species, but evidence r norepinephrine as a transmitter subance in invertebrates is slight.[39]

While biochemical identity of the ansmitter substances remains doubtful many instances, the fact that a transitter substance is involved in transmison at synapses seems to be rather genally accepted. Thus it is considered that most neurons a chemical change proced by a transmitter substance results an electrical change (local generator otential) which sets off a conductile rocess (propagated action potential) nding in an effector action—the secreon of another transmitter substance. he action of the stimulus upon receptor ells probably also produces secretion of transmitter substance which induces e depolarization of the afferent neuron. rom this point of view the molecular echanism for activation of various synpses may be quite similar in principle, espite diversity of transmitter substances.[37]

Inhibition at Synapses. Inhibition of naptic transmission is part of the mechnism of integration of responses to imuli. Attempts to explain synaptic in-

hibition on the basis of electrotonic spread from presynaptic to postsynaptic membranes have been as unsuccessful as those purporting to explain synaptic transmission of excitation by electrotonic spread, and for the same reasons. However, inhibitory effects of some secretions and drugs have been known for a long time.

An example of inhibition is the action of the vagus nerve (tenth cranial nerve) upon the heart beat. It is known that stimulation of the vagus releases acetylcholine which causes hyperpolarization or stabilization of the resting potential of the heart muscle fibers and results in slowing or stopping the heart beat. The mechanism, seemingly, is a change in ionic conductance, but the channel opened in this case is restricted to K^+ and does not include Na^+. As a consequence the membrane of the muscle cells affected tends to be held at the K^+ equilibrium potential which is somewhat greater than the existing resting potential.[37]

In the synapses of the vertebrate central nervous system some evidence of an inhibitory substance ("I" substance) has been gathered on the basis of the action of perfusates from inhibited synapses. Such substances generally act as hypopolarizers of the postsynaptic junctions (Table 22.2). An inhibitory substance is also found at synapses to lobster muscle fibers and is thought to be γ-aminobutyric acid. It is likely that different inhibitory substances occur in different groups of animals. It is also possible that different inhibitory substances act in different parts of the nervous system of the same species. These problems are the basis of much current research.[39]

Drugs may also inhibit the passage of the nerve impulse across a synapse. Perhaps the best known action of this type is *curare*, the active ingredient in South American arrow poison, which paralyzes animals by preventing transmission of the nerve impulse across the myoneural junction. Curare competes with acetylcholine

TABLE **22.2.** *Changes Induced in Excitable Cells by Stimulation*[1]

EXCITABLE CELLS	EXCITATION INDUCED	EXCITOR	IONIC CHANGES AT MEMBRANE
Dendrites	Local (non-propagated), graded, decremental depolarization	Acetylcholine in some, X[2] in others	Simultaneous Na^+ influx and K^+ efflux
Axon of neuron	Propagated all-or-none action potential (spike), with overshoot	see text	Na^+ influx followed by K^+ efflux
Vertebrate skeletal muscle fiber	Spike with overshoot	Acetylcholine	Na^+ influx followed by K^+ efflux
Invertebrate muscle fiber	Local, graded, decremental depolarization (slow fiber) or	X	Ionic flux[3] increased
	spike with overshoot (fast fiber)	X	Ionic flux increased sequentially for different ions
Receptor cell and afferent neuron junction[4]	Local, graded, decremental, depolarizing generator potential (at transducer)	Sensory substance?	Ionic flux increased
Synapse: excitatory	Local, graded, decremental depolarization	In some, acetylcholine; in others, norepinephrine; in still others, X	Simultaneous Na^+ influx and K^+ efflux; possibly other ions
Synapse: inhibitory	Local, graded, decremental hyperpolarization; or stabilization of resting potential	Substance "I"	Change in ionic flux of some ions[5]
Synapse of vagus on vertebrate heart	Local, graded, decremental hyperpolarization	Acetylcholine	K^+ efflux
Nitella cell	Depolarization and spike which may be all-or-none or decremental, no overshoot	?	Ionic flux changed

[1] Data mainly from Katz,[37, 38, 43] Florey[39] and Frank and Fuortes.[40]
[2] X—an unknown substance present in extracts; electrical transmission in some crayfish synapses.[41]
[3] May involve entry of divalent cations in some, sodium and other ions in others, see Katz.[38]
[4] The axon of the afferent neuron acts like any other axon.
[5] Hyperpolarization could occur by entry of Cl^-.

for the receptor sites on the postsynaptic membrane and sets the end plate potential at a lower value, presumably by increasing the permeability to Na^+ and K^+. Acetylcholine liberated on stimulation of the presynaptic neuron cannot then lower the potential on the curarized postsynaptic membrane to the level required for excitation of a propagated action potential on the muscle fiber.

Facilitation at Synapses. At most synapses more than one incoming impulse is required to excite a postsynaptic neuron to a propagated action potential. When each successive impulse induces an increment of local postsynaptic potential greater than the preceding one, rather than merely adding to the preceding one (as in summation), *facilitation* is said to have occurred. On the basis of the chemical transmitter theory of synaptic transmission, facilitation could be explained as the release of larger and larger amounts of the transmitter substance with each successive impulse. When the transmitter substance has induced sufficient depolarization of the postsynaptic junction, a propagated axon potential is initiated.[39] Facilitation thus prevents impulses generated by minor stimuli from spreading immediately through the nervous system and serves as a device to keep responses proportional to stimulation.[48] In this way, facilitation, like inhibition, serves as a mechanism for coordination of responses of an organism. In some giant fiber systems, there are cases where one presynaptic impulse induces one postsynaptic response, but they are unusual.[34, 48]

APPENDIX

2.1 Chemical Chain Potentials

When different kinds of electrolytes are used on the two sides of a membrane, the magnitude and sign of the potential developed depend upon a number of factors: whether the membrane is perme-

able to anion or cation; the difference in concentration, if any, of anions and cations on the two sides of the membrane; and the relative mobilities of the ions.[8] Four cases are considered below and in Figure 22.13.

1A. If a membrane, permeable to cations but not to anions, separates two electrolytes, e.g., NaCl and KCl, of *equal* molal concentration, a potential develops because of the difference in mobilities of the two cations (e.g., the mobility of K^+ is 7.61×10^{-4} cm./sec., whereas that of Na^+ is 5.19×10^{-4} cm./sec.). The solution with the cation of greater mobility becomes negative to the other solution and then the potential gradually declines as the ions distribute themselves on the two sides of the membrane. The magnitude of the potential reached depends upon the ratio of the mobility of the cations.

2A. If a membrane, permeable to anions but not to cations, separates two electrolytes of equal molal concentration, the relations are the converse of those holding in case 1A, and the solution with the anion of greater mobility becomes positive to the other solution. The magnitude and duration of the potential reached depend upon the ratio of the mobilities of the anions.

3A. If the salts on the two sides of the membrane are present in different concentrations and contain different kinds of cations or anions, the potential developed is the sum of the potential due to differences in concentrations plus the potential due to differences in mobilities of the ions. In this case it is assumed that the membrane is selectively permeable to anions *or* to cations, but not to both.

4A. When a membrane, permeable to both anions and cations, but more permeable to cations than to anions, separates two solutions of different kinds of ions present in equal concentrations, the side with the cation of greater mobility becomes negative to the side with the cation of lesser mobility. Conversely, if the

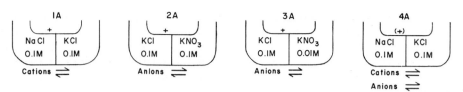

Fig. 22.13. Chemical chain potentials developed across a membrane separating electrolytic solutions of the same, or different, molal concentrations but with ions of different mobilities. In this case chemical "chain" potentials are developed, the sign and duration of a potential depending upon the permeability of the membrane to the ions. Case 1A illustrates what happens when the membrane is permeable to cations only. Cases 2A and 3A show what happens when the membrane is permeable to anions only. (Note that in case 3A the two solutions separated by the membrane differ in concentration as well as in the mobilities of the penetrating ions.) Case 4A shows what happens when a membrane is equally permeable to anions and cations. In case 4A the sign, which is only temporary, depends upon the relative mobilities of the ions. A fifth case might be added; namely, one in which anions *and* cations differ, with both solutions at the same concentration (e.g., 0.1M NaCl and 0.1M KNO_3). What would happen in this case if the membrane were permeable to anions? Cations? Both?

membrane is more permeable to anions than to cations, the side with the anion of greater mobility becomes positive to the one of lesser mobility. In both cases the potential then declines as fast as the various ions reach an equilibrium in their distribution.

Since chemical chain potentials are not found to contribute significantly to cell membrane potentials, quantitative formulations on the basis of relative mobilities of the varoius ions and of their concentration is omitted, but may be found in handbooks on the subject.[55]

GENERAL REFERENCES

Abbott, B. C., Hill, A. V., and Howarth, J. V., 1958: The Positive and Negative Heat Production Associated with a Nerve Impulse. Proc. Roy. Soc. London B *148*:149–183.

Blinks, L. R., 1955: Some Electrical Properties of Large Plant Cells, *in* Electrochemistry in Biology and Medicine (Shedlovsky, T., ed.). Wiley, New York, pp. 187–212.

Bullock, T. H., 1959: Initiation of Nerve Impulses in Receptor and Central Neurons, *in* Biophysical Science—A Study Program (Oncley, J. L., ed.). Wiley, New York, Ch. 54, pp. 504–514.

Comparative Neurophysiology, Feb., 1962. Am. Zoologist *2*:1. An excellent account.

Connelly, C. M., 1959: Recovery Processes and Metabolism of Nerve, *in* Biophysical Science—A Study Program (Oncley, J. L., ed.). Wiley, New York, Ch. 51, pp. 475–484.

Davson, H., 1959: A Textbook of General Physiology. Little, Brown, Boston, Sect. 4.

Eccles, J. C., 1957: The Physiology of Nerve Cells. Johns Hopkins Univ. Press, Baltimore.

van Euler, U. S., 1961: Neurotransmission in the Adrenergic Nervous System. Harvey Lectures *55*:43–65.

Florey, E., 1961: Transmitter Substances. Ann. Rev. Physiol. *23*:501–528.

Frank, K., and Fuortes, M. G. F., 1961: Excitation and Conduction. Ann. Rev. Physiol. *23*:357–386.

Furshpan, E. J., and Potter, D. D., 1959: Transmission at the Giant Motor Synapses of the Crayfish. J. Physiol. *145*:289–325; 326–335.

Gerebtzoff, M. A., and Schoffeniels, E., 1960: Nerve Conduction and Electrical Discharge, Comp. Biochem. *2*:519–544.

Grundfest, H., 1957: The Mechanisms of Discharge of Electric Organs in Relation to General and Comparative Electrophysiology. Progr. Biophys. *7*:3–85.

Hartline, H. K., 1959: Receptor Mechanisms and the Integration of Sensory Information in the Eye, *in* Biophysical Science—A Study Outline (Oncley J. L., ed.). Wiley, New York, Ch. 55, pp. 515–523.

Hodgkin, A. L., 1958: Ionic Movements and Electrical Activity in Giant Nerve Fibers. Proc. Roy. Soc London. B *148*:1–37.

Katz, B., 1959: Mechanisms of Synaptic Transmission *in* Biophysical Science—A Study Outline (Oncley J. L., ed.). Wiley, New York, Ch. 56:524–531.

Katz, B., 1959: Nature of the Nerve Impulse. Biophysical Science—A Study Program (Oncley, J. L., ed. Wiley, New York, Ch. 50, pp. 466–474.

Katz, B., Sept. 1961: How Cells Communicate. Sc Am. *205*:209–238.

Keynes, R. D., Dec. 1958: The Nerve Impulse and the Squid. Sci. Am. *199*:83–90.

Loewenstein, W. R., Aug. 1960: Biological Transducers. Sci. Am. *203*:99–108.

IRRITABILITY AND CONTRACTILIT

Nachmansohn, D. (ed.), 1959: Chemical and Molecular Biology of Nervous Activity. Academic Press, New York.

Ruch, T. C., and Fulton, J. F., 1960: Medical Physiology and Biophysics. Saunders, Philadelphia, Ch. 1–4.

LITERATURE CITED

1. Grundfest, H., 1952: in Modern Trends in Physiology and Biochemistry (Barron, E. S. G., ed.). Academic Press, New York, p. 193.
2. Grundfest, H., Shanes, A. M., and Freygang, W., 1953: J. Gen. Physiol. 37:25.
3. Boyarsky, L. L., 1953: Biol. Bull. 105:370.
4. Blinks, L. R., 1940: Cold Spring Harbor Symp. 8:204.
5. Osterhout, W. J. V., 1936: Bot. Rev. 2:283.
6. Osterhout, W. J. V., 1936: Physiol. Rev. 16:216.
7. Gardner, E., 1958: Fundamentals of Neurology. Saunders, Philadelphia, Ch. 6 and 7.
8. Höber, R. (ed.), 1945: Physical Chemistry of Cells and Tissues. Blakiston, New York.
9. Michaelis, L., 1929: Molecular Sieve Membranes. Bull. Nat. Res. Council, No. 69, p. 119.
10. Blinks, L. R., 1949: Proc. Nat. Acad. Sci. 35:566.
11. Blinks, L. R., 1955: in Electrochemistry in Biology and Medicine (Shedlovsky, T., ed.). Wiley, New York, p. 187.
12. Hodgkin, A. L., 1951: Biol. Rev. 26:339.
13. Conway, E. J., 1954: Symp. Soc. Exp. Biol. 8:297.
14. Fenn, W. O., 1950: J. Gen. Physiol. 33:195.
15. Hodgkin, A. L., and Keynes, R. D., 1953: J. Physiol. 119:513.
16. Keynes, R. D., 1951: J. Physiol. 113:99; 114:119.
17. Davson, H., 1959: Textbook of General Physiology. 2nd Ed. Little, Brown, Boston. Section 4.
18. Nachmansohn, D., ed., 1950: The nerve Impulse. Trans. First Conference. Josiah Macy, Jr. Foundation, New York.
19. Hodgkin, A. L., and Huxley, A. F., 1945: J. Physiol. 104:176.
20. Hodgkin, A. L., and Huxley, A. F., 1945: Nature 144:710.
21. Keynes, R. D., and Lewis, P. R., 1951: J. Physiol. 113:73.
22. Hodgkin, A. L., Huxley, A. F., and Katz, B., 1949: Arch. Sci. Physiol. 3:129.
23. Hodgkin, A. L., and Huxley, A. F., 1952: Cold Spring Harbor Symp. 17:43.
24. Brazier, M. A. B., 1960: The Electrical Activity of the Nervous System. 2nd Ed. Macmillan, New York.
25. Keynes, R. D., 1949: Arch. Sci. Physiol. 3:165.
26. Erlanger, J., and Gasser, H. S., 1937: Electrical Signs of Nervous Activity. Univ. Pennsylvania Press, Philadelphia.
27. Dudel, J., and Kuffler, S. W., 1961: J. Physiol. 155:514, 530, 543.
28. Robertson, J. D., 1955: Exp. Cell. Res. 8:226.
29. Rosenblueth, A., 1950: The Transmission of the Nervous Impulse at Neuro-Effector Junctions and Peripheral Synapses. Wiley, New York.
30. Nachmansohn, D., and Wilson, I. B., 1955: in Electrochemistry in Biology and Medicine (Shedlovsky, T., ed.). Wiley, New York, p. 167.
31. Ling, G., and Gerard, R. W., 1949: J. Cell. Comp. Physiol. 34:382.
32. Bishop, G. H., 1951: The Nerve Impulse (Nachmansohn, D., ed.). Trans. Second Conference, Josiah Macy, Jr. Foundation, New York, p. 50.
33. DeRobertis, E. D. P., 1958: Exp. Cell. Res. Suppl. 5:347.
34. Bullock, T. H., 1959: in Biophysical Science, a Study Program (Oncley, J. L., ed.). Wiley, New York, Ch. 54, pp. 504–514.
35. Connelly, C. M., 1959: in Biophysical Science, a Study Program (Oncley, J. L., ed.). Wiley, New York, Ch. 51, p. 475.
36. Hartline, H. K., 1959: in Biophysical Science, a Study Program (Oncley, J. L., ed.). Wiley, New York, Ch. 55, p. 515.
37. Katz, B., 1959: in Biophysical Science, a Study Program. (Oncley, J. L., ed.). Wiley, New York, Ch. 56, p. 534.
38. Katz, B., 1959: in Biophysical Science, a Study Program (Oncley, J. L., ed.). Wiley, New York, Ch. 50, p. 466.
39. Florey, E., 1961: Ann. Rev. Physiol. 23:501.
40. Frank, K., and Fuortes, M. G. F., 1961: Ann. Rev. Physiol. 23:357.
41. Furshpan, E. J., and Potter, D. D., 1959: J. Physiol. 145:289; 326.
42. Hodgkin, A. L., 1958: Proc. Roy. Soc. London B 148:1.
43. Katz, B., Sept. 1961: Sci. Am. 205:209.
44. Keynes, R. D., Dec. 1958: Sci. Am. 199:83.
45. Loewenstein, W. R., Aug. 1960: Sci. Am. 203:99.
46. Gaffey, C. T., and Mullins, L. J., 1959: J. Physiol. 44:505.
47. Prosser, C. L., and Brown, F. A., Jr., 1961: Comparative Animal Physiology. 2nd Ed. Saunders, Philadelphia.
48. Bullock, T. C., and Horridge, G. A., The Anatomy and Physiology of the Invertebrate Nervous System Manuscript chapters on Conduction and Transmission kindly loaned by Dr. Bullock.
49. Goldman, D. E., 1943: J. Gen. Physiol. 27:37.
50. Hodgkin, A. L., and Katz, B., 1949: J. Physiol. 108:37.
51. Gerebtzoff, M. A., and Schoffeniels, E., 1960: Comp. Biochem. 2:519.
52. Schmitt, F. O., 1959: in Biophysical Science, a Study Program (Oncley, J. L., ed.). Wiley, New York, p. 455.

53. Magoun, W. H. W. (ed.), 1959: Handbook of Physiology Sect. I: Neurophysiology (3 vols.), Williams & Wilkins, Baltimore.
54. Eccles, J. C., 1957: The Physiology of Nerve Cells. Johns Hopkins Press, Baltimore.
55. MacInnes, D. A., 1947: Principles of Electrochemistry, 2nd Ed. Dover, New York.
56. Baker, P. F., Hodgkin, A. L., and Shaw, T. I., 1961: Nature 190:885.
57. Davis, H., 1961: Physiol. Rev. 41:391.
58. Dale, H. H., Feldberg, W., and Vogt, M., 1936: J. Physiol. 86:353.
59. Hill, S. E., and Osterhout, W. J. V., 1937–38: J. Gen. Physiol. 21:541.
60. Hoyle, G., 1962: Am. Zool. 2:5.
61. See ref. 57 for a discussion of the more complex sequence of events which occur when specialized receptor cells excite the afferent neurons (e.g., in taste buds). Only the case in which the distal portion of the afferent neuron acts as a receptor is considered in Ch. 22.

CHAPTER

23

CONTRACTILITY

Contractility, that is, the capacity for movement, is one of the fundamental properties of the cell. While some cells lack the power of independent motion, their cellular structures move actively in at least some stage of their development (e.g., mitosis) and probably slowly at all times. Two kinds of cell contractility are manifested: one by which the cytoplasm moves about inside the cell, e.g., cytoplasmic streaming (*cyclosis*), and the other by which the cell makes a movement relative to its surroundings. Four types of motion relative to the surroundings are recognized in living cells: ameboid, ciliary, flagellar and muscular movement or muscular contraction. Ameboid, ciliary and flagellar movements are the primary means of locomotion in unicellular organisms and larval forms. In mature plants, movement relative to the surroundings is primarily by growth or by turgor changes, except for the movement by flagella of zoospores and gametes of some plants. In mature animals only gametes, ciliated epithelia, wandering ameboid cells and muscle cells perform easily visible movements. Embryonic cells in animals move from places of formation to places often distantly located where the cells become parts of organs. Cells in tissue culture, healing wounds, and some cancer cells also show free movement.

Cytoplasmic Streaming

Cytoplasmic streaming is readily seen in a great number of cells, e.g., *Nitella*, mycelia of molds (*Neurospora*), slime molds and protozoans (*Amoeba, Paramecium*). It is a well-known fact that during mitosis the contents of both plant and animal cells move actively and in a well-defined pattern. Streaming is also readily seen in epidermal cells, hair cells and phloem cells of the seed plant.

Cytoplasmic streaming has long been the subject of study, and the effects of various environmental conditions upon streaming have been extensively investigated. It has been found that streaming can be initiated in some cells by visible light and also by certain chemicals. Within the biokinetic zone, streaming slows when the cell is chilled and increases when the temperature is raised. It is stopped by various stimuli, such as electric shock and ultraviolet radiation. The rate of streaming is affected by various physiological and chemical factors in much the same manner as the viscosity of cytoplasm.[1-3, 46]

Although it is inherently a fascinating problem, relatively little is known of the mechanism by which cytoplasmic movement or streaming occurs. It is likened by some to a type of ameboid movement studied in foraminiferan protozoans (for discussion, see below).

Ameboid Movement

Ameboid movement is the characteristic motion of amebas, hence the name. It is the motion also of various wandering ameboid cells present in the blood and body fluid of diverse animals. Ameboid wandering cells serve as scavengers and regenerate injured regions in many invertebrates. Phagocytosis of foreign particles by ameboid white blood cells is important as a defense mechanism in multicellular animals. In organogenesis during embryonic development, some cells disperse to their definitive locations in organs by ameboid movement. In rare instances, as in *Ascaris*, sperms are ameboid. Ameboid motion is found rarely in plant cells; an example is the plasmodium of the slime mold, a huge multicellular ameboid mass formed by the aggregation and coalescence of vast numbers of small ameboid cells.[4] The plasmodium, as a unit, then moves about like a giant ameba.

Despite a considerable body of research, a satisfactory analysis of ameboid movement is still not available. The most generally accepted explanation of the mechanism of ameboid movement is the conception of a reversible gel-sol transformation.[45] Solation of the anterior end of the ameba accompanied by the contraction of the cortical gel at the posterior end ("tail") results in propulsion of a pseudopod (see Fig. 23.1A, B, C). This theory has also been used to explain the accumulation of some basic dyes (e.g., neutral red) in the interior of an ameba. According to this view, protein molecules present in the cell membrane (when in the unfolded state so that acitve combining sites are exposed) take up the dye

molecules, but they liberate the dye molecules when they contract, at which time the combining sites are covered. This mechanism supposedly could serve for active transport of materials into the cell as well as for propulsion. However, it has been shown that the ectoplasm at the posterior end of an ameba has a lower viscosity than that at the anterior end, as judged by the movement of particles in the ameba during centrifugation.[57, 60] Furthermore, it was found that when amebas are sucked into small glass capillaries, which are then broken under oil (or water) in such a way as to tear off the ectoplasm, vigorous streaming in the isolated endoplasm continues for an hour afterward in what is essentially the subcellular contractile apparatus of the ameba.[41-44] It would appear that the theory of ameboid movement by contraction of the posterior ectoplasm as outlined above is not in keeping with the facts.

Allen and his co-workers suggest instead that an ameba literally pulls itself forward by contraction in the endoplasm at the anterior end.[41-44] They found that when amebas are subjected to precisely controlled centrifugal exposures, the particulates in the axial endoplasm move only after a certain yield value has been reached, indicating structure such as is found in some colloids (see Fig. 4.5). The only regions which show a low viscosity and where the particles move with high velocity are the "shear zone," surrounding axial endoplasm, and the posterior endoplasm or "recruitment zone" (Fig. 23.1D). The latter is so named because endoplasm is recruited from the walls of the ectoplasm in the posterior third of the cell. The endoplasm appears to contract actively as it enters the "fountain zone" (see Fig. 23.1D) just posterior to the hyaline cap, where the axial endoplasm becomes everted to form part of the ectoplasmic tube. The tension developed between the anchored advancing rim of the ectoplasmic tube and the movable endoplasm displaces the latter ante-

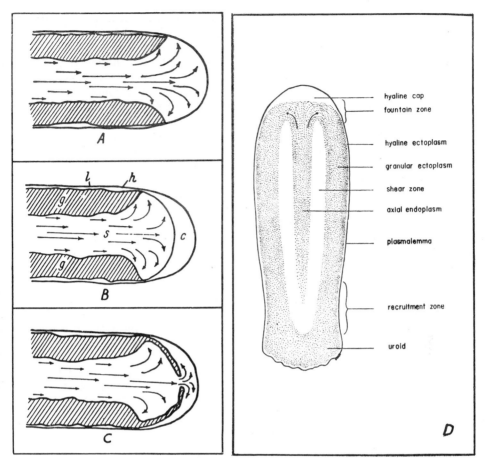

Fig. 23.1. *A, B,* and *C,* ameboid movement illustrating the growth of a pseudopod. The shaded region represents gelled cytoplasm. In *A* the flowing endoplasm reaches the plasmalemma (membrane) at the tip of the advancing pseudopod. In *B* there is a well defined hyaline cap (*c*). In *C* the hyaline cap has broken. (*s*), Plasmasol; (*g*), plasmagel; (*h*), hyaline layer; (*l*), plasmalemma. (After Mast, 1931: Protoplasma, *14*:323.) *D,* a new scheme for ameboid structure and movement based on studies of cytoplasmic flow. A new terminology is proposed for regions of the cell which are differentiated with respect to consistency. *Uroid* refers to the tail process. (From Allen, 1960: J. Biophys. Biochem. Cytol., *8*:395.)

riorly. Continuous streaming is maintained by propagation of the contraction posteriorly along the ectoplasm at the same velocity as that at which the endoplasm advances relative to the pseudopodial tip. At the anterior end of the cell the contraction phase of the contractility cycle expresses water and solutes to form the hyaline cap.[60]

A third theory postulates gel-endoplasm sliding in the shear zone (Fig. 23.1).[60] A chemical reaction is envisaged to occur between molecules in the gel and in the solated endoplasm such that the fluid endoplasm is moved forward by a mechanism perhaps akin to that proposed for muscular contraction.

A type of "ameboid" movement has been described for foraminiferan protozoans, e.g., *Allogromia*, which possess *reticulopodia*, forming a network instead of simple lobose or thread-like pseudopodia. In each of these relatively stiff filamentous reticulopodia, which may extend for many millimeters about the body of the shelled protozoan, the streaming is always in two directions simultaneously— toward and away from the body—as can be seen by watching the ever moving particles adhering to the moving surfaces on the two sides of the reticulopod (Fig. 23.2). The reticulopod is unlike a pseudopodium inasmuch as no gel-sol differences between its outer and inner cytoplasm can be detected, such as are described in a pseudopod (see above). When the cell is injured the reticulopod breaks into two filaments. It is postulated that this type of movement consists of shearing forces in opposite directions on the part of the two opposing faces of the filament, except at the tip where the filaments appear to be continuous as if one filament turned back upon itself (Fig. 23.2B). This concept has been extended to explain cyto-

plasmic movement in *Nitella* and other cells as well. This movement is thought to be similar, on a gross scale, to muscular contraction at the molecular level.[55] The filaments in a reticulopodium suggest the two types of protein filaments present in muscle cells which have been demonstrated by electron microscopy to move along one another in the course of contraction (see Chapter 24) but on a different scale.

Perhaps akin to ameboid movement is the movement of slime molds, e.g., *Physarum polycephalum*, the "many-headed" one, which produces many pseudopodia, sometimes moving in several directions.[56] An interesting aspect of the movement is its pulsating nature, the pseudopodium advancing for a while, then retreating. Movement is usually greater in one direction than in the other; therefore the slime mold as a whole advances or retreats. The nature of the pul-

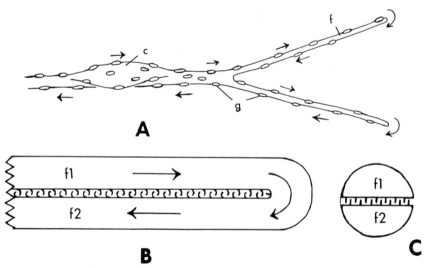

Fig. 23.2. Movement in a foraminiferan protozoan. *A*, the general shape and structure of the tip of one of the finer pseudopodia with a single bifurcation into branches about one micron in diameter. Arrows show movement of the granules (g), and of a small cytoplasmic mass (c), all of which are attached to the actively moving filament (f). *B*, arrangement of actively moving filaments (f1, f2) of pseudopod as seen in side view. The direction of movement is shown by arrows. The moving material is assumed to be in the form of a semi-cylindrical filament turned back upon itself at the tip with the flat surfaces opposed. The shearing force is assumed to be between the adjacent surfaces and is designated by the short curved lines. *C*, cross section of a filament. (From Jahn and Rinaldi, 1959: Biol. Bull. *117:* pp. 103, 111.)

IRRITABILITY AND CONTRACTILITY

sations and the motive force has been recorded by measuring the pressure just necessary to prevent movement (see Fig. 23.3). A contractile protein has been iso-lated from *Physarum,* and some evidence indicates that adenosine triphosphate may play a role in movement here as in muscle cells.[30]

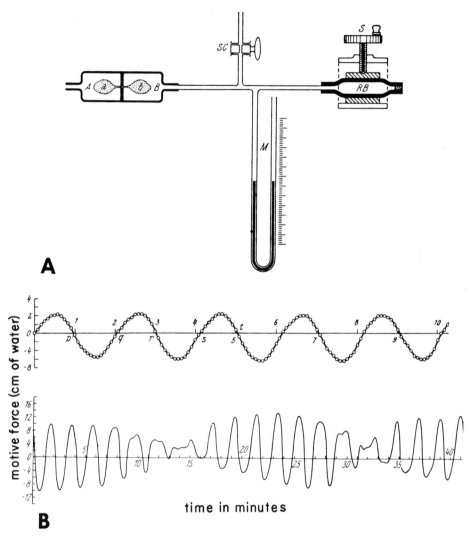

A

B

time in minutes

Fig. 23.3. *A,* diagram showing the general arrangement for measuring the motive force of proto-plasmic streaming in a myxomycete plasmodium. Note double chamber (A, B) with myxomycete (a, b) connected through a small hole between the chambers. (M) is a water-filled manometer, (SC) a stopcock, and (S) is a screw to control the pressure applied to the bulb (RB). *B,* a recording of the motive force in cm. of water. Note the beat-like wave pattern under normal conditions. The upper line is a recording showing all the points recorded several times a minute. The lower line shows a record in which the points are left out and the abscissa is compressed to make possible the showing of data for a longer period of time. It is possible to study the effect of temperature, anesthetics and various injurious agents on the wave pattern using this equipment. (From Kamiya, 1959: Proto-plasmic Streaming. Protoplasmatologia 8: sect. 3a, pp. 41, 43.)

Movement of Pigment Granules in Chromatophores

Pigment cells, or chromatophores, are of great interest in the present discussion because of the remarkable movements which they show.[37] They are found in the skin of many types of animals, and enable the animal to simulate the background in many cases, e.g., the chameleon. While chromatophores are classified in a variety of ways with regard to the pigment they contain, there are essentially three main structural types: (1) individual reticulate cells such as those found in vertebrates (Fig. 23.4A, B); (2) larger reticulate units made up of several fused cells (syncytia), such as those found in Crustacea; and (3) multicellular units consisting of a central pigment-containing cell surrounded by radially arranged muscle cells, found in some cephalopods (Fig. 23.4C, D).

The pigments in chromatophores are of diverse colors and chemical nature. Thus, the black and brown pigments are melanins, the red and yellow are carotenoids, the blue are protein-carotenoid complexes, and the reflecting white ones are guanine crystals. The latter type of pigment granules are usually immobile and the reflecting chromatophores are deeper seated. A single chromatophore may contain several types of pigment

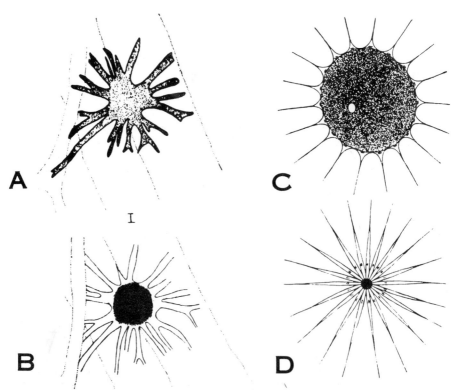

Fig. 23.4. Chromatophores. *A* and *B* represent camera lucida drawings of a melanophore from a scale of the killifish, *Fundulus* in the expanded and contracted state. *C* and *D* represent the expanded and contracted states of the pigment in the chromatophore of the squid, *Loligo*. Expansion of the pigment in this case results from contraction of the circle of muscle cells surrounding the pigment cell. (*A* and *B* from Matthews, 1931: J. Exp. Zool, 58:471. *C* and *D* from Bozler, 1928: Z. Verg. Physiol., 7:379.)

granules that move independently of one another, each pigment granule individually moving from the central mass into the branching ramifications of the cell or flowing back into the central zone. Three stages of pigment spread are recognized: punctate or contracted, stellate or intermediate, and reticulate or fully expanded. Some chromatophores respond directly to light, electricity and hormones. For example, the squid chromatophore[40] showed a response much like that obtained for the twitches and summation of a muscle fiber.

The mechanism by which the pigment moves in the reticulate chromatophore cell is not fully understood. The pigment granules appear to flow into the arborizations or channels of the cells. The channels seem to be permanent structures clearly visible, at least in tissue cultures of such cells, even when the cell is in punctate form and the pigment is in the fully contracted stage.[39] However, it has been stated that in some cases the channels collapse when the punctate state is assumed.[37]

Experiments show that application of pressure to the chromatophores of the killifish *Fundulus* brings about pigment dispersion in the chromatophores. Since the pressure required to do this (7000 to 8000 pounds per square inch) usually induces a sol-like condition in cytoplasm, it was thought that perhaps dispersion of pigment is caused by solation, whereas, conversely, the contraction of pigment is caused by gelation. To test this hypothesis Marsland[38] centrifuged the chromatophores in the punctate state and was unable to stratify the pigment granules even with a force 70,000 times gravity, while he was able to easily stratify the pigment granules in the reticulate state with less centrifugal force. However, if solation and gelation do accompany pigmentation, the exact method by which this achieves the movement of the pigment granules is not clear.

In cephalopods the pigment cell is in an expanded state when the radial muscle cells are contracted, and in a punctate state when these muscle cells are relaxed. The muscle cells are under the control of the nervous system. The chromatophores of crustaceans are coordinated by hormones while those of fishes are controlled by both hormones and nerve impulses. Since problems of regulation and coordination are beyond the realm of cell physiology, appropriate references should be consulted.[37]

Ciliary and Flagellar Movements

Cilia, the numerous hair-like motile processes on a cell, occur in all animal phyla except in nematode worms and arthropods, but they are especially prominent in members of the protozoan class Ciliata and in free-swimming larvae of many marine animals (see Fig. 23.5). A flagellum is a whip-like motile organelle, present singly or in small numbers at one end of a cell. It is present in members of the protozoan class Flagellata, in the spermatozoa of most animals and plants and in the flagellated cells of sponges and coelenterates, zoospores of algae, etc. In the flagellate *Noctiluca*, the beat of the flagellum is accompanied by an action potential.[61]

Cilia and flagella have many characteristics in common, but flagellar motion is often much more complicated than ciliary motion. The flagellum may be used like an oar, or it may move only at the tip—like a propeller, whereas the cilium is always stroked like an oar although not always in the same manner.[5, 59] Cilia and flagella serve many purposes and their movements propel the organism. They usually beat continually and act as independent effectors. However, in a few invertebrate embryos they are probably under nervous control since their movement may be stopped upon stimulation of the embryo.[9] In ciliates they are

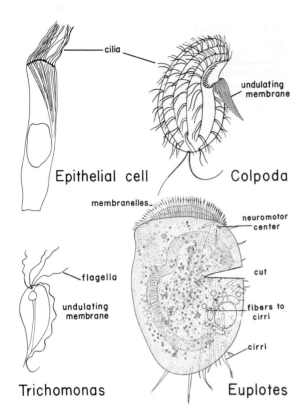

cilia

undulating membrane

Epithelial cell

Colpoda

membranelles

neuromotor center

flagella

cut

undulating membrane

fibers to cirri

cirri

Trichomonas

Euplotes

Fig. 23.5. Cilia and flagella of various types of cells. The epithelial cell is from the hepatic duct of a snail. (After Gray, 1928: Ciliary Movement. Macmillan, New York). In *Colpoda duodenaria*, a ciliate, note the fusion of cilia to form an undulating membrane and the orderly arrangement of cilia in rows. In *Trichomonas*, from the intestine of a termite, note especially the undulating membrane made by fusion of one flagellum to the cell membrane and the supporting skeletal rod (the endostyle). *Euplotes* is a ciliate with cilia fused to form membranelles at the top and along the groove leading to the mouth and into cirri, or walking appendages, on the ventral surface of the animal. Each *cirrus* is innervated by a fiber from the *neuromotor center* near the anterior end of the animal. A cut across this set of fibers causes uncoordinated movement of the cirri to which the fibers connect. A similar cut elsewhere in the body has no effect on coordination. The large sickle-shaped body is the macronucleus. Note also the numerous vacuoles. In this species the contractile vacuole is formed by fusion of many small vacuoles. (After Taylor, 1923: J. Exp. Zool., *37*:259; and 1920: Univ. Calif. Publ. Zool. *19*:403.)

thought to be coordinated by a neuro-motor center near the mouth since destruction of the fibers connecting the center to the cilia results in uncoordinated movement.[58]

Numerous studies of ciliary and flagellar movements have been made[5, 9-12, 31, 59] and a great deal of information is available on the effect of various environmental conditions on the motion of cilia and flagella. It is interesting to note that on electron micrographs of all cells tested each cilium and flagellum has a characteristic pattern of nine circumferential and two central paired filaments, the latter filaments being somewhat more delicate than the former (Fig. 23.6). Attempts have been made to interpret ciliary movement in terms of principles of muscular contraction.[13-16] Experiments show that glycerin-extracted cilia and flagella beat many times in a solution of ATP.[49]

Some evidence has been presented that the two inner filaments of a cilium transmit excitation while the nine outer filaments are the seat of ATP splitting.[27]

Akin to the cilia are the contractile myonemes seen, for example, as longitudinal fibers in the stalk of *Vorticella* (also found in *Spirostomum* and a few other ciliates). Studies on such myonemes indicate that they show many similarities to muscular movement.[47, 48] Also, the energy source seems to be the same as that for muscular contraction.[49, 54, 62]

Muscular Movement

Contractility has reached its highest development in muscle cells where, perhaps, it is most exaggerated and diagrammatic. Being adapted to their special function, the muscle cells are modified in many ways. In general the units of struc-

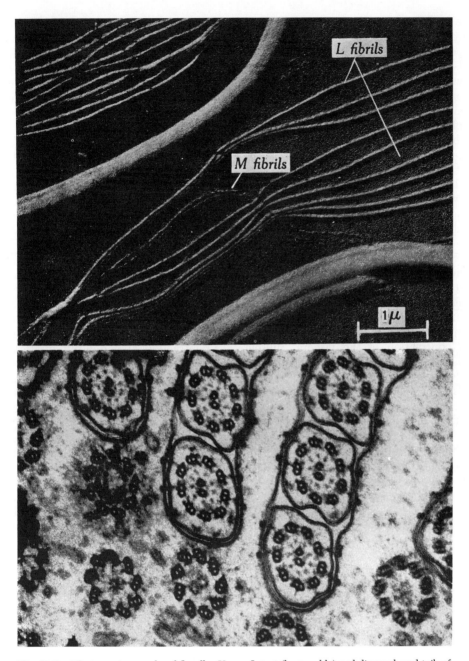

Fig. 23.6. Electronmicrographs of flagella. *Upper.* Intact (large cable) and dismembered tails of cock spermatozoons, showing the eleven fibrils of which the flagellum is composed. (M fibrils) refers to the two, median, more delicate fibrils, while (L fibrils) refers to the nine, larger, lateral fibrils. (From Grigg and Hodge, 1949: Austral. J. Sci. Res., *B2*:271.) *Lower.* Cross sections of flagella of *Pseudotrichonympha* (a flagellate from a termite). Note that the median fibrils are single while the lateral fibrils are double. Sections through basal granules are seen below the flagella. (From Gibbons and Grimstone, 1960: J. Biophys. Biochem. Cytol., 7:697.)

ture are elongate and spindle shaped, and they consist either of single cells (e.g., visceral muscle cells) or of "composite cells" called *muscle fibers* (skeletal muscle fibers). In each case the muscle cells, or fibers, possess *contractile myofibrils* (fine elongate structures) and one or more nuclei and are enclosed in a membrane. Although some studies have been made upon single muscle fibers,[23-25] most investigations of muscle contraction deal with the entire muscle or with muscle-nerve preparations, even though the major concern is the nature of cellular contractility. It will become clear that the behavior of muscle is explainable only in terms of the cells or fibers of which it is composed. Three kinds of vertebrate muscle cells are recognized: visceral, heart, and body or skeletal. The contents of the gut and various other tubular internal organs are propelled by the contraction of the visceral muscle cells lining their walls. The blood is propelled by contraction of cardiac muscle cells. Locomotion is made possible by skeletal muscle fibers, and the development of these highly differentiated structures indicates the premium placed upon speed in the animal world. Only the high points of the contractile properties of these various types of muscle cells can be discussed here.

Contraction of Visceral Muscle Cells

Contraction of visceral muscle cells shows some interesting and unique features. In structure, visceral muscle consists of tiny, elongate spindle-shaped cells, each with a single nucleus and with interconnecting bridges[8] (see Fig. 23.7 and 23.8). Minute longitudinal myofibrils (units of contraction) have been described in these cells and clearly seen in electron micrographs.[19] The cells are arranged in the wall of the tubular organ in circular and longitudinal layers, which oppose one another in action, in such a way that contraction of the longitudinal layer

shortens an organ and contraction of the circular layer lengthens it. The single cells are too small to be studied individually; therefore, for experiments on contraction, organs (e.g., stomach, intestine or parts of them) containing visceral musculature have been used.

A striking property of the contraction of visceral muscle cells of the digestive tract is their rhythmic "beat," which occurs even when all nervous connections are severed if the preparation is aerated and bathed in a balanced salt solution. The tendency to contract is therefore inherent or *myogenic*, that is, the contractions are initiated in the muscle cells themselves. This rhythmic contraction leads to *peristalsis*, or waves of contraction, at intervals of about 1 minute. A peristaltic wave is highly coordinated; coordination is achieved by a slow spread of excitation (action potential). Preceding a contraction, an action potential can be measured at a "segment" (a small portion between two regions of contracted circular muscle) of the intestine, and after it has contracted, the electrical wave excites another segment, causing it to contract, until the contraction wave has passed the full length of the intestine.[17] Long before this contraction wave has completed its course, another series of contraction waves has been initiated.

While contraction can be induced and maintained in visceral muscle cells without nervous connections, it is generally controlled by the nervous system through double innervation, that is, by excitatory and inhibitory (autonomic) nerve fibers. When denervated visceral muscle cells are stimulated with electricity, they remain contracted for many seconds before they relax. The time for a complete cycle of contraction and relaxation is called a *muscle twitch*. The twitch time for visceral muscle is generally long and the *refractory period* (that is, the period during which the muscle cells cannot be induced to contract) is relatively short. This means that a sustained state of contraction can be maintained even by a small number of periodic impulses from the nervous system.[17]

Visceral muscle cells maintain *tonus* (the mild state of sustained contraction of a muscle brought about by contraction of a few of its units) over a wide range of levels of contraction. For example, the cells of the stomach distend as the organ receives food, yet similar tonus is exerted for each distention. As food is used up, the cells of the stomach contract and maintain a fairly constant tension on the food that remains. Visceral muscle cells are capable of contraction down to within a few per cent of the lengths of the maximal stretch, a contractility far greater than that of any other muscle cells.

Visceral muscle cells have relatively low sensitivity to stimuli for contraction. For example, the chronaxie for bladder musculature of a rat is about 50 to 100 msec., and for uterine muscle of a guinea pig it is 1500 to 2000 msec., as compared with the chronaxie for skeletal muscle of man, which is 0.15 to 0.5 msec.

The contraction of visceral muscle cells is influenced by the action of hormones. This field of research is very active, but it is beyond the realm of this discussion. It will suffice to mention that, in the vertebrate, epinephrine (adrenaline) inhibits the contraction of visceral muscle cells and acetylcholine enhances it, while female sex hormones and the pituitary gland make possible powerful contractions of the uterine musculature.[18]

Contraction of Cardiac Muscle Cells

An invertebrate heart may be a very simple organ—merely a contractile tube resembling a more active visceral muscle, as in the annelid worms. In fishes the heart is still a simple tube, but in all other vertebrates it is a fairly complex structure.[5] The vertebrate heart muscle, viewed in sections under the light microscope, appears to be composed of an interlacing network of muscle fibers and

Fig. 23.7. Isolated smooth muscle cells from the wall of the stomach of a cat. ($\times$220) (From Maximow and Bloom, 1960: A Textbook of Histology. 7th. Ed., Saunders, Philadelphia. p. 159.)

was thought to be a syncytium, i.e., to form a single multinucleate unit. However, electron micrographs show that the network is composed of separate cells (fibers) which are in intimate contact rather than in a continuous syncytium.[22] The separate fibers can be demonstrated also by treatment with strong alkali. Each cell is indicated by a nucleus, and each mass of cytoplasm is separated from the next by membranes called intercalated disks.

The vertebrate heart, even when removed from the body, still continues to beat. The beat is, therefore, said to be myogenic, although a particular balance

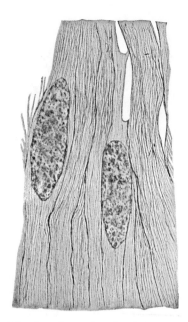

Fig. 23.8. Smooth muscle cells of the intestine of *Triton vulgaris*, a salamander. Note the myofibrils. (×1430) From Maximow and Bloom, A Textbook of Histology. 7th. Ed. Saunders, Philadelphia, p. 160. (After Levi.)

of ions is necessary for maintenance of this activity (see Chapters 8 and 12).

Although the entire heart is capable of beating or contracting, a gradient of excitability is found in its parts, and the most irritable portion is called the *pacemaker*. In the frog heart the pacemaker is the sinus venosus (see Fig. 23.9). In the mammal heart the sinus venosus is represented by a vestige, the *sinoauricular node*, which is the pacemaker from which the wave of excitation (depolarization) sweeps over the heart, initiating the beat in the auricles, from which it spreads by way of the auriculoventricular node and the *bundle of His* to the ventricle (see Fig. 23.10). Modified muscular fibers (Purkinje fibers in the bundle of His) in the ventricle carry the action potential at the rate of about 5 meters per second to various portions of the heart, making possible a coordinated contraction.[20, 32]

Initiation of the heart beat, as seen in the frog, is not the prerogative of the sinus venosus alone, since if the sinus is cut from the auricles, or the auricles from the ventricle, each piece, after it has recovered from the shock of the operation, will continue to beat. However, only the rate of beat of the portion containing the sinus venosus equals that of the intact heart, while the isolated auricles and ventricles beat more slowly. The severed tip of the ventricle shows the least ability to initiate a contraction.[20, 32] Apparently the pacemaker is the most irritable portion of the heart and therefore the first to contract. If it is affected locally, by the application of a cold or hot rod, the rate of the heart beat is lowered or increased, respectively.

If a ligature is tied between the pacemaker and the rest of the heart, the ventricle no longer beats at its regular rate (see Fig. 23.11). If the ventricle, physiologically isolated in this manner, is stimulated by electrical means, a threshold stimulus evokes contraction to the full extent characteristic of the normal tonus level of the heart. Increasing the stimulus does not increase the degree of contraction.[20, 32] The cardiac muscle contraction therefore obeys the all-or-none rule, under the conditions of these experiments.

The refractory period for cardiac contraction is fairly long, being about 1 second in man.[32] It depends upon the size of the animal, being shorter for the rapidly beating heart of a small animal. It is shorter also in a warm-blooded animal than in a cold-blooded one of the same size. Because of the long refractory period, the heart muscle fibers cannot be tetanized on continued stimulation. Electrical stimulation is effective only if the heart muscle fibers are in the relative refractory phase (see Fig. 23.12), when an extra contraction may be induced. The extra contraction is followed by a compensatory phase (refractory time) during which contraction cannot be induced by further stimulation.

The long refractory period of the heart probably results from permeability changes and ionic fluxes at the cell membranes. The Na$^+$ influx is not cut off as rapidly as in nerve, nor does the K$^+$ efflux rise above the steady state condition. Repolarization is therefore delayed.[62]

The force of the heart beat depends upon the stretch to which the fibers are subjected, e.g., upon the degree to which the heart is filled with blood. This relation is known as *Starling's law of the heart.* The heart muscle fibers maintain tonus at various levels of contraction; they can contract from any one of these levels. Such a response is adaptive and of importance in maintaining a good blood supply, since the heart may respond to varied demands upon it by a change in the strength or frequency of contraction.[20, 32]

The beat of the vertebrate heart, while self-initiated, is regulated by inhibitory and excitatory nerve fibers from the autonomic nervous system. Stimulation of the inhibitory nerve fibers, which come by way of the tenth cranial nerve (the vagus), slows or stops the heart beat (see Fig. 23.13). Loewi demonstrated that something diffusible appears in the heart after stimulation of the vagus and that the per-

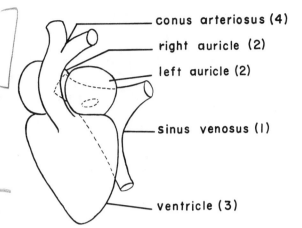

Fig. 23.9. Sequence (shown by numbers) of contraction of the parts of a frog's heart.

fusate from such a heart, when circulated to another heart, will inhibit the beat of the second heart also (see Fig. 23.14). For studies in this field he received the Nobel prize in 1936. The diffusible substance, or "vagusstoff," was later identified as acetylcholine (equation 21.1), application of which slows or stops the heart beat.[20, 32] The mechanism by which this occurs has been considered in Chapter 22.

A heart with the beat slowed by acetyl-

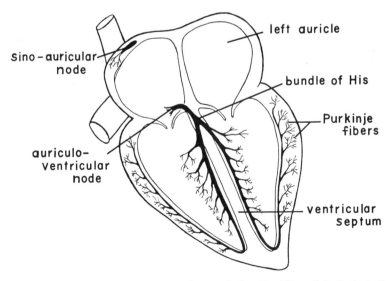

Fig. 23.10. Diagram of a mammalian heart, showing the bundle of His and the Purkinje fibers.

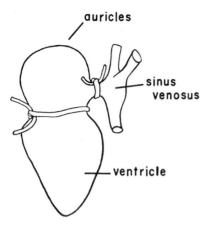

auricles

sinus venosus

ventricle

Fig. 23.11. Isolating the sinus venosus from the auricles and the auricles from the ventricle by means of ligatures.

choline, or by brief stimulation of the vagus nerve, usually beats more forcibly for a while and then resumes a normal rate of beating.

The beat is resumed because the acetylcholine is decomposed to choline and acetic acid. Decomposition is accelerated greatly by a highly active enzyme, choline esterase, which is widely distributed, especially in nervous and muscle cells. Sometimes, even if vagal stimulation is continued, the heart may occasionally "escape" from the inhibitory influence of the vagus and beat more forcibly than normally, thus indicating the strong tendency of the heart muscle cells to continue rhythmic contraction.

Stimulation of the excitatory nerve fibers, which comes by way of the sympathetic nerve, accelerates the heart beat (Fig. 23.15). It is found that the perfusate of a heart excited in this manner contains sympathin, probably chiefly norepinephrine (differing from epinephrine by lack of a CH_3 radical[34]). Application of epinephrine to the surface of the heart and its injection into the heart are familiar methods for stimulating heart muscle contractions.[34]

Contractions of some invertebrate hearts share many of the properties of contraction of the vertebrate heart. There are other invertebrate hearts, however (like that of the adult king crab *Limulus*), in which the heart contraction is *neurogenic*, that is, the heart will not beat when severed from nervous connections. It is also interesting to note that in the larval stage of this animal, the heart beat is myogenic, suggesting that the neurogenic heart beat is the result of a more specialized structure than a heart in which the contractions are myogenic. Studies on vertebrate and invertebrate hearts and their control are discussed in books on human and comparative physiology.[5, 32]

Contraction of Skeletal (Body) Muscle Fibers

Individual muscle cells of the body musculature of lower invertebrates are relatively simple cells much like visceral muscle cells of vertebrates and show similar rhythmic pulsations.[21] It is only in some higher invertebrates (cephalopod mollusks and insects) and in the vertebrates that skeletal muscle cells become much elongated and show striking transverse striations. It must be realized that such muscle cells probably represent highly specialized structures[5] in which certain properties of contractility have been exaggerated while other properties, such as myogenicity, have been lost. Only the essential features of vertebrate skeletal muscle movement will be illustrated here.

The skeletal muscles, which move the body and its appendages, are under voluntary control and are made up of multinucleate muscle fibers containing contractile fibrils, across which run transverse striations (see Fig. 23.16). The contractile fibrils of a muscle fiber practically fill it, but a certain amount of cytoplasm surrounds the fibrils, and in the cytoplasm are found the spindle-shaped nuclei, the entire fiber being a multinucleate unit. It is interesting that such multinucleate fibers have arisen not only in the vertebrates, but also in several invertebrate groups.[5] This suggests an evolutionary advantage of a unit of this type in which the contractile fibrils may become much longer than would be possible in a single cell. A long muscle fiber has an advantage in the propagation of excitation for contraction and in the mechanical work performed.

The skeletal muscle fibers of vertebrates are innervated only by excitatory nerve fibers (single innervation). An efferent neuron innervates a small number of muscle fibers, each branch of the distal portion of the axon attaching to a muscle fiber by a muscle end plate or *myoneural junction* (see Fig. 23.17 and 22.12). The motor neuron and the muscle fibers innervated by it respond as a unit and constitute the *motor unit.* A large number of motor units make possible a fine gradation of force exerted—from delicate movements to powerful sustained ones—depending upon the number of motor units called into action. When the nervous impulse traveling on the efferent neuron reaches the myoneural junction, it first induces a local excitatory state (local potential) on the muscle fiber near the myoneural junction. If this change is of sufficient magnitude (above threshold), an action potential (Chapter 21) sweeps the muscle fiber, following which the muscle fiber contracts (Fig. 23.18).

The muscle fibers may also be directly stimulated by heat, light, chemicals, pressure or electricity, and the excitation is always accompanied by action potentials. When a muscle fiber is electrically stimulated with a current below threshold, a local excitatory state develops around the cathode. This state of excitation grows with continued stimulation, but only when the current is above threshold and the time of application is sufficiently long will the excitation become propagated and induce contraction of the muscle fiber. Muscle fibers, like nerve fibers, maintain a resting potential of about 50 to 100 millivolts, the outside being posi-

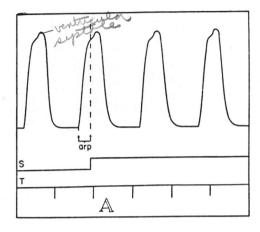

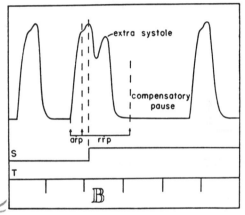

Fig. 23.12. *A,* demonstration of the absolute refractory period (arp) of the heart. Each spike is a kymograph record of a heart beat, the peak being the height of ventricular systole, after which the heart begins to relax. When the heart is contracting, a single electric shock (S) has no effect. (T) is the time in seconds. *B,* demonstration of the relative refractory period (rrp). When a single electric shock is sent into the ventricle at about the peak of ventricular contraction or soon afterwards, an extra systole appears, subnormal in strength and followed by a compensatory phase. (T) is the time in seconds. (From Amberson and Smith, 1948: Outline of Physiology. 2nd Ed. Williams & Wilkins, Baltimore, p. 277.)

tive to the inside. This sign of the potential reverses during excitation. Evidence indicates that during the development of the propagated action potentials the same type of ionic changes occur in muscle fibers as in nerve fibers. The action potential travels over the muscle

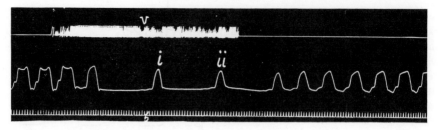

Fig. 23.13. A kymograph record of the inhibition of heart beat by stimulation of the vagus. The tuning fork record at v shows the tetanic stimulation of the vagus. At (i) and (ii) the heart "escapes" from the inhibitory influence, indicating the strength of the tendency to beat. The lower markings are 0.2 second intervals. (Classroom experiment.)

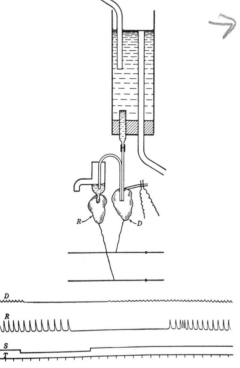

Fig. 23.14. Perfusion apparatus containing Ringer's solution and two hearts with fluid intercommunication to demonstrate Loewi's classic experiment on regulation of the heart by a hormone. Heart (D) is stimulated electrically by way of the vagus nerve, and it stops beating, as shown in kymograph record (D) below. Fluid pumped from donor heart (D) into recipient heart (R) stops heart (R) somewhat later, as shown in record (R) below. The effective substance in the perfusate has been shown to be acetylcholine. (S) (below) indicates the time at which the electric stimulus is applied to the vagus. (T) represents the time in seconds for the three records above it. (From Scheer, 1953: General Physiology, Wiley, New York, p. 457.)

fibers at the rate of 1 or 2 meters per second, which is much slower than in nerve fibers. Just how the electrical excitation induces muscular contraction is unknown.[26]

The chronaxie for muscle fibers is comparable to that for the motor neurons innervating it. The strength-duration curve resemble those of nerve fibers, only the absolute values being different. Muscle fibers are therefore highly excitable systems and have many properties in common with nerve fibers.

If a muscle fiber is stimulated with current above rheobase but of duration insufficient to excite, contraction does not occur. If the stimuli are frequently repeated, they may summate, each subliminal excitation producing a local potential which may be added to other until the local potential sets off a propagated action potential (spike), which, in turn, is followed by a contraction. When single muscle fibers are isolated by removal or destruction of surrounding muscle fibers, and then stimulated with graded series of shocks, the individual muscle fiber always contracts as a unit and to the same extent. When individual muscle fibers in an intact muscle are tagged by spraying with mercury and then excited with electrodes small enough to contact only single fibers, individual fibers are seen to contract completely not at all. These experiments show that single muscle fibers in the intact muscle like single neurons, obey the all-or-none

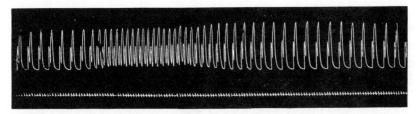

Fig. 23.15. Kymograph record showing acceleration of the heart of a frog by stimulation of the sympathetic nerve. (From Zoethout and Tuttle, 1952: Textbook of Physiology. 11th Ed., Mosby, St. Louis, p. 219.)

aw under the conditions of the experiment.

An interesting but little understood exception to the all-or-none principle occurs in some frog muscle fibers of the back, which are innervated by small nerves. Stimulation of these nerves causes individual muscle fibers to contract sometimes to a greater degree than at other times. Analysis has shown that a local excitatory state in such muscle fibers is accompanied by a local contraction, the degree of local contraction depending upon the magnitude of the local excitatory potential. The purpose served by local contractions in these muscle fibers is unknown. On the other hand, in some invertebrates, such as the crustacea, local contractions are the main method for obtaining graded responses, since the number of motor units is very small.[29]

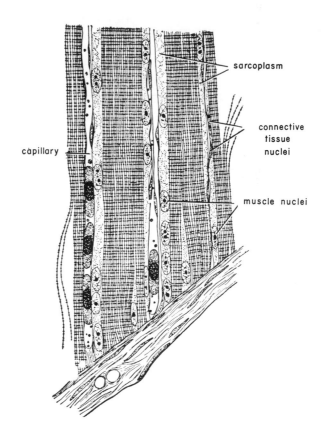

sarcoplasm

connective tissue nuclei

càpillary

muscle nuclei

Fig. 23.16. Longitudinal section of striated muscle from the sucker *Catostomus*. (From Dahlgren and Kepner, 1925: Principles of Animal Histology. Macmillan, New York, p. 81.)

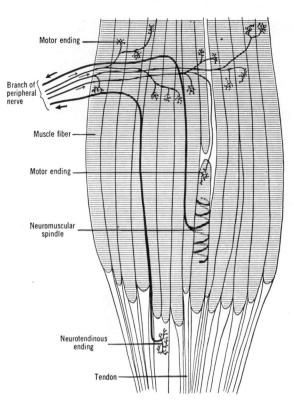

Fig. 23.17. Relations between neurons and muscle fibers. Efferent neurons end in myoneural junctions (muscle end-organs). Two afferent neurons are also shown, one from a muscle spindle and the other from a tendon receptor. (From Gardner: Fundamentals of Neurology. 2nd Ed. Saunders, Philadelphia.

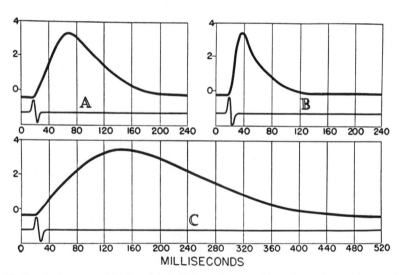

MILLISECONDS

Fig. 23.18. Action potentials (lower record in each example) and muscle twitches in three muscles. A, the mainly white-fibered gastrocnemius; B, the wholly white-fibered internal rectus; C, the red-fibered soleus. (From Amberson and Smith, 1948: Outline of Physiology. 2nd Ed. Williams & Wilkins, Baltimore, p. 128.)

When a muscle is stimulated with electricity, by varying the voltage, it is possible to find a minimal stimulus threshold below which no response is observed. As the voltage is increased above the threshold, the force of contraction of the muscle increases in degree, until a maximal contraction is observed[27, 32] (see Fig. 23.19). The same graded response is found upon stimulation, by way of the nerve, of an intact muscle in the animal, and is the consequence of the response of successively larger numbers of motor units, as stimulation increases in strength. A muscle has many motor units, each of which has a characteristic threshold. In a population of fibers some have low, some high, and some intermediate thresholds, the sensitivity being distributed about a mean. When a muscle is stimulated, gradation is obtained by calling into action all those fibers for which the stimulus is above threshold.[27, 28, 32]

A single electric shock induces a single twitch of a muscle fiber. The twitch is a laboratory phenomenon primarily useful for analysis of the properties of muscular contraction. The record of a muscle twitch may be spread out by being recorded on a rapidly moving drum of a kymograph, thereby making possible a study of the time relations in the contraction and relaxation of the muscle fiber. The entire cycle for the "form" curve of the gastrocnemius muscle of a frog occupies about 0.1 second (Fig. 23.18). Immediately after stimulation, a latent period of about 0.0075 second elapses before the contraction begins. During this period the action potential, beginning at the point of stimulation, sweeps the muscle. Contraction occupies about 0.04 second, relaxation about 0.05 second. The exact times vary with the type of muscle fiber and the temperature. After stimulation muscle fibers becomes *refractory* for a period lasting a fraction of a millisecond several milliseconds, during which they cannot be excited again. Since the

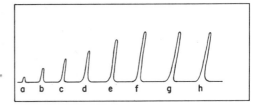

Fig. 23.19. Graded response of a skeletal muscle to increasing stimulation. A maximal response is reached at f. (Classroom experiment.)

twitch of a frog gastrocnemius muscle reaches its full contraction 0.04 second after excitation and relaxes only after another 0.05 second, it is evidently excitable long before it has relaxed. Consequently, it is possible for a skeletal muscle fiber to maintain continuous tension if stimulated frequently enough within a given time. A sustained contraction of this type is called *tetanus* (see Fig. 23.20).

If the stimuli are spaced so that they reach the muscle after it has begun to relax, incomplete tetanus is obtained (Fig. 23.20). The record shows that a relaxing muscle may be induced to contract from any degree of relaxation, as might be expected from the shortness of the refractory period.

Contractions of the muscle fibers in the living animal are normally initiated by continuous volleys of discharges along motor neurons. The impulses are spaced about a hundredth of a second apart, leading to tetanic contractions of some muscle fibers in various muscles of the body. By this means, muscular *tonus* is maintained. This tonus is responsible for maintenance of posture and for keeping the musculature in readiness for action. In a muscle stimulated to tetanic contraction, the degree of contraction increases during the course of the volley of impulses, and the final state of contraction achieved is greater than the initial state. This indicates that a muscle kept contracted does more work per stimulus than one just stimulated from a state of

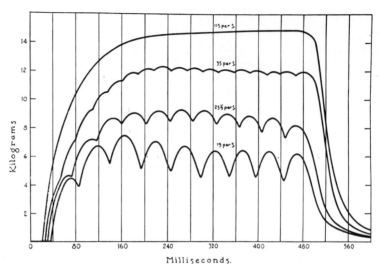

Fig. 23.20. Partial and complete tetanus caused by varying rhythms of stimuli applied to the gastrocnemius muscle. (From Amberson and Smith, 1948: Outline of Physiology. 2nd Ed. Williams & Wilkins, Baltimore, p. 131.)

rest (Fig. 23.20), a behavior in apparent contradiction to the all-or-none principle. The fact is, individual skeletal muscle fibers will also contract to a greater extent if stimulated when already contracted than if stimulated from a state of rest, thus showing increased capacity for work under these conditions. The all-or-none law, then, holds under a given set of circumstances only.

When a stimulated muscle is unable to move its load and does not shorten, the muscular contraction is said to be *isometric* ("same length"). Although tension (force) is developed and the muscle tonus is increased, no mechanical work is done and all the expended energy appears as heat. For recording the maximum tension exerted by a particular muscle, use may be made of a lever and an attached spring (see Fig. 23.21). Muscles used for maintaining posture are contracting isometrically. On the other hand, if a muscle is able to move a load, that is, when the resistance offered by the load is less than the tension developed, the muscle shortens and performs mechanical work. The same tonus is maintained, irrespective of the degree of contraction; hence this contraction is said to be *isotonic* ("same tonus") (see Fig. 23.22). The muscle used in lifting a load are contracting isotonically. In lifting a load, an average of 20 to 25 per cent of the total chemical potential energy expenditure appears as mechanical work, the remainder being dissipated as heat. The muscle is therefore more efficient than the steam engine and comparable in efficiency to the gasoline engine.[20, 32]

A muscle fiber is capable of maintaining tetanus for a considerable period, the limit being set by development of *fatigue* and resultant failure of contraction. Fatigue is also observed if individual twitches are induced continually, by electricity, for example, although a frog leg muscle contracts about 12,000 times before fatiguing.[33] As a muscle fatigues, the degree of contraction decreases gradually because some of the component fibers fail to contract; consequently, the capacity for work of the muscle as a whole decreases (see Fig. 23.23). The cause of muscular fatigue is not known with certainty. It is thought to be due to a number

IRRITABILITY AND CONTRACTILI

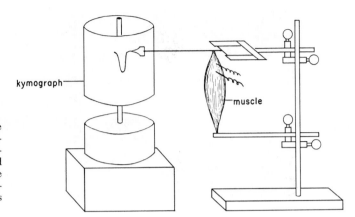

Fig. 23.21. Isometric muscle contraction. The muscle is attached to a lever which is soldered to a steel spring held tightly in the clamp. It therefore exerts tension with only a minimum of contraction which is magnified by the lever.

ber of changes occurring concurrently: first, the exhaustion of the substrate serving as the immediate source of energy and, second, the accumulation of waste products. Experiments have demonstrated that removal of wastes by continuously washing a thin sheet of muscle in balanced salt solution delays fatigue. In any event, if stimuli are applied at such intervals that the muscle fibers have a chance to recover, they may be able to contract for hours without fatigue. Apparently, recovery is complete, or nearly so, in about 1 second. Intact muscle fibers, stimulated *in vivo* through a nerve, fatigue much more rapidly (e.g., frogs are fatigued after 29 to 82 jumps in 1 to 2 minutes[33]. In this case the impulse

passes by way of the myoneural junction and thence to the muscle fiber. The myoneural junction fatigues quite readily, even though the muscle fibers of a fatigued animal will continue to contract on direct stimulation. The nerve fiber fatigues even more slowly than the muscle fiber it innervates. The myoneural junction apparently acts as a safety valve, preventing injury to the muscle fiber by too prolonged a period of contraction.

Relaxation of a skeletal muscle fiber could conceivably be a passive process, since skeletal muscles occur in pairs which are opposite in action, e.g., an extensor and a flexor. Studies of an isolated muscle show that without any pull or friction upon it, a muscle after contraction relaxes and ex-

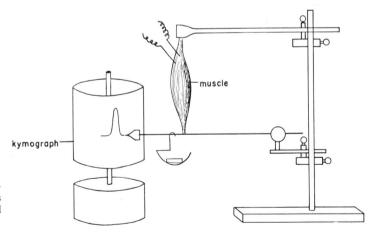

Fig. 23.22. Isotonic contraction. The muscle pulls an easily movable lever and shortens as it does so.

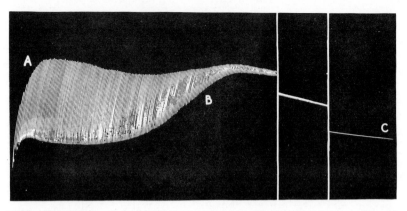

Fig. 23.23. Kymograph records of fatigue curve, showing staircase (A), contracture (B), and complete fatigue (C). (From Zoethout and Tuttle, 1952: Textbook of Physiology. 11th Ed., C. V. Mosby, St. Louis, p. 109.)

tends itself, but is not capable of doing work. Thus, if the muscle is placed in a bath of mercury it cannot become extended against the weight of the mercury. Nonetheless, evidence indicates that relaxation is a spontaneous process,[20, 32] and not merely the absence of the active state.

Contracture is the name given to muscular contraction which is sustained, reversible, and which occurs with the liberation of heat but shows no propagated spike potentials. It is brought on by various stimuli, e.g., strong electric currents, heat, acids, narcotics, potassium, citrate, caffeine, acetylcholine, nicotine, veratrine and many other drugs. When veratrine, for example, is dropped on a single muscle fiber, it gives rise to several propagated spikes, after which a prolonged negativity (after-potential) develops, accompanied by a contracture. Spontaneous normal repolarization of the membrane of the muscle fiber, or anodal stimulation, brings the contracture to an end. Contracture precedes fatigue in a muscle which is continuously stimulated.

If skeletal muscle fiber is stretched by weights, it may be considerably extended. After removal of the weights it returns to its original length, indicating that it is highly elastic. The elasticity is due in part

to the contractile fibrils and in part to the sarcolemma membrane which encloses each muscle fiber, since the membrane remains elastic, even when the contents of the muscle fiber have been expressed,[23] although not as elastic as the whole fiber.

Work and Heat Relations in Muscle Contraction

A muscle can contract with shortening (isotonic contraction) or without shortening (isometric contraction). The muscle fibers can exert maximal tension (force) when they do not shorten; for example, a striated muscle can exert a tension of 3 kilograms per square centimeter of cross section. Even though a muscle fiber in this state does no visible work in the physical sense of moving an object through a given distance, it needs energy to maintain the state of tension, and this energy, on degradation, appears as heat.[35, 50]

When a muscle fiber shortens it exerts less tension than when it does not shorten. The tension also decreases as the speed of shortening increases. This decrease in tension is not due to changes in internal viscosity of the muscle cells (friction) since a muscle fiber shortening rapidly should liberate more heat than one short

496

ening slowly over the same distance, yet this is not found to be the case. Therefore, the decrease in tension is presumably caused by other factors.[35, 36]

A shortening muscle fiber liberates heat in proportion to the distance of shortening, and not to the speed. But the "shortening heat" is independent of the load on the muscle fibers—a muscle fiber produces no more and no less "shortening heat" (i.e., at the time of shortening) when it lifts a large load than when it lifts a small one. Since the muscle fiber carrying a larger load does more work than the one carrying a small load, the total energy expended by the muscle fiber increases with the load. A muscle cell therefore shows some remarkable properties, and the chemical reactions which provide the energy for contraction must consequently be controlled, not only by change in length of the muscle fiber, but also by the tension placed on it during this change.[36]

Forced lengthening of a muscle fiber during contraction decreases the energy liberated. A. V. Hill[36] has gathered evidence to indicate that the chemical processes which are induced in a muscle fiber by applying a stimulus are reversed by the application of external mechanical work (force working through a distance), although it is not possible to store energy in the muscle fiber in this way.

GENERAL REFERENCES

Allen, R. D., 1961: Ameboid movement, in The Cell (Brachet, J., and Mirsky, A. E., eds.). Academic Press, New York, vol. 2, pp. 135–186.

Allen, R. D., Feb. 1962: Ameboid Movement. Sci. Am. 206:112–122.

Bourne, C. (ed.), 1960: Structure and Function of Muscles. Academic Press, New York, 2 vol.

Davson, H., 1959: A Textbook of General Physiology. 2nd Ed. Little, Brown, Boston. Ch. 18 and 19.

Fawcett, D., 1961: Cilia and Flagella, in The Cell (Brachet, J., and Mirsky, A. E., eds.). Academic Press, New York, 2:217–297.

Fingerman, M., 1959: The Physiology of Chromatophores. Internat. Rev. Cyt. 8:175–210.

Harmon, J. W., 1956: The Cytochondria of Cardiac and Skeletal Muscle. Internat. Rev. Cyt. 5:89–146.

Hayashi, T., Sept. 1961: How cells move. Sci. Am. 205:184–204.

Hill, A. V., 1960: Production and Absorption of Work by Muscle. Science 131:897–903.

Hoffmann-Berling, H., 1958: Physiologie der Bewegungen und Teilungsbewegungen tierischer Zellen. Fortschr. der Zool. (N. F.) 11:142–207.

Holtzer, H., 1959: Some Further Uses of Antibodies for Analyzing the Structure and Development of Muscles. Exp. Cell. Res. (suppl.) 7:234–243.

Huxley, A. F., 1957: Molecular Structure and Theories of Contraction. Progr. Biophys. 7:255–318.

Huxley, H. E., 1960: Muscle Cells, in The Cell (Brachet, J., and Mirsky, A. E., eds.). Academic Press, New York, vol. 4, pp. 365–481.

Kamiya, N., 1960: Physics and Chemistry of Protoplasmic Streaming. Ann. Rev. Plant Physiol. 11:323–340.

Marsland, D., 1956: Protoplasmic Contractility in Relation to Gel Structure: Temperature and Pressure Experiments on Cytokinesis and Ameboid Movement. Internat. Rev. Cyt. 5:199–228.

Perry, S. V., 1956: Relation between Chemical and Contractile Function and Structure of the Skeletal Muscle Cell. Physiol. Rev. 36:1–76.

Physiology of Voluntary Muscle. British Med. Bull. 12 no. 3, 1956.

Prosser, C. L., and Brown, F. A., Jr., 1961: Comparative Animal Physiology. 2nd Ed. Saunders, Philadelphia. Sections on muscles and chromatophores.

Slater, E. C., 1957: Sarcosomes (Muscle Mitochondria). Symp. Soc. Exp. Biol. 10:110–133.

Wilkie, D. R., 1959: Facts and Theories about Muscles. Progr. Biophys. 4:288–324.

LITERATURE CITED

1. Heilbrunn, L. V., 1952: An Outline of General Physiology. 3rd Ed. Saunders, Philadelphia, Ch. 14.
2. Seifriz, W., 1953: Nature 171:1136.
3. Ewart, A. S., 1903: Protoplasmic Streaming in Plants. Clarendon, London.
4. Bonner, J. T., 1952: Morphogenesis. Princeton Univ. Press, Princeton, N. J.
5. Prosser, C. L., and Brown, F. A., Jr., 1961: Comparative Animal Physiology. 2nd Ed. Saunders, Philadelphia.
6. Schaeffer, A. A., 1920: Ameboid Movement. Princeton Univ. Press, Princeton, N. J.
7. Kriszat, G., 1949: Arkiv. Zool. 1:81, 477.
8. Thaenert, J. C., 1957: J. Biophys. Biochem. Cyt. 6:67.

9. Gray, J., 1928: Ciliary Movement. Cambridge Univ. Press, London.
10. Metz, C. B., Pitelka, D., and Westfall, J. A., 1953: Biol. Bull. *104*:408.
11. Bradfield, J. R. G., 1953: Quart. J. Micros. Soc. *94*:351.
12. Sedar, A. W., and Porter, K. R., 1955: J. Bioph. Biochem. Cyt. *1*:583.
13. Seaman, G. R., and Houlahan, R. K., 1951: J. Cell. Comp. Physiol. *37*:309.
14. Maroney, S. P., and Ronkin, R. R., 1953: Biol. Bull. *105*:378.
15. Bulbring, E., Burn, J. H., and Shelley, H. J., 1952: Proc. Roy. Soc., London, B *141*:445.
16. Bulbring, E., et al., Brit. J. Pharmacol. 7:67.
17. Fisher E., 1944: Physiol. Rev. *24*:467.
18. Turner, G. D., 1960: General Endocrinology. 3rd Ed. Saunders, Philadelphia.
19. Hanson, J., and Lowy, J., 1957: Nature *180*:906.
20. Zoethout, W. D., and Tuttle, W. W., 1961: Textbook of Physiology. 14th Ed. Mosby, St. Louis, Ch. 10.
21. Pantin, C. F. A., 1952: Proc. Roy. Soc. London, B *140*:147.
22. Sjostrand, F. S., Andersson-Cedergran, E., and Dewey, M. M., 1958: J. Ultrastructure Res. *1*:271.
23. Ramsey, R. W., and Street, S. F., 1941: Biol. Symp. *3*:9.
24. Nastuck, W. L., and Hodgkin, A. L., 1950: J. Cell. Comp. Physiol. *35*:39.
25. Nastuck, W. L., 1953: J. Cell. Comp. Physiol. *42*:249.
26. Tiegs, D. W., 1953: Physiol. Rev., *33*:90.
27. Hayashi, T., Sept. 1961: Sci. Am. *205*:184.
28. Davson, H., 1959: A Textbook of General Physiology. 2nd Ed. Little, Brown, Boston, Sect. 5.
29. Wiersma, C. A. G., 1952: Ann. Rev. Physiol. *14*:159.
30. Loewy, A. G., 1942: J. Cell. Comp. Physiol. *40*:127.
31. Potts, B. P., and Tomlin, S. G., 1955: Biochim. Biophys. Acta *16*:66.
32. Ruch, T. C., and Fulton, J. F., 1960: Medical Physiology and Biophysics. 18th Ed. Saunders, Philadelphia, Ch. 4.
33. Heilbrunn, L. V., 1952: An Outline of General Physiology. 3rd Ed. Saunders, Philadelphia, Ch. 27.
34. Vogt, M., 1954: J. Physiol. *123*:451.
35. Huxley, H. E., 1956: Endeavour *15*:177. Nov. 1958: Sci. Am. *199*:67.
36. Hill, A. V., 1960: Science *131*:897.
37. Nicol, J. A. C., 1960: The Biology of Marine Animals. Interscience, New York, Ch. 12.
38. Marsland, D., 1944: Biol. Bull. *87*:252.
39. Matthews, S. A., 1931: J. Exp. Zool. *58*:471.
40. Hill, A. V., and Solandt, D. Y., 1934: J. Physiol. (London) *83*:13P.
41. Allen, R. D., Cooledge, J. W., and Hall, P. J., 1960: Nature *187*:896.
42. Griffin, J. L., and Allen, R. D., 1960: Exp. Cell Res. *20*:619.
43. Allen, R. D., 1960: J. Biophys. Biochem. Cyt. *8*:379. Also, 1961: Exp. Cell. Res. suppl *8*:17–31.
44. Allen, R. D., and Roslansky, J. D., 1959: J. Biophys. Biochem. Cyt. *6*:437.
45. Zimmerman, A. M., Landau, J. V., and Marsland D., 1958: Exp. Cell. Res. *15*:484.
46. Smirnova, N. A., 1955: Fiziol. Rastenii Akad Nauk S.S.S.R. *2*:578.
47. LaPique, L., and Faure-Fremiet, E., 191? Compt. Rend. Soc. Biol. *74*:1194.
48. Hou, C. L., and Brücke, E., 1931: Arch. ge Physiol. *226*:411.
49. Hoffmann-Berling, H., 1958: Biochim. Biophy Acta 27:247.
50. Kishimoto, U., and Akabori, H., 1959: J. Ger Physiol. *42*:1167.
51. Kishimoto, U., 1958: J. Gen. Physiol. *41*:120? 1223.
52. Kamiya, N., and Kuroda, K., 1958: Protoplasm *50*:144.
53. Kelso, J. M., and Turner, J. S., 1955: Australian Biol. Sci. *8*:19.
54. Roth, L. E., 1958: J. Ultrastructure Res. *1*:223.
55. Jahn, T. L., and Rinaldi, R., 1959: Biol. Bu *117*:100.
56. Kamiya, N., 1959: Protoplasmic Streaming. P toplasmatologia 8, Sect. 3a, pp. 1–199.
57. Harvey, E. N., and Marsland, D. M., 1932: Cell. Comp. Physiol. *2*:75.
58. Taylor, C. V., 1920: Univ. California Publ. Zo *19*:403.
59. Fawcett, D., 1961: *in* The Cell (Brachet, J., a Mirsky, A. E., eds.). Academic Press, N York, vol. 2, p. 218.
60. Allen, R. D., 1961: *in* The Cell (Brachet, J., a Mirsky, A. E., eds.). Academic Press, N York, vol. 2, p. 135.
61. Hisada, M., 1957: J. Cell. Comp. Physiol. (suppl. 1):57.
62. Katz, B., 1959. Biophysical Science, a Study P gram. Wiley, New York, p. 466.

CHAPTER 24

THE CHEMICAL BASIS
OF CONTRACTILITY

Movements such as are seen in cytoplasmic streaming, ameboid and ciliary movement or muscular contraction are, of course, possible only because of molecular and ionic movements that are taking place inside the living cells. The nature of these molecular and ionic movements and the source of energy by which they occur are fundamental to an understanding of the mechanism of contractility.

Because energy conversions occur on such a large scale in muscle fibers, and because the quantities of enzymes and metabolic intermediates are large, muscle fibers have long been a favorite object for studies on contractility. Many of the enzyme systems have been isolated, and their reactions have been studied *in vitro*.[7, 8] However, the objective here is to consider only the broader aspects of muscle metabolism and the possible manner in which the muscle fiber uses the energy released to do mechanical work.

For studies of the chemistry of muscular contraction, vertebrate skeletal muscle fibers have been used most exten-

sively because, being highly differentiated, they are likely to show most clearly the basic features of a contractile system. Only such studies will be presented here. However, some parallel studies on vertebrate cardiac and visceral and on invertebrate muscle fibers are also available in the literature and they indicate essential similarity in the chemical systems involved.[13, 49-51]

Evidence of Molecular Orientation in Muscle Fibers

To perform work it is necessary that a muscle fiber exert force in a system with a favorable spatial relation. Muscle cells and individual muscle fibers are always elongate and they may even run the whole length of a muscle and join with the tendon. Around each muscle fiber is an electrically polarized membrane (the sarcolemma), the inside being about a tenth of a volt negative to the outside. A muscle fiber contains elongate *myofibrils* (Fig. 24.1), which lie in the cytoplasm or, more specifically, the sarcoplasm. The

499

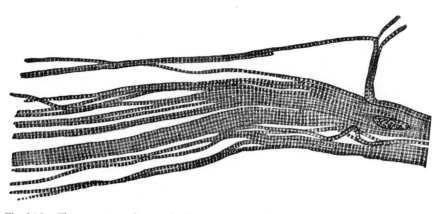

Fig. 24.1. The separation of a muscle fiber into a mass of myofibrils after treatment with nitric acid. One nucleus is seen within a spindle-shaped mass of sarcoplasm. ($\times 530$) (A. A. M.)

nuclei of the muscle fiber lie in the sarcoplasm around or between the myofibrils. The myofibrils may be liberated for study by appropriate methods. Each myofibril is about a micron in diameter and is presumably the seat of muscle contraction.

The striated appearance of a skeletal muscle fiber seen under the microscope is due to the striations on the myofibrils, the striations being similarly oriented across all the myofibrils of a fiber and arising from a repeating variation in the density along the myofibrils. Under the polarizing microscope the dark bands are found to be doubly refracting, and the light bands are found to be singly refracting. This suggests molecular orientation.[1]

Under high power of the light microscope the striation pattern on isolated myofibrils is seen as a regular alternation of isotropic I-bands (or light bands, through which light passes equally in all directions) and anisotropic A-bands (or dark bands, possessing different refractive indices in different directions). These bands are on the myofibrils of the muscle fibers (see Fig. 24.3, top). When a vertebrate striated muscle fiber is almost fully relaxed, the length of one A-band of a myofibril is commonly about 1.5 microns and that of one I-band is about 0.8

micron. In the middle of the A-band is a portion called the H-zone which is lighter than the rest, and in the middle of the I-band is a darker Z-line which bisects the band. From one Z-line to the next is one repeating unit (*sarcomere*) of the myofibril[37, 39] (Fig. 24.2 and 24.3).

Evidence of molecular orientation in muscle fibers comes also from x-ray diffraction studies. Briefly, such studies are based on the fact that x-ray wavelengths are diffracted by layers of molecules (or ions). If a beam of x-rays is passed through a crystal, the diffracted beam forms a circle of discontinuous images about the central beam (Fig. 3.7). If a beam of x-rays is passed through a powdered salt crystal, the diffracted beam forms a series of continuous rings about the central beam, indicating less perfect orientation in masses of the small crystalline fragments. When x-rays are passed through muscle fibers, the diffracted beam forms a series of continuous rings surrounding the central beam, indicating less perfect orientation than in a true crystal. Each ring is the result of diffraction of the x-rays by a different set of oriented molecules. By measuring the angles between the central beam of x-rays and the ring it is possible to deduce the distance between the molecular units in the muscle

IRRITABILITY AND CONTRACTILI

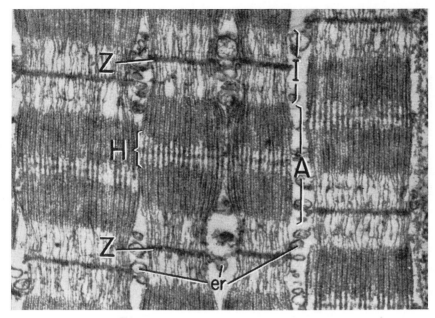

Fig. 24.2. Electron micrograph of four myofibrils, showing the alternating sarcomeres with the Z-lines and the H-, A- and I-bands. The sarcoplasmic reticulum (er) is situated between the myofibrils. The finer structure of the myofibril represented by the thin (actin) and the thick (myosin) filaments is also clear. (×60,000) (Courtesy of H. Huxley.)

er and the dimensions and arrangements of the structural units.[2-6] Without going into details, it is possible to state that the contractile units in the fibrils are oriented along the length of the fibrils with a regularity suggestive of a crystal. Since the indicated size of the contractile unit is that of a large protein molecule in every case, the x-ray studies make it seem likely that the regularly arranged constituents are protein molecules.[18]

When the myofibril is examined under the electron microscope it is found to be made up of two kinds of smaller filaments, one twice as thick as the other. The thicker filaments are about 100 Å in diameter and 1.5 microns long, and the thinner ones are about 50 Å in diameter and 2 microns long. Each filament is seen arrayed with the other filaments of the one kind, and the two arrays overlap for part of their length. It is apparently this overlapping that gives rise to the

cross bands of the myofibril: the dense A-band consists of overlapping thick and thin filaments; the lighter I-band consists of thin filaments alone; the H-zone consists of thick filaments alone. Halfway along their length, the thin filaments pass through a narrow zone of dense material; this constitutes the Z-line.[37, 39] Usually the two kinds of filaments are arranged in such a manner that each thin filament lies in a spatial symmetry among three thick ones (Fig. 24.4 and 24.5). The two kinds of filaments are linked together by cross bridges which project outward from the thick filaments at a fairly regular interval of about 60 to 70 Å, each bridge being 60 degrees further around the axis of the filament, so that the bridges form a helical pattern that is repeated every six bridges, or about every 400 Å along the filament (see Fig. 24.6).

The structures seen with the electron microscope are, of course, being observed

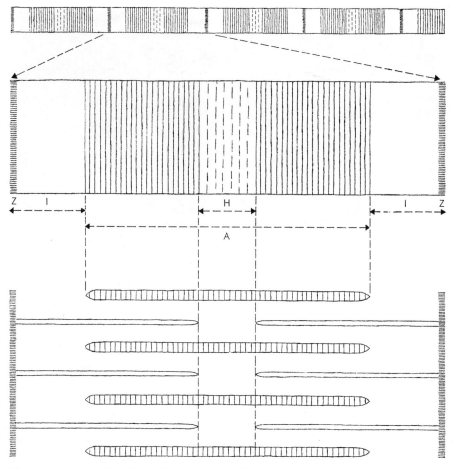

Fig. 24.3. Organization of a myofibril showing, at the top, the alternate light (isotropic) and dark (anisotropic) bands as seen with the light microscope. A single band is shown enlarged in the middle, the I-band at each end being half of a light band. The bottom figure shows the pattern of thick (myosin) and thin (actin) filaments as visualized with the electron microscope. The light bands are regions where thin filaments alone are present; the dark bands are regions where the two types of filaments overlap. The myofibril varies in diameter from 1 to 2μ and in length from a few millimeters to many centimeters depending on the muscle from which it is taken. The I-band is about 0.8μ wide; the A-band is about 1.5μ wide. The thin filament is about 50Å in diameter and the thick filament is about 100 Å in diameter.[55] (From Huxley Nov., 1958: Sci. Am. *199*:68.)

on fixed and dried material. However, the regularity of filaments and their cross linkages is also indicated in x-ray diffraction studies although the evidence is indirect and difficult to present.

The Structural Proteins of Muscle

About 20 per cent of the weight of the muscle fibers is represented by proteins.

If a mass of muscle fibers is mince wrapped in cheesecloth and squeezed a press under many atmospheres of pr sure, a fluid exudes which is called t *press juice*. If the muscle residue, l after squeezing out the press juice, washed in very dilute salt solution, wat soluble albumins and readily solul globulins are removed. The remaini material contains, among other substanc

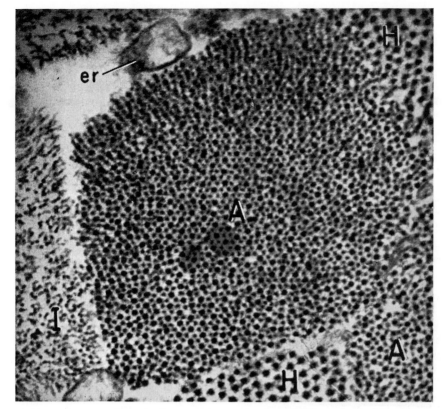

Fig. 24.4. Electron micrograph of cross sections passing through different levels of the sarcomere. The A-bands show the thick and thin filaments; the I-band only thin filaments; the H-band only thick ones. (er) represents the sarcoplasmic reticulum. (×120,000) (Courtesy of H. Huxley.)

vo major proteins, namely *myosin* and *tin,* and one minor protein present in nall quantities called *tropomyosin.* If is remaining material is extracted with solution of 0.3 molar KCl, buffered with 0.15 molar potassium phosphate to give the solution a pH of 6.5, and if the extraction is not too prolonged, myosin, being more soluble than actin, dissolves into the solution. It can be purified

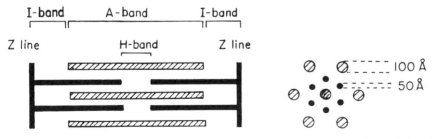

Fig. 24.5. Diagram to show disposition of thick and thin filaments in longitudinal view (left) and cross section (right). A single sarcomere is shown on the left and a section through the A-band is shown on the right. (Courtesy of H. Huxley.)

CHEMICAL BASIS OF CONTRACTILITY

503

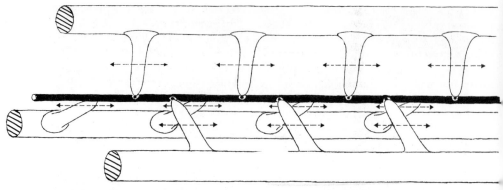

Fig. 24.6. Arrangement of cross-bridges suggests that they enable the thick filaments to pull the thin filaments by a kind of ratchet action. In this schematic drawing one thin filament lies among three thick ones. Each bridge is a part of a thick filament, but it is able to hook onto a thin filament at an active site (*dot*). Presumably the bridges are able to bend back and forth (*arrows*). A single bridge might thus hook onto an active site, pull the thin filament a short distance, then release it and hook onto the next active site. (From Huxley, Nov., 1958: Sci. Am., *199*:80.)

by diluting the solution slightly, whereupon its complex with actin, namely actomyosin, precipitates out.

Myosin is an α-helix type of protein[55] of high molecular weight (about 450,000).[31] As seen in electron micrographs[55] myosin molecules appear to be long and thin (2000 Å by 50 Å). Myosin is composed of many dicarboyxlic acids; therefore it has many ionizable residues, and, near neutrality, it has one charge for almost every angstrom of its length. This very high charge density explains why the molecule maintains its fibrous form, since one part of the molecule repels another part of the same molecule as well as another molecule of its own kind. Because of its needle-like, linear form, myosin shows beautiful streaming birefringence (see Chapter 14).[11-15]

Myosin is presumably present in the muscle fiber as the magnesium salt, magnesium myosinate. It binds monovalent ions, not distinguishing between sodium and potassium ions, as well as divalent ions. Calculations also indicate that practically all the ATP present in muscle fibers is probably bound to myosin.[13-17] Apparently ATP is strongly bound to the magnesium of the myosinate since the ultraviolet absorption spectrum of the

myosin-ATP complex is different from that obtained by summing up the absorption of myosin and ATP measured separately. One mole of ATP is bound per 18,000 grams of myosin. In balanced salt solutions like those of the cell, myosin is made soluble by ATP. Since ATP is ionized with an over-all negative charge, the myosin becomes negatively charged when ATP is added to it. When purified myosin, dissolved in 0.3 molar KCl, is added to distilled water, it precipitates in the form of a thread. However, this thread does *not* contract when ATP is added, even though it binds ATP in the presence of salts.

Myosin has been fragmented into two fractions, a heavy one and a light one, which together make up the myosin unit.[14] These fractions are of particular interest because electron microscope photographs indicate them to be of the right order of magnitude to account for some of the angular deviations of the x-ray diffraction rings (Fig. 3.7). The light and heavy units of myosin are each made up of much smaller subunits (protomyosins) held together by secondary links.[29]

Actin, the other major structural protein of muscle fibers, is less soluble in solutions of KCl than is myosin and dissolve only when the concentration of KCl is raised to about 0.6 molar.[13-17] An alternative method of extraction is also available.[13, 14] Actin binds four equivalents of calcium per molecule, and apparently it exists normally as calcium actinate. In the absence of salts, actin exists in globular form, with a molecular weight of about 70,000, but upon addition of ATP it forms dimers, and in the presence of 0.1 M KCl and ATP, it polymerizes to long fibers. Polymerization is accompanied by splitting of ATP, the ADP being firmly bound to the actin and inorganic phosphate being given off. Each molecule of actin appears to bind one ADP. The actin is in the α-helix with a period of 400 Å indicated by both x-ray diffraction and electron microscope studies.[55] It is not clear what role, if any, the globular-to-fibrous transformation that actin undergoes may play in muscular contraction.

In polymerized form, actin shows streaming birefringence like myosin, another sign of the linear units of which it is composed. Like logs in a stream of water, the long molecules are lined up in the solution, thus differentially affecting light passed at right angles to the long axes as compared with light passed parallel to the long axes of the molecules.

When actin and myosin are mixed in the presence of salts normally found in the muscle fibers, a striking change occurs. The viscosity of the mixture becomes much greater than the sum of the viscosities of the two constituent solutions. Electron micrographs show that a network is formed by electrostatic association between the two proteins. This complex is called actomyosin. Actin and myosin have been found to combine in stoichiometric ratios.

It has been possible, through studies with the electron microscope, to localize the proteins in the filaments of the muscle fibrils. Thus, when myosin of a muscle fiber is extracted with an appropriate KCl solution, the thicker filaments of the fibrils show only as ghosts, which indicates that they had contained the myosin. When muscle fibers are treated to remove actin, the electron micrographs show absence of the thin filaments in the fibrils, indicating that these consist mostly of actin (they also have some tropomyosin). Corroborating data come from analyses of the filaments using immunochemical techniques, fluorescent antibodies being produced against either myosin or actin.[45]

Tropomyosin makes up about 2.5 per cent of the muscle fiber protein.[55] While it seems to be present in all muscle fibers, its function is still unknown. To obtain it, the muscle fibers are extracted with 1 M solution of KCl (or weak acid) after preliminary treatment with alcohol (or ether). It has a relatively low molecular weight (about 60,000) and crystallizes readily.[32] In water it aggregates to form strands 200 to 300 Å thick. Its localization in the muscle fiber is uncertain; it may be in the Z-line, since this remains after extraction of myosin, or it may be in the bridges between the filaments.

Still another kind of muscle protein, *paramyosin,* is found in the catch muscles of mollusks and annelids. It is extracted with weak acid (or strong salt solutions) after the muscle fibers are first treated with ethanol (or ether). It has a molecular weight of about 137,000 and a length of 1400 Å. The molecule shows pronounced asymmetry. Catch muscle fibers hold tension for prolonged periods with exceedingly low metabolic activity and without the characteristic tetanus of vertebrate striated muscle fibers, the "catch" mechanism being the setting of structural bonds of the paramyosin at a given length.[32, 33, 53]

Source of Energy for Contraction

While the fibrils of the muscle fiber are the seat of muscular contraction, the sarcoplasm is the seat of the biochemical reactions from which high energy compounds are made available to the muscle fibrils. Mitochondria, with all the essential oxidation-reduction and phosphorylation enzyme systems of the Krebs cycle, have been identified in muscle fibers. These mitochondria are especially prominent in size and number in the flight muscle fibers of birds and insects.

The press juice of minced muscle fibers is largely extracted from the sarcoplasm and contains most of the high energy phosphate compounds, as well as salts and the globular proteins which constitute almost all of the enzymes. Many of the glycolytic enzymes characteristic of the Krebs cycle may be identified in the press juice.

Glycogen constitutes about 1 per cent of the wet weight of whole muscle fiber; creatine phosphate (CP), about 0.5 per cent; and adenosine triphosphate, (ATP) about 0.025 per cent, indicating a considerable store of ready nutrient. Experiments show that during muscular contraction, glycogen disappears and a corresponding quantity of lactic acid appears when the rate of activity is too rapid to permit complete oxidation of the pyruvic acid formed during glycolysis. The excess lactic acid is carried by the blood to the liver where about four fifths of it is resynthesized into glycogen, while one fifth of the lactic acid is completely oxidized to carbon dioxide and water in the process.[7] New supplies of glucose are continually delivered to muscle cells by the blood.

The diagram of the anaerobic breakdown of glucose (Fig. 17.6) reveals the mechanism whereby pyruvic acid produced in glycolysis is converted into lactic acid. In the absence of oxygen, lactic acid accumulates, since the reactions cannot go any further. When oxygen is available, lactic acid is oxidized in the reactions of the Krebs cycle as shown in the diagram of the metabolic mill (Fig. 17.9). The glycolytic reactions occur whether oxygen is present or absent. If oxygen is present the glycolytic reactions are then followed by the reactions of the Krebs cycle* (Fig. 17.8).

According to measurements of the heat produced during muscular contraction, energy is liberated in two stages. A small amount of heat is given off upon contraction, and a much greater amount of heat is liberated for many seconds, or even for several minutes, after contraction (see Fig. 24.7). Studies indicate that the initial heat is evolved during breakdown of high energy phosphates and that the large amount of heat measured later is evolved during glycolysis and the complete breakdown of some of the lactic acid to carbon dioxide and water.[18] Actually, the sequence of events is much more complex, the initial and delayed heat each being made up of several components. (For example, tension or shortening heat, maintenance heat and relaxation heat all contribute to the initial heat. The delayed heat phase has anaerobic and aerobic components.[30]) Hill and Meyerhof received the Nobel Prize in 1922 for their pioneer studies on muscle metabolism.

If a muscle fiber is stimulated in the presence of adequate oxygen, it fatigues slowly. In the absence of oxygen, the muscle fatigues much more rapidly because it must then depend upon glycolysis for its energy, and anaerobic processes always yield considerably less energy than aerobic processes. Since glycolysis precedes aerobic oxidations and continues in their absence, is it, then, the immediate source of energy for contraction of muscle fibers? To test this, Lundsgaard used iodoacetic acid to poison the enzymes catalyzing the glycolytic reactions, and he found that contraction still continued but that the muscle fatigued even

* Muscle cells make use of fat as well as glycogen; red muscles more so than white. During migration butterflies, fishes and birds make extensive use of fat for muscular contraction and show a corresponding low respiratory quotient.[56]

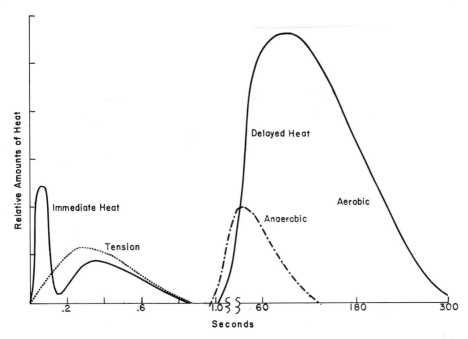

Fig. 24.7. Immediate and delayed heat formation in frog muscle (schematic). (Data from several sources, mainly after Hartree.)

more rapidly than an unpoisoned anaerobic control.[9] Clearly, some immediate source of energy for muscular contraction, other than glycolysis, had to be sought.

Analyses showed that the high energy phosphate compounds decreased in amount as contractions continued in the poisoned anaerobic preparations. Presumably, these compounds were being used in muscular contractions, but in the absence of both glycolysis and aerobic reactions these high energy phosphate bonds could not be replenished, and the muscle fibers fatigued very rapidly.

If ATP is the immediate source of energy for contractility it should provoke contraction when applied directly to a muscle fiber.[10] As expected, it has been demonstrated that when a solution of ATP is injected into an artery, tetanus is induced in the muscle fiber supplied with blood by this artery. If a muscle is cut up into small bundles and placed at

low temperature in glycerin, all the soluble constituents leach into the glycerin, but the structural proteins presumably remain intact and arranged as they were in the live muscle. Muscle strands leached in this manner are called *muscle models* and have been extensively used in research. Contraction with a tension equal to that exerted by living muscle fibers may then be induced by placing the dead leached muscle fibers in either fresh muscle press juice or a balanced salt solution containing ATP. Press juice in which the ATP has been decomposed does not induce contraction.[14]

That ATP is involved in some way in muscular contraction is incontestable. The decomposition of ATP to ADP, liberating the energy of one high energy phosphate bond, appears as the likely immediate source of energy for muscular contraction. ADP is "recharged" to ATP by glycolysis during which glucose is decomposed to pyruvate (or lactate in absence of oxygen), and by oxidation of pyruvate to CO_2 and H_2O in the reactions of the Krebs cycle. ATP can be immediately replenished by the reaction between ADP and creatin phosphate which occurs as a reserve of high energy phosphate bonds in the muscle cells.

Working with other motile systems such as fibroblasts, histiocytes, amebas, flagella, contractile myonemes (*Vorticella*) and mitotic spindles extracted with glycerol, Hoffman-Berling has shown that they, too, contract when ATP is added. Contraction does not occur if the adenosine triphosphatase present on the fibers is first poisoned with Salyrgan, specific to this type of enzyme. This suggests that all of these systems, like muscle contraction, depend upon ATP as a source of energy for contraction.[34] Proteins, which contract on addition of ATP, have been extracted from embryonic fibroblasts and from the flagella of sperm.[54]

Actomyosin—Muscle Fibril Analogues

Actomyosin dissolved in 0.6 molar KCl solution shows brilliant streaming birefringence. The electron microscope discloses actomyosin particles to be long threads of about 150 Å diameter and ten or more times the length of a myosin unit. If the salt solution is diluted to 0.1 molar KCl, actomyosin is precipitated in the form of loose flakes. On addition of ATP the precipitate becomes more tightly set ("super precipitate"). At higher concentrations of KCl, however, the actomyosin seems to be dispersed into solution by ATP, and the viscosity of the mixture drops to the sum of the viscosities of actin and myosin taken separately. Salts present in very high concentrations (0.6 molar KCl) in solution also disperse (dissolve) the molecules, even in the absence of ATP.

When actomyosin dissolved in 0.6 molar KCl is squirted into 0.01 M KCl (see Fig. 24.8), a gelled thread of actomyosin is obtained.[19] When such a thread is placed in ATP solution, it contracts.[13] Actomyosin is also found to possess an enzymatic function (adenosine triphosphatase), splitting ATP to ADP and inorganic phosphate. These observations created a sensation when they were first announced, because actomyosin thus appeared to be a model, or analogue, of muscular contraction. However, important differences were soon found between a muscle fibril and an actomyosin thread. The latter loses about 40 per cent of its water on contraction, whereas a muscle fibril does not. Furthermore, study of the actomyosin thread under the electron microscope shows that the molecules are in disarray, resembling the brush network in a protein gel rather than the linearly arranged and regularly spaced units disclosed by x-ray analysis of a muscle fiber. Moreover, if the thread represents a model of a muscle fibril, it should perform work like a muscle fibril, yet when the actomyosin thread is loaded, and then ATP is added, the thread stretches instead of contracting.

A few years later an actomyosin model which contained linearly oriented actomyosin molecules was constructed. It had many properties in common with a muscle fibril. Because protein molecules become oriented at a surface, a film can be made by dropping a solution of actomyosin on the surface of 0.06 molar KCl solution in a trough. Since the monomolecular film formed is too weak to support weight, it is thickened[20-23] by sweeping the trough (see Fig. 24.9), thus folding the surface sheet into an accordion-pleated thread which holds together because of cohesive forces. Such an actomyosin thread has tensile strength (see Fig. 24.10). Loaded with a weight, it contracts and performs work, on addition of ATP to the bathing fluid. It becomes relaxed when washed with appropriate salt solutions and it can again be contracted by the addition of ATP (see Fig. 24.11). Further more, water is not lost during contraction.

It was reasoned that if the energy for contraction of an actomyosin thread comes from ATP, the ATP should be used up when work is done by the model contracting thread. Quantitative determinations of ATP showed that this, in fact, is the case, and actomyosin therefore serves as an adenosine triphosphatase, liberating the energy of ATP to make possible the contraction of the actomyosin thread. Still the model is not a complete analogue to a muscle fibril, because the time required for its contraction is longer than that for the control muscle fibrils.[23]

The Sliding Filament Theory of Muscular Contraction

Another approach to the study of muscular contraction has been used by H. E. Huxley and A. F. Huxley, and J. Hanson, who investigated the structural changes occurring during a cycle of contraction, as seen in a series of electron micrographs of ultrathin sections (about 150 Å) of muscle fibers.[39, 47] Such an electron micrograph is shown in Figure 24.2 and an interpretation of what is seen is given diagrammatically in Figures 24.3 and 24.5.

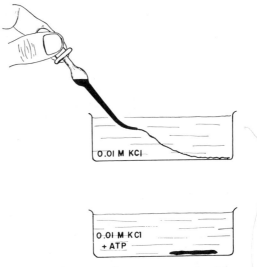

Fig. 24.8. Formation of an actomyosin thread by adding a jet of actomyosin to a dilute solution of KCl. Contraction of the thread is shown after addition of ATP.[25]

During muscular contraction, as seen with electron micrographs, the A-band remains constant, but the length of the I-band varies with the state of contraction. Since the A-band is apparently equal to the length of the thick filaments it can be assumed that the length of

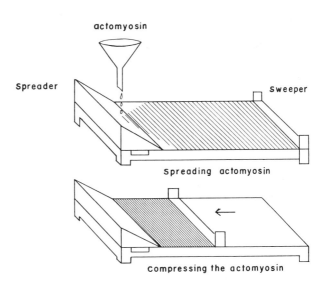

Fig. 24.9. Diagram to show the formation of an oriented thread by sweeping a trough containing a layer of actomyosin.

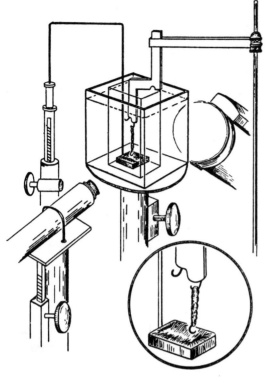

Fig. 24.10. Apparatus for measuring loaded contraction of the actomyosin thread. The small hook at the bottom of the mass of actomyosin serves as the load. (From Hayashi, 1952–53: J. Gen. Physiol., *36*: 141.)

these filaments is constant. The length of the H-zone in the middle of the A-band increases and decreases with the length of the I-band, so that the distance from the end of one H-zone to the beginning of the next H-zone remains approximately the same. Since this distance is equal to the length of the thin filaments, they also appear to remain approximately constant in length. Consequently, it is concluded that when a muscle fiber changes length the two sets of filaments slide past one another.[47, 54]

When a muscle fiber is contracted to its fullest extent, the filaments now meet and their ends may even crumple (see Fig. 24.12). Under such conditions, new bands appear on the electron micro-

graphs, which are explained as a result of the shortening process, not as a cause of contraction.[38]

As was pointed out earlier, actin and myosin must be combined to contract in the presence of ATP. However, since the actin and myosin filaments in the fibrils are too far apart for any "action at a distance," the motive power for muscular contraction is postulated to be the formation of chemical couplings between the myosin and actin filaments through the bridges between the two (Fig. 24.6). The bridges are permanent parts of the myosin filaments jutting outward toward the actin filaments and the number of such bridges appears to be the same as the number of molecules of myosin. A chemical reaction is postulated to occur between the myosin and actin filaments, as a result of which the actin filament slides along the myosin filaments for perhaps 100 Å, and then returns to its original configuration, ready for another pull, completing a cycle.[37, 47] To account for the rate of contraction and of energy liberation in the rabbit psoas muscle fiber, for example, it is necessary for each bridge to go through 50 to 100 cycles per second. Each such reaction is thought to be at the expense of 1 ATP molecule. When removal of phosphate groups from ATP stops (presumably as a result of the action of an inhibitor or relaxing factor—see below), the myosin and actin dissociate from each other and the fiber returns to its relaxed state. There is evidence to show that in the presence of the relaxing factor, ATP can break the combination between actin and myosin.[4]

The sliding filament theory effectively explains a number of the features of muscular contraction. For example, it is possible to envisage why a rapidly contracting muscle fiber exerts less tension than one contracting slowly, i.e., because it takes a certain amount of time to form the bridges between actin and myosin; hence, if the contraction is too fast, fewer bridges can form, and fewer bridges

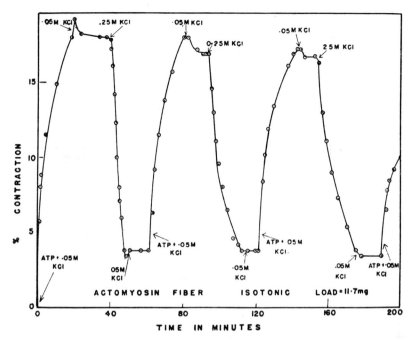

Fig. 24.11. A graph showing contraction of the actomyosin thread upon addition of ATP in 0.05 molar KCl, and showing relaxation upon washing in 0.25 molar KCl. (From T. Hayashi, and R. Rosenbluth, 1952: J. Cell. and Comp. Physiol., 40:501.)

means less tension exerted. Again, it is possible to see why a muscle fiber carrying a larger load uses more energy (heat plus work) than one under a lesser load. When the load is larger, more bridges form and more ATP molecules are used up. It is also possible to conceive how a muscle fiber can continue to exert tension, since at any site the reaction can occur more than once, the bonds between actin and myosin breaking and re-forming, permitting a muscle fiber to continue to do work.[54] Bridges have not yet been identified in electron micrographs of contractile systems other than striated muscle.[54]

Excitation of Muscular Contraction

Although evidence for activation of the muscle fiber by acetylcholine secreted by the terminations of the efferent neurons at the myoneural junction is convincing (see Chapter 22), the problem still re-

mains, however, as to how the individual units of the filaments are activated. It has been shown that if minute microelectrodes (about 2 μ in diameter) are brought alongside the isotropic and anisotropic bands of a single isolated muscle fibril and the flow of current is allowed to depolarize it, contraction occurs when the stimulating electrode is against the Z-line, but not if it is placed midway between the two Z-lines, even though the current is increased severalfold.[30, 39] The Z-lines appear to line up and perhaps connect transversely through a whole series of muscle fibers. It is attractive to suggest that the Z-lines are involved in excitation coupling, but the mechanism by which this is accomplished is unknown.[39]

Electron micrographs of the myoneural junction show a tubular system extending from the membrane of the muscle fiber inward as a sort of microsynaptic system to the fibrils. Such a system would help

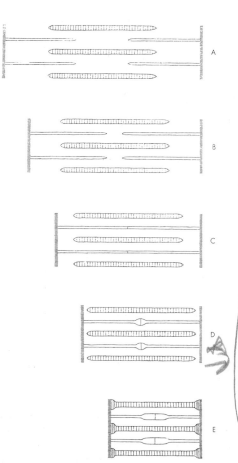

Fig. 24.12. Muscular contraction as envisaged from the contractile filament theory. Change in length of the muscle fiber changes the arrangement of the filaments. In *A* the muscle fiber is stretched; in *B* it is at its resting length; in *C, D* and *E* it is contracted. In *C* the thin filaments meet; in *D* and *E* they crumple up. In *E* the thick filament also meet adjacent thick filaments (not shown) and crumple. The crumpling gives rise to new band patterns. The central thick filaments are presumably myosin; the thin filaments, actin. (See text.) (From Huxley, Nov., 1958: Sci. Am. 199:76.)

explain spread of excitation since no ordinary diffusion of a substance across a membrane would be fast enough to account for the rapidity of a contractile response.[40, 52]

It is tempting to assume that in the living muscle fibers ATP must play the same role as in contraction of muscle fiber models and actomyosin threads. That ATP is present in muscle fibers in abundance is shown by biochemical extraction. Furthermore, a muscle fiber which has exhausted its ATP goes into a state of rigor (stiffness) which is reversed by addition of ATP. In fact, one of the major functions of ATP is believed to be the maintenance of suppleness and plasticity of muscle fibers.[46]

An attempt has been made to localize ATP in the bands of the fibrils by autoradiography, using tritiated adenine in the ATP. The resolution of the photographs is not quite adequate to make localization certain, but concentration in the boundary between the A-bands and the I-bands is suggested.[47, 48]

Since ATP is used in muscular contraction, either it is present in an inactive form to be released for action only when the impulse reaches the muscle fiber, or the enzymatic breakdown of ATP is in some way normally inhibited by some substance until the action potential reaches the muscle fibers, at which time the inhibitory influence vanishes and the ATP in the region of the active enzyme is decomposed.[14] An inhibitor, called the *relaxing factor*, or the *Marsh-Bendall* (MB) factor,* which is active in the presence of ATP and magnesium, has been extracted from muscle but has not yet been identified.[26, 27, 31] In the presence of this factor, a muscle fiber model fails to contract, even in the presence of ATP. However, when a solution of calcium $(10^{-3}$ molar) is added, contraction occurs. The importance of calcium to muscle contraction was emphasized by Heilbrunn long before this.[28] It is possible that release of calcium in the muscle fiber by the nerve impulse results in muscular contraction

---

* This factor appears to be microsomal, or bound to particles (vesicles). Incubation of these particles with ATP yields an active soluble relaxing factor, which is not myokinase (the enzyme catalyzing transfer of phosphate from one ADP to another to yield AMP and ATP), as indicated in earlier experiments.[31]

by negating in some way the inhibitory influence of the MB factor. It is also possible that the MB factor inhibits the adenosine triphosphatase activity of myosin. Only when this inhibition is removed can contraction occur.[41, 42]

While in all of our thinking ATP is closely linked with muscular contraction, the evidence for its action in the live muscle fiber can only be inferred. In live muscle fibers it is difficult to demonstrate any changes in ATP concentration of sufficient magnitude, even by spectrophotometric means. Changes in concentration of creatine phosphate, however, can be demonstrated, and the decrease in creatin phosphate is proportional to the number of contractions of the muscle. Creatin phosphate, it will be remembered, is always ready to donate its high energy phosphate bond to ADP, resulting in the formation of ATP and creatin (see Ch. 17).[44]

Here in the muscle fiber is a machine which elegantly converts chemical energy into mechanical energy. The biochemical machinery for liberation of the chemical potential energy in the living cell is well known. In fact, the whole series of discoveries in muscle and nerve biochemistry and structure make one of the most interesting chapters in cell physiology. One large and critical portion of the puzzle yet remains to be found: How is the final chemical to mechanical energy conversion completed inside the living muscle fiber?[29, 54]

Hill, A. V., 1960: Production and Absorption of Work by Muscle. Science *131*:897–903.

Hodge, A. J., 1959: Fibrous Proteins of Muscle. Biophysical Science: A Study Program (Oncley, J. C., ed.). Wiley, New York, pp. 409–425.

Hoffman-Berling, H., 1960: Other Mechanisms Producing Movements. Comp. Biochem. *2*:341–370.

Huxley, A. F., 1957: Molecular Structure and Theories of Contraction. Progr. Biophys. *7*:89–146.

Huxley, H. E., 1957: The Double Array of Filaments in Cross-Striated Muscle. J. Biophys. Biochem. Cyt. *3*:631–646.

Huxley, H. E., 1960: Muscle Cells *in* The Cell (Brachet, J., and Mirsky, A. E., eds.). Academic Press, New York, vol. 4, pp. 365–481.

Mommaerts, W. F. H. M., Brady, A. J., and Abbott, B. C., 1961: Major Problems in Muscle Physiology. Ann. Rev. Physiol. *23*:529–576.

Morales, M. F., 1959: Mechanism of Muscle Contraction, 426–432, *in* Biophysics: A Study Program (Oncley, J. C., ed.). Wiley, New York.

Needham, D. M., 1960: Biochemistry of Muscular Action, *in* Structure and Function of Muscle (Bourne, G. H., ed.). Academic Press, New York, vol. 2, pp. 55–104.

Perry, S. V., 1956: Relation between Chemical and Contractile Function and Structure of Skeletal Muscle Cell. Physiol. Rev. *36*:1–76.

Szent-Györgyi, A., 1953: Chemical Physiology of Contraction in Body and Heart Muscle. Academic Press, New York.

Szent-Györgyi, A. G., 1960: Proteins of the Myofibril, *in* Structure and Function of Muscle (Bourne, G. H., ed.). Academic Press, New York, vol. 2, pp. 1–54.

The Sarcoplasmic Reticulum, J. Biophys. Biochem. Cyt. (suppl.) *10*:1961.

Weber, H. H., 1954: Adenosine Triphosphate and Motility of Living Systems. Harvey Lect. *49*:37–56.

Weber, H. H., and Portzehl, H., 1954: Transference of Muscle Energy in Contraction Cycle. Progr. Biophys. *4*:60–111.

Weber, H. H., 1958: The Motility of Muscle and Cells. Harvard Univ. Press, Cambridge, Mass.

Wilkie, D. R., 1954: Facts and Theories about Muscle. Progr. Biophys. *4*:288–324.

GENERAL REFERENCES

Dubuisson, M., 1954: Muscular Contraction. Thomas, Springfield, Ill.

Hanson, J., and Huxley, H. E., 1955: The Structural Basis of Contraction in Striated Muscle, *in* Fibrous Proteins and Their Biological Significance. Symp. Soc. Exper. Biol. *9*:228–264.

Hermann, H., 1952: Muscle Development. Ann. New York Acad. Sci. *55*:99–108.

LITERATURE CITED

1. Barer, R., 1948: Biol. Rev. *23*:159.
2. Astbury, W. T., 1950: Proc. Roy. Soc., London, s. B. *137*:58.
3. Bluhm, M. M., Sitaramayya, C., 1951: Quart. J. Micros. Sci. *92*:323.
4. Jakus, M. A., and Hall, C. E., 1949: Exp. Cell. Res. (suppl.) *1*:262.

5. Weinstein, H. J., 1954: Exp. Cell. Res. 7:130.
6. Pauling, L., and Corey, R. B., 1951: Proc. Nat. Acad. Sci. U. S. 37:235–282.
7. Mommaerts, W. F. H. M., 1950: Muscular Contraction. Interscience Press, New York.
8. Dubuisson, M., 1954: Muscular Contraction. Thomas, Springfield, Ill.
9. Lundsgaard, E., 1930: Biochem. Ztschr. 217:162; 220:8.
10. Bozler, E., 1953: J. Gen. Physiol. 37:63.
11. Mommaerts, W. F. H. M., 1954: Ann. Rev. Biochem. 23:381.
12. Mommaerts, W. F. H. M., 1954: J. Appl. Physiol. 6:1.
13. Szent-Györgyi, A., 1950: Chemistry of Muscular Contraction. 2nd Ed. Academic Press, New York.
14. Szent-Györgyi, A., 1953: Chemical Physiology of Contraction in Body and Heart Muscle. Academic Press, New York.
15. Sandow, A., 1949: Ann. Rev. Physiol. 11:297.
16. Szent-Györgyi, A., 1955: Adv. Enzymol. 16:313.
17. Dubuisson, M., 1952: Ann. Rev. Biochem. 21:387.
18. Davson, H., 1959: A Textbook of General Physiology. 2nd Ed. Little, Brown, Boston, Sect. 5.
19. Weber, H. H., and Porzehl, H., 1954: Progr. Biophys. 4:60.
20. Hayashi, T., 1951: Science 114:684 (Abstr.).
21. Hayashi, T., 1952: J. Gen. Physiol. 36:139.
22. Hayashi, T., and Rosenbluth, R., 1952: J. Cell. Comp. Physiol. 40:495.
23. Hayashi, T., and Rosenbluth, R., 1953: Proc. Nat. Acad. Sci., U. S. 39:1285.
24. Porzehl, H., 1951: Z. Naturf. 6b:355.
25. Harris, R. J. C. (ed.), 1961: Cell Movement and Cell Contact. Academic Press, New York.
26. Weber, H. H., 1953–54: Harvey Lect. 49:37.
27. Marsh, B. B., 1952: Biochim. Biophys. Acta 9:247.
28. Heilbrunn, L. V., 1956: The Dynamic Aspects of Living Protoplasm. Academic Press, New York, Chapter 7.
29. Szent-Györgyi, A., 1958: Science 128:699.
30. Ruch, T. C., and Fulton, J. F., 1960: Medical Physiology and Biophysics. Saunders, Philadelphia, ch. 4.
31. Mommaerts, W. F. H. M., Brody, A. J., and Abbott, B. C., 1961: Ann. Rev. Physiol. 23:529, 538.
32. Szent-Györgyi, A. G., 1960: in Structure and Function of Muscle (Bourne, G. H., ed.). Academic Press, New York, vol. 2, p. 1.
33. Jewell, B. R., 1959: J. Physiol. London 149:154.
34. Hoffmann-Berling, H., 1960: Comp. Biochem. 2:341.
35. Huxley, H. E., and Niedergerke, R., 1954: Nature 173:971.
36. Huxley, H. E., 1956: Endeavour 15:177.
37. Huxley, H. E., Nov. 1958: Sci. Am. 199:67.
38. Huxley, H. E., 1957: J. Biophys. Biochem. Cyt. 3:631.
39. Huxley, A. F., 1957: Progr. Biophys. 7:255.
40. Bennett, H. S., 1960: The Structure and Function of Muscle (Bourne, G. H., ed.). Academic Press, New York, vol. 1, p. 137.
41. Bendall, J. R., 1954: Proc. Roy. Soc. B 142:409.
42. Gergeley, J., 1959: Ann. New York Acad. Sci. 81:490.
43. Briggs, F. N., and Fuchs, F., 1960: Fed. Proc. 19:257 (Abstr.).
44. Davies, R. E., Cain, D., and Delluva, A. M., 1959: Ann. New York Acad. Sci. 81:468.
45. Marshall, J. M., Jr., Holtzer, H., Finck, H., and Pepe, F., 1959: Exp. Cell. Res. (suppl.) 7:219.
46. Weber, H. H., 1959: Ann. New York Acad. Sci. 81:409.
47. Huxley, H. E., and Hanson, J., 1959: Ann. New York Acad. Sci. 81:403.
48. Hill, D. K., 1959: J. Physiol. London 145:132.
49. Murayama, K., and Matsumiya, H., 1957: J. Biochem. (Tokyo) 44:537.
50. Hoffmann-Berling, H., 1958: Biochim. Biophys. Acta 27:247.
51. Tso, P. O. P., Eggman, L., and Vinograd, J., 1959: Biochim. Biophys. Acta 25:532.
52. Peachey, L. D., and Porter, K. R., 1959: Science 129:721.
53. Johnson, W. H., and Kahn, J. S., 1959: Science 130:160.
54. Hayashi, T., Sept. 1961: Sci. Am. 205:184.
55. Huxley, H. E., 1960: in The Cell (Brachet, J., and Mirsky, A. E., eds.). Academic Press, New York, vol. 4, p. 365.
56. Drummond, G. I., and Black, E. C., 1960: Ann. Rev. Physiol. 22:169.

SECTION
VI

GROWTH AND CELL DIVISION

In preceding chapters an actively functioning cell has always been assumed without a question as to its origin or its fate. In turn, the cell's structure and chemical organization, its environment, its manner of achieving a steady-state relationship with its environment, its release of energy for cell activities and its use of the energy in maintaining within itself a state of irritability have been considered. In this section the temporal parameter of cell physiology is explored, with the fate of the cell as the main theme. What is the mechanism of cell growth and cell division, and how does the cell derive the energy for these processes?

Either the cell continues to function until it ages and dies or it grows and divides. In dividing it reproduces its kind, for all cells arise only from pre-existing cells. While it is almost impossible to study cell growth apart from cell division, since growth precedes cell division, it is desirable to focus attention first upon one problem and then upon the other, although it must be recognized that the two are always intimately related. To the degree that separation of the two subjects is possible, cell growth is considered in Chapter 25 and the cell division in Chapter 26.

Multicellular organisms grow by an increase in number and a differentiation of cells. Because the problem of differentiation of cells is usually considered in embryology it is omitted from discussion here.[85]

CELL GROWTH

Aging and Death of Cells

A bold view, largely attributed to Weismann,[1] holds that unicellular organisms are potentially immortal, but that in multicellular organisms only cells of the "germ plasm," which are passed, during reproduction, from generation to generation, are potentially immortal, while the specialized cells of the body (soma) must die.

It has been thought in the past that a stock of protozoans always grows old and dies after prolonged subculture.[3] Thus individuals of the protozoan *Paramecium bursaria*, for example, isolated from cultures which had been kept in the laboratory for many years, divide more and more slowly with time, and often contain nuclei in the process of degenerative fragmentation. Ultimately such cultures die out.[2] Similar results had been observed in other species of protozoa, and attempts were made to determine the span between youth, old age and death for various kinds of protozoans. It was also demonstrated that, after conjugation, some individuals in each of many kinds of protozoans were rejuvenated and more viable.[3] It was concluded that unicellular organisms age and ultimately die unless periodically rejuvenated by conjugation or some other type of nuclear reorganization. But it was soon realized that this conclusion, though suggestive, is not valid, because it is based on observations of protozoans grown in the presence of diverse bacteria which might be the cause of unfavorable growth, and because the protozoans were grown in a medium which might be lacking in the growth factors required for maintenance of a vigorous culture.

To control conditions of growth, it is necessary to grow the protozoans in pure culture, in the absence of any other microorganisms, and preferably on a synthetic nutrient known to be fully adequate. *Tetrahymena pyriformis* (*geleii*), grown under such conditions, has been kept in pure culture for years by Lwoff, Kidder and Dewey, growing at a rate even in excess of the wild state and without loss of vigor.[4] Conjugation has never been observed in any of these stocks, yet wild stocks of *Tetrahymena*, isolated from ponds, undergo conjugation when the proper mating types are mixed.[5] Furthermore, similar experiments with a variety of other kinds of microorganisms in repeated transfer or in steady-state growth devices show that many microorganisms may be

517

grown at a constant growth rate for thousands of generations.[6] It must therefore be concluded that microorganisms are probably potentially immortal and that growth of protoplasm and cell division follow without abatement if nutrient is available and other conditions are favorable.

Yet a growth cycle ending in death will occur in pure culture if microorganisms are grown in a limited or unbalanced environment. This may be the result of limited nutrient or of other unfavorable conditions. For example, if a single vigorous protozoan is inoculated into a limited volume of a known culture medium, it divides regularly until lack of food limits its growth. A plot of the number of divisions against time gives a characteristic curve (see Fig. 25.1, A). The initial curve is a rising straight line. The curve then flattens out and forms a plateau (the stationary phase) as food becomes a limiting factor. The curve declines as the individuals begin to die because of inanition. If an identical medium is initially inoculated with a starving individual, a lag precedes the rising straight line (Fig. 25.1, B), rep-

resenting the period of recovery from the effects of starvation. If individuals are removed from a culture in which they are about to die for lack of food, and are inoculated into fresh medium identical to the first one, after a long lag phase they resume growth and continue to multiply at the same rate as in the preceding experiments.

In some cultures of microorganisms death may result, even if food is available, when other conditions become unfavorable. For example, yeast grown anaerobically produces alcohol and carbon dioxide; alcohol, as it accumulates, eventually becomes toxic to the yeast. Similarly, lactic acid bacteria produce lactic acid in such concentrations that it kills off all other microorganisms and finally the lactic acid bacteria themselves.[6] For this reason lactic acid bacteria are effective in preserving ensilage, cabbage (in sauerkraut), etc.

If microbes did not die for lack of food or because of other unfavorable conditions, like the accumulation of waste products or the presence of enemies, they

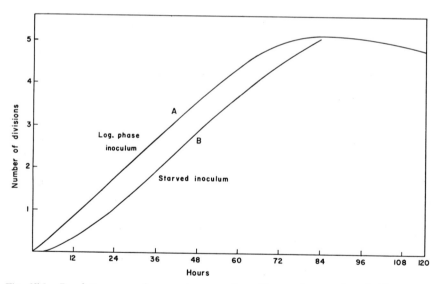

Fig. 25.1. Population curve for a protozoan culture (*Paramecium caudatum*). If paramecia dividing at the maximal rate (logarithmic phase) are used as inoculum, division continues at a maximal rate. If starved animals are used as inoculum, a lag precedes division at the maximal rate.

GROWTH AND CELL DIVISION

would soon exhaust the nutrients of the earth, since their growth is exponential:

$$N = 2^n \quad (25.1)$$

In this equation N is the number of individuals, and n is the number of divisions.

It will be seen that such a growth curve resembles a compound interest curve,* because each increment resulting from a cell division doubles the population, which will double again at the next division. Such an exponential increase in population is often said to be explosive.

In population growth studies, it is found that equation 25.1 is more convenient in its logarithmic form:

$$\text{Log } N = n \log 2 \quad (25.2)$$

$$\text{or } n = \frac{\log N}{\log 2} \quad (25.3)$$

Equation 25.3 is used in plotting the data in Figure 25.1.

In multicellular organisms cells divide actively in the early embryo, but the rate of cell division rapidly declines. When maturity is reached, cell division occurs only in restricted "immature" tissues. These statements apply more strictly to animals than to plants, since plants generally reproduce also from cuttings, buds, etc.

Although mature and aging cells are no longer growing and dividing, replacement apparently continues at all times. Schoenheimer and his associates, using radioactive tracers, have claimed that proteins in the cells of even such relatively inert tissues as tendons are continually being replaced.[8] Because microorganisms synthesize proteins and nucleic acids only during growth, this conclusion for mature cells in multicellular organisms has been questioned. In fact, some studies suggested that it is probably not biochemical replacement in old cells that accounts for the incorporation of radioactive materials into tissues but rather that these materials are incorporated into new cells which are continually being formed to replace dying and disintegrating cells. Apparently such a replacement of cells takes place at a much more rapid rate than had been expected.[42] However, evidence now indicates that animal cells kept for a long time from dividing do indeed incorporate new material.[95] Cells of aging multicellular individuals usually become somewhat dehydrated, respire more slowly[9, 10] and accumulate calcium, various pigments and other inert matter.[12-15] The inert matter may be insoluble excretory materials of metabolism which are incapable of passing through a cell membrane. Dehydration of the cytoplasm, perhaps because of insolubilization of proteins and loss of their water-binding capacity, is noted in cells of many but not all species. A decrease in enzymatic activity of such cells has also been noted.

Why do cells of multicellular organisms age? Is it because the individual cells making up the body have completed their life span or because the body no longer is able to provide adequately for the constituent cells, like an exhausted culture medium for unicellular organisms? To some extent this question might be answered by studies on growth of cells in tissue culture in which tissue cells are periodically transferred to fresh medium (subcultured) in the same manner as is done with unicellular organisms.

Growth of Cells in Tissue Culture and in Tumors

Cells from various plant or animal tissues have been successfully cultured in the absence of other living things. In a typical culture medium for cells of animal tissues, plasma serves as a substrate for attachment of the cells, while an extract from an embryo usually serves as nutrient, although synthetic media are available.[11] The cells must be periodically

* $S = P (1 + r)^k$ where r is a decimal, or rate of interest per interest period, P is the original principal, and S the compound amount to which P accumulates at the end of k interest periods.

washed free of metabolic wastes. If these conditions are met, the tissue cells are capable of living, growing and dividing at a constant rate year after year and may be alive and fully vigorous many years after the animal from which the tissue cells were taken would have normally died. Thus Carrel isolated a piece of chick heart and kept it alive in culture from 1913 to 1946, when the experiment was terminated by choice. Plant cells too have been grown in tissue culture and in completely synthetic media, and the requirements for different types of plant tissues have been determined.[11]

When cells of human tissues, kept in tissue culture, are dissociated, clones can be grown from single cells in colonies much like microorganisms.[43] Such cultures are invaluable for studying many problems. They indicate that cells of man, like those of the chick, grow rapidly and multiply indefinitely if supplied with the proper nutrients and conditions and washed free of wastes, e.g., epithelial cells and fibroblasts (cells of connective tissue).[44-47] Protein-free culture media have been developed for this purpose.[48]

Under certain conditions a cell previously in stasis (not growing or dividing) begins to grow and divide actively, forming a tumor, or a cancerous growth.[77, 78] A cancer is the result of uncontrolled proliferation of undifferentiated cells of a tissue. The cells grow at an exponential rate comparable to that of microorganisms, as shown in Figure 25.2. The cancer may remain localized in a given area, or it may metastasize (spread by way of the lymph or blood stream) to all parts of the body. The undifferentiated cells grow and disorganize the tissues among which they become located. To prevent or cure cancer it will be necessary to gain a fundamental knowledge of the nature of cell growth and of the mechanism by which the body normally holds the growth and division of cells under control.

At present cancer is treated by various techniques which aim only to suppress its rate of growth once it has started. Most of these techniques originated from a study of cell activities. These techniques include ionizing radiations, to suppress division of cells in certain types of cancer;[62] radioactive salts selectively incorporated into a tissue containing cancerous cells, to suppress cell division; and substances which block the synthesis of metabolites necessary for the growth and division of cancerous cells.[16, 17, 54]

On a cellular basis interpretation of cancer induction is still lacking, in spite of many attempts. However, one interesting explanation is that cancer results from injury of the cellular respiratory equipment, with a consequent increase in fermentation. Fermentation is considered a lower order of energy-liberating mechanism, incapable of maintaining structural integrity and organization in cells of higher forms. Many poisons and other agents that induce cancer have such effects upon the respiratory mechanisms of cells.[18] The question arises whether such changes are a consequence, rather than the cause, of cancer. When cells from a tumor are grown in tissue culture, they often behave and respire like normal cells under similar conditions. However, when placed inside an organism, tumor cells multiply, whereas normal cells do not. They synthesize protoplasm so actively that they soon exhaust the supplies of high energy phosphates required for the normal pathways of aerobic respiration. It is then that they obtain a major part of the required energy from reactions proceeding along other pathways. They also become more susceptible to injury or death from hydrogen peroxide much like anaerobic cells.[49]

It has been suggested that a mutation could so change a normal cell as to remove it from the control of hormone and other influences which normally repress multiplication of cells in the body. For example, bone marrow cells from a normal individual and bone marrow cells from a leukemic individual, both grown

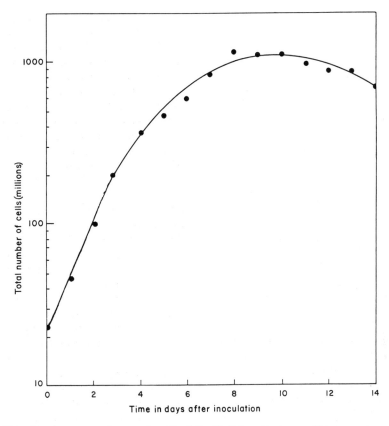

Fig. 25.2. Population growth curve for cells of the Ehrlich ascites tumor. This tumor is made up of individual cells growing in the body (ascitic) fluid. The initial injection on "0" days consisted of 22 × 10⁶ cells. Note the initial logarithmic rise for almost four days, the later decline in rapid growth, and then the decrease in number of cells as some of them die, the whole curve resembling that in Fig. 25.1. The mean survival time for mice with the tumor so inoculated is 14 days. Each point is the average of six determinations. (Courtesy of A. Furst and M. Dollinger, Standford Univ.)

in tissue culture, are inhibited by antagonists to folinic acid, one of the B vitamins required for cell division (see Table 3.10). Within 15 minutes, division dramatically stops. Normal cells remain inhibited from dividing as long as exposed to the antagonist. However, the leukemic cells begin to divide actively after 24 hours, though still exposed to the antagonist. During this time they appear to have inactivated the antagonist because the filtrate from this culture no longer affects either normal cells or leukemic cells, whereas the filtrate from the experiment with the normal cell culture is still inhibitory. (The inactivated material has been separated, crystallized and reactivated.) It would appear that the leukemic cells differ from the normal ones in being able to develop an enzyme system capable of handling the folinic acid antagonist. Since enzymes are considered to be produced by genes, it would seem likely that the leukemic cells differ genetically from the normal ones.[84]

Another interpretation is also possible. It will be recalled that lysogenic viruses "hide" in bacterial cells, remaining inactive except under certain circumstances. But they have produced a change in the

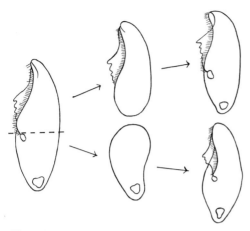

Fig. 25.3. Regeneration of missing parts in two pieces of a bisected *Blepharisma*. Note especially the regeneration of the hypostome (mouth region) in the posterior segment. Regeneration occurs within about six hours at room temperature. (From a classroom experiment. For details, see Moore, 1924: J. Exp. Zool., 39:249.)

host cell since the bacterium is now not infected by the active or lytic variety of the same species of phage (see Chapter 6). It is conceivable that cells become leukemic as a result of invasion by viruses which change the properties of the cells, enabling them to escape the various controls that the body normally exerts upon the bone marrow cells which restrict multiplication to a level adequate for replacement of lost cells. Unfortunately, at the present time, such a change would be difficult to distinguish from a direct gene mutation and lysogeny has not yet been detected in animal cells.

A variety of evidence for viral and for genetic origins of cancer has accumulated, none yet completely convincing. Cancer remains an interesting and important problem to the cell physiologist.[65, 86]

Regulation of Form and Size in Cells

The ability of a cell to maintain its organization and characteristic size at a given temperature and in the presence of adequate nutrients is perhaps best shown by the regeneration of protozoans after removal of parts of a cell. The mouth parts are the first to regenerate (see Fig. 25.3). In fact, a *Blepharisma*, from which the entire hypostome (mouth area) has been removed, regenerates it sufficiently well to feed within 6 hours.[19] If large portions of the cell are removed, but macronuclear fragments and micronuclei remain present, regeneration will result in a miniature edition of the species. After feeding, however, the regenerated organism rapidly regains its original size. Redifferentiation is usually restricted to portions of the cell adjoining those removed by microsurgery; however, even then, materials required for regeneration must be obtained by the hydrolysis of existent structures. In some species of ciliates, on the other hand, even a small injury results in dedifferentiation of the entire animal and redifferentiation of all the organelles (such as membranelles, motile organs and mouth parts). *Stentor* cut into about 40 adherent pieces survives and regenerates its normal form.[83] As a result of this morphogenetic activity, organelles which have been removed are regenerated, and the characteristic form and size of the species are reconstituted.[19]

When pieces are removed from eggs of some chordates and echinoderms, the eggs produce embryos of reduced size. This shows that the egg maintains a certain pattern, just as does the unicellular organism. When pieces are removed from the eggs of annelids or mollusks, the eggs develop into partial embryos only. In such cases the pattern is supposedly laid down earlier than in the eggs of chordates and echinoderms, and each part is already destined to form a particular organ.[20]

It is probable that most vertebrate cells can recover from minor injuries, although experimental studies on this subject have been limited. The neuron of a vertebrate, for example, regenerates damaged axons or dendrites provided the cell body is intact. Like any other cell, the neuron needs a nucleus for normal functioning.

The nature of the process of cell regeneration and redifferentiation, as well as the nature of the cellular interactions leading to differentiation in development and morphogenesis, is not known. In the slime mold *Dictyostelium* it has been shown that chemical attraction and cellular interactions result in the aggregation of the ameboid cells to form the plasmodium, and also result in the differentiation of the fruiting stalks.[7]

Some ciliates, such as *Stylonychia* and *Blepharisma*, both of which are ordinarily bacterial feeders, may be fed successively a series of protozoans of increasing size, ultimately including their own kind (cannibalism). As a result they become considerably enlarged, having many times the bulk of the normal bacteria-fed individuals. The mouth parts, membranes, motile organs, macronuclei, etc., become proportionally enlarged, and the large size is maintained so long as the abnormal diet is continued. In all cases, however, it has been noticed that when the giants are again put on a bacterial diet, division is more rapid than it is in controls fed continuously on bacteria, so that the giants soon return to the characteristic species size.[22, 23]

Conversely, ciliates may be starved for long periods, during which they undergo reduction in size. *Tetrahymena*, for example, will become a minute particle with little resemblance to its former self. Yet on addition of nutrients it quickly enlarges to the normal size, and when it has grown double this size it divides, thus maintaining the normal size of the species.

That size of cells is regulated by division is most clearly demonstrated with *Amoeba proteus*.[24, 55, 56] During growth of an ameba the mass increases until it just doubles. Then no further increase occurs, and after a lapse of time it divides, each daughter receiving half the mass of the mother. If a part of an ameba is cut off during the period of growth, division will not occur at the time it does in control amebas, but only after the mass of protoplasm removed has been replaced by growth. An ameba may be prevented from dividing, presumably indefinitely, by the periodic removal of a piece of protoplasm although there is some evidence to the contrary.[96]

Heredity plays an important role in the maintenance of size and shape of cells. This is evident since clones of a given species of microorganisms under a given set of environmental conditions tend to be quite constant in size and form for a long series of generations, i.e., a constant nuclear to cytoplasmic ratio is maintained. However, size was found to vary with a change in each environmental factor studied.[25]

Experiments have shown that increasing the number of chromosomes by polyploidy is apparently often attended with an increase in cell size.[26] If the number of chromosomes is increased, each chromosome maintains its characteristic size; therefore the amount of chromatin present in the polyploid nucleus is correspondingly increased. The nucleus increases proportionally in size, and the cytoplasm compensates. A polyploid salamander, for example, has giant cells. The same is true of certain mosses which are usually haploid but may be experimentally produced in diploid, triploid or tetraploid form. Polyploidy has been found in a wide variety of animal and plant cells almost always correlated with increased size of the polyploid cell.[27]

In plant cells, growth might appear to be limited by the rigidity of the cell walls. However, the cell wall is known to be rendered plastic by the plant growth hormone, auxin (indole acetic acid). This softening of cell walls is presumably what occurs to cells in the region of growth, for example when plants, illuminated on one side only, turn toward the light. Auxin has been shown to accumulate on the side away from the light. The curvature induced by the auxin generally results from the extra elongation of young cells in the region of growth, not from cell multiplication. Application of auxin to one side of a plant kept in the dark results in curvature from more rapid growth on that side. Similar softening of cell walls occurs whenever plant cells increase in volume after cell division, but here the action of auxin is less evident than in tropistic responses.

During embryogeny plant cells lack a central sap vacuole. Differentiation usually involves the development of a large central sap vacuole, along with the resultant enlargement of the cell. During such increases in cell size, auxins render the cell walls plastic. It is conceivable that regulation of growth in plant cells may be controlled in part by the auxin supply to different parts of the plant.[92]

Biosyntheses

Cell growth remains a challenging problem and is being attacked not only by biologists, but also by biochemists and biophysicists, often in experimental teams.

The cell grows from within (by intussusception). Growth occurs only if temperature, pH, oxygen and other conditions are favorable, and if the required nutrients and adequate water are available. In the absence of water, the cell may pass into such dormant resting stages as cysts or spores, and remain thus for many years (see Chapters 3, 7, 10). If nutrient is lacking, or if certain required nutrients are limiting factors, growth may stop or become abnormal. Growth is also easily inhibited by poisons, radiations, and, in fact, by all agents that injure the cell or interfere with normal cell functions; a large amount of literature on such effects has accumulated.[57]

Growth is the result of a series of syntheses. For example, the illuminated green plant cell synthesizes all the organic constituents it needs from inorganic salts, carbon dioxide and water. Carbohydrates are produced in photosynthesis, while amino acids, proteins, lipids and vitamins are produced in subsequent syntheses catalyzed by enzymes which are formed from certain proteins and prosthetic groups. Enzymes catalyze the synthesis of components of the nucleus, microsomes, mitochondria, etc.

The animal cell derives its carbohydrates, lipids and proteins ultimately from plant cells. However, with the aid of numerous enzymes, an animal cell also actively synthesizes compounds, but it requires a supply of ready-made glucose, fatty acids, amino acids, vitamins (cell foods), etc., from which it produces the proteins it needs for its cellular structures.

Many of the simpler biosyntheses performed by cells have been successfully duplicated and studied in the laboratory. Biochemists have synthesized large polypeptides and by using amino acids tagged with radioactive tracers, the rate of incorporation of amino acids into proteins has been determined. It has also been found that for the synthesis of polypeptides from amino acids and for the incorporation of amino acids into proteins, high energy phosphate compounds are required. The nucleic acids, DNA and RNA, have also been synthesized *in vitro*.

Perhaps the most successful attack on the problem of biosynthesis is that pioneered by Beadle and Tatum,[58] largely with the bread mold *Neurospora*, for which they received the Nobel Prize in 1958. Wild type *Neurospora* supplied with a base medium of sucrose, certain salts and the B vitamin, biotin, produces all the other growth factors and all the amino acids and other compounds it needs. However, when wild type *Neurospora* is irradiated with ultraviolet radiations or x-rays, gene "blocks" occur, and mutants may appear that are unable to synthesize some growth requirements synthesized by the wild type. These mutants grow only if the particular required compound is added to the base medium (see Fig. 25.4 and 25.5). This finding provides a tool for studying the synthesis of many cell requirements and has yielded results that would have been impossible by other means. To illustrate, a number of mutants of *Neurospora* have been found that fail to produce either tryptophan (an aromatic amino acid) or some precursors of tryptophan. All these mutants will grow if tryptophan is added to the base medium. But by adding a variety of possible precursors of tryptophan to the medium of the mutants, and by studying the metabolic intermediates that accumulate in the medium, the course of the tryptophan synthesis can be analyzed. In this manner, as illustrated in Figure 25.6, it has been found that after mutation of gene 1, a culture of the mutant *Neurospora* synthesizes tyrosine or phenylalanine but is unable to make anthranilic acid from these. If it is supplied with anthranilic acid, it forms indole, which is then coupled with serine to form tryptophan.

Mutation of gene 2 "blocks" synthesis of indole from anthranilic acid, although all the preceding syntheses occur. Provided with indole, *Neurospora* with a mutated gene 2 readily synthesizes tryptophan. In a culture of *Neurospora* with a mutation at gene 2, anthranilic acid accumulates.[28]

Many naturally occurring defects in the metabolism of animals have been found that lead to the accumulation in the urine of peculiar intermediates. By identification of these, it has been possible to map the pathways of biosynthesis and degradation of a great number of compounds. However, the agreement between data gathered on biosyntheses in cells of animals and data on biosynthesis in *Neurospora* is impressive and leads one to a realization of the unity in the biochemistry of the cell, be it in the plant, animal or microorganism. Such unity for degradation of nutrients was realized

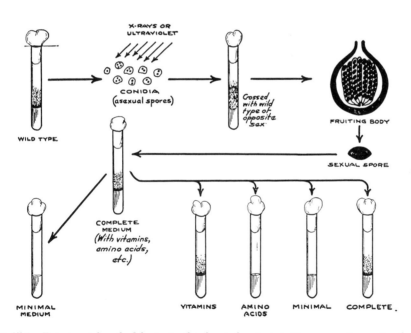

Fig. 25.4. Experimental method for testing biochemical mutants in *Neurospora*. In practice the irradiated asexual spores must be sprouted to form a mycelium, which is fused with another mycelium developed from a nonirradiated asexual spore (see life cycle in Fig. 25.5). The fused mycelia form a fruiting body in which are developed the ascospores. It is the ascospores which are isolated for the tests shown. (From Beadle, 1947: Science in Progress, 5:176.)

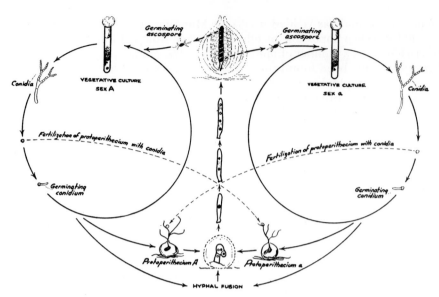

Fig. 25.5. Diagram of the life cycle of *Neurospora crassa*. In addition to the sexual cycle shown, the mold is able to multiply asexually by microconidia and by means of fragments of the mycelium. (From Beadle, 1946: Am. Scientist, *34*:36.)

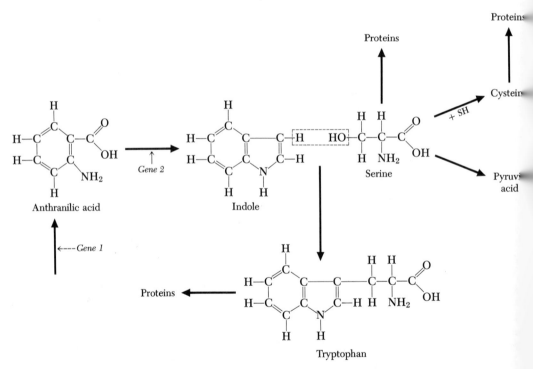

Fig. 25.6. The action of various genes on tryptophan synthesis in *Neurospora*. (After Tatum and Bonner, from Beadle: Am. Scientist, *34*:37, 1946.)

long ago[30] but is now also apparent for the synthetic processes as well. The oldest homologies in life are therefore at the cellular level.[31]

The biosynthetic method used by Beadle and Tatum on *Neurospora* has been applied by many workers to other organisms, especially bacteria, e.g., the colon bacillus, *Escherichia coli*. By this method much has been learned about biosyntheses in cells of various growth factors, purines, pyrimidines, amino acids, etc. In both organisms it has been possible to go a step further, by isolating the enzymes concerned and attempting to duplicate the biosynthetic reactions *in vitro*.[87]

Biosynthesis of DNA. The biosynthesis of deoxyribonucleic acid (DNA) *in vitro*, through polymerization of nucleoside triphosphates in the presence of the appropriate enzyme, was successfully completed by Kornberg, and for this he received the Nobel Prize in 1959.[37] The nucleic acid DNA consists of four kinds of nucleotides or nucleoside phosphates (units of purine or pyrimidine attached to a phosphoric acid residue through a pentose sugar) attached to one another, the phosphoric acid and pentose forming the backbone of the spiraling structure of the Watson-Crick DNA model (see Fig. 3.16). The two complementary DNA fibers are connected to one another by hydrogen bonds between their respective purine and pyrimidine bases—thymine (T) to adenine (A), and guanine (G) to cytosine (C).

The first step in the synthesis of DNA is the formation of the activated nucleoside phosphates by the union of an ATP molecule with each of the four nucleoside monophosphates (phosphorylation). This mechanism is not unique—it is the means whereby amino acids are activated before protein synthesis and fatty acids are activated before any of their synthetic reactions. It is also the means whereby coenzymes are phosphorylated (e.g., nicotinamide mononucleotide to diphosphopyridine nucleotide).

For the four deoxyribonucleoside phosphates, the reactions are:

$$dAMP + ATP \rightarrow dAPPP + P_i \qquad (25.4)$$

$$dGMP + ATP \rightarrow dGPPP + P_i \qquad (25.5)$$

$$dCMP + ATP \rightarrow dCPPP + P_i \qquad (25.6)$$

$$TMP + ATP \rightarrow TPPP + P_i \qquad (25.7)$$

where d refers to the pentose deoxyribose, a component of the nucleoside; ATP refers to adenosine triphosphate; AMP, to adenosine phosphate; GMP, to guanosine phosphate; CMP, to cytidine phosphate; TMP, to thymidine phosphate; APPP, to adenosine triphosphate; GPPP, to guanosine triphosphate; CPPP, to cytidine triphosphate; TPPP, to thymidine triphosphate; and P_i, to inorganic phosphate. An enzyme (phosphorylase) must be present to catalyze the reaction in each case. The nature of the reaction of the ATP with each nucleoside phosphate is shown in Figure 25.7A.

The next step in the synthesis of DNA is polymerization of the activated nucleoside triphosphates, as they are added one at a time at the end of a DNA molecule supplied to serve as a primer or template in the synthesis. A pyrophosphate (PP) of low energy content is given off. This reaction is shown in Figure 25.7B. The high energy bonds of the triphosphates supply the energy required for the synthesis. This occurs only in the presence of an enzyme, nucleotide polymerase, which in this instance was extracted from the colon bacillus. It also proceeds only if some DNA is supplied as a primer. The over-all reaction is shown in Figure 25.7C. The material enzymatically synthesized *in vitro* has been shown to have physical and chemical properties indistinguishable from the natural products.[37]

The function of the DNA primer in the synthesis of DNA is to supply a model to serve as a template. The exactness of the duplication is perhaps best illustrated by the nature of the DNA produced when different models are supplied.

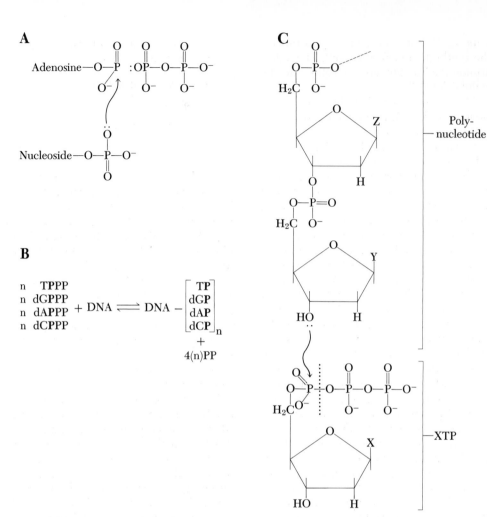

Fig. 25.7. Biosynthesis of DNA. *A*, reaction between adenosine triphosphate and a nucleoside phosphate. *B*, over-all equation for polymerization of the nucleoside triphosphates formed as a result of the reaction shown at *A*. *C*, mechanism of attachment of a nucleoside to the polynucleotide chain. (From Kornberg, 1960: Science *131* : 1505.)

Each DNA, it will be recalled, always has an equal number of adenine and thymine residues (A = T) and an equal number of guanine and cytosine (G = C) residues, but the ratio of A + T to G + C is a characteristic property of each type of DNA. In Table 25.1 are listed the primers used and the base analysis of the primer and product. The agreement is remarkably close. The enzyme, in some unknown and perhaps unique way, takes directions from the template and adds the nucleo-tides in the order and in the numbers appropriate to the primer supplied. It is always the double-stranded DNA that is produced by the enzyme, even when a single-stranded DNA, such as that from the tiny φ X174 virus,[38] was provided. When DNA, which is normally double-stranded but which had uncoiled and become single-stranded in heating, was used as a template, the formation of only the normal double-stranded DNA was obtained. Evidently enough information is available in a single strand of DNA to enable the enzyme to synthesize the appropriate double-stranded DNA. With highly purified enzymes[37] the single-stranded DNA (obtained by heating the double-stranded one) alone is effective.

When a co-polymer, made up only of two nucleotides—deoxyadenylate and deoxythymidilate—is supplied as a template, only the co-polymer is duplicated even though all four nucleoside triphosphates are present in the reaction mixture. This polymer (Table 25.1, last line) indicates the extent to which the enzyme copies what is presented as a template and also shows that the hydrogen bonding between pyrimidine and purine must be of considerable importance in the structure of the polymer produced.

Biosynthesis of RNA. The biosynthesis of RNA by Ochoa, for which he shared the Nobel Prize in 1959 with Kornberg, may be accomplished either (1) from nucleoside diphosphates, or (2) from the triphosphates. In both cases the nucleosides required are adenosine phosphate, guanosine phosphate, cytidine phosphate and uridine phosphate.

In the method first discovered, the nucleotide monophosphates are converted (phosphorylated by use of ATP) to the nucleoside diphosphates. Ochoa and his colleagues[39, 40] isolated from the microorganism *Azotobacter vinelandii* an enzyme (polynucleotide phosphorylase) which, they found, could catalyze the synthesis of high molecular weight ribopolynucleotides from nucleoside diphosphates with the release of inorganic phosphate:

$$nBRPP \rightarrow (BRP)_n + nP_i \qquad (25.8)$$

where B stands for base: adenine, hypoxanthine, uracil or cytosine; R, for ribose; and P_i, for inorganic phosphate. The enzyme is found in bacteria and plant cells but so far has been identified in few animal cells. In the early experiments the enzyme was only partially purified.

Single polymers containing one of the nucleotides—AMP (adenosine monophosphate), UMP (uridine monophosphate),

TABLE 25.1. *Chemical Composition of DNA Enzymatically Synthesized with Different Primers**

DNA PRIMER	A	T	G	C	$\dfrac{A+G}{T+C}$	$\dfrac{A+T}{G+C}$
Mycobacterium phlei						
Primer	0.65	0.66	1.35	1.34	1.01	0.49
Product	0.66	0.65	1.34	1.37	0.99	0.48
Escherichia coli						
Primer	1.00	0.97	0.98	1.05	0.98	0.97
Product	1.04	1.00	0.97	0.98	1.01	1.02
Calf thymus						
Primer	1.14	1.05	0.90	0.85	1.05	1.25
Product	1.12	1.08	0.85	0.85	1.02	1.29
Bacteriophage T2						
Primer	1.31	1.32	0.67	0.70	0.98	1.92
Product	1.33	1.29	0.69	0.70	1.02	1.90
A-T copolymer	1.99	1.93	<0.05	<0.05	1.03	40

* A, adenine; T, thymine; G, guanine; C, cytosine
From Kornberg, 1960: Science *131*.

CMP (cytidine monophosphate) and IMP (inosine monophosphate)—as the only basic units have been obtained by incubating the enzyme with the corresponding nucleoside diphosphate in each case, even nucleosides not normally present in RNA being polymerized. Mixed polymers of adenine and uridine ribonucleoside phosphates or of all four nucleoside phosphates of RNA can be obtained if two or four of the nucleoside diphosphates, respectively, are supplied.

The polymers have molecular weights of the order of 30,000 to 2,000,000; therefore they are in the range of molecular weights for RNA from different sources. Also, they display many RNA-like properties. For example, the polynucleotides even react with tobacco mosaic virus protein to form noninfective virus-like particles.

Success has also now been obtained in the synthesis of RNA using methods[92a] much like those used in the synthesis of DNA. A single enzyme, RNA-polymerase, was found to be responsible for incorporating the four ribonucleotides (containing the bases adenine, guanine, cytosine and uracil) in the highly energetic triphosphate form. RNA appeared to be needed as a template, but it was later discovered that DNA, present in the impure extracts, was necessary for RNA synthesis. The synthesized RNA is specific to the DNA (template) used for its induction. Thus when the DNA is obtained from the colon bacillus, the ratio of adenine plus uracil to guanine plus cytosine (i.e., $\frac{A + U}{G + C}$) is 1.0 in the RNA synthesized, which is characteristic of the colon bacillus RNA. When the DNA is obtained from calf thymus, the $\frac{A + U}{G + C}$ ratio in the RNA synthesized under DNA influence is 1.3, which is characteristic of calf thymus RNA.

Additional evidence of the specificity of DNA as an inducer of RNA was ob-

tained by using a synthetic DNA-like polydeoxyribonucleotide; for example, containing adenine and thymine deoxyribonucleotides (AT co-polymer). In this case the RNA-like polyribonucleotide, synthesized under DNA influence, consisted of polymers of uracil and adenine polyribonucleotides in alternating sequence. When polythymine deoxyribonucleotide was used as the template, adenine polyribonucleotide consisting of only adenine ribonucleotide units was synthesized.[92a]

Biosynthesis of Protein. Biosynthesis of proteins has been of great interest for many years and a great deal is known of protein composition and much has been learned about protein synthesis. Use of radioactively labeled amino acids has made it possible to measure their rate of incorporation into proteins, and thus follow the steps of protein synthesis in the living cell. An important early observation that dinitrophenol, which is known to uncouple phosphorylations, also inhibits protein synthesis led to the realization that not the amino acids but, rather, their "activated" phosphorylated forms are probably used in synthesis of proteins in the cell. Histochemical and cytological studies, especially by Brachet and Caspersson (see Chapters 3 and 6), had implicated RNA of the ribosomes of the cytoplasm in protein synthesis.

Although the pathway by which the present knowledge of protein synthesis has been achieved is somewhat devious,[50] it is now known that the synthesis of protein in the cell involves a number of steps and the participation of several forms of RNA. The first step involves activation of the amino acid by reaction with ATP in the presence of an enzyme, forming an amino acid—adenosine monophosphate complex (aa-AMP) (Step 1, Fig. 25.8A). Another step is the preparation of an acceptor site for the amino acid on soluble RNA (the low molecular weight fraction of RNA dissolved in the hyalo-

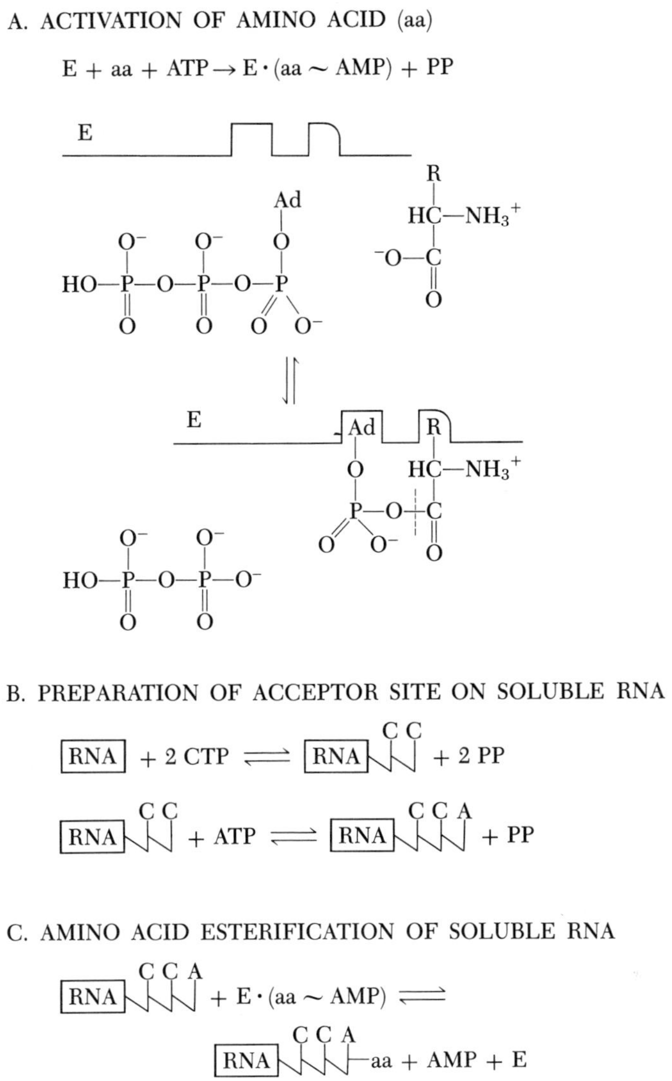

A. ACTIVATION OF AMINO ACID (aa)

$$E + aa + ATP \rightarrow E \cdot (aa \sim AMP) + PP$$

E

R
|
Ad   HC—NH$_3^+$
|
O$^-$ O$^-$ O $^-$O—C
| | ‖   ‖
HO—P—O—P—O—P   O
‖   ‖   \\
O   O   O O$^-$

⇕

E

          Ad   R
                  |
          O   HC—NH$_3^+$
          | |
          P—O—C
         O O$^-$ ‖
                   O

O$^-$ O$^-$
| |
HO—P—O—P—O$^-$
‖   ‖
O   O

B. PREPARATION OF ACCEPTOR SITE ON SOLUBLE RNA

$$\boxed{RNA} + 2\,CTP \rightleftharpoons \boxed{RNA}\overset{C\;C}{\wedge\!\!\wedge} + 2\,PP$$

$$\boxed{RNA}\overset{C\;C}{\wedge\!\!\wedge} + ATP \rightleftharpoons \boxed{RNA}\overset{C\;C\;A}{\wedge\!\!\wedge\!\!\wedge} + PP$$

C. AMINO ACID ESTERIFICATION OF SOLUBLE RNA

$$\boxed{RNA}\overset{C\;C\;A}{\wedge\!\!\wedge\!\!\wedge} + E \cdot (aa \sim AMP) \rightleftharpoons$$

$$\boxed{RNA}\overset{C\;C\;A}{\wedge\!\!\wedge\!\!\wedge}\!\!-aa + AMP + E$$

Fig. 25.8. Schematic representation of preparatory steps in protein synthesis concerned with amino acid activation. A, phosphorylation. (ATP) represents adenosine triphosphate; (AMP) adenosine monophosphate; (aa) amino acid, reaction and schematic representation of mechanism; (E) enzyme surface; (Ad) adenine; (R) a radical on the amino acid; (PP) pyrophosphate. Only the alpha amino group and the carboxyl group are shown in detail. (From Hoagland, Keller and Zamecnik, 1956: J. Biol. Chem., 218:345.) B, preparation of the acceptor site on soluble RNA by phosphorylation. (CTP) represents cytidine triphosphate; (C) cytidine. C, addition of amino acid to the soluble RNA. Note that the enzyme is released for further activity after esterification is completed. (From Zamecnik, 1960: Harvey Lect., 54:265.)

plasm, liberated into the supernatant of disintegrated cells and precipitated at pH 5—therefore called the pH 5 fraction) by reaction with cytidine triphosphate (CTP) and adenosine triphosphate (ATP) (Step 2, Fig. 25.8B). The activated amino acid complex is next attached to the phosphorylated soluble RNA and AMP is

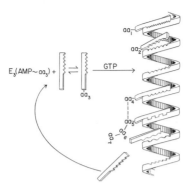

Fig. 25.9. The synthesis of amino acid into a protein. The activated amino acid is shown attached first to an enzyme at the far left, then attached to transfer RNA. This, in turn, in the presence of guanosine triphosphate, attaches to the template RNA shown as a spiral. The activated amino acid then forms a peptide linkage with another amino acid at the expense of phosphate bond energy at the same time liberating the soluble RNA which can repeat the cycle. (From Hoagland, Zamecnik and Stephenson, 1959: *in* A Symposium on Molecular Biology (Zirkle ed.). Univ. of Chicago Press, Chicago, p. 105.)

released, as shown in Step 3, Fig. 25.8*C*.

Presumably, twenty such soluble transfer RNA molecules (also called adapter RNA) occur, one for each amino acid. Thus, when a particular amino acid (labeled) is added until the saturation level is reached, addition of any other labeled amino acid at this time leads to further labeling of the protein, indicating a lack of competition between the two amino acids.[41, 51] This could best be explained by postulating for the second amino acid, a separate soluble RNA molecule different from that involved with the first amino acid. These RNA molecules are now being fractionated and identified. A separate enzyme is probably involved in the attachment of each of the twenty amino acids to the respective molecule of soluble RNA. The enzyme is liberated at the time the amino acid becomes attached to the soluble RNA (see Fig. 25.8 and 25.10).

It was also observed that not only soluble RNA but also ribosomal RNA is needed for amino acid incorporation into protein.[41, 51, 94] Presumably, the soluble RNA carries the activated amino acid to the ribosomal RNA, and in the presence of guanosine triphosphate (GTP) as a source of energy, the amino acid is transferred to the ribosome (RNA) while the soluble RNA is liberated, as shown in Figure 25.9.

This process can be better followed by using ascites tumor cells at 20° C. instead of at body temperature (37° C.). It has been shown in this case that incubation of tumor cells with a C^{14}-labeled amino acid is followed by the appearance of radioactivity first in the transfer RNA fraction, more slowly in the ribosomal RNA, then in the ribosome protein and finally in the soluble protein of the cell. For these reactions guanosine triphosphate is needed, probably as a source of high energy phosphate bonds.

Just what happens on the surface of the ribosome is at present largely speculative. Presumably the base sequences of the transfer RNA molecules carrying the amino acids are located on the ribosomal RNA according to complementarity of base sequences which encode the message from the gene. When this location has been achieved, the particular ribosome RNA would carry along its length a series of transfer RNA molecules, each with an attached amino acid. Peptide bonding between successive amino acids attached to the ribosome then takes place by what has been described as a "zipper action," apparently starting with the amino acid valine at one end of the chain and closing bond after bond until the protein molecule is finished in accordance with the template presented.[8] Meanwhile, each soluble transfer RNA is liberated as its amino acid joins in the formation of protein (Fig. 25.9). New amino acid molecules are added to the growing chain at the rate of two a second, and a protein molecule of 150 amino acids is finished in 1.5 minutes. The amino acids are in an activated state.

and presumably need only to be juxtaposed in the appropriate steric relationships for this to happen. Following protein synthesis, the next step would be the separation or "peeling off" of the protein molecule from its template on the ribosome (Fig. 25.9).[41, 50] The over-all scheme of protein synthesis is shown in Figure 25.10.

The big question, of course, is how does the nuclear DNA give to the ribosomal RNA its coded information as to the kind of protein to make. It is possible to envision each strand of DNA laying down along its length a series of RNA nucleotides, creating thus a set of working dyes identically coded for the amino acids. According to this theory[41, 51] the master DNA template is thus preserved in the genes, but the "messenger" RNA (formed on the DNA with the corresponding message) can proceed to coat the RNA of the ribosome with the message from the gene. An alternate theory is that the DNA may produce ribosomes directly. While RNA is known to be produced in the nucleus, how it reaches the ribosomes is not known. With the "messenger RNA hypothesis" it is necessary to postulate that as many types of DNA molecules exist as there are proteins in the cell. There must also exist even a few more types of RNA (ribosomal and soluble RNA) than types of proteins.[51*]

Protein synthesis occurs to some extent also in the nucleus as is shown by uptake of labeled amino acids into proteins of nuclei. The nucleus, like the cytoplasm, contains the enzymes for activation of amino acids and for their incorporation into proteins. Nuclei depleted of DNA by treatment with deoxyribonuclease lose their capacity for incorporation of ATP and of amino acids, but upon addition of DNA, synthesis is restored.[41, 52]

It is of great importance to note that specific protein syntheses may be induced in cells. For example, it will be recalled that enzymes can be induced in

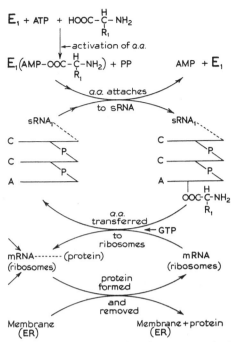

Fig. 25.10. Overall scheme of protein synthesis. Stages in protein biosynthesis. (E_1) is the activating enzyme for the amino acid $R_1CH(NH_2)COOH$ and ($sRNA_1$) is the corresponding transfer RNA for this amino acid. (mRNA) indicates the microsomal RNA found in the ribosomes. (ER) represents the endoplasmic reticulum. (From Davidson, J. N., 1960: The Biochemistry of the Nucleic Acids, 4th. Ed. Methuen, London, p. 240.)

microorganisms in response to the presence of a specific nutrient for which the organism does not have a constitutive enzyme. Thus the colon bacillus develops a β-galactosidase in response to the presence of lactose in the medium (see Chapter 13). Another case of induced protein synthesis is the development of immunity, that is, the production of antibodies in response to antigens. The active group (haptene) in the antigen is generally a carbohydrate (polysaccharide) or a protein, and the antibody protein is highly

*Acetabularia continues to synthesize protein for several weeks after enucleation. This apparent paradox is resolved if the report that DNA is present in some chloroplasts is found to be general, in view of the role of DNA in protein synthesis.

discriminatory in its action, indicating its "custom-built" synthesis.

Protein synthesis in cells is readily inhibited by the antibiotic chloramphenicol. RNA and DNA synthesis, however, may continue under these conditions. Radiation can inhibit DNA synthesis without immediately affecting the others, indicating partial separateness of the three processes. Stopping both protein and RNA synthesis, however, also stops DNA synthesis.[82]

The Origin of Life

It is inevitable that the question of the origin of life should arise whenever the spectacular advances in biosynthesis of cellular constituents in recent years are reviewed. As the synthesis of various organic compounds—amino acids, polypeptides, nucleic acids, and proteins—are studied, one asks how these substances were first formed on the lifeless planet. Much has been learned about the synthesis of various organic compounds from inorganic precursors that have been subjected to heat, radiations and electric discharges which simulate conditions on the surface of the primeval earth. It is also of greatest interest to know how the aggregations of such materials attained life and the ability to replicate. The viruses which duplicate themselves may represent an experiment in this direction, but their inability to liberate energy from organic compounds makes them dependent upon host cells; consequently they do not appeal to many as the first forms of life. It is not possible to consider here the many experiments and speculations present in the large literature.[90, 91, 93]

Synthesis of Organelles of the Cell

Little is known about the origin and development of the various organelles of the cell. Some attempts have been made to gain an insight into the processes by studying what appears to be analogous reactions in colloidal systems.[53] The interaction of colloids of opposite charge in the formation of tactoids and coacervates has already been considered in Chapter 4. Some globular inclusions in the cell have been likened to coacervates,[59] and the spindle-shaped fibers, and even structures such as the division spindle, have been likened to tactoids.[61]

It is thought by some workers that many of the organelles in the living cell may arise *de novo* as outgrowths of the cell membrane,[66] while others postulate that they result from replication of existing organelles which act as templates, guiding the enzymes in depositing the new material[67] (for evidence, see ref. 97).

Balanced and Unbalanced Growth

When a mutant form of the colon bacillus, which requires for its growth the pyrimidine base thymine, is grown in a medium deficient in thymine but adequate in all the other nutrients, growth appears to occur (as measured by turbidity). However, when the growing material is plated out, even on a balanced medium containing all necessary nutrients, including thymine, it is observed that about 90 per cent of the individuals fail to produce colonies if they have been grown in the deficient medium for a period equivalent to that required for one generation. If so grown for two generations, about 99 per cent fail to form colonies. Tests show that protein and RNA increase in the cells, but there is only a slight increase in DNA.[36] Such disproportionate growth of different cell constituents is spoken of as *unbalanced growth*. A similar phenomenon has been observed in yeast[70] and *Neurospora*.[7] However, it does not appear to be general, since some cells recover even after becoming much enlarged.[95]

An interesting experiment is one in which a mutant requiring some nutrient mmon to synthesis of both RNA and NA is maintained without apparent ange on a medium deficient in the nu ent.[71] In this case, no growth, or very tle, can occur. Presumably it is only en growth is unbalanced, that is, en most constituents can increase in antity but one does not, that injury curs, as in the experiments above. The ll is already so unbalanced in content at even when the required nutrient is stored, it has no way of rectifying the sarrangement.[36]

It might be expected that any factor, her than limitation of nutrients, which ds to unbalanced growth might simi ly kill the cell. Experiments with ultra let radiations (to which synthesis of NA is one of the most susceptible proc ses in the cell[68]) show that the irradiated lls in which DNA synthesis is just in bited may continue to grow and be me giants accumulating RNA and oteins. Plated out, however, they also il to produce colonies—i.e., they are able to divide.[36] It is argued that the owth of various structures in the ab nce of DNA synthesis has deranged the ll so that it is no longer able to divide d reproduce, even when the DNA nthesis has recovered from the radia n injury. If the cells are irradiated suf iently to stop DNA synthesis and kept non-nutrient solution so that they can t grow or divide, DNA synthesis covers slowly, and addition of balanced trients will restore balanced growth.[88]

These derangements indicate that the owth processes in the cell must be ad sted to maintain some sort of balance. is clear that the rate of enzymatic re tions must be controlled. How is this hieved?

At least part of this control must come feedback from each reaction. Most actions occur in series. Evidence exists at in some instances the products of e last reaction of a series serve to re ice the initial reaction in the series, in is way serving as a negative feedback.

The over-all effect of such a control is to adjust the amount of precursor formed to the demand for the products. If the products are quickly used, there will be no negative feedback and the reaction will proceed at maximal rate.[72, 74, 79, 80]

Another control is perhaps structural and steric. It is known, for example, that ribosomes occur in a range of sizes, the large sizes appearing to result from combination of several small ones. The large particles may be forty times as active in protein synthesis as the small ones. Presumably the rate of protein synthesis can be adjusted to any level by variation in the size of the particles. Control of this type may have great importance in syntheses carried out by the ribosomes. This may possibly be true for other cases.[73]

Still another type of control is genetic. Evidence for this exists in the colon bacillus in which genes at several loci are found which apparently, directly or indirectly, control the activity of some of the enzymes involved in protein synthesis. One of the genes, for example, at the structure-determining locus, is concerned with the production of the RNA template for protein synthesis. The rate of production of this RNA template material, however, is determined by two *controller genes:* an *operator* gene, closely linked to the structure-determining locus, which switches the production on and off, and a *regulator* gene. The regulator gene controls the rate of production of a low molecular weight substance (perhaps a nucleic acid[89]) called a *repressor,* which probably interferes with the action of the template (or possibly with the gene itself).[74] The operator gene may regulate the production of RNA template, shutting it off, at a signal from the repressor. The inhibitory action of the repressor substance appears to be overcome by the competition of a particular substrate acting as an *inducer,* evoking the formation of new enzyme by this means (e.g., galactose induces the formation of β-galactosidase). It is possible that the interaction of operator genes with the repressor and inducer substances leads to a steady state favorable for continued synthesis of enzymes at a rate adjusted to the needs of the cell.[75, 81] Occasionally the regulatory machinery of the cell fails as a result of a mutation, and the cell produces much more of a given protein (e.g., an enzyme) than it can use. In nature, such defective strains are soon eliminated through survival of the fittest.[75, 79]

Changes in Syntheses—Mutations

It is to be expected, on the basis of probabilities, that in the course of a long series of replication of genic DNA a mistake will occur. Such a mistake might well produce changes in synthesis of the specific protein with profound effects on the organism.

The method of "fingerprinting" proteins has made it possible to document some mutations and to demonstrate that a mutation with gross effects on the cell or organism may rest upon a simple alteration in synthesis of a protein. Thus a protein of a mutant type may differ from the corresponding protein of the normal by only one amino acid at a given location in the protein molecule. For example, the hereditary disease of man, known as sickle cell anemia, results during development of hemoglobin in the cells of the mutant individual from the substitution of a molecule of the amino acid valine for glutamic acid, the fourth amino acid of the β chain of the hemoglobin molecule. As a result, the hemoglobin of the mutant (diseased individual) is so altered in its physical properties that the entire erythrocyte takes on a new form—that of a sickle instead of a disk—which is much less effective in transporting oxygen. In another mutant type, replacement of the glutamic acid by the amino acid lysine at the same position on the

hemoglobin molecule gives rise to s another pathological condition. Seve other amino acid substitutions on hem globin in other mutants have correspon ing effects on the protein molecule a on the red blood cell.[76]

Other changes in proteins produced mutations have also been analyzed. Th in Neurospora crassa several mutatic affect the enzymes tyrosinase and tryp phan synthetase, 100 mutants being ava able in the latter case, of which 30 ha been examined in biochemical and netic tests. It is shown that a single ge mutation involves single amino ac alteration in the enzymic proteins p duced, and this causes drastic effects the properties of the enzyme. In Esch ichia coli, tryptophan synthetase, alkali phosphatase and β-galactosidase have been similarly studied. In all cases, t fully analyzed "fingerprint" shows subs tution of an amino acid at one locus the enzyme protein molecule.[69]

It seems quite clear that the concept "one gene—one enzyme" has consid able evidence to support it. The ge expresses itself by the formation of a p tein which, if enzymatic, carries out t syntheses designated by the code in t DNA. A slight change in this protein even the replacement of a single ami acid at a critical point on the molecule results in such a change of its properti that the reaction it catalyzes is carri out more slowly or not at all. This de ciency in the genic DNA template is th reflected in a deficiency of the prote produced under direction of the partic lar gene. The resultant deficiency show up as a mutant in the cell or t organism.[81]

What now remains is an exciting pro pect, almost within reach—namely, t determination of the sequence of bases the DNA of the gene, thereby elucid ing the nature of the genic coded me sage to the enzymes of the cell.[69, 98]

536

GENERAL REFERENCES

Adolph, F., 1931: The Regulation of Size as Illustrated in Unicellular Organisms. Thomas, Springfield, Ill.

Allen, J. M. (ed.), 1961: The Molecular Control of Cellular Activity. McGraw-Hill, New York.

Andrew, W., 1952: Cellular Changes with Age. Thomas, Springfield, Ill.

Anfinsen, C. B., 1959: The Molecular Basis of Evolution. Wiley, New York.

Beadle, G. W., 1959: Genes and Chemical Reactions in *Neurospora*. Science *129*:1715–1719.

Bernal, J. D., 1955: Une Discussion sur l'Origine de la Vie. Union Rationaliste, Paris.

Biesele, J. J., 1958: Mitotic Poisons and the Cancer Problem. Elsevier, New York.

Blum, H. F., 1957: On the Origin of Self Duplicating Systems. Society for Study of Development and Growth, 15th Symposium. pp. 155–170.

Cohen, S. S., and Barner, H. D., 1954: Studies on Unbalanced Growth in *Escherichia coli*. Proc. Nat. Acad. Sci. U. S. *40*:885–893.

Comfort, A., 1956: The Biology of Senescence. Rinehart, New York.

Comfort, A., Aug. 1961: The Life Span of Animals. Sci. Am. *205*:108–119.

Davidson, J. N., 1960: The Biochemistry of the Nucleic Acids. Methuen, London.

Florkin, M., (ed.), 1960: Aspects of the Origin of Life. Pergamon Press, London.

Fox, S. W., 1957: Chemical Problem of Spontaneous Generation. J. Chem. Educ. *34*:472–479.

Fraenkel-Conrat, H., 1961: Design and Function at the Threshold of Life: The Viruses. Academic Press, New York.

Gross, L., 1961: Oncogenic Viruses, Pergamon Press, New York.

Hieger, I., 1961: Carcinogenesis. Academic Press, New York.

Jacobson, W., 1958: The Toxic Action of Drugs on the Bone Marrow, *in* Symposium of the Evaluation of Drug Toxicity (Walpole, A., and Spinks, A., eds.). Little, Brown, Boston, pp. 76–101.

Kornberg, A., 1960: Biologic Synthesis of Deoxyribonucleic Acid. Science *131*:1503–1508.

Kornberg, A., 1959: Enzymatic Synthesis of Deoxyribonucleic Acid. Harvey Lect. *53*:83–112.

Lederberg, J., 1959: Bacterial Reproduction. Harvey Lect. *53*:69–82.

Lederberg, J., 1960: A View of Genetics. Science *131*:269–276.

Lerner, M., 1954: Genetic Homeostasis. Wiley, New York.

Lotfield, R. B., 1957: The Biosynthesis of Protein. Progr. Biophys. *8*:347–386.

Magasanik, B., 1961: Feedback Mechanisms in Biological Syntheses, *in* Biological Approaches to Cancer Chemotherapy (Harris, R. J., ed.). Academic Press, New York.

Miller, S. L., and Urey, H. C., 1959: Organic Compounds on the Primitive Earth. Science *130*:245–251.

Morgan, J. F., 1958: Tissue Culture Nutrition. Bact. Rev. *22*:20–45.

Moscona, A. A., May 1959. Tissues from Dissociated Cells. Sci. Am. *200*:132–144. Sept. 1961: How Cells Associate. Sci. Am. *205*:143–162.

Needham, A. E., 1959: The Origination of Life. Quart. Rev. Biol. *34*:189–209.

van Niel, C. B., 1955: Natural Selection in the Microbial World. J. Gen. Microbiol. *13*:201–217.

Nigrelli, R. F., (ed.), 1957: Modern Ideas on Spontaneous Generation. Ann. New York Acad. Sci. *69*:255–376.

Ochoa, S., 1959: *in* Enzymes of Polynucleotide Metabolism (Roth, J. S., ed.). Ann. New York Acad. Sci. *81*:511–804.

Oparin, A. I., 1957: The Origin of Life on the Earth. 3rd Ed. Academic Press, New York.

Paul, J., 1960: Cell and Tissue Culture. Williams & Wilkins, Baltimore.

Puck, T. T., 1957: The Mammalian Cell as Microorganism. 15th Symp. Society for Study of Development and Growth, 15th Symposium, pp. 1–18.

Sagan, C., 1961: On the Origin and Planetary Distribution of Life. Rad. Res. *15*:174–192.

Shock, N. W., Jan. 1962: The Physiology of Aging. Sci. Am. *206*:100–110.

Strehler, B. L., 1959: Origins and Comparisons of Time and High Radiations on Living Systems. Quart. Rev. Biol. *34*:117–142.

Sutton, H. E., 1961: Genes, Enzymes and Inherited Diseases. Holt, New York.

Thompson, D. W., 1942: Growth and Form. Macmillan, New York.

Weisz, P. B., 1954: Morphogenesis in Protozoa. Quart. Rev. Biol. *29*:207–229.

Zamecnik, P. C., 1960: Historical and Current Aspects of the Problem of Protein Synthesis. Harvey Lect. *54*:256–281.

Zarrow, M. X. (ed.), 1961: Growth in Living Systems. Basic Books, New York.

LITERATURE CITED

1. Weismann, A., 1913: Vorträge über Deszendenztheorie. Jena, Germany.
2. Jennings, H. S., 1945: J. Exp. Zool. *99*:15.
3. Calkins, G. N., 1933: The Biology of the Protozoa. Lea and Febiger, Philadelphia.
4. Kidder, G. W., 1953: Biochemistry and Physiology of Nutrition (Invertebrates). Vol. 2, Chapter 15.

5. Elliott, A. M., and Hayes, R. E., 1953: Biol. Bull. *105*:269.
6. Carpenter, P. L., 1961: Microbiology. Saunders, Philadelphia.
7. Bonner, J. T., 1952: Morphogenesis. Princeton Univ. Press, Princeton, N. J.
8. Schoenheimer, R., 1942: The Dynamic State of Body Constituents. Harvard Univ. Press, Cambridge, Mass.
9. Zeuthen, E., 1947: Compt. Rend. Lab. Carlsberg *26*:17.
10. Zeuthen, E., 1953: Quart. Rev. Biol. *28*:1.
11. White, P. R., 1953: The Culture of Animal and Plant Cells. Ronald Press, New York.
12. Child, C. M., 1915: Senescence and Rejuvenescence. Univ. Chicago Press, Chicago.
13. Comfort, A., 1954: Biological Aspects of Senescence. Biol. Rev. *29*:251.
14. McCay, C. M., 1942: Trans. & Stud. Coll. Physicians *10*:1–10.
15. Slonaker, J. R., 1939: Stanford Univ. Publ. Biol. Sci. Vol. 6, no. 4, p. 257.
16. Kidder, G. W., Dewey, V. C., and Parks, R. E., Jr., 1949: Science *109*:511.
17. Woodside, G. L., Kidder, G. W., Dewey, V. C., and Parks, R. E., 1953: Cancer Res. *13*:289.
18. Warburg, O., 1956: Science *123*:309.
19. Balamuth, W., 1940: Quart. Rev. Biol. *15*:290.
20. Scheer, B. T., 1953: General Physiology. Wiley, New York, Ch. 16.
21. Muggleton, A., and Danielli, J. F., 1958: Nature *181*:1738.
22. Giese, A. C., and Alden, R. H., 1938: J. Exp. Zool. *78*:117.
23. Giese, A. C., 1938: Trans. Am. Micr. Soc., *57*:245.
24. Mazia, D., 1956: Am. Sci. *14*:1; Prescott, 1956: Exp. Cell Res. *11*:94.
25. Adolph, E. F., 1931: The Regulation of Size as Illustrated in Unicellular Organisms. Thomas, Springfied, Ill.
26. Fankhauser, G., 1952: Int. Rev. Cyt. *1*:165.
27. White, M. J. D., 1961: The Chromosome. 5th Ed. Wiley, New York.
28. Beadle, G. W., 1949: Science in Progress (Baitsell, G., ed.). *6*:184. Yale Univ. Press, New Haven.
29. Duncan, G. G., ed., 1959: Diseases of Metabolism. 4th Ed. Saunders, Philadelphia.
30. Kluyver, A. J., and Donker, H. J. L., 1926: Chemie der Zelle und Gewebe, *13*:134.
31. Szent-Györgyi, A., 1940: *in* The Cell and Protoplasm (Taylor, C. V., ed.). Science Press, New York, p. 159.
32. Thompson, E. O. P., 1955: Sci. Am. *192*:36. Sanger, F., and Smith, L. F., 1957: Endeavour *16*:48.
33. Caspersson, T., 1950: Cell Growth and Cell Function. Norton, New York.
34. Brachet, J., 1952: Symp. Soc. Exp. Biol. *6*:173.

35. Pollister, A. W., 1954: Science *120*:789 (abstr.).
36. Cohen, S. S., and Barner, H. D., 1954: Proc. Nat. Acad. Sci. U. S. *40*:885.
37. Kornberg, A., 1960: Science *131*:1503.
38. Sinsheimer, R. L., 1959: J. Molec. Biol. *1*:43; July, 1962: Sci. Am. *207*:109.
39. Grunberg-Manago, M., Ortiz, O. J., and Ochoa, S., 1956: Biochim. Biophys. Acta *20*:269.
40. Ochoa, S., and Heppel, L. A., 1957: *in* The Chemical Basis of Heredity (McElroy, W. D., and Glass, B., eds.). Johns Hopkins Press, Baltimore, p. 615.
41. Davidson, J. N., 1960: The Biochemistry of the Nucleic Acids. 4th Ed. Methuen, London.
42. LeBlond, C. P., and Walker, B. E., 1956: Physiol. Rev. *36*:255.
43. Puck, T. T., 1957: Society for Study of Development and Growth, 15th Symposium, p. 1.
44. Paul, J., 1960: Cell and Tissue Culture. Williams & Wilkins, Baltimore.
45. Morgan, J. F., 1958: Bact. Rev. *22*:20.
46. Deschner, E. E., and Allen, B. R., 1960: Science *131*:419.
47. Salzman, N. P., 1961: Science *133*:1559.
48. Eagle, H., 1960: Proc. Nat. Acad. Sci. U. S. *46*:427.
49. Warburg, O., Gewehn, K., and Geissler, A. W., 1957: Z. Naturforsch. *12*:393.
50. Zamecnik, P., 1960: Harvey Lect. *54*:256.
51. Hoagland, M. B., Dec. 1959: Sci. Am. *201*:55.
52. Crick, F. H. C., 1958: Symp. Soc. Exp. Biol. *12*:138.
53. Frey-Wyssling, A., 1953: Submicroscopic Morphology of Protoplasm. 2nd Ed. Elsevier, Houston.
54. Pullman, A., and Pullman, B., 1955: Adv. Cancer Res. *3*:117.
55. Prescott, D. M., 1956: Exp. Cell. Res. *11*:86, 94.
56. Mazia, D., 1956: Adv. Biol. & Med. Physics *4*:70.
57. Hughes, A., 1952: The Mitotic Cycle. Academic Press, New York.
58. Beadle, G. W., and Tatum, E. L., 1941: Proc. Nat. Acad. Sci. U. S. *27*:499.
59. Bungenberg de Jong, H. G., 1932: Protoplasm *15*:110.
60. Mazia, D., 1954: Symp. Soc. Exp. Biol. *9*:335.
61. Bernal, J. D., and Fankuchen, I., 1941: J. Gen. Physiol. *25*:111.
62. Strangeways, T. S. P., and Hopwood, F. L., 1926: Proc. Roy. Soc. London s.B, *100*:283.
63. Huxley, J., 1956: Biol. Rev. *31*:474.
64. Alfrey, V. G., Mirsky, A. E., and Stern, H., 1955: Adv. Enzymol. *16*:411.
65. Hoffman, J. G., 1957: The Life and Death of Cells. Hanover House, Garden City, N. Y.
66. Robertson, J. D., 1960: Progr. Biophys. *10*:343.
67. DeRobertis, E. D. P., Nowinski, W. W., and Saez, F. A., 1960: General Cytology, 3rd Ed. Saunders, Philadelphia.

68. Kelner, A., 1953: J. Bact. *65*:252.
69. Yanofsky, C., and St. Lawrence, P., 1960: Ann. Rev. Microbiol. *14*:311.
70. Ridgeway, G. J., and Douglas, H. C., 1958: J. Bact. *76*:163.
71. Strauss, B. S., 1958: J. Gen. Microbiol. *18*:658.
72. Roberts, R. B., 1959: Rev. Mod. Physics *31*:170.
73. Tissieres, A., Schlessinger, D., and Gros, F., 1960: Proc. Nat. Acad. Sci. U. S. *46*:1450.
74. Niedhardt, F. C., and Magasanik, B., 1960: Biochim. Biophys. Acta. *42*:99.
75. Jacob, F., Perrin, D., Sanchez, C., and Monod, J., 1960: Compt. Rend. Acad. Sci. *250*:1727.
76. Ingram, V. M., Jan. 1958: Sci. Am. *198*:68.
77. Breton, E. L., and Moulé, Y., 1961: The Cell (Brachet, J., and Mirsky, A. E., eds.). Academic Press, New York, vol. 5, p. 497.
78. Oberling, C., and Bernhard, W., 1961: The Cell (Brachet, J., and Mirsky, A. E., eds.). Academic Press, New York, vol. 5, p. 405.
79. Yates, R. A., and Pardee, A. B., 1956: J. Biol. Chem. *221*:757.
80. Umbarger, H. E., 1956: Science *123*:848.
81. Yanofsky, C., 1960: Bact. Rev. *24*:221.
82. Doudney, C. O., and Billen, D., 1961: Nature *190*:544.
83. Tartar, V., 1960: J. Exp. Zool. *144*:187; 1961: The Biology of Stentor, Pergamon Press, Oxford.
84. Jacobson, W., 1958: *in* A Symposium on the Evaluation of Drug Toxicity (Walpole, A., and Spinks, A., eds.). Little, Brown, Boston, p. 76.
85. Berrill, N. J., 1961: Growth, Development and Pattern. Freeman, San Francisco.
86. Hieger, I., 1961: Carcinogenesis. Academic Press, New York.
87. Beadle, G. W., 1959: Science *129*:1715.
88. Giese, A. C., Iverson, R. M., and Sanders, R., 1957: J. Bact. *74*:271.
89. Jacob, F., and Wollman, E. L., June 1961: Sci. Am. *204*:93.
90. Nigrelli, R. F. (ed.), 1957: Annals New York Acad. Sci. *69* (Art. 2):255.
91. Florkin, M. (ed.), 1960: Aspects of the Origin of Life. Pergamon Press, London.
92. Leopold, A., 1955: Auxins and Plant Growth. Univ. California Press, Berkeley.
92a. Hurwitz, J., and Furth, J. S., Feb. 1962: Sci. Am. *206*:41.
93. Oparin, A. I., 1957: The Origin of Life on Earth. 3rd. Ed. Academic Press, New York.
94. Allfrey, V. C., and Mirsky, A. E., Sept. 1961: Sci. Am. *205*:74.
95. Mazia, D., 1961: *in* The Cell (Brachet, J., and Mirsky, A. E., eds.). Academic Press, New York, vol. 3, p. 77.
96. Hirshfield, H. I., Tulchin, N., and Fong, B. A., Ann. New York Acad. Sci. *90*:523–528.
97. Manton, I., 1959: J. Mar. Biol. Assoc. U.K. *38*:319.
98. Yanofsky, C., and Hening, U. (in press). Proc. Nat. Acad. Sci. U.S.
99. Aisenberg, A. C., 1960: The Glycolysis and Respiration of Tumors. Academic Press, New York.

CHAPTER

26

CELL DIVISION

Synchronized Cell Division

In many of the studies of cell division it has been found desirable to have all of a population of cells divide at one time. Such synchronized cell division makes possible more effective analysis of the components of the process than would be possible with a population of cells in which only a small number of cells are dividing at any one time, the others being in various stages of readiness for division. Eggs of marine animals have been favorite objects for such studies. Practically all the eggs divide at one time in a suspension of cells which are perfectly healthy and normal (Fig. 26.1).

This synchrony in dividing marine eggs implies that some event has occurred to achieve the synchrony, e.g., the almost simultaneous entry of sperm in all eggs starts a train of events that takes about the same amount of time in all of the cells. Cleavage continues in synchrony for several generations unless cells are separated from one another.[1] When the eggs have been affected by unfavorable conditions, e.g., heat, or ultraviolet, division may be delayed, and when it starts, some eggs cleave before others. Therefore, as seen in Figure 26.1, since the sus-

ceptibility of the cells to the unfavorab conditions varies about a mean for th population, a characteristic distributic curve is obtained for the population.

Cells that are growing are destined divide. In a culture of bacteria, protozo or tissue cells in which the cells are n in continuous contact, the number cells in division at any one time is limite being from 5 to 10 per cent. The ratio the number of cells in division to th total number of cells is called the *mitot index*. The mitotic index appears to be function of the time between division for a given species (*generation tim* under the conditions provided and th time a given cell takes to divide und those conditions.[2] The mitotic index ma be increased by selecting a single ce from such an asynchronous culture an using it as the progenitor of a cultur For a few generations thereafter, syr chrony is obtained, but it also graduall disappears, as shown in Figure 26.2.

The failure to achieve synchrony division in a culture of cells is probably result, in part, of differential exposure t various environmental conditions, bt perhaps it is mainly due to lack of con munication between cells. The division nuclei in a syncytium (multinucleate cel

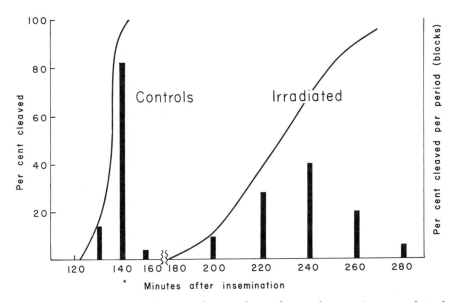

Fig. 26.1. High degree of synchrony in division of normal sea urchin eggs (inseminated simultaneously) as shown in the curve for "controls." Note that the histogram plotting the number of eggs cleaving in a 10 minute period indicates that over 80 per cent of the eggs cleave simultaneously. The same sample of eggs fertilized with ultraviolet-radiation-treated sperm (50 ergs/mm.^{2} of wave length 2654 Å) show much less synchronous division. The division figures were recorded photographically over a period of about 100 minutes. (Data from P. Wells, 1952: PhD. Thesis, Stanford Univ.)

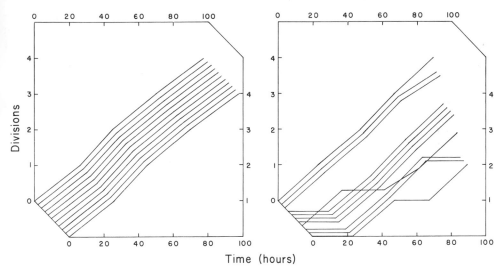

Fig. 26.2. Synchrony and asynchrony in division of the ciliate *Blepharisma undulans*. *A*, the plot of the division of 11 isolated individuals which are descended from a single individual four generations back. Perfect synchrony is maintained for the four divisions that were traced. *B*, the relatively asynchronous division of 11 other individuals of the same species and stock taken at random from a large stock culture, many generations removed from a common ancestor. The time and division axes are staggered to make more evident synchrony and asynchrony. (Data by courtesy of B. McCaw.)

where mixing of all materials occurs is usually perfectly synchronized. Also, in the syncytial insect, egg nuclear division continues synchronously for as many as eleven generations.[2] The same is true for the nuclei in the syncytial endosperm of plant embryos. It is therefore likely that nuclei in division secrete division-stimulating materials. To explain the low mitotic index in most cell cultures it has been suggested that the division-stimulating material from the few cells in division does not affect many other cells, either because they are distant or because the membranes of such cells are relatively impervious to the hypothetical division-controlling substances.[2]

This concept of control of synchrony by secretion of materials from nuclei has some experimental backing. For example, grafts can be made between two multinucleate amebas (*Chaos chaos*) with nuclei synchronously dividing but out of phase with each other. After one cycle the division of all nuclei from both amebas is synchronous, the larger piece imposing its time upon the smaller.[2] Similarly, cells in a tissue in synchronous division—as for example, in spermatogenic cells lining the lumen of a germinative tubule—have been found to be connected to one another by cytoplasmic bridges.[51] It would therefore appear that cell contact is not enough to insure entry of the division-stimulating material from one cell to another, but cytoplasmic contact appears to insure it. However, more data are needed.

It is important at this time to emphasize that a suspension of cells, whether they are cells in tissue culture, protozoans, yeast or bacteria, are fundamentally different from a suspension of marine eggs. Marine eggs have undergone a period of growth in the ovary and they have self-contained supplies which will serve for many cell divisions before intake of nutrients need take place. Even DNA is stored in the cytoplasm of many eggs and needs only to be incorporated in the nuclei resulting from mitosis. Cells, other than eggs, however, must incorporate nutrients and grow before they can divide. Perhaps not all cells are able to incorporate the same nutrients at the same rate. Studies on *Tetrahymena* (ciliate protozoan) show that the mass of the cell increases linearly during the entire *synthetic period*, from the onset of furrowing in one division until about 10 to 20 minutes before the next division, in a division cycle with a generation time of 2.25 to 2.5 hours at 28 to 29° C.[2] During the 10 to 20 minute *predivision period*, which precedes furrowing, there is no increase in mass while the cell gets ready to divide. Such a period has also been found in other cells, e.g., in *Amoeba* it occupies about one-sixth of the generation time (Fig. 26.3).

Since it is not possible to achieve synchrony of cell suspensions other than marine eggs, attempts have been made to *shock* cells into synchrony. Two methods have been used: chemical shock and physical shock. Chemical shock consists of withholding or limiting the supply of some nutrient necessary for division and then supplying it to the culture at one time in a large quantity, inducing in this manner simultaneous metabolic activity, much like the stimulus supplied by fertilization of marine eggs. The physical shock is unfavorable for the act of cell division yet favorable to other metabolic activities preceding division, thus allowing the cells in earlier stages of the division cycle to catch up with those in the predivision stages. Removal of the shock should then permit simultaneous metabolic activities leading to division in a large segment of a population.

Let us consider experiments using a chemical shock. Cell division and DNA synthesis in *Escherichia coli* 15$_T$, a thymine-requiring mutant (thymineless), are blocked immediately upon transfer of the organism to a thymine-free medium. However, RNA and protein synthesis

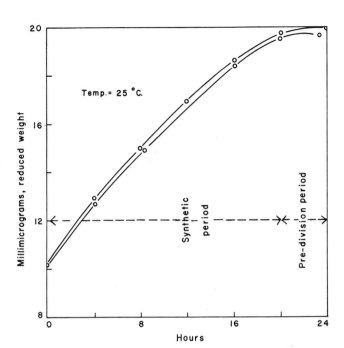

Fig. 26.3. Growth in mass of *Amoeba proteus.* The pair of lines represents the growth of a pair of sister cells from the time of division of their mother cell to the time they themselves divide. "Reduced weight" is defined as the total weight of the object (in this case the cell) minus the weight of water which is displaced by the object. It is the value obtained with the Cartesian diver balance for weighing single cells (see Zeuthen, 1948: Compt. Rend. Lab. Carlsberg. Series Chimique, *26*:243). (Data from Prescott, D. M., after Mazia, 1956: Am. Scientist, *44*:9.)

The chart axes read: y-axis "Millimicrograms, reduced weight" from 8 to 20; x-axis "Hours" from 0 to 24. Label "Temp.= 25 °C." Regions labeled "Synthetic period" and "Pre-division period."

continue, apparently at the original rate. When thymine is added 30 minutes later, DNA synthesis is resumed and nearly all the cells are found to divide simutaneously after a lag of 35 to 40 minutes.[3] Similarly, in *Lactobacillus acidophilus,* synchrony can be induced by the addition of thymidine to a thymidine-starved culture.[4] Yeast cells starved in succinate buffer until some of the reserves are gone will divide synchronously after return to complete nutrient, including carbohydrate and nitrogen sources.[5] Similar results were obtained with a variety of cells needing some particular metabolite. For example, division in the cells of the epidermis of the insect *Rhodnius* follows its periodic ingestion of blood. In *Chlorella* and various algae, all photosynthetic, the daily periodic lighting regimen makes possible synchronization of cell division, presumably by periodic accumulation of food reserves during the period of illumination.[6, 9]

Use of temperature, as a physical shock to obtain synchronized division, stems from the notion that the processes that occur during the division cycle are differentially sensitive to temperature. If some reaction in the predivision period is more sensitive to heat than are the reactions in the synthetic period, then a high temperature might prevent division without stopping syntheses. Thus, cells lagging behind might be given a chance to catch up with the others. As expected, single shocks synchronize only a small proportion of the cells, but a series of temperature shocks which block division—alternating with an exposure to near-optimal temperature but for a period insufficient to allow the cells in the predivision stages to divide— gradually accumulate practically all the cells in the predivision stage. Zeuthen and Scherbaum found that alternate exposure of suspensions of the ciliate *Tetrahymena,* for half-hour periods at 28 to 29° C. (optimal) and 34° C. (inhibitory) for seven cycles resulted in 85 per cent of the cells in division[2] when the cultures were subsequently kept at 28° C. Synchrony persisted for several cell generations then disappeared (Fig. 26.4). Thermal shocks have also been effective for synchronizing division of many other kinds of cells, including bacteria[8] (Fig. 26.5).

Cold shocks have also been used to induce synchronization of cell division in a number of protozoans and bacteria. Nutritional deficiency, coupled with temperature shocks, has also been very effective.[6] X-rays have also been shown to induce synchrony in division, again presumably by holding back the cells in the radiation-sensitive predivision stages and causing accumulation of these cells which will ultimately divide at nearly the same time.[7]

Much effort has gone into production of synchronized cultures of cells because in much cultures division and growth are essentially uncoupled. Therefore, growth can be studied in the cells prior to division, and the process of division and its accompaniments can then be studied in the cells accumulated in the predivision stages. The cells shocked into synchrony, such as marine eggs, have accumulated sufficient reserves for a series of divisions, which follow one another more rapidly than the usual generation time for the species until the accumulated reserves have been partitioned among the descendants. Heat-shocked cells thus grow until they are considerably larger than controls (Fig. 26.4b). In a heat-shocked culture of *Tetrahymena*, the generation time for the first few synchronized divisions is about 60 per cent of that required for a culture that was not subjected to heat shock.

Synchronized cultures of various cells in suspensions are now being widely used in biochemical and cytochemical research.[8] It is important to note, however, that changes in size and composition of the cells after synchronization must be taken into consideration. For example, resistance of such cells to ultraviolet radiations is markedly altered.[54]

Synchronization of cell division in the photosynthetic dinoflagellate *Gonyaulax*, in the normal diurnal rhythm of day and night, occurs in 85 per cent of all cells destined to divide during a 5-hour period spanning the end of darkness and the beginning of the light period.[9] Although it might appear that cell division here, as in *Chlorella*, is related to periodic changes in nutritional conditions, keeping *Gonyaulax* in continuous dim light only sufficient to maintain nutritional balance in the cells does not stop synchronous division for at least 14 days. The synchronous division here is also relatively independent of small variations in light intensity and temperature. In high light intensity, however, synchrony is lost in 4 to 6 days (Fig. 26.6). This is an interesting case worthy of detailed study. At present it is interpreted as an example of inherent biological rhythm[9] (see Chapter 9).

Source of Energy for Cell Division

That synchronization of cells results from feeding them with energy-yielding nutrients after starvation, as in the case of yeast cited above,[5] suggests the need of energy for cell division. It has been shown that addition of glucose to isolated epidermal tissue culture cells results in division of many cells, presumably blocked by lack of a nutrient source because little glycogen is stored in the cells.[11] Even if glucose is supplied division fails if oxygen is not available. Glucose may be replaced by lactate, glutamate, fumarate or citrate. This suggests that operation of the Krebs cycle supplies the energy for division of the cells. As expected, mitosis is inhibited by Krebs' cycle poisons such as malonate, cyanide, carbon monoxide, and by phlorhizin—a phosphorylation inhibitor.[11] The latter finding suggests that high energy phosphate bonds are an energy reservoir or are used in building this reservoir. Marine eggs and protozoans require oxygen for division, but frog eggs and many embryonic tissue cells do not, presumably supplying their energy for cell division by glycolysis. Cells which require oxygen for division have a low

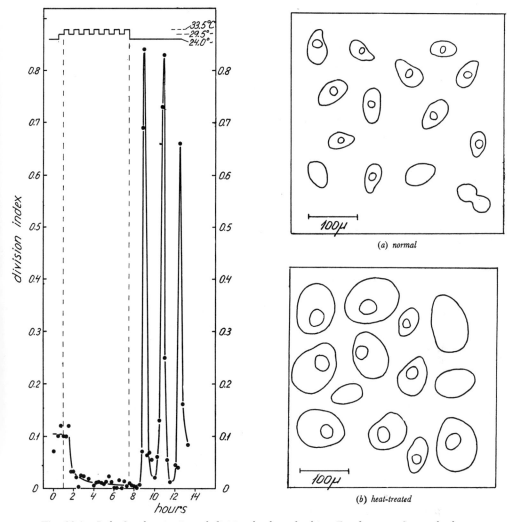

Fig. 26.4. *Left,* Synchronization of division by heat-shocking *Tetrahymena.* Seven shocks at 33.5° C. are given in succession, alternating with 29.5° C. At the conclusion of the heat shocks, the temperature is dropped to 24.0° C. The three post-heat-treatment divisions are synchronized to the extent indicated by the division index. *Right (a),* normal *Tetrahymena* drawn with camera lucida and *(b) Tetrahymena* after heat treatment. The circles inside the cell are the macronuclei. (From Zeuthen and Scherbaum, 1954: Colston Papers, Symposium Colston Res. Soc., 7:141.)

rate of glycolysis compared to the rate of respiration. Cells which divide in absence of oxygen have rates of glycolysis much higher than respiration, sometimes several-fold greater.[11] As might be expected, cells which can supply their energy needs for division by glycolysis are very sensitive to glycolytic inhibitors such as iodoacetic acid.

In order to have an effect, the energy sources must be supplied early in the cell division cycle during what Bullough calls the *antephase.* Once a critical concentration of the energy-rich substances has been built up and the prophase begins, nothing short of killing the cell will stop it from dividing. This has been noticed, not only for cells deprived of oxygen or

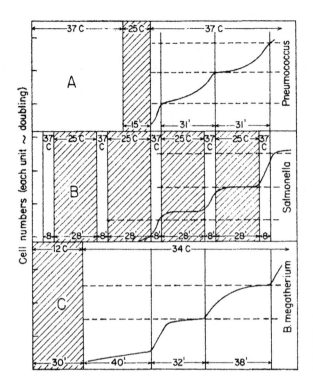

Fig. 26.5. Three different examples of synchronization in Bacteria. (*A*) *Pneumococcus* (Hotchkiss, 1954). (*B*) *Salmonella typhimurium* (Maaløe and Lark, 1954). (*C*) *Bacillus megatherium* Szybalski and Hunter-Szybalska, 1955).

metabolically poisoned, but also for those damaged by radiations or subjected to other injuries; such cells may divide and soon thereafter cytolyze. Initiation of mitosis appears to begin a series of concatenated and irreversible reactions which stop only when the cells have divided.

By employing carbon monoxide to block cytochrome oxidase in sea urchin eggs and releasing the block by shifting from green light (which is not absorbed by the enzyme-CO complex) to white light, Swann[12] has been able to get information on the nature of the energy source necessary for division. If inhibition is applied before sea urchin eggs enter mitosis, the first cleavage is delayed by a time about equal to the time of application of CO (Fig. 26.7). If inhibition is applied after the cells have entered mitosis, they complete mitosis and cleave with little or no delay, but the second cleavage is delayed for a time which is roughly equal to the period of inhibition. It is sug-

gested that the results can best be explained by a hypothetical *energy reservoir*. Energy is stored for a cell division during the preceding mitosis and cleavage. The reservoir which is continuously being filled, "siphons out" when it is full. Once the energy has siphoned out it carries the cell through mitosis and cleavage; if at this time the cell is poisoned by monoxide and energy is no longer being accumulated in the reservoir, cleavage will nevertheless continue to completion. However, no energy, will accumulate until the block is removed; consequently, the next cell division is delayed for an interval equal to the period of application of the poison. It might be expected that lack of oxygen and various poisons that affect the aerobic enzymes would also affect cell division in a similar manner.

Poisons which do not affect energy-liberating systems act in a different manner. For example, ether (1 per cent) is almost without effect if applied before the mitotic spindle has formed, but if applied

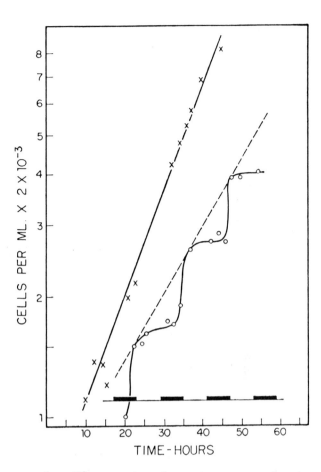

Fig. 26.6. Increase in cell population of the photosynthetic dinoflagellate *Gonyaulax polyhedra* in continuous light (X) and in alternating light and dark periods of 12 hours (open circles). Light intensity, 900 foot candles; temperature, 21.5°C. Average generation time in continuous light, 1 day; in alternating light and darkness, 1.5 days. Note the synchronization achieved by the alternating light-darkness regime. (From Sweeney, B. M., and Hastings, J. W., 1958: J. Protozool. 5:217.)

after that time it blocks development of the spindle fibers, maintaining the proteins in a solvated state. If the treated eggs are then washed free of the ether, development proceeds at once, the only delay being the period during which the eggs were subjected to the ether. It would appear that the energy reservoir is unaffected by ether.[13]

Heat shock, as pointed out above, does not stop growth although it prevents division, and, consequently, the cells may reach a size four times the average volume of a cell in the control culture. Returning the cells to the optimal temperature after one or more heat shocks permits cleavage in less than the generation time. Thus, it would appear that the energy reservoir is partially full at all times (or the process is now speeded up).

The question then arises as to what is happening to the energy reservoir of heat-shocked cells. Presumably the mitogenic and growth channels are separate at their definitive ends, but both are fed by the same sources of energy and materials and are therefore interrelated. When the mitogenic channel is blocked by physical or chemical means, the energy and material which might normally go through this channel pass instead into synthetic reactions leading to cell growth. Consequently, after release from temperature block, some time must elapse before the energy reservoir specific to division is filled. The evidence for such a reservoir is admittedly indirect.[8]

It is interesting to note that if heat shocks continue well beyond seven cycles, *Tetrahymena* may ultimately divide,

Diagrams to illustrate the working of the reservoir hypothesis under normal conditions, carbon monoxide and ether inhibitions. Times slightly modified for simplicity—critical point for siphoning out of reservoir, 40 minutes after fertilisation; cleavage 60 minutes after fertilisation.
1, Normal conditions.
2 and 3. Carbon monoxide.
Action: complete block to filling of reservoir.
2. Inhibition: from 20–50 minutes after fertilisation.
   Result: 1st cleavage delayed 30 minutes.
3. Inhibition: from 50–80 minutes.
   Result: 1st cleavage not delayed.
          2nd cleavage delayed 30 minutes.
4. 1 per cent ether.
Action: (a) no effect on filling of reservoir.
        (b) block to building up of mitotic figure, either by preventing siphoning out or by preventing effect of reservoir contents.
Inhibition: from 20–50 minutes.
Result: 1st cleavage delayed 10 minutes.
5. 2 per cent ether.
Action: (a) halving of rate of filling of reservoir.
        (b) block to building up of mitotic figure, as with 1 per cent ether.
Inhibition: from 20–70 minutes.
Result: 1st cleavage delayed 30 minutes.

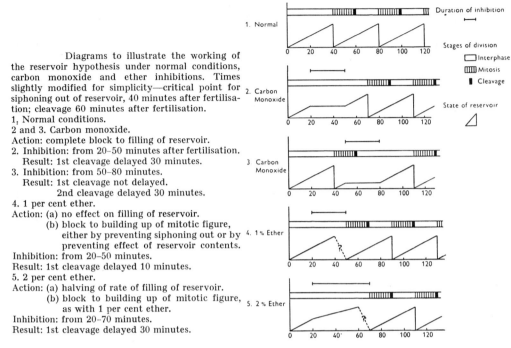

Fig. 26.7. Interpretation of the action of poisons on cell division based on the energy reservoir hypothesis. (From Swann, 1954, Exp. Cell Res., 7:513.)

even during a heat shock. It seems that accumulation of products of growth in a cell, and thus the effective siphoning of the energy reservoir along these synthetic channels, has its limitations, and the energy overflows into the division channel. Division can then no longer be prevented by thermal shocks that previously blocked it.[6]

Perhaps an even more clear-cut separation of growth processes from cell division is shown in experiments with *Tetrahymena* cells which are heat shocked in nutrient medium and then transferred to balanced salt medium with no nutrients.[14] Such cells subsequently divide at least twice without addition of nutrients. Cleavage of such cells can be "set back" or delayed by various metabolic poisons or physical shocks. The set-back is best interpreted as an effect of the agent on the filling of the energy reservoir, since

in this case growth can no longer occur.[53]

Experiments with dinitrophenol also distinguish two fractions of metabolism in *Tetrahymena*. One fraction (about 30 per cent) relies on endogenous reserves and can support cell division. Another fraction (about 70 per cent) depends upon exogenous supplies and is coupled with growth.[58]

The energy reservoir for mitosis cannot be considered to be just a storage of high energy phosphate bonds, because such compounds as ATP and CP do not vary sufficiently or in a regular fashion during the division cycle.[6] However, high energy phosphates are probably being produced continuously and used in the formation of the various compounds of complex nature and the structures necessary for cell division. The identity of these substances or structures specifically correlated with cell division is at present unknown.[59]

Blocking Cell Division by Radiations

Inhibition of cell division by x-radiation was observed soon after the discovery of x-rays, and this led to the use of ionizing radiations in the treatment of cancer (see Chapter 9). Cells already well along in the division cycle complete the division, but those in earlier stages regress. Almost without exception dividing cells are most sensitive to x-rays for a short period just prior to the onset of mitosis.[15] The type of tissue cell seems of little consequence provided the cell is growing and dividing in culture or in tissue.[16, 17] (The cells in a mature tissue are apparently radioresistant, i.e., not killed, when they have ceased dividing.) As a consequence, x-rays produce a degree of synchronous division of cells in tissue culture.[7]

The locus of action of the x-rays is not fully known. The rate of incorporation of precursors into DNA is decreased or inhibited in cells of tissues subjected to x-rays. Since in most cases assays were made many hours or even days after the irradiation, at which time the cell population may have declined as a result of x-raying, the results from this type of experiment have been questioned. However, by using cell suspensions, it has been shown that application of a certain x-ray dosage, at a time just before synthesis of DNA has begun, is much more effective in stopping DNA synthesis than if the radiations are applied after synthesis has started. There thus appears to be a system connected to, but not identical with, DNA synthesis that is even more sensitive to x-rays than DNA synthesis itself. Larger dosages affect both this process and synthesis of DNA as well.[18]

It is interesting that synthesis of protein and RNA continue in a radiation-sterilized cell, that is, one that will not divide again. The result is the production of giant cells. Unbalanced growth of this type is followed by death, but the undivided cell may live for a considerable time. During this time, materials leak from the cells that are useful in growth of normal tissue cells. Consequently, Puck has used mats of similar nondividing (sterilized) cells on which to place a single normal unirradiated human tissue cell. The cell gives rise to a colony, the cells of which form a clone, that is, they are all the descendants of the single cell placed there.[16]

Ultraviolet radiations retard or stop cell division, but, because the radiations are absorbed so superficially, they are not suitable for cancer therapy. The action spectrum for division-inhibition in a suspension of cells resembles the absorption spectrum of nucleic acids or nucleoproteins. Also, it has been shown that DNA synthesis is retarded by small dosages of ultraviolet radiations.[19] However, as in the case of x-rays, exceedingly small dosages may inhibit division of cells without having any detectable effect on DNA synthesis, indicating the existence of a process even more sensitive than DNA synthesis but probably closely related to it. The action spectrum for the effect implicates nucleic acid.[20, 21]

In general, synthesis of DNA appears more sensitive to ultraviolet radiations than is RNA synthesis or protein synthesis. Since the blockage of DNA synthesis leads to unbalanced growth and larger dosages of ultraviolet radiation inhibit RNA and protein syntheses, the interrelations between all these syntheses are complex.

Blocking Cell Division by Poisons

A great number of poisons block cell division (Fig. 26.7 and 26.8), but only those which help identify metabolic reactions or events in the complex which makes up cell division can be mentioned here. The action of such poisons has been studied extensively because of its theoretical interest and its possible use in control of cancer.

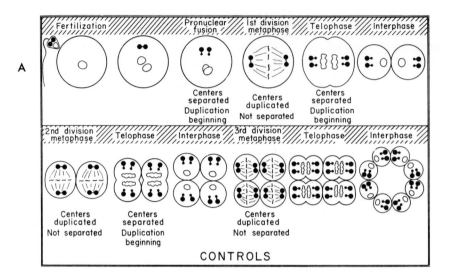

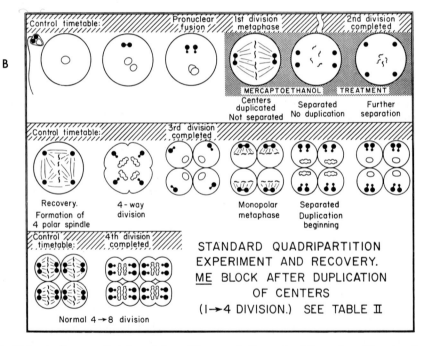

Fig. 26.8. *A*, diagrammatic interpretation of the reproductive cycle of the centers. All nuclear figures shown are purely symbolic and are introduced merely to identify mitotic stages. Functional units of the centers are represented by solid dots. Small dots indicate newly formed unit. Bars connecting the units indicate that they have not yet split from each other. *B*, an interpretation of the basic quadripartition experiment, in which it is assumed that the mercaptoethanol block is imposed after the duplication of the centers but before they have split. During blockage, the centers split and separate, forming four poles, each of which is composed of half the normal number of units. The following mitosis is monopolar. (From Mazia, Harris, and Bibring, 1960: J. Biophys. Biochem. Cytol., 7:17.)

Many mitotic poisons interfere with interphase growth. For example, metabolic poisons, such as inhibitors of respiration and glycolysis, or those which uncouple phosphorylations from energy-yielding reactions, prevent the accumulation of high energy compounds and prevent release of energy for synthesis or division. Another group of mitotic poisons—the antimetabolites—interfere with syntheses. Still others, such as the antibiotic chloramphenicol (isolated from *Streptomyces*), which resembles phenylalanine and presumably competes with the latter on the surface of the protein-synthesizing enzymes, block protein synthesis. If applied in sufficient concentration early in the division cycle, chloramphenicol blocks cell division.[22] Tetracyclines (isolated from *Streptomyces*) interfere with protein synthesis, although probably in some manner other than that of chloramphenicol.[23]

A few mitotic poisons block nucleic acid synthesis. These compounds resemble some normal metabolite, and thus compete with the normal metabolite for the surface of the particular cell enzyme (competitive inhibition). For example, azaguanine, which resembles the purine, guanine, acts in this manner, and many other purine and pyrimidine analogues have been tested. However, whereas such agents may act in this manner, they may also act in other ways.[24] Unfortunately, many such analogues have too great an effect on cell division in germinative areas (e.g., on blood-forming cells of man) to be useful for treatment of cancer.

Antagonists to folic acid (a B vitamin, see Table 3.10) such as A-methopterin and aminopterin affect a specific step in the separation of the chromosome between metphase and anaphase. They may therefore be classed as specific metaphase inhibitors.[27] These experiments demonstrate that one of the B vitamins controls a specific step in the mitoses of the cells (chick fibroblasts) upon which they were tested.

Alkylating agents (e.g., those which replace an H atom of a compound with an alkyl group such as the methyl or ethyl) do not affect growth but prevent cell division. The nitrogen mustards (used as mutagens and in the treatment of cancer) and methane sulfonates (e.g., Myleran used in treatment of chronic myeloid leukemia) are such alkylating agents. The exact manner in which inhibition of cell division occurs is unknown, but some of these alkylating agents cause chromosome breakage or failure of normal chromosome movement similar to the effects following x-radiation.[28] This could presumably occur as a result of translocation of parts of two chromosomes, resulting in two kinetochores (chromosome constrictions for spindle fiber attachment) at two places on a single chromosome which is torn in half during anaphase. Abnormal disjunction could occur from failure of attachment of kinetochores.[29] These agents also appear to affect the formation of spindle fibers, generally reducing the viscosity of the cytoplasm. Esterification of carboxyl groups of proteins and combinations with nucleic acids have also been demonstrated, but the precise nature of the reactions is unknown.[24]

A large group of antimitotic agents, for example, colchicine, podophyllin and the urethans, inhibit the formation, or the breakdown, of the mitotic apparatus. Colchicine has been used quite extensively, especially by plant cytologists to obtain polyploids. It apparently does not interfere with other events in the cell division cycle; chromosomes duplicate themselves, but the fibers that form are disoriented, resulting in polyploidy which, in some species, persists even after the poison is removed. Colchicine therefore inhibits cell division by disorganizing the mitotic spindle, without stopping growth or duplication of various organelles in the cell. It does not even interfere with the making or breaking of disulfide bonds between proteins forming the fibers. It seems to interfere with the secondary bonding in the formation of an oriented and symmetrical mitotic spindle.[29]

The sulfhydryl reactants (e.g., chloracetophenone), on the other hand, block cell division by interfering with the disulfide and sulfhydryl cycle which is necessary for the formation and dissolution of the spindle fibers. All the other processes continue up to the formation of the spindle.[30]

Another interesting poison which has given considerable insight into mitosis is mercaptoethanol which prevents the duplication of *mitotic centers* (centrioles) of the cell, although all other events proceed normally (Fig. 26.8). Centrioles always appear in animal cells in pairs. Both members of a pair must divide before they act as division centers for the cell. The precise way in which mercaptoethanol affects the pattern of cell division depends upon when it is applied during the division cycle. Exposure of the eggs to the poison delays cell division to the extent that it delays duplication of the mitotic centers which divide only after the cells are removed from the poison. In addition to this delay, division of the cell is made abnormal because, although the division of centrioles is inhibited by mercaptoethanol, the separation of the centrioles from one another is not. Therefore, along with all the other processes preparing for cell division, the members of the pair of centrioles must separate and take their positions at the poles of the cell. If an egg cell, inhibited just before its first division when it has two pairs of centrioles is kept in mercaptoethanol beyond the time for the first division, it will prepare for the second division except that the required duplication of the centrioles will not occur. The two pairs of centrioles separate and single centrioles now occupy four areas of the egg. Released from mercaptoethanol after being washed in sea water, the centrioles first divide and then the egg divides into four cells at once (Fig. 26.8). The data are of interest because they show that the poison specifically affects only the duplication of cell centers, not their separation or movement in the cell.[31] (Poisons of this type have not yet been exploited in cancer therapy.)

Some antibiotics, such as penicillin, prevent cell division of bacteria by interfering with the incorporation of amino acids into the cell walls. Presence of penicillin in the medium causes some bacteria to develop as protoplasts—without cell walls. Such protoplasts cannot divide—apparently the cell wall is necessary for bacterial cell division. Since animal cells do not form cell walls they are unaffected by this action of penicillin.[23]

The Trigger for Cell Division

The cell, as we have seen, grows to a certain stage and then divides. In some unknown way each unit (organelle?) in the cell presents a template upon which duplication occurs. Thus, for example, the genes in the chromosomes duplicate themselves preceding the division of chromosomes. When cell division occurs, each daughter cell contains in itself a duplicate of the varied structures present in the mother cell.

Cell division has been studied in a multitude of cells, and most cells, under normal conditions, are known to divide by mitosis. Chromosomes condense and appear on an equatorial plane. The daughter chromosomes, produced by splitting, separate from one another, and a duplicate set of chromosomes is moved toward each of the two poles. Finally the cytoplasm separates into two portions. The complete process may take no more than half an hour in some marine eggs. Mitosis is described in detail in textbooks of cytology.[48] The interest here centers on the mechanism initiating cell division.

The trigger which sets off the cell division has been of interest for many years, and numerous suggestions have been made about the nature of this process. One possibility that suggests itself is the doubling in mass of the cell, since this might be the last growth requirement for a series of processes, each resulting in doubling of cell organelles. Division then occurs because the ratio of cytoplasm to nucleus is upset. Some evidence points this way. As previously indicated, when an ameba has doubled its mass it divides, but not immediately (see Fig. 26.3). The division takes place after a lapse of time during which something occurs which triggers the division of the cell.[32, 33] This time lapse before division is about 4 hours, or about one-sixth of the generation time of 24 hours for *Amoeba proteus*. Also, when an ameba about to divide is shaken, it divides unequally, but each daughter ameba grows until it equals the mass of the mother ameba before it divides again (see Fig. 26.9). Moreover, amputation of a part of a growing ameba is followed by replacement of the mass removed before division occurs at all. In all these cases division takes place 4 hours after the ameba has doubled its mass. Growth in all cells, however, is not alike. *Tetrahymena* shows an increase in mass followed by a predivision "rest period" like *Amoeba*,[2] but in *Escherichia coli* B,

synthesis proceeds in exponential fashion.[6]

Another suggestion for the trigger in cell division is the upsetting of the surface to volume ratio. However, if a piece of cytoplasm is removed at a "critical" time just before an ameba has doubled its mass, division will still occur, even though smaller offspring than normal are produced. This experiment might be taken to indicate that, by this time, division has been determined and follows even if the ameba is not as large as a typical mother cell about to divide, and that neither the ratio of nucleus to cytoplasm nor the ratio of surface to volume can in itself be the probable trigger for cell division.

Doubling the DNA content has been suggested as still another possibility. By the use of labeled precursors, it has been shown in most cells, however, that DNA is doubled in the interphase, long before division actually occurs,[29, 32] in fact even before the formation of the extra pairs of chromosomes. Thereafter, DNA recedes in compactness and visibility. Doubling of DNA content is therefore not the likely trigger. As the nucleolus re-forms in the "resting" nucleus, intense protein synthesis appears to occur just outside

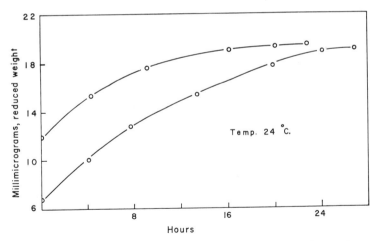

Fig. 26.9. Relation between the weight of *Amoeba proteus* at "birth" and the weight at maturity. Curves represent the growth of sister cells following unequal division of their mother cell. The last point on each curve gives the weight at the time of division. (Data from Prescott, D. M., after Mazia, 1956: Am. Scientist 44:11.)

the nuclear membrane. The interphase is apparently not a period of rest for the cell but rather a period during which the necessary proteins are manufactured by it (see Fig. 6.13).

The possibility that the nucleolus has a vital role in initiating cell division is suggested by experiments in which microbeam irradiation of a nucleolus (neuroplast of a grasshopper) at certain critical times (telophase to middle prophase) permanently stops mitosis in the cell, while comparable irradiation of the surrounding areas of the cell does not.[49]

It was also thought possible that the chromosomes or other organelles produce a specific substance which induces the division of a cell. One team of workers found that kinetin (6-furfurylaminopurine) serves this function in some plant cells in which division is otherwise infrequent.[34] No convincing evidence has accumulated to show this to be a general phenomenon. In fact, it has been shown that nuclear structures need not be present for the cytoplasm of the sea urchin egg to divide, since non-nucleated egg fragments can be excited to divide by parthenogenetic agents.[35] However, such cells develop abnormally and eventually die.

According to Heilbrunn, cell division is initiated by a coagulative process similar to the formation of a clot in blood, and any stimulus which induces clot formation is likely to initiate formation of spindles and cell division. It has been shown that agents which inhibit clot formation, e.g., heparin, interfere with the division of normal fertilized eggs. Agents which release calcium, which is also required for clotting blood, facilitate cell division, while agents which bind calcium, such as oxalate or citrate, inhibit cell division.[36]

Whatever the immediate cause of cell division, there are apparently many factors that contribute toward a favorable state for division of the cell. Preparations must be completed along many parallel lines before cell division can occur.

The Nature and Formation of the Mitotic Apparatus

That the division spindles are gels has long been known from micromanipulative experiments and from studies in which intact mitotic figures have been isolated by Mazia from dividing eggs by the use of mild detergents which solubilize the rest of the cell[37] (see Fig. 26.10). The spindle is made up of about 3 to 5 per cent ribonucleic acid (RNA), and the remainder appears to be largely one type of protein. Electrophoretic diagrams indicate two peaks, one of which is the protein, the other is its conjugate with RNA. Electron microscope studies of fixed cells demonstrate that the spindle gel consists of definitely organized and oriented fibers of protein, the centers of orientation being the centrioles[60] (see Chapters 2 and 5). When three pairs of centrioles are present, as in polyspermic eggs, the orientation is toward three poles. Presumably, something is liberated from the centrioles which leads to the development of such oriented fibers, although no evidence for its origin or transport has yet been obtained.

On the basis of chemical evidence, the linkages between protein molecules in the fibers of the mitotic spindle appear to be disulfide (S—S) bonds.[29] The mechanism by which the spindle is thought to be formed is illustrated in Figure 26.11. In the preparatory phase the *intramolecular* disulfide bonds of protein molecules are presumably reduced by glutathione. This is considered to take place before the metaphase, at a time when the glutathione content of the egg is known to be declining.[38] When the mitotic apparatus is fully formed and growing, the disulfide bonds are supposedly restored, but now as *intermolecular* disulfide bonds (Stage II, Fig. 26.11), binding the protein molecules into fibers and liberating the glutathione, a suggestion in accordance with the rising concentration of the glutathione in the egg cell at this time.[38] Postulation

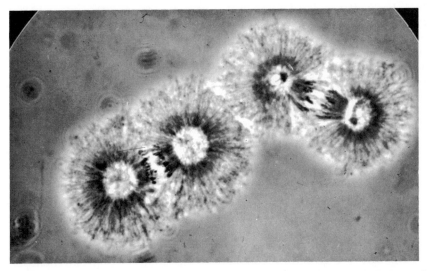

Fig. 26.10. Isolated mitotic apparatus at anaphase (developing eggs of the sea urchin *Strongylo-centrotus purpuratus*). Note mitotic centers, astral rays, chromosomal fibers connecting chromosomes to centers, and interzonal regions of spindles between separated chromosomes. (From Mazia, 1956: Am. Scientist, *44*:21.)

of intermolecular disulfide bonds rests on the assumption that the probability of forming a bond between sulfur atoms on two protein molecules would be greater than the probability of re-forming the original intramolecular disulfide bonds. In essence, then, the sulfhydryl cycle has converted intramolecular disulfide bonds into intermolecular disulfide bonds, the glutathione acting essentially like a cata-lyst, being recovered unaltered at the end of the cycle.[29]

If orientation and organization of fibers are a prime necessity for cell division, then any agent which interferes with the spindle should interfere with cell division, even if this agent permits gelation. This is exactly what happens when a cell is poisoned with colchicine. Disulfide bonds are formed and a gel appears, but the

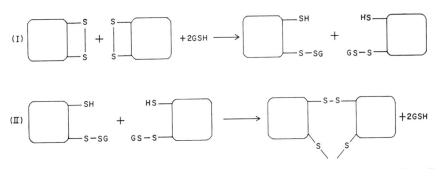

Fig. 26.11. A possible scheme for the gelation of the mitotic apparatus. The preparatory phase (I) involves the reduction of intramolecular S—S by glutathione. This would take place during the period before metaphase and corresponds to the decline in free glutathione. In phase (II), when the mitotic apparatus is forming fully and growing, the S—S bonds are restored as *intermolecular* bonds. GSH = glutathione (a tripeptide). (From Mazia, 1956: Am. Scientist, *44*:26.)

secondary bonds fail to develop, the gel is disoriented and separation of the doubled chromosomes fails to occur ("flabby anaphase"). Because of this, as we have already seen, polyploid cells are produced by the use of colchicine. When such cells are washed free of colchicine, they later divide, but the polyploid condition is maintained.

When Hoffman-Berling placed cells about to divide (i.e., showing spindle fibers) in glycerin solutions, the division process ceased. When they were later placed in a balanced salt solution, the spindle fibers remained, but division still failed to occur. It seemed possible that some material necessary for cell division had leached into the glycerin solution. When he applied adenosine triphosphate (ATP) to such mitotic models (glycerin-extracted dividing cells) the spindle fibers contracted and the chromosomes moved toward the poles.[39] Furthermore, an enzyme for decomposing ATP is present in the spindle.[60] On the other hand, ATP added to alcohol-hardened spindles of the sea urchin egg isolated in the manner used by Mazia and his co-workers does not produce movement.[32] Hoffman-Berling[39] points out that hardening the spindles denatures the proteins of the fibers, making them incapable of contraction in response to ATP, even though hardening permits their separation and purification from other cellular constituents.

It is an oversimplification to consider only the shortening of the spindle fibers. Careful analysis of the movements indicates that only the early part of mitosis (to anaphase) occurs by contraction. This is indicated not only by the loss of birefringence of the fibers, but also by the broadening of the spindle. However, evidence suggests that in anaphase the two sets of chromosomes are actually pushed apart by the fibers between the poles. For example, when the spindles of grasshopper neuroblasts are immersed in hypertonic solutions which reduce the volume of the cell and thus crowd the mitotic figure, the chromosomes are crumpled and spiraled during the anaphase and pushed against the ends of the cell.[39]

The active elongation of the spindle poses the same problems as relaxation and elongation of muscle fibers, which are known to be active processes. Low concentrations of ATP applied to the mitotic models cause contraction; higher concentrations, elongation.[39] Mazia,[29] on the other hand, has pointed out that the spindle fibers appear to consume themselves as contraction occurs, unlike a muscle which maintains its mass in spite of shortening. A single contraction of the spindle fibers, however achieved, suffices to separate the duplicated chromosomes from one another. It would almost appear as if the chromosomes, as they move toward the poles, release some material which dissolves the spindle fibers. The fact that glycerin-extracted models of dividing cells contract when placed in ATP, and the chromosomes on the metaphase plate separate, could conceivably be explained as the result of contraction of the entire cell in such a way as to actually simulate mitosis rather than by contraction of the spindle fibers.[29] The problem of chromosome movement should not be considered solved, despite the appeal of the contractile fiber hypothesis.

Furrow Formation and Cleavage (Cytokinesis)

The formation of a furrow in a dividing egg or other animal cell appears to be accompanied by increased viscosity in the area of the furrow. High pressures, which liquefy protein gels, also prevent the formation of cleavage furrows and cause such dividing cells to fuse again. The furrow disappears with even the slight pressure applied to both sides with a microneedle, but cell division resumes when the pressure is released.[52] An egg ruptured at the time of furrow formation disintegrates, but a part of the cortex and the furrow remain intact. The furrow is apparently a rigid part of the cell. Furthermore, it has been noticed that as the cortex forms in the cleaving eggs, a slight separation between the cortical layers of the two blastomeres (the two-celled stage) is maintained for a time, indicating that some change has occurred which prevents coalescence of the two layers.[40]

An attempt has been made to explain the formation of a furrow in a dividing cell by means of the *contractile ring theory* (or *cortical gel contraction theory*). According to this theory the gelated ring in the cortex of the dividing cell is considered to contract like the nonmotile portion of an ameba, and it might be expected, therefore, to decrease the surface area. However, measurement in some cells showed that before division the surface increased by about 26 per cent[41] (Fig. 26.12).

The increase in surface area accompanying cell division does not invalidate contraction theories of cell division. It is essential that the cell elongate before it cleaves, and at this time the surface area increases. But elongation is part and parcel of any contractile system, as already seen in muscle fibers (Chapter 24). When relaxation of muscle cells is better understood it may also be possible to understand cell division better. In modified form the contractile furrow theory, illustrated in Figure 26.12, allows for a passive increase in surface at the poles as a result of active contraction of the furrow region.[55]

The *expanding surface theory*,[44] on the other hand, suggests that a nuclear substance is liberated (probably from chromosomes) which causes expansion of the cellular membrane at the poles (Fig. 26.13). As the polar area expands the equator contracts, leading to division. This theory is supported by two lines of evidence. First, movement of material on the surfaces of cells, consistent with such a suggestion, has been observed.[42] Secondly, expansion at the poles should

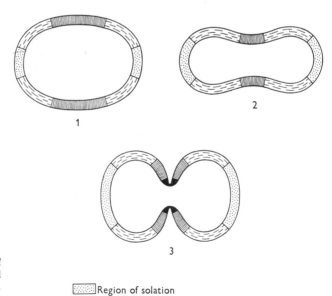

Fig. 26.12. Diagram of the *cortical gel contraction theory* of Marsland and Landau. *1*, early telophase; *2*, early furrow; *3*, late furrow. From Swann and Mitchison 1958: Biol. Rev. 33:109. (After Marsland and Landau, 1954.)

::::::: Region of solation
≡≡≡ Region subjected to stretching
▓▓▓ Contracting region
████ Fully contracted region being passively pushed

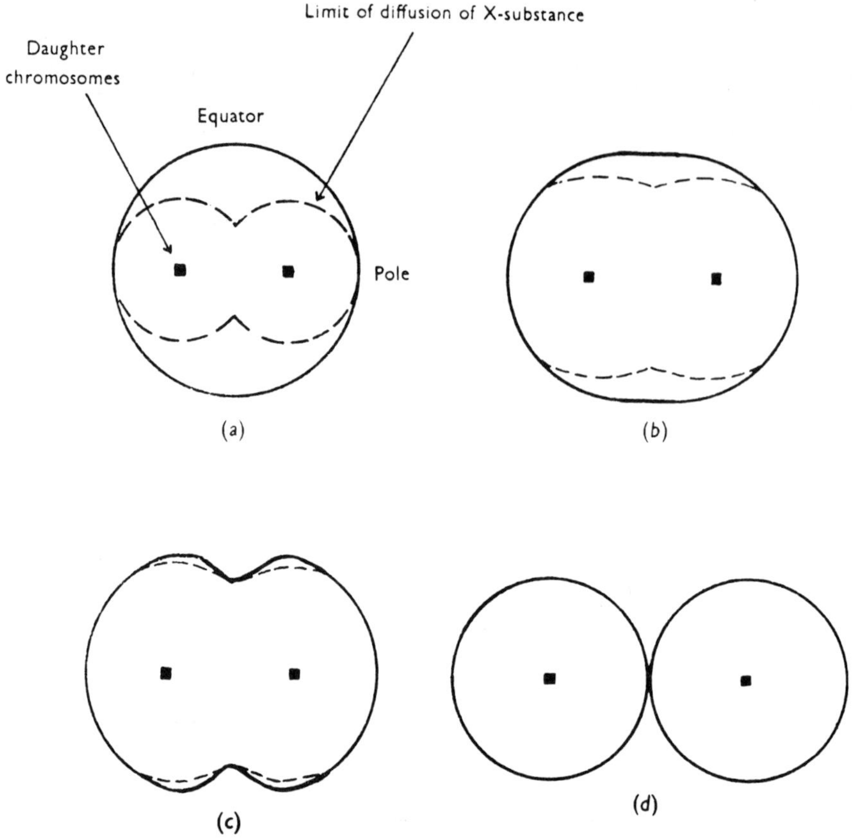

Fig. 26.13. Diagram to illustrate the *expanding membrane theory* of cleavage of Mitchison and Swann. The X-substance is the hypothetical substance which presumably comes from the chromosomes, and which leads to an increase in polar surface area upon contact with the poles. (From Mitchison, 1952: Symp. Soc. Exp. Biol. 6:105.)

weaken the membrane there. The fact that cytolysis of an egg occurs more readily during division than during interphase suggests some change in the cell membrane at the poles.[44] The equatorial part persists after cytolysis, apparently being more rigid. However, even cells without nuclei or chromosomes, cleave;[35] therefore, the excitant may have origins other than the nucleus. Another form of this theory postulates expansion of surface area as a result of growth.[57]

Somewhat similar to the expanding surface theory is the conception of the mechanism of *cytokinesis* in ameba.

Here, at anaphase, large pseudopodia form at opposite poles and literally pull an ameba in two.[56] This method of division is possible in ameboid cells only.

The *spindle elongation theory*[42, 45] assigns a decisive role to the spindle and asters in cell division. The evidence comes from observation of movement with respect to one another, of kaolin particles attached to the surface of an egg membrane. The basic observation is that the elongation of the cell at anaphase is accompanied by a shrinkage at the equator, the two particles on either side of the equator coming closer together

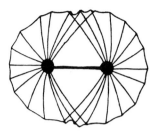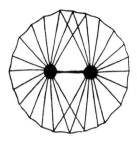

Fig. 26.14. Model illustrating Dan's *spindle elongation theory.* Note especially the effect of the spindle elongation upon the astral ray attachments at the surface of the cell. Spindle elongation results in a pull at the furrow region and furrow formation. (From Dan, 1948: Physiol. Zool. *21*:191.)

while there is a corresponding stretching at the poles. Since the spindle and asters appear to be rigid structures, as tested with a micromanipulator, the driving force is believed to be the elongation of the spindle which pushes the centers apart, bringing the astral rays attached to the equator close together (Fig. 26.14).

Because an egg even without a nucleus or a spindle will cleave, as in the case of parthenogenetic merogony in a nucleus-free half of a sea urchin egg[35] (Fig. 6.4), the *astral relaxation theory,* based only on changes produced by the asters, has been proposed.[50] Surface tension and elasticity measurements show that an egg surface is under uniform tension before cleavage begins. When the asters reach the poles of the egg they produce a change (the nature of which is unknown), and the surface tension at the poles is lowered. This permits the furrow region, which maintains its surface tension, to contract while the polar regions expand.

Work with eggs under pressure and subjected to various inhibitory reagents suggests that the ATP system accounts for the energy of whatever movements occur during cleavage, since addition of ATP often relieves the effect of an inhibitor.[43] The energy required for division of an egg has been calculated to be about three times that normally available from respiration. Since the rate of respiration rises only a few per cent during cleavage (Fig. 26.15), it would appear that the energy for cleavage must come from a specific source. It is suggested that com-

pounds with high energy phosphate bonds, formed by the cell in preparation for each successive cleavage, might well serve this purpose.[46, 47]

It is apparent that all of these theories have much in common and that they are developed primarily from data on the marine egg cell. They do not apply to such phenomena as multiple fission, which occurs in some plant and animal cells, nor do they take into consideration the division of plant cells with cell walls —where the laying down of a new wall is of prime importance for cytokinesis (see Chapter 2). In bacteria and yeast, as was seen above, removal of the cell wall prevents cell division even though the cells continue to grow.[61] We are still without a generalized theory of cytokinesis.[62]

GENERAL REFERENCES

Abraham, E. P., 1959: Antibiotics in Microbiology. Endeavour *18*:212–220.

Anderson, N. G., 1956: Cell Division. Quart. Rev. Biol. *31*:169–199; 243–269.

Bass, A. D., 1959: Chemical Influences on Cell Division and Development. Ann. Rev. Physiol. *22*:49–68.

Bullough, W. S., 1952: Energy Relations of Mitotic Activity. Biol. Rev. *27*:133–168.

Ducoff, H. S., and Ehret, C. F., 1959: Mitogenesis. Univ. Chicago Press, Chicago.

Frydenberg, O., and Zeuthen, E., 1960: Oxygen Uptake and Carbon Dioxide Output Related to the Mitotic Rhythm in the Cleaving Eggs of *Dendraster excentricus* and *Urechis caupo*. Compt. Rend. Lab. Carlsberg *31*:423–455.

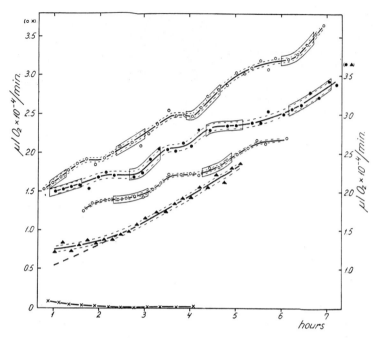

Fig. 26.15. Respiration in populations of *Tetrahymena* cells plotted on arithmetical scales against time in hours. Open and full circles: three experiments with synchronized populations. Upper curve: 10 cells initially present, about 100 cells after the experiment. Second curve from above: 11 cells initially present. Third curve from above: 9 cells initially present, 70 in the end. In the three curves, frames indicate division periods observed in the divers. The fourth curve (triangles) is a control run with 20 cells from an unsynchronized population. A control run with empty diver is represented by crosses. (Experiments by H. Thormar.) (From Zeuthen and Scherbaum, 1954: Colston Papers, Colston Res. Soc., 7th. Symposium, 7:151.)

Gross, P., and Mazia, D. (eds.), 1960: Second Conference on the Mechanisms of Cell Division. Ann. New York Acad. Sci. *90*: Art. 2:345–613.

Harvey, E. B., 1936: Parthenogenetic Merogony or Cleavage without Nuclei in *Arbacia punctulata.* Biol. Bull. *71*:101–121.

Heilbrunn, L. V., 1952: The Physiology of Cell Division, *in* Modern Trends in Physiology and Biochemistry (Barron, E. S. G., ed.). Academic Press, New York, pp. 123–134.

Hoffman-Berling, H., 1960: Other Mechanisms Producing Movements. Comp. Biochem. *2*:341–370.

Hughes, A. F. W., 1950: The Effect of Inhibitory Substances on Cell Division. Quart. J. Micr. Sci. *91*:251–278.

Hughes, A., 1952: The Mitotic Cycle. Academic Press, New York.

Huxley, J., 1957: Cancer Biology: Virus and Epigenic. Biol. Rev. *32*:1–37.

Jacobson, W., 1958: The Toxic Action of Drugs on the Bone Marrow. A Symposium on the Evaluation of Drug Toxicity (Walpole, A. C., and Sparks, A., eds.). Little, Brown, Boston.

Jacobson, W., and Webb, W., 1952: Nucleoprotein and Cell Division. Endeavour *11*:200–207.

Kopac, M. (ed.), 1951: The Mechanism of Cell Division. Ann. New York Acad. Sci. *51*:1279–1546.

Marsland, D., 1957: Temperature-pressure Studies of the Role of Sol-Gel Relations in Cell Division, *Influence of Temperature on Biological Systems* (Johnson, F. H., ed.). Am. Physiol. Soc., Washington, pp. 111–126.

Mazia, D., 1956: The Life Cycle of the Cell. Am. Scientist *44*:1–32.

Mazia, D., 1961: Mitosis and the Physiology of Cell Division, *in* The Cell (Brachet, J., and Mirsky, A. E., eds.). Academic Press, New York, vol. 3, p. 77–412.

Mazia, D., Sept. 1961: How Cells Divide. Sci. Am. *205*:100–120.

Mitchison, J. M., 1952: Cell Membranes and Cell Division. Symp. Soc. Exp. Biol. *6*:105–127.

Prescott, D. M., 1955. Relations between Cell Growth and Cell Division. Exp. Cell Res. *9*:328–337.

Puck, T. T., Aug. 1957: Single Human Cells *in vitro.* Sci. Am. *197*:91–100.

Ris, H., 1955: Cell Division, *in* Analysis of Development (Willier, Weiss and Hamburger, eds.). Saunders, Philadelphia.

Roberts, H. S., 1961: Mechanisms of Cytokinesis: a Critical Review. Quart. Rev. Biol. *36*:155–177.

Scherbaum, O., 1960: Possible Sites of Metabolic Control during the Induction of Synchronous Cell Division. Ann. New York Acad. Sci. *90*:565–579.

Scherbaum, O. H., 1960: Synchronous Division of Microorganisms. Ann. Rev. Microbiol. *14*:283–310.

Schrader, F., 1953: Mitosis. Columbia Univ. Press, New York.

Stern, H., 1956: The Physiology of Cell Division. Ann. Rev. Plant Physiol. *7*:91–114.

Swann, M. M., 1954: The Control of Cell Division, *in* Recent Developments in Cell Physiology (Kitching, J., ed.). Academic Press, New York, pp. 185–196.

Swann, M. M., and Mitchison, J. M., 1958: The Mechanism of Cleavage in Animal Cells. Biol. Rev. *33*:103–135.

Wolpert, L., 1960: The Mechanics and Mechanism of Cleavage. Internat. Rev. Cyt. *10*:163–216.

Zeuthen, E., 1949: Oxygen Consumption during Mitosis: Experiments on Fertilized Eggs of Marine Animals. Am. Naturalist *83*:303–322.

Zeuthen, E., 1958: Artificial and Induced Periodicity in Living Cells. Adv. Biol. & Med. Physics *4*:37–73.

Zeuthen, E., and Scherbaum, O., 1954: Synchronous Divisions in Mass Cultures of the Ciliate Protozoan *Tetrahymena pyriformis*, as Induced by Temperature Changes. Colston papers *7*:141–156 (Proc. 7th. Symp. Colston Res. Soc.).

LITERATURE CITED

1. Ducoff, H. S., and Ehret, C. F., 1959: Mitogenesis. Univ. Chicago Press, Chicago.

2. Zeuthen, E., and Scherbaum, O., 1954: Recent Developments in Cell Biology (Kitching, J. A., ed.). Academic Press, New York, p. 141.

3. Barner, H. D., and Cohen, S. S., 1956: J. Bacteriol. *68*:80.

4. Burns, V. W., 1959: Science *129*:566.

5. Sylvan, B., Tobias, C. A., Malmgren, H., Otteson, R., and Thorell, B., 1959: Exp. Cell. Res. *16*:75.

6. Scherbaum, O., 1960: Ann. Rev. Microbiol. *14*:283.

7. Spoerl, E., and Looney, D., 1959: Exp. Cell. Res. *17*:320.

8. Zeuthen, E., 1958: Adv. Biol. & Med. Physics *4*:37.

9. Sweeney, B. M., and Hastings, J. W., 1958: J. Protozool. *5*:217.

10. Baldwin, W. F., and Salthouse, T. N., 1959: Canad. J. Zool. *37*:1061.

11. Bullough, W. S., 1952: Biol. Rev. Cambridge Phil. Soc. *27*:133.

12. Swann, M. M., 1953: Quart. J. Micr. Sci. *94*:369.

13. Swann, M. M., 1954: Recent Developments in Cell Biology (Kitching, J. A., ed.). Academic Press, New York, p. 185.

14. Hamburger, K., and Zeuthen, E., 1957: Exp. Cell. Res. *13*:443.

15. Gray, L. H., 1959: Rad. Res. Suppl. *1*:73.

16. Puck, T. T., 1960: Progr. Biophys. *10*:237.

17. Puck, T. T., Aug. 1957: Sci. Am. *197*:91. April 1960: Sci. Am. *202*:142.

18. Stocken, L. A., 1959: Rad. Res. Suppl. *1*:53.

19. Kelner, A., 1953: J. Bact. *65*:252.

20. Deering, R. A., and Setlow, R. B., 1957: Science *126*:397.

21. Deering, R. A., 1958: J. Bact. *76*:123.

22. Taylor, E. W., 1959: J. Biophys. Biochem. Cyt. *6*:193.

23. Abraham, E. P., 1959: Endeavour *18*:212.

24. Bass, A. D., 1959: Ann. Rev. Physiol. *22*:49.

25. Jacobson, W., 1954: J. Physiol. *123*:603.

26. Jacobson, W., 1954: J. Physiol. *123*:618.

27. Jacobson, W., and Webb, M., 1952: Endeavour *11*:200.

28. Alexander, P., Jan. 1960: Sci. Am. *202*:99.

29. Mazia, D., 1956: Adv. Biol. & Med. Physics *4*:69.

30. Hughes, A. F. W., 1950: Quart. J. Micr. Sci. *91*:251.

31. Mazia, D., Harris, P. J., and Bibring, T., 1960: J. Biophys. Biochem. Cyt. *7*:1.

32. Mazia, D., 1956: Am. Sci. *44*:1.

33. Prescott, D., 1956: Exp. Cell. Res. *11*:94.

34. Miller, C. O., Skoog, F., Von Saltza, M. H., and Strong, F. M., 1955: J. Am. Chem. Soc. *77*:1392.

35. Harvey, E. B., 1936: Biol. Bull. *71*:101.

36. Heilbrunn, L. V., 1955: Dynamics of Living Protoplasm. Academic Press, New York.

37. Mazia, D., 1954: Symp. Soc. Exp. Biol. *9*:335.

38. Rapkine, L., 1931: Ann. Physiol. et Physiochim. biolog. *7*:382.

39. Hoffman-Berling, H., 1960: Comp. Biochem. *2*:341.

40. Marsland, D., 1957: Influence of Temperature on Biological Systems (Johnson, F. H., ed.). Am. Physiol. Soc., Washington, p. 111.

41. Swann, M. M., and Mitchison, J. M., 1958: Biol. Rev. *33*:103.

42. Dan, K., and Dan, J. C., 1947: Biol. Bull. *93*:139.

43. Zimmerman, A. M., Landau, J. V., and Marsland, D., 1957: J. Cell. Comp. Physiol. *49*:395.

44. Mitchison, J. M., 1952: Symp. Soc. Exp. Biol. *6*:105.

45. Dan, K., 1958: J. Exp. Biol. *35*:400.

46. Zeuthen, E., 1949: Am. Naturalist *83*:303.

47. Scholander, P. F., Leivestad, H., and Sundnes, G., 1958: Exp. Cell. Res. *15*:505.

48. DeRobertis, E. D. P., Nowinski, W. W., and Saez, F. A., 1960: General Cytology. 3rd Ed. Saunders, Philadelphia.

49. Gaulden, M. E., and Perry, R. P., 1958: Proc. Nat. Acad. Sci. U. S. *44*:554.

50. Wolpert, L., 1960: Internat. Rev. Cyt. *10*:163.

51. Fawcett, D. W., Ito, S., and Slautterback, D., 1959: J. Biochem. Biophys. Cyt. *5*:453.
52. Guttes, E., and Guttes, S., 1960: Nature *187*:520.
53. Thormar, H., 1959: Compt. Rend. Lab. Carlsberg *31*:207.
54. Iverson, R. M., and Giese, A. C., 1957: Exp. Cell. Res. *13*:213.
55. Marsland, D. A., and Landau, J. V., 1954: J. Exp. Zool. *125*:507.
56. Chalkley, H. W., 1951: Ann. New York Acad. Sci. *51*:1303.
57. Selman, G. G., and Waddington, C. H., 1955: J. Exp. Biol. *32*:700.
58. Scherbaum, O. H., 1960: Ann. New York Acad. Sci. *90*:565.
59. Zeuthen, E., 1958: Adv. Biol. & Med. Physics *6*:37.
60. Mazia, D., Sept. 1961: Sci. Am. *205*:100.
61. Robinow, C. F., 1960: The Cell (Brachet, J., and Mirsky, A. E., eds.). Academic Press, New York Vol. 4, p. 57.
62. Anderson, N. G., Fisher, W. E., and Bond, H. E., 1960: Ann. New York Acad. Sci. *90*:486.

SECTION
VII

HISTORY OF
CELL PHYSIOLOGY

CHAPTER

27

A BRIEF HISTORY OF
CELL PHYSIOLOGY

When the subject of cell physiology is presented, one cannot help inquiring into its origins, yet no comprehensive historical account is available. Perhaps such an account is lacking because the subject is little more than a hundred years old, and it is difficult to gain perspective on so young a subject. The summary that follows here is an attempt to outline the origins of some of the major trends in cell physiology, rather than to give a chronological history of it, and it was written with the feeling that these developments may be seen in quite a different light in another few years.

Three phases in the history of cellular physiology might be recognized: the first, an exploratory period which began with the acceptance of the cell doctrine and continued through the beginning of the twentieth century; the second, an analytical period which has occupied the time since; and the third, a new period of development, just beginning, which might be best characterized as molecular biology. In the limited space available here it is impossible to name all the investigators of merit in the field of cell physiology.

Therefore only a few are chosen as examples, with the understanding that those omitted are not necessarily of lesser merit.

It is perhaps self-evident that cellular physiology, as a separate field of study, could develop only after the cell was recognized as a unit of structure in plants and animals, but many of the sources from which cell physiology sprang are of much older origin. The cell doctrine was fairly widely accepted by 1839, although it would be difficult to give the credit for its inception to any one or two individuals. Even before that time, some workers had pointed out that the cell had a sort of double existence as part of an organism and as an independent unit, and Schleiden wrote, "It is, however, apparent that the vital process of the individual cell must form the very first absolutely indispensable basis of vegetable physiology and comparative physiology."[3] Conklin, in a number of scholarly essays on the early history of the cell doctrine, points out that Schleiden and Schwann contributed to it primarily by publicizing the idea and bringing to a culmination the work of a large number

563

of other investigators who already clearly understood the cell to be a unit of structure.[1, 2, 13]

Before 1839 biological research had progressed independently in a variety of directions in zoology, botany and physiology. The cell doctrine was the first of the great unifying principles that caused botanists, zoologists and physiologists to realize that organisms—whether animals or plants—and their functions were not quite so unrelated as had been previously supposed. The cell principle led to a better understanding of the unity of life, a concept which was to grow as other principles of biology were developed, not the least of which came from cell physiology.

In the period following 1839, in addition to cellular physiology, two other new fields of biological study arose, histology and cytology, initially concerned with the structure of tissues and of cells, respectively. Until recent times, cytologists centered their attention on the structure and behavior of the nucleus. Cell physiologists, to the extent that they could be identified as such, continued their interest in cytoplasmic structure and used both cells and tissues in their studies, but they were interested in structure primarily as a means of interpreting the way in which the cell performs its functions.

During the early or exploratory period, cell physiology developed along three major lines: the amassing of a fund of information, the development of various experimental techniques, and the attempts to formulate theories to correlate findings. It was necessary, first, to find out what types of cells and cell organelles were present in various plants, animals and unicellular organisms.[4-7] It was also necessary to observe the properties and behavior of the cell under a variety of conditions and to determine the types of substances that enter and leave cells. Various kinds of movements made by cytoplasm, such as streaming or movement by means of cilia, flagella, pseudopodia or by massed cells in various types

of muscles, had to be studied and characterized. The nature of the irritability process in diverse organisms and the role of the individual cells in these responses of organisms had to be ascertained. The nature of cell division and cell growth had to be investigated and the information codified. And so, throughout the nineteenth century and into the twentieth century, this type of information accumulated, serving as a springboard for later analytical studies.

All these objectives and the investigations preformed in succeeding years indicate that many cell physiologists had accepted the point of view introduced by Descartes (1596–1650) and developed by others—namely, that the phenomena of life are explainable in terms of the organism as a machine expending energy, rather than in terms of supernatural forces.[4]

Early investigators, using cells, studied their structure and spoke of the cell as a unit of function, but few did more than assume this fact. Perhaps the earliest studies of the functions of cells were those by Purkinje (who introduced the term protoplasm) on the physical properties of protoplasm, and those on cell division in connection with the chromosome cycle. These studies, culminating in the interpretation of the chromosomal behavior in mitosis and meiosis (Strasburger, 1875; Farmer and Moore, 1905), covered a span of about 65 years following the acceptance of the cell doctrine, and they were greatly stimulated by the introduction of staining by Gerlach in 1858. Toward the end of the nineteenth century the botanists Pfeffer and Overton used plant cells in studies on permeability About this time embryologists began manipulating single blastomeres of larger embryos, and during the early part of the twentieth century micromanipulators were devised, enabling workers (Kite Seifriz, Taylor, Barber, Chambers, Peterfi to handle single small cells and even to dissect them. These workers were thereby able to demonstrate that many of the cell organelles seen in stained preparations were not mere artifacts produced by fixation and staining.

In parallel with these events, organic chemistry arose and was to contribute tools of vast importance to cell physiology. Wöhler synthesized urea in 1828, beginning the study of organic syntheses and organic chemistry which, at its inception at least, was concerned with biological compounds and was therefore closely allied to biology. The great work of Liebig (1803–1873) demonstrated some of the food transformations and contributed methods of organic analysis of importance to the biochemist. Various organic acids occurring in plant and animal cells were identified and synthesized. Proteins were recognized and characterized as early as 1838 (Mulder; Boussingault). Various amino acids were isolated and then synthesized, and by 1842 a difference between plant and animal proteins was recognized. It was further determined that the animal remakes its proteins from amino acids found in the digest of plant proteins (Johnson). In 1902 the peptide bond was discovered independently by Fischer and Hofmeister, and it was recognized that the protein molecule could be made from a relatively small number of amino acids. At about the beginning of the twentieth century Ostwald studied catalysts, and the concept of catalytic action was accepted into biological thinking (Fischer) to explain the many oxidations and syntheses found occurring in animal and plant cells (Bertrand).[5]

Miescher's researches on nucleic acid, from 1868 to 1892, laid the foundation for the study of these cellular constituents, the importance of which has been fully realized and exploited only in recent years.[5]

In the meantime, techniques for handing cells and for using them in experiments continually improved. During this time also, biologists adapted many pieces of physical equipment for measuring and recording changes in organs and cells. In this respect, the physiologist Ludwig (1816–1895), one of the great teachers of his time, is outstanding. Many pieces of equipment used now in elementary physiology courses are traceable to his adaptations and inventions. Du Bois-Reymond (1818–1896) devised methods to measure potentials and action currents in animal cells. Contributions were made by many investigators over the entire early period, and ways were found to measure muscle tension and electrical changes on nerve and muscle and in individual cells. The turn of the century found a new burst of activity in physics, with the discovery of radioactivity, x-rays and other phenomena, but the main impacts of these discoveries on cellular physiology were to be felt only later.

A great impetus to many fields of biological research, including cellular physiology, was the foundation of a number of marine laboratories, where investigators from all parts of the world could study together and exchange ideas. Four such laboratories of especial note are the first marine laboratory, established at Concarneau, France, in 1859; the international biological station at Naples, Italy, established by Anton Dohrn about 14 years later; the Marine Biological Laboratory at Woods Hole, Massachusetts, which succeeded the small laboratory set up by Louis Agassiz on the island of Penikese in 1873; and the Plymouth Laboratory of the Marine Biological Association, founded in England in 1888.

The main theoretical efforts of many of the cell physiologists, operating on the broad concept of a mechanical interpretation of life, were attempts to formulate analogues by which they could visualize or duplicate the structure and the operation of the cell. Unquestionably, many an investigator had a tongue-in-cheek attitude when he presented his analogue, realizing that it was far from reality, but the information available at the time was inadequate for more than suggestive models.[4-10]

Various conceptions were proposed to account for the structure of cytoplasm. Altmann (1893) thought cytoplasm was granular; Bütschli (1894), that it was alveolar; and Flemming (1882), that it was fibrillar, while E. B. Wilson (1925) thought that it was a colloid. The last of these conceptions makes room for all these types of organization; the colloidal state can account for granules, fibrils and emulsified materials, all of which occur in the cell. The viscosity of cytoplasm, its resistance to deformation and the irregular zigzag movement of particles through it, all indicated a structure of elastic scaffolds; yet the free flow of cytoplasm that occurs during division of cells or in streaming, and the Brownian movement in portions of it, all suggested a liquid. In 1899 Hardy and Fischer independently showed that some of the structures in cytoplasm could be duplicated by action of fixatives upon albumin. A resolution of some of these puzzling facts was to come later only when much more effective tools became available for study of cytoplasmic structure.

In the last decade of the nineteenth century the cell membrane was conceived as a lipoidal film by Overton. Michaelis later made collodion analogues of the cell membrane to study the dynamics of movements of substances through it. Using iron wire, Lillie (1929) made a model that shows many of the characteristics of the nerve impulse. From such a model Lillie predicted saltatory conduction in nerve fibers. Another model, constructed by Ebbecke to show the origin of potentials on the nerve fibers, was later made of a collodion sac filled with a salt solution. A variety of models for muscular contraction, ciliary movement, ameboid movement, cell division and even for contraction of the heart appeared during this period

of cellular physiology. Some of the models are crude; others are quite ingenious and elaborate and are still useful pedagogically.[8, 12]

Many biologists sought some particles in the cell which were as fundamental to an explanation of the properties of life as are the atoms to an explanation of the properties of matter in the physical world. Perhaps one of the most prominent of these attempts was the biogen hypothesis of Verworn (1863–1921). The biogen was conceived of as a hypothetical albuminoid molecule whose chief characteristic consisted of high energy content and chemical lability, "a constant and simultaneous alternation of disintegration and reconstruction." This property, according to Verworn, is the true essence of life, there being no difference between animate and inanimate matter except that brought about by the very extraordinary metabolic possibilities of the biogen molecule. His book *Allgemeine Physiologie* treated effectively many other phases of physiology, however, and had a profound influence on the biology of his day; his monograph on *Irritability* included many important contributions from his laboratory.

If, in retrospect, the general theories developed at this time are often inadequate, it must be remembered that in terms of what the early investigators had to build on, their theories were worthy accomplishments. The mass of data on various cell activities and properties which they accumulated was also foundation for further work.

During the next period, the analytical period of cell physiology, the newer and more precise methods of the chemist and physicist were applied to the problems of cell physiology.[9, 10] This approach was the basis of the famous textbook by Höber, called the *Physical Chemistry of Cells and Tissues*, the first German edition of which appeared in 1902. An edition in English with the collaboration of a number of eminent American physiologists appeared in 1945. Perhaps a quotation from the preface to the last edition will serve to illustrate the tenets of this phase of physiology: ". . . not physiology originated essentially to fill human needs and help suffering individuals, but physiology as a branch of physical science dealing with life as a physical, though exceedingly complex, system that may be subjected to scientific analysis like any other natural object."[14] Bayliss' equally famous *General Physiology** was modeled along somewhat similar lines, but in addition treated the effects of light on organisms, as well as studies on many aspects of what is essentially mammalian physiology. Both these books had a considerable amount of influence on training and thinking in the field of cell physiology. In recent years perhaps the most influential book in cell physiology has been Heilbrunn's *An Outline of General Physiology*, which first appeared in 1937.

At the time of World War I, the concept of molecular orientation at surfaces was developed by Langmuir, Hardy and Jarkins. This concept was to have far-reaching effects in research of cellular activities and organization of cellular membranes. Somewhat later, by x-ray diffraction, it became possible to determine the size of regularly arranged units in such structures as cell membranes, intact tendon and muscle cells. With more effective application of the polarizing microscope, the probable orientation of molecules in cell structures was demonstrated. The application of the phase microscope, invented in 1934 by Zernicke, in making observations needs no further emphasis here. With it many structures of the living cell have been clearly identified, and cyclic changes have been readily followed for the first time. After the invention of the electron microscope in 1938, the size and shape of many submicroscopic structures in the cell and many other molecules or molecular

aggregates of biological interest could be determined.

Electronic methods adapted to the investigation of biological problems also have been of tremendous importance. These studies were begun in 1922 by Gasser and Erlanger (Nobel Prize, 1944) who made use of the oscilloscope to investigate features of the nervous impulse not previously susceptible to analysis by slower methods.

In recent years, following the pioneering work of Schoenheimer, radioactive tracers have facilitated investigation of many fundamental problems in the metabolism of cells and in the dynamic aspects of bodily and cellular constituents. In the hands of a large number of workers the tracer technique has led to many other important discoveries in cell physiology. For example, quantitative analysis had previously failed to demonstrate movement of sodium into cells. Yet by use of radioactive sodium, Brooks demonstrated that it went in, exchanging places with its nonradioactive isotope. Again Calvin, Benson, Arnon and Bassham have used tracers to analyze the pathway of synthesis of carbon compounds in photosynthesis.[23]

Biochemistry, also, has been applied to cell physiology, leading to the elucidation of the degradation of nutrients and the dynamics of energy liberation in cells. The field of enzyme chemistry has had a spectacular development and the Nobel Prize in 1955 went to Theorell for his studies on enzymes of respiration. Syntheses, as well, have been studied in cells, and many enzymes and enzyme reactions in cellular activities have been studied by a large number of workers. The enzymes and coenzymes concerned with these activities have been isolated and purified, following pioneer experiments by Fischer. Protein chemistry has

---

* A new edition of this book has recently appeared in two volumes.[15]

also shown great progress; e.g., Pauling's contribution to the knowledge of the structure of the protein molecule won him the Nobel Prize in 1954. Sanger's analysis of the sequence of amino acids in a protein, for which he received the Nobel Prize in 1958, opened the way for "fingerprinting" proteins with an opportunity to analyze how genes work. The study of nucleic acids has been intensely stimulated by the greater insight achieved by the Watson-Crick double-helix model of DNA. The synthesis of DNA and RNA *in vitro* by Kornberg and Ochoa, respectively, for which they received the Nobel Prize in 1959, makes possible an attack on the most basic of biological problems—the nature of inheritance—at the molecular level.

Perhaps the contrast between the thinking in the two periods of development of cell physiology can be best brought out by examples comparing the conceptions of some cellular problems in both periods.[5]

Forty years ago mitochondria would have been described as cell organelles which stain specifically with Janus green B. They were known to vary in size, shape, position and number, depending on cellular activity and treatment of the preparation. They were thought to play some part in cell respiration, but the issue was controversial. Some workers even thought that mitochondria were symbiotic microorganisms. At present, mitochondria, which may be separated from other constituents of cells by the fractional centrifugation of ruptured cells, are known to be cell organelles bounded by selectively permeable membranes. Washed free of contaminants, mitochondria have been analyzed and found to consist primarily of proteins, lipids and ribonucleic acid, the proteins being present in greatest proportion. In fragmented mitochondria many of the enzymes concerned with aerobic oxidations in the cell have been identified, as have also many of the enzymes concerned with phosphorylations and transfer of high energy phosphate bonds. It is thought that in the mitochondria occur all the reactions of the Krebs tricarboxylic acid cycle, as a result of which most of the energy required for the work of the cell is liberated. The positions of some of the enzymes in a mitochondrion have been identified, and very recently Palade has demonstrated by electron microscopy that the structure of a mitochondrion consists of a matrix in which are found cristae or lamellae which give a large surface for enzyme activity.

In like fashion, the vague conception of protoplasm as a colloid has given place now to the more critical physical-chemical appraisal of the types of forces and bonds that give cytoplasm its rigidity and at the same time its fluidity (Frey-Wyssling, Bernal). In fact, the word protoplasm has lost its meaning as the structure and function of all parts of the cell are becoming clearer.[16]

The early workers considered cell membranes to be lipoidal films, and cells to be simple osmometers. At the present time, data are available from many lines of inquiry to show that cell membranes contain both proteins and lipids (Parpart). Furthermore, the arrangement of these substances in the membrane has been ascertained to some extent (Schmitt, Danielli, Wolpers). Studies on permeability have demonstrated that while some materials pass through the cell membrane in response to a concentration gradient, many ions and molecules move against concentration gradients, being taken up actively with expenditure of energy by the cell (Blinks, Steinbach, Rothstein, Ussing). For example, potassium is often accumulated inside cells in greater amounts than are present outside the cells, and many wastes are carried into the kidney tubules against a concentration gradient (Richards, Smith). The cell membrane is now viewed, therefore, as dynamic and changeable. Some enzymes have been located on the cell surface, which also shows that it is apparently an active structure rather than just a selective sieve.

A great change has also taken place in the conceptions of biological oxidation-reduction reactions and of energy liberation in the cell. The early work of Lavoisier (1780) and the later studies of Liebig (1803–1873) had demonstrated that animals liberate energy from foodstuffs. About 1903, Wieland (Nobel Prize, 1927) and Thunberg emphasized the need for activation of hydrogen, and Wieland made models, with activated platinum as a catalyst, for the dehydrogenation of organic molecules. He found that vigorous oxidations occurred only if a substance which can carry hydrogen to oxygen is added.

Warburg (1908) emphasized that activation of oxygen preceded oxidations in cells. He made models of cellular oxidation, using as a catalyst animal blood charcoal, which contains iron. Many organic materials, shaken with such charcoal in the presence of oxygen, were oxidized. Warburg (Nobel Prize, 1931) insisted that the iron activated the oxygen, making possible its reaction with substrate molecules, and he postulated an iron-containing, oxygen-activating enzyme, which was later isolated by others and is now known as cytochrome oxidase.

Michaelis next elucidated the stepwise nature of electron transfer in biological oxidation-reduction reactions. Since that time biochemists and cell physiologists have succeeded in identifying the steps in the decomposition of cell nutrients, especially in yeast and muscle cells. The enzymes concerned in most of the steps have been identified, isolated and in some cases purified. The two Nobel Prize winners in medicine and physiology in 1953 were Krebs and Lipmann, who did much to elucidate the cyclic changes in metabolism, but many others contributed to the discoveries which enabled them to relate all the reactions into the cyclic oxidations. The function of the B vitamins as prosthetic groups in the enzymes has in many cases been clarified, and attempts are being made to put the enzymes together on particles in order to simulate their action in the sequences operative in the cell (Green).

The conception of muscular contraction has also undergone a striking change. Fundamental researches by Hill and Meyerhof on the heat production and the lactic acid cycle in the anaerobic metabolism of muscle cells led to the awarding of the Nobel Prize to these men in 1922. More recently aerobic muscle metabolism and the enzymes involved have been studied (Krebs, Warburg, the Needhams). In the last two decades the structural proteins of muscle have been isolated, and two of these, actin and myosin, have been found to combine in various stoichiometric ratios (Weber, Edsall, Szent-Györgyi, Mommaerts). Compressed films of actomyosin with oriented molecules, which contract to lift a load when placed in salt solutions containing adenosine triphosphate and relax when placed in other salt solutions, show many, though not all, of the properties of the contractile fibrils of muscle (Hayashi). This muscle model is illustrative of the type of molecular models sought for by workers at the present time. H. E. and A. F. Huxley, on the basis of electron micrographic studies of ultra-thin sections of muscle fibers and of x-ray diffraction studies, have demonstrated that myosin and actin occur in the muscle in the form of separate filaments. They postulate contraction to be a stero-spatial sliding of the two kinds of filaments as they react in the presence of ATP. The concept is in accord with most of our present knowledge of muscular contraction.

Studies on action potentials and injury potentials were made by Nernst (1899), Bernstein (1913), and Höber (1910). The work of Lucas (1906) and Adrian (1912) developed many of the basic concepts of the irritability process, and that of Sherrington (1892) and Pavlov (1910) formulated reflexes as functions of the nervous system. With advances in knowledge of electronic devices, fundamental researches on the nerve impulse at the cellular level were made possible by the use of the cathode ray oscilloscope. The work of many distinguished investigators (among them Gasser, Erlanger, Osterhout, Blinks, Bronk, Curtis, Cole, Gerard, Grundfest, Hodgkin, Katz, Kuffler, Nachmansohn, Rushton and Wiersma) has led to a better understanding of resting and action potentials of cells. To the success of this work, the discovery and use of large plant cells and the squid giant axon have contributed much, since it is easier to make electrical measurements upon them.

The development of biochemical genetics, pioneered by Beadle and Tatum (1941), for which they received the Nobel Prize jointly with Lederberg, in 1958, has led to a better understanding of biosyntheses. Tailor-made mutants, each lacking capacity to produce some required nutrient, have made possible precise determinations of many biosynthetic pathways, adding a powerful tool to other biochemical techniques for studies of metabolic deficiencies. We now know the steps by which cells make many amino acids and many vitamins, and we know some of the steps in the formation of purines, pyrimidines, and, somewhat incompletely, even the synthesis of nucleotides, nucleic acids and proteins.

Startling advances in understanding photosynthesis have come as a result of the application of comparative biochemical approaches (van Niel), and of radioactive tracers (Calvin, Bassham, Arnon, Benson and others). Recently, most of the enzymes (Racker) and many of the conditions required for both the photochemical and the thermochemical reactions in photosynthesis have been analyzed, and the biochemical pathway has been indicated. For his analysis of the dark reactions in photosynthesis, Calvin received the Nobel Prize in 1961.

Newer techniques have made possible studies on cell division which promise to untangle the complex series of reactions involved, but analytical work has just begun. Here might be mentioned the isolation and analysis of the division spindle and the study of the trigger mechanism that initiates cell division (Mazia). Development of a synthetic medium for culture of plant cells (White) and the possibility of developing a similar one for animal cells offer further opportunities for an analysis of cell division.

Gradually a new approach to cell physiology is crystallizing in all these fields. Research workers, too numerous to be mentioned, in both the western[17] and eastern countries[18, 19, 20] are attempting to construct for each cellular structure a molecular concept from the chemical constituents of that structure, and they are attempting to analyze the operation of each cell organelle in terms of physics and chemistry by any tool available. These investigations reveal new facts, sometimes making possible a choice between alternate views or a formulation of new hypotheses. A few books representing steps in this direction are: *Modern Trends in Physiology and Biochemistry* (1952), honoring Michaelis, edited by Barron and containing articles by various leaders in their fields; the book by Johnson, Eyring and Polissar called *The Kinetic Basis of Molecular Biology* (1954); and *A Textbook of General Physiology* (1959), by Davson, and *Biophysical Science, a Study Program* (edited by Oncley), which emphasize the biophysical aspects of cell physiology. It is important that the role of cells as part of an organism not be forgotten.[21] Cell biologists interested in the fundamental aspects of development are bridging this gap.[22]

Contributions of Cell Physiology to Biological Thought

Cell physiology has reinforced the mechanistic concept of life, since the behavior of cells has proved to be explainable in terms of the principles of chemistry and physics. For example, utilization of energy and matter in the cell appears to be governed by the principles of conservation of energy and matter, as in the physical world.

A second contribution of cell physiology is the observation that basic cell activities, as well as cell organelles and their constituents, are remarkably similar in cells of all organisms, no matter how diverse the organisms may be. Many of the cell organelles are common to all cells and are alike in chemistry and function; for example, the plasma membrane, the nucleus and its constituents, the mitochondria and the microsomes are the oldest structural homologies of the living world. Many of the chemical constituents of cells are universal. This is true not only of the proteins, lipids and carbohydrates, but also of substances present in only catalytic quantities. For example, vitamin B_1 has been found in all organisms assayed and forms part of the enzyme system involved in conversions of that universal metabolite, pyruvic acid. Again, the flavoproteins, which carry hydrogen from a dehydrogenase to some hydrogen acceptor, are omnipresent, and according to Barron, represent the most archaic enzymes—presumably having been present in the primeval anaerobic cells. For their synthesis, flavoproteins require vitamin B_2, which the animal gets from plants, or from microorganisms in its gut. Szent-Györgyi (Nobel Prize, 1937), speaking of the role of vitamins and other chemicals universally required in cells but in many cases obtained by an animal cell from plant food, says: "This simple fact involves a point of greatest philosophical importance. If I look upon the cell as a mechanism and upon the molecule as a wheel of this mechanism, then by saying that I take my vitamins from the plant, I say that there are two mechanisms, the plant cell and my cells, whose parts, the single wheels, are interchangeable. Two mechanisms, whose parts are interchangeable, cannot be very different. This is the first scientific evidence for the great, fundamental chemical unity of living Nature. There is no real difference between cabbages and kings, we are all recent leaves on the old tree of life."[11]

The past history of cell physiology indicates that advances in knowledge have not always followed along a perfectly smooth and continuous curve. There have been some false starts, overlaps and dead ends, but there also have been many ascending jumps. Decisive advances have been the result of the operation of several factors: (1) Choice of some exceedingly favorable experimental cell material in which one kind of phenomenon can be studied with a minimum of other biological complications, e.g., the use of *Neurospora* in biosynthetic studies. (2) Advances in chemistry and physics, and the development of new experimental tools which make possible new kinds of study and measurment, e.g., radioactive tracer techniques which have played so vital a role in investigations of metabolism, in studies of photosynthesis and also in an analysis of the function of the nucleus. (3) The imagination and thorough scholarship which has enabled an investigator to develop a generalization based on previously uncorrelated information, e.g., the Krebs cycle and the metabolic mill, which together correlate a vast mass of biochemical information and make possible a logical attack on unsolved problems.

The great number of original publications, reviews and symposia on cell physiology is evidence of an actively growing field. The advances made in so short a span of time as the last 5 years* present a prospect for the future which is both interesting and exciting.

---

* This is the elapsed time since the literature was reviewed for the first edition.

LITERATURE CITED

1. Conklin, E. G., 1940: *in* The Cell and Protoplasm (Moulton, F. R., ed.). A.A.A.S., Washington, p. 6.
2. Conklin, E. G., 1940: Biol. Symp. *1*:5.
3. Conklin, E. G., 1940: *in* The Cell and Protoplasm (Moulton, F. R., ed.). A.A.A.S., Washington, p. 11.
4. Nordenskiold, E., 1936: The History of Biology. Tudor, New York.
5. Dawes, B., 1952: A Hundred Years of Biology. Macmillan, New York.
6. Franklin, K. J., 1949: A Short History of Physiology. Staples, London.
7. Singer, C., 1950: A History of Biology. Schuman, New York.
8. Barnes, T. C., 1937: Textbook of General Physiology. Blakiston, New York.
9. Some of the information from reference 5; other information from annual prefatory chapters in the Annual Review of Physiology, beginning with volume 12.
10. Veith, I., 1954: Perspective in Physiology. Am. Physiol. Soc., Washington.
11. Szent-Györgyi, A., 1940: *in* The Cell and Protoplasm (Moulton, ed.). A.A.A.S., Washington, p. 160.
12. Bayliss, W. M., 1931: Principles of General Physiology. 4th Ed. Longmans, New York. Bayliss gives the historical background for many subjects of interest to the cell physiologist.
13. Five articles by Baker, J. R., evaluating the cell theory and containing much interesting information: 1948: Quart. J. Micros. Sci. *89*:103. 1949: Quart. J. Micros. Sci. *90*:87. 1952: Quart. J. Micros. Sci. *93*:157. 1953: Quart. J. Micros. Sci. *94*:407. 1955: Quart. J. Micros. Sci. *96*:449.
14. Höber, R., 1945: Physical Chemistry of Cells and Tissues. Blakiston, New York, p. v.
15. Bayliss, L. E., 1959–1960: Principles of General Physiology. Longsman, New York, 2 vols.
16. Hardin, G., 1956: Meaninglessness of the Word Protoplasm. Sci. Month. *82*:112–120.
17. Hughes, A., 1959: A history of Cytology. Abelard-Schuman, New York.
18. Christman, R. (ed.), 1952: Soviet Science. Am. Assoc. Adv. Sci., Washington.
19. Suskind, S. R., 1960: Microbial Genetics in the USSR. Quart. Rev. Biol. *35*:41–79.
20. Setlow, R. B., and Setlow, J. E., 1961: Soviet Cellular Biophysics, 1950–60. Quart. Rev. Biol. *36*:1–49.
21. Commoner, B., 1961: In Defence of Biology. Science *133*:1745–1748.
22. Picken, L., 1960. The Organization of Cells and Other Organisms. Clarendon Press, London, Ch. 10, Becoming Multicelluar as Seen in the Light of Cell Properties.
23. Arnon, D. I., 1961: Changing Concepts of Photosynthesis. Bull. Torrey Bot. Club *88*:215–259.

INDEX

Page numbers in *italics* refer to illustrations; page numbers followed by the letter T refer to tables.

573

adenosine diphosphate, in muscular contraction, 507
adenosine triphosphate, 328, *330*
    in muscular contraction, 507, 510, 512
adenylic acid, formula, *48*
adenyl-luciferin, 387
ADP, 330, *330*
    in muscular contraction, 507
Adrian, 569
adsorption, 66
    chromatography, 418
aerobic decomposition, of glucose, 334–336, 334T, *335*
aerobic metabolism, 370–374
afferent neurons. See *neurons.*
after-potentials, negative and positive, 431, 463
agglutinogens, 52
aging of cells, 517–519
albumins, solubility of, 41
alcohols, partition coefficients, 228, 229T
aldehydes, permeability of, 230, 232T
alkylating agents, 551
all or none principle, 430
    exception in some muscle fibers, 491
alpha particles, 163, 189
Altmann, 566
ameba, viscosity of, 77
ameboid movement, 476–479
amino acid(s), 37–40
    bonding of, 37
    dissociation of, 152
    in collagen molecule, 44
    in Krebs cycle, 336
    in polypeptide chains, 41
    in representative proteins, 40T
    representative formulas, *39*
    sequences in insulin, 41
    synthesis into protein, *532*
    types, 38, 38T
aminopolypeptidases, 306
ampholytes, 152
anaerobic bacteria, 383
anaerobic decomposition, of glucose, 332–334, *333*, 337, *338*
anaerobic metabolism, 382–385
anaerobiosis, effect on viscosity of protoplasm, 78
anelectrotonus, definition, 438
anesthetics, effects on action potential of neuron, 444
    on permeability, 239
anilin dyes, 22
animal(s) cells. See *cell.*
    life activities of, compared with plants and micro-organisms, 4
    nutrition, general scheme of, 284, *284*
    physiology, comparative, definition, 6
    tissues, classification, 16
anion(s), gradients, effects on resting potential, 456
    Hofmeister series, 72
    of cells, 37
    permeability of, 233
anisotropic substances, definition, 275
anoxia, effects on action potential of neuron, 443

antagonism, salt, 238, *238*
antephase, 545
antibiotics, as mitotic poisons, 552
antimetabolites, 551
aperture, numerical, of light microscope, 22
arc, reflex. See *reflex arc.*
D-arginine, formula, *39*
arginine phosphate, 330
Arrhenius, 199, 205
artifact(s), organelles as, 12
    stimulus, 432
ash, relative amounts in different organisms, 34T
astral relaxation theory, of cleavage, 559
asynchrony, in cell division, 540–544, *541*
atmospheric blanket, of water vapor, 134
atmosphere, oxygen in, 138
    ozone layer, 163
atomic bomb, biological effects of, 187
ATP, 328, *330*
    as source of energy for muscular contraction, 507, 510, 512
auxins, 425, 523
axon, 16, 427
    diameter, effect on conduction rate of nerve impulse, 432, 433T
axoplasm, 438
azide, as respiratory inhibitor, 377, *378*

BACTERIA. See also *microorganisms.*
    anaerobic, 383
    barophilic, 143
    cell walls of, 268
    compared with viruses, 19
    conjugation in, *123*
    effects of bacteriophages, 20
    flagella, structure, 101
    gram-negative and gram-positive, differences between, 18
    luminous, 385, *385*
    lysogeny in, 124, *124*
    photosynthetic, pigments in, 412T
    plasma membrane, 18
    transduction in, 124
bacteriophage(s), 20, *20*
    DNA of, 121
    lysogenic, 21
    multiplication in bacterial cell, 121, *122*
balanced growth, 534–536
Barger's method, for determination of osmotic pressure, 218
base(s), definition, 144
    strong, definition, 144
    weak, and salt, use in buffer mixtures, 160
Bayliss, 567
Beadle, 524, 570
beam, comparison, in interference microscope, 25
Beer law, 188
Bernstein, 569

cytochrome C, structure, *342*
cytochrome oxidase, 339, 340
cytokinesis, 556–559
cytoplasm, 9
    as polyphasic colloid, 74
    chemical composition, 56
    communications with nucleus, 280
    early studies of, 566, 568
    pH, 58
    relationship with nucleus, 105–108
    relative sensitivity to ionizing radiations, *186*, 186
    staining of, 58
    strands, in plasmolyzed cells, *75*, 75
    structural bonds, nature of, 76–78, *76*
    viscosity, 77, *77*
cytoplasmic streaming, 475
cytosine, formula, *48*

DALTON's law 139
dark adaptation, of human eye, 168, *168*
    field microscope. See *microscope.*
de Candolle, 424
death of cells, 517–519
decomposition, of glucose, 328, 329T
        aerobic, 334–336, 334T, *335*
        alternate pathways, 341–345
        anaerobic, 332–334, *333*, *337*, *338*
    of organic materials, in microorganisms, 344
degradation, of energy, 289–291
dehydrating agents, 21
dehydration, effect on respiration, 377, *379*, *380*
    in dormant cells, 198
dehydrogenases, 311, 339
denaturation, of proteins, 46, *47*
        temperature coefficient for, 201
dendrite(s), 16, 427, *428*
deoxyribose, *51*
deoxyribonucleic acid. See *DNA.*
deplasmolysis, *214*, 224
Descartes, 564
dichroism, definition, 275
dielectric constants, 135
diffraction, x-ray, of DNA, 53
        of fibrous proteins, 43, *44*
diffusion, effects of temperature, 202
digestion, 304
    in plants, 306
    of starch, 305
dilatometry, 47
dimming time, 394
dinitrophenol, 332
dipeptidases, 306
diphosphopyridine, 311, *311*
disaccharides, 52
disperse phase, in heterogeneous systems, 64, 65T
dispersing medium, 64, 65T
dissociation, 144
    effects on pH, 158
    of proteins, 152

disulfide bonds, in mitosis, 554
diurnal rhythms, 172–174
division, cell. See *cell division.*
DNA, 52–56. See also *ribonucleic acid.*
    and genetic code, 128
    as transmitter of hereditary information, 121
    constituents, 53T
    content, as factor in cell division, 553
        relation to absorption of ionizing radiations, 182, *183*
    differences from RNA, 52, 53T
    enzyme tests for, 113
    in chromosomes, 114
    in Feulgen reaction, 111
    in protein synthesis, 125, 128, 533
    in transformations of pneumococcus, 121, *123*
    molar proportions of bases, 55T
    molecular weight, 53
    of multiplying bacteriophage, 121
    proportion in total nucleus, 113, 119
    relative number of molecules in cell, 35T
    replication, 125, *126*
    staining of, 111, 113
    structure, 53, *54*, *55*
    synthesis of, 125, 527–529, *528*, 529T
        inhibition by ionizing radiations, 187, 549
            by ultraviolet radiation, 178, 181
    template, 125
Donnan equilibrium, 235, *235*
drugs, as synaptic inhibitors, 469
Du Bois-Reymond, 385, 428, 565
dye(s). See also under specific dyes.
    in active transport studies, 244, *245*
    natural, 22
    photosensitization by, 166
    reaction with protein, effect of isoelectric pH, 42T
    types of, 22
    use in measurement of redox potentials, 365
        in permeability studies, 223
        in pH measurement, 153
    vital, 21

ECTOPLASM, 9
effector, definition, 424
efferent neurons. See *neurons.*
egg, polarity of, 74
Einstein, theory of relativity, 300
Einstein-Starck law, 165
elasticity, of skeletal muscle, 496
electric resistance, of cell membrane, 270
electrocardiogram, 445, *445*
electrode(s), potentials, normal, 353T
    redox potentials at, 352–356
    types, 352
electrolytes, in cell environment, 144–160
    osmotic pressures of, 216
    relation between concentration and activity, 158
    strong, 227
    weak, 227

electrolytes, dissociation of, calculation, 144
electrometric method, of pH measurement, 154, *155*
electromotive potentials, *354*
   series, 353, 353T, *354*
     biological, 358
electron microscope. See *microscope.*
   paramagnetic resonance, 363, *363*
   range of, 189
   spin resonance, 363, *364*
   transfer, in oxidation-reduction reactions, 339–341, *340*
electronmicrography, in study of chromosomes, 115, *116*
electrophoresis, in purification of enzymes, 308
electroplax, 445, *446*
emanations, radioactive, 163
Emerson effect, 412
   action spectrum, *415*
emulsions, 66–68, *67*
   size ranges of, 68T
en passant synapses, 465
encystment, effect on respiration, 377, *379*
end feet synapses, 465
end group analysis, in purification of enzymes, 309
endergonic reactions, definition, 292
endopeptidases, 306
endoplasm, 9
endoplasmic reticulum, 12, 83–88, *84, 86, 87*
   development, 83
   enzymes in, 348
   membranes of, 84, *84*
   organization, 74
   of muscle, 85, 88
   origin, 88
   relationship to cell membrane, *96*
   structure, 83
energy, available for photosynthesis, 418, *419*
   conservation of, law of, 287–289
   conversion of mass to, 300
   definition, 287
   degradation of, 289–291
   exchange, law of, and life, 295–298
   for cell division, source of, 544–548, *548*
   free, 291
     changes in, 330, *331*
   in muscle contraction, 505–508
   kinds of, 287
   kinetic, definition, 287
   liberation in hydrolysis and oxidation, comparison, 327, *327*
   of activation, 199, *201*
     determination of, 205
     lowering by enzymes, 303, *304*
   potential, definition, 287
     storage of, 291
   release, in active transport, 245
     in cells, 326–351
   requirements for photochemical action, 418, *419*
   reservoir, 546, *548*
   stepwise release during oxidation-reduction reactions, 327

energy, surface, 65, *65*
engines, heat, and Carnot cycle, 301
enhancement effect. See *Emerson effect.*
entrainment, of luminescence rhythm, 173, *174*
entropy, 289
   and second law of thermodynamics, 293
enucleation, 105, *105*
environment of cell, 131–207
   anaerobic, effects on animals and plants, 383
   buffering systems in, 149–152
   carbon dioxide in, 137, 137T
   effects on active transport, 254
     on enzyme activity, 314–318
   electrolytes in, 144–160
   oxygen in, 138–141, 139T, *140*
   pH of, 151T
   pressure as factor in, 141–143, 142T
   radiations in, 161–192
   response to, as cellular function, 3
   temperature as factor in, 193–207
   water as factor in, 133–137
enzymes, activation, *322*
   activity of, effect of environment, 314–318
   adding, 311
   as catalysts, 303
   cellular, 303–325
   concentration of, effect on activity, 314, *315*
   effects of heat, 195
     of hydrogen peroxide, 345
     of pressure, 142
   hydrolytic, 304–306, *305*
     activation of, 309, 310T
     chemical nature of, 308
     specificity of, 306–308
   in cellular oxidation-reductions, 310–314
   in glycolysis, 333T
   in Krebs cycle, 336T
   in muscle, 506
   in organelles, 347–349
   in photosynthesis, 405
   inhibition, *322*
     by poisons, 320–323, *321, 322*
   mechanism of action, 318–320, *319*
   molecules, number in cell, 12
   of hyaloplasm, 88
   of lysosomes, 95
   of mitochondria, 92
   of nucleus, 112
   oxidative, elements necessary for, 313, 314T
   poisons, 321, 323
   prosthetic groups, 311, *312*
   purification of, 308
   reactions, measurement of, 347
   redox systems, coupling, 360–362
   role in lowering energy of activation, 303, *304*
   splitting, 311
   transferring, 311
   transport by permease system, 253
   union with substrates, 318
   use in identification of nucleic acids, 61
epithelial cells, description, 16

glycerol, effect on freezing, 196
glycine, formula, *39*
glycogen, 51
  in muscle, 506
glycolysis, 332–334, *333*, 382–385
  enzymes in, 333T
  in muscle, *334*
    contraction, 506
glycoproteins, in cell membrane, 272
Golgi apparatus, *11, 12*, 93–95, *93, 94*
    appearance in stained cells, 12
    chemical composition, 58
    function, 15
    membranes, 94
    size, 94
    structure, 93
    study by centrifugation, 95
    visualization of, 15
gradient, concentration, See *concentration gradient.*
gram-negative bacteria. See *bacteria.*
gram-positive bacteria. See *bacteria.*
grana, of chloroplasts, 97, *98, 99*
granule, secretory. See *secretory granule.*
gray matter, water content, 36
Grotthus-Draper law, 166
ground substance, 12
    chemical composition, 56
    effect of centrifugation on, 13
    organization, 74
    proteins of, bonding, 76, *76*
    relationship to cell membrane, *96*
    viscosity, 74
growth, 517–539
  as cellular function, 3
  balanced and unbalanced, 534–536
  effect of pressure, 142
  factors, 56
  genetic control of, 535
  hormone, 425, 523
  in tissue culture and tumors, 519–522
guanine, formula, *48*
gut, active transport in, 250
guttation, 248

HARDY, 566, 567
heart, action potential of, 445
  beat, force of, 487
    inhibition of, 487, *490*
    initiation of, 486
  muscle. See *muscle, cardiac.*
  of frog, 486, *487*
  pacemaker, 486
  structure of, 485
heat and work relations, in muscle contraction, 496
  capacity, definition, 134
  death, of cells, 193–195
  during respiration, 379–381
  engines, and the Carnot cycle, 301

heat and work relations, in muscle contraction, 506, *507*
  latent, of vaporization, 133
  of adsorption, 66
  of combustion, of organic compounds, 290T
  of fusion, 134
  production, during nerve activity, 442, *444*
  resistance, of cells, 193–195
  specific, 133
Heilbrunn, 75, 238, 554, 567
helix, of DNA, 53, *55*
α helix, 43, *45, 46*
heme, 47
hemoglobin, 47
  combination of oxygen with, 140, *140*
hemolysis, as method for studying permeability, 225
Henderson-Hasselbalch equation, 147
heterogeneous systems, 64, 65T
    interfaces, 65
    surfaces, 65
heteropolar cohesive bonds, 76, *76*
heteropolar valency bonds, 76, *76*
heterotrophic microorganisms, 344
hexoses, 50
Hill, 569
histochemistry, aims of, 58
  of chromosomes, 114
  of nucleus, 108–115
  of organelles, 58–62
  of RNA, 113
history of cell physiology, 563–572
Höber, 566, 569
Hoffman-Berling, 556
Hofmeister, 565
Hofmeister series, 71
    anionic, 72
homeostasis, definition, 131
homogenation, *85, 87*
homogeneous systems, 64
homopolar cohesive bonds, 76, *76*
homopolar valency bonds, 76, *76*
hormone, growth, 425, 523
Huxley, 569
hyaline plasma layer, of sea urchin egg, 265, *266*
hyaloplasm, 74, 84, 88
  RNA of, 127
hyaluronic acid, 52
hyaluronidase, 52
hydration, 67, *67*
  effect on size of ions, 233
hydrogen, activation of, 346
  bonds, of water, 137
  donors and acceptors, definitions, 327
  electrode, compared to calomel electrode, 368
    potential, 353, *355*
  ion, concentration. See *pH.*
    definition, 144
  transfer, in oxidation-reduction reactions, 339–341
hydrogen peroxide, as end product in cellular oxidation, 345
hydrolases, 304

hydrolysis, 304–306, *305*
  energy liberation in, compared with oxidation, 327, *327*
hydrolytic enzymes. See *enzymes.*
hydronium ions, 159
hydrophilic radicals of proteins, 69T
hydrophobic radicals of proteins, 69T
hydroquinone, oxidation of, 361, *361*
hydrostatic pressure, 141
hypertonic solutions, effect on viscosity of cytoplasm, 78

ICE, formation of, 134
  melting of, 137
imbibition, 70
immersion oil, use with light microscope, 22
impulse, nerve. See *nerve impulse.*
inclusions, visualization of, 15
index, mitotic, 540
inducer substance, in control of growth, 535
inductorium, 434, *436*
inhibition, at synapses, 469–471
  competitive, definition, 321
  of cell division, by poisons, 549–552
    by radiations, 549
injury potential, 450
inorganic materials, relative number of molecules in cell, 35T
insulin, amino acid sequences, 41
  structure of, *40*
intercellular fluid, 16
interfaces, in heterogeneous systems, 65
interfacial tension, in heterogeneous systems, 65
interference microscope. See *microscope.*
interneurons, 425
intestine, active transport in, 250
intrinsic birefringence, definition, 275
iodopsin, 171
ion(s). See also specific ions and *electrolytes.*
  concentrations in cells and bathing media, 453, 453T
  content, of muscle and blood, *36*
  lyotropic series, 71
  sizes of, effects of hydration, 233
ionic compounds, 227
  partition coefficients, 228
ionization, effect on permeability, 231–234
ionizing radiations. See *radiations.*
irritability, 423–514
  definition, 423
isoelectric pH, 152
  of proteins, 41, *42*, 42T
isoelectric point, 152
isolated system, definition, 288
isomerases, 310
isometric contraction, of skeletal muscle, 494, *495*
isotonic contraction, of skeletal muscle, 494, *495*
isotropic substances, definition, 275

JARKINS, 567
jelly layer, in sea urchin egg, 265, *266*
junction, myoneural, 465, 489, *492*
  neuromuscular, 467
  synaptic. See *synapse.*

KEILIN, 340
keratin-myosin-elastin-fibrinogen group, 43
kidney, active transport in, 250, *251*
  glomerular, 250
  tubule cells, as example of active transport, 244, *245*
kinetic energy. See *energy.*
kinetin, 554
Kornberg, 125, 568
Krebs, 569
Krebs cycle, 335–339
  as source of energy for cell division, 544
  compared with photosynthesis, 404
  enzymes in, 336T

LANGMUIR, 567
Laplace, 296
Lavoisier, 296, 569
lecithin, formula, *49*
Lederberg, 570
leptoscope, 273, *274*
leucocytes, 17
leucoplasts, 15
leukemia, 520
Liebig, 565, 569
life activities, vitalistic and mechanistic interpretations of, 5
  origin of, 534
light, absorption of, 188
  effect on synchrony, 544, *547*
  microscope. See *microscope.*
  polarized, 274
  reactions, in photosynthesis, 399–404
  ultraviolet. See *ultraviolet.*
lignin, 52
Lillie, 566
limiting reactions, temperature coefficients and, 203
linin, 11, *11*
lipases, 307
lipids, cellular, 49, *49*, 50
  chemical composition, 49
  examples of, 33T
  solubility of, 33T
  subclasses of, 33T
  effects of heat, 195
  in cell membranes, 269
    evidence for, 270, *271*
    structural arrangement of, 274–279
  of nucleus, 113
  relative amounts in different organisms, 34T

Lipmann, 336, 569
literature, of cell physiology, 7
local circuit theory, of propagation of action potential, 461
Loewi, 487
London-van der Waals forces, 76, *76*
long-night plants, 175
loop synapses, 465
Lucas, 569
luciferase, 385
luciferin, 385
Ludwig, 565
lumen, of cytoplasm, 84
luminescence, 385–388
    effects of heat, 194
    of firefly, 387
    physical nature of, 388, *389*
    rhythm of, 172, *174, 175*
lymphocytes, 17
    chromosomes of, 114
lyophilic colloids, 69
lyophobic colloids, 69
lyotropic series, 71
lysis, of cell membranes, 271
lysogenic phages, 21
lysogeny, DNA in, 124, *124*
lysosomes, 88, 95

MACROMOLECULES, entry into cell by pinocytosis, 261
magnetic moments, of free radicals, 362–365
manometers, 390
marine laboratories, founding of, 565
Marsh-Bendall factor, 512
mass, conversion to energy, 300
matrix, of mitochondrion, *90,* 91
matter, conservation of, law of, 298–300
    definition, 287
Maxwell-Boltzmann law, 205
mechanistic interpretation of life activities, 5
medical physiology, definition, 6
meiosis, chromosomes in, visualization of, 14
melting point, determination of, 219, *219, 220*
membrane(s). See also under specific membranes, e.g., *cell membrane.*
    artificial, concentration chain potential across, 451–453, *451*
        passage of water across, 211–213
    extraneous, 265–269
    selectively permeable, definition, 213
    semipermeable, definition, 212
mercapto ethanol, 552
mercury osmometer, 212, *213*
metabolic mill, 336–339
metabolism, activity, of neurons, 442
    aerobic, 370–374
    anaerobic, 382–385
    definition, 326

metabolism, in poisoned cells, 344
    in tumor cells, 345
    intermediary, methods for investigating, 345–347
    relation to resting potential, 456–458
    resting, of neurons, 441
methionine, formula, *39*
5-methyl cytosine, formula, *48*
methylene blue, used in study of Golgi apparatus, 15
Meyerhof, 569
Michaelis, 361, 362, 566, 569
Michaelis-Menten law, 323
microdissection, 29
microincineration, 61, *61*
micromanipulators, 28, *28,* 29
microorganisms. See also *bacteria.*
    compared with plants and animals, 4
    death of, 518
    decomposition of organic materials in, 344
    mutations produced by ultraviolet radiation, 178
microscope, centrifuge, *13*
        stratification seen with, 13, *13*
    dark field, 23, *23*
    development of, 567
    electron, 27, 28
    interference, 25–27, *26*
    light, 22, *22*
        compared with electron microscope, 28
        numerical aperture, 22
        organelles seen with, 13
    phase, 14, 23, *24,* 25
    polarizing, 23
        use in study of cell membrane structure, 274, *275*
    techniques, 22–28
    ultracentrifuge. See *microscope, centrifuge.*
microsomes, *86, 87,* 88
    chemical composition, 56
    number in cell, 12
    revealed by centrifugation, 14
microsurgery, 28
Miescher, 565
mill, metabolic, 336–339
mitochondria, *11,* 89–92, *90, 91*
    appearance in stained cells, 12
    chemical composition, 58, 90
    early studies of, 568
    enzymes in, 92, 347, *349*
    fragmentation, 92
    in dividing cells, 15, 92
    in muscle fibers, 506
    membrane, *90,* 91
    movement, 89
    number in cell, 12, 89
    organization, 90, *90*
    origin of, 15, 92
    relationship to cell membrane, *96*
    size, 89
    visualization of, 14
mitosis. See also *cell division.*
mitotic apparatus, nature and formation of, 554–556, *555*

neuron(s), resting metabolism of, 441
  stimulation of, effects on permeability, 240
    threshold current, 434
Neurospora, biosynthesis in, 524, *525, 526*
neutrons, fast and slow, 190
Nicol prism, 274, *275*
Nissl bodies, 88
Nitella, action potential in, 446, *447*
nitrogen cycle, 298, *300*
  solubility, 137T
nodes of Ranvier, 440
  sinoauricular, 486
nonelectrolytes, osmotic pressure of, 214–216
nonionic polar compounds, 227
nonpolar compounds, *226*, 227
    partition coefficients, 227
norepinephrine, 468
normality, relation to pH, 146T
nuclear membrane. See *nucleus, membrane.*
nucleic acid(s), 52–56. See also under specific acids.
  functions of, 125–128
  identification by enzymes, 61
    by microincineration, 61, *61*
    by radioautography, 59, *60*, 61
    by spectrophotometry, 59, *59*
  in cell membranes, 270
  measurements of, 111
  molar proportions of bases, 55T
  of bacteriophage, 20
  purines and pyrimidines of, *48*
  structure, *49*
  synthesis, blocking by mitotic poisons, 551
nucleolus, 11, *11*
  formation, 120, *120*
  organizer, 120
  role in cell division, 554
  structures and constituents, 112
nucleoplasm, 11
nucleoproteins, 49
nucleotides, formulas, *48*
  of RNA, 127
nucleus, 9
  appearance in stained cell, 9, 11
  centrifugation of, 108
  chemical composition, 56
  chemical organization and function, 105–130
  communication with cytoplasm, 280
  constituents of, 109
  DNA content, 113, 119
  enzymes of, 112, 348
  histochemistry of, 108–115
  in cell division, 108
  lack of, in bacteria, 18
  lipids of, 113
  mass of, 109
  membrane of, 9, 108, *109, 110*
    permeability of, 279
    relationship to cell membrane, *96*
  protein synthesis in, 533
  relationship to cell membrane, *96*
    with cytoplasm, 105–108

nucleus, relative sensitivity to ionizing relations, *186,*
  removal of, 105, *105*
  ring centriole, *110*
  RNA content of, 119
  role in control of synchrony, 542
  sap, constituents, 112
  staining of, 58
  study by ultraviolet photomicrography, 111, *111*
  transfer to different species, 106
  ultrastructure of, 108, *109, 110*
  visualization of, 14
nutrition, animal, general scheme of, 284, *284*
  as cellular function, 3
  of plants, 3. See also *photosynthesis.*
    scheme of, 284

OCEANS, evaporation of, 134
Ochoa, 529, 568
oil, coalescence with cell membrane, 270
  droplets, as cell inclusions, 15
  immersion, use with light microscope, 22
opsin, 170
open system, cell as, 295
operator genes, 535
ordinary ray, definition, 275
organ physiology, definition, 6
organelles, as artifacts, 12
  as seen in fixed and stained cells, 9–13
  chemical composition, 56, 58
  enzymes in, 347–349
  histochemistry, 58–62
  in living cells, experimental evidence for, 13–15
  localization of chemical ink, 58–62
  numbers in cell, 12
  structure and functions, 83–104
  synthesis of, 534
organic chemistry, early development of, 565
oscilloscope, cathode ray, 429, *429*
osmometer(s), cells as, 220, 220T
  mercury, 212, *213*
  simple, *212*
osmosis, 211–222
osmotic pressure, 211
    determination of, 218
      colligative properties and, 216–220
    of electrolytes, 216
    of nonelectrolytes, 214–216
    of sugar, 215T
osmotic relations, in presence of protein, 234, *235*
Ostwald, 565
Overton, 564, 566
oxidases, 311
oxidation, cellular, hydrogen peroxide as end product,
    345
    oxidation-reduction potentials in, 352–369
  definition, 326
  energy liberation in, compared with hydrolysis, 327,
    327
  of hydroquinone, 361, *361*

phagosomes, 99

phase microscope. See *microscope.*

phase(s), of homogeneous and heterogeneous systems, 64

shift, 172, *173*

phenylalanine, formula, *39*

phloem, 18

phosphagens, 330

phosphatides, bonding, 77

phosphatidic acid, as possible carrier molecule in active transport, 255

phospholipids, 49, *49*

in cell membranes, 269

phosphorylated organic compounds, 328

phosphorylation, photosynthetic, 401, 403T

photobiological reactions, effects of temperature, 203

photochemical action, energy requirements for, 418, *419*

photochemical equivalence, law of, 165

photochemical reactions, effects of temperature, 203

in photosynthesis, 399–404

photodynamic sensitization, 165–167

photography, time-lapse, used in study of chromosomes, 14

photomicrographs, ultraviolet, use in study of chromosomes, 14

photomicrography, use in study of nucleus, 111, *111*

photoperiodism, 175–177

photoreactivation, 179, *180, 181*

photoreceptor cells, 167–172

photoreduction, in photosynthesis, 399–404

photoreversal, 179, *180, 181*

photosensitizers, 166

photosynthesis, 3, 97, 397–422

as oxidation-reduction reaction, 398

carbon dioxide in, 138

chloroplasts in, 407

compared with Krebs cycle, 404

energy available for, 418, *419*

enzymes in, 405

importance of, 397

in Chromatium, 403

light reactions in, 399–404

modern theories of, 570

pigments in, 407–416

quantum efficiency of, 416–418, 417T

rate of, effects of temperature and light intensity, 399, 399T

temperature coefficient, 203

thermochemical reactions in, 404–407

phototropism, 424

phycobilins, 411

phycocyanin, 411

absorption spectrum, *414*

prosthetic group, structure, *414*

phycoerythrin, 411

absorption spectrum, *414*

physiological studies, categories of, 6

physiology, cell. See *cell physiology.*

phytochrome, 176, *176*

pigment granules, in chromatophores, movement of, 480, *480*

in photosynthesis, 407–416

pinocytosis, 256–262

cell types in which found, 257

channels, 256, *256*

compared with active transport, 262

induction of, 257, *258, 261*

mechanism of, 259–261

occurrence, 256

salts in, 257, *258*

significance of, 261

pinosomes, 99, *258, 259, 260*

pKa, 146

plant cells. See also *cell.*

action potentials in, 446, *446*

permeability to water, 214, *214*

walls of, 266–269　,

digestion in, 306

fluids, pH of, 153, 153T

growth in, 523

life activities of, compared with animals and microorganisms, 3

movements of, 4

nutrition of, 3. See also *photosynthesis.*

phosynthesis in. See *photosynthesis.*

photosynthetic, pigments in, 412T

physiology, definition, 6

respiratory quotient, 382

short-night and long-night, 175

skeletons of, 18

temperature of, 381

plasma membrane. See *cell membrane.*

plasmodesmata, 12

plasmolysis, *214*

plastids, 12, 96. See also under specific plastids, e.g., *chloroplasts.*

visualization of, 15

platinum electrode, 352, *395*

pneumococcus, transformations of, role of DNA in, 121, *123*

poise, 80

poisons, inhibition of cell division by, 549–552

of enzymes by, 320–323, *321, 322*

polar compounds, nonionic, 227

partition coefficients, 228

polarity, of egg, 74

polarization, of neurons, 463

of synapse, 465

polarized light, 274

polarizing microscope. See *microscope.*

polypeptide chains, 40

polyphasic colloidal system, cell as, 73–76

polysaccharides, 52

porosity, of extraneous membranes, 269

postsynaptic membrane, 465

potassium, accumulation in cells, as example of active transport, 247

ion concentration, changes in, effects on resting potential, 454, *455*

effects of temperature, 247

potassium, ion concentration, in cells and bathing media, 453, 453T
  movement through cell membrane, 248
  osmotic activity, 247
potential. See under specfic potentials, e.g., *oxidation-reduction potential.*
potential energy. See *energy.*
precipitation, of proteins, 72
press juice, 502
pressure, as factor in environment, 141–143, 142T
  effect on growth, 142, 142T
  hydrostatic, 141
  osmotic. See *osmotic pressure.*
  receptors, 463
  root, 248
  tolerance adaptations, 141
presynaptic membrane, 465
prism, Nicol, 274, *275*
procaryotic cell, definition, 18
prosthetic groups, of enzymes, 311, *312*
protein(s), amino acid content, 40T
  as zwitterions, 41
  attachment to bound water, 36
  cellular, 37–49
    examples of, 33T
    subclasses of, 33T
  coagulation of, 46
  colloidal properties, 69–72
  composition, 37
  conjugated, 47
  denaturation, 46, *47*
    temperature coefficient for, 201
  dissociation of, 152
  effects of heat, 194
  empirical formulas for, 39
  entry into cell by pinocytosis, 261
  fibrous, 43–46
    types of, 43
    x-ray diffraction, 43, *44*
  gelation, 70
  globular, 43–46
    structure, 46
  hydrolysis of, 305
  hydrophobic and hydrophilic radicals, 69T
  in cell membranes, 269
    evidence for, 271–273
    structural arrangement of, 274–279
  in oil-water emulsions, 67
  isoelectric pH of, 41, *42*, 42T
  molecules, attraction and repulsion, 69
  of ground substance, bonding, 76, *76*
  osmotic relations in presence of, 234, *235*
  peptide backbone, 38, *38*
  precipitation of, 72
  reaction with dyes, effect of isoelectric pH, 42T
  relative amounts in different organisms, 34T
  relative number of molecules in cell, 35T
  residual, of chromosomes, 115
  salting out, 72
  solubility of, 33T, 41
  state as sol or gel, 70
protein(s), structural formulas for, 40, *40*
  structural, of muscle, 502–505
  surface binding of, 261
  synthesis of, 530–534, *531–533*
    inhibition by ionizing radiations, 187
      by ultraviolet radiation, 178
    role of DNA, 125, 128
      of ribosomes, 89 127
      of RNA, 126
proteolysis, 305
  unfolding of, 47
  water uptake, 70, *71*
protoplasm, chemical constituents, 35
protoplast, 18
  retraction of, *19*
protozoans, active transport in vaculoar output, 249, *249*
  aging of, 517
  regeneration of, 522
pseudopod, growth of, *477*
pump, sodium, 248, *459*
purification, of enzymes, 308
purine nucleus, formula, *48*
Purkinje, 564
  fibers, 486, *487*
purple, visual, 169
pyrenoid, *11*
pyrimidine nucleus, formula, *48*
pyruvic acid, oxidation of, 334, *335*

QUANTITATIVE analyses, in study of permeability, 225–227, *226*
quantum efficiency, of photosynthesis, 416–418, 417T
  theory, 165
quinhydrone electrode, in measurement of pH, 368

RAD, definition, 165
radiation(s), effects on permeability, 236
  in cell environment, 161–192
  ionizing, absorption of, 182
    characteristics of different kinds, 189
    compared wih ultraviolet radiations, 182, 183T
    effects on cells, 182–187
    mutations produced by, 184
  measurement of, 163–165, *164*
  natural, 161–165
  nature of, 165
  of sunlight, 161–163, *162*
  sickness, 188
  use in inhibition of cell division, 549
  wavelengths of, 164T
radical, free. See *free radical.*
radioactive emanations, 163
radioactive tracers, in studies of permeability, 225 226
radioautography, 59, *60, 61*
radiolarian, 73

radiosensitivity, variations in, 186
range, of electrons, 189
Ranvier, nodes of, 440
rate-limiting reactions, 203
rays, cosmic, 163
   ordinary and extraordinary, definition, 275
reaction. See under specific reactions, e.g., *Feulgen reaction.*
reaction rate theory, 206
Reamur, 385
receptor cells, 463
   definition, 424
recruitment zone, in ameboid movement, 476, *477*
red blood cells. See *erythrocytes.*
redifferentiation, of cells, 522
redox potentials. See *oxidation-reduction potentials.*
reduction level, 377–379, 381T
reflex arc, 425
refractory period, 430
   absolute and relative, 431
   in cardiac muscle, 486, *489*
   in skeletal muscle, 493
   in visceral muscle, 484
regeneration, of cells, 522
regulator genes, 535
relative refractory period, 431
relativity, Einstein's theory of, 300
relaxation, of skeletal muscle, 495
relaxing factor, 512
renucleation, 106
reciprocity law, Bunsen-Roscoe, 166
repressor substance, in control of growth, 535
reproduction. See also *cell division.*
   as cellular function, 3
resonance, paramagnetic, 363, *363*
   spin, 363, *364*
respiration, 370–396
   definition, 370
   heat evolved during, 379–381
   inhibition of, 377, *378*
   measurement of, 370–374
      Cartesian diver method, 391–393, *392*
      chemical methods, 389
      manometric methods, 390, *391*
      polarographic methods, 393, *393*
      volumetric methods, 389
   rate of, 370–374, 371T
      compared with size of organism, 371T, 372, *373, 374*
      effects of encystment, 377, *379*
      of oxygen tension, 376, *376*
      of temperature, 375, *375, 376*
      of water, 377, *379, 380*
   role in active transport, 246
respiratory quotient, 377–379
   measurement of, 381
   of animals, 382
   of plants, 382
spirometer, 370, *372*
response, definition, 423
resting potentials, across cell membrane, 450–458

resting potentials, origin of, 453–456
   changes during propagation of action potential, 458
   definition, 450
   effects of anion gradients, 456
      of increased potassium ion concentration, 454, *455*
      of oxygen, 456, *457*
   experimental demonstration of, 450, *451*
   in muscle, 489
   relation to metabolism, 456–458
reticulopod, 478, *478*
retina, 167
   rod cells of, 101–103, *103*
reticulum, endoplasmic. See *endoplasmic reticulum.*
retinene, 169
rheobase, 434
Rhodopseudomonas, 166
rhodopsin, 169
   effect of light, *170*
rhythm, diurnal. See *diurnal rhythms.*
riboflavin, oxidation-reduction of, 361, *362*
ribonuclease, empirical formula, 39
ribonucleic acid. See *RNA*
ribonucleoprotein particles, 86, *87*
ribose, *51*
ribosomes, 88
   in protein synthesis, 89, 127, 532
Rickettsia, 19
RNA, 52–56. See also *nucleic acids.*
   constituents, 53T
   differences from DNA, 52, 53T
   enzyme tests for, 113
   histochemistry of, 113
   in chromosomes, 115
   in Feulgen reaction, 111
   in protein synthesis, 126
   lability of, 120
   molar proportions of bases, 55T
   molecular weight, 53
   nucleotides of, 127
   proportion in total nucleus, 119
   relative number of molecules in cell, 35T
   role in biosynthesis of protein, 530–534
   of hyaloplasm, 127
   staining of, 111, 113
   structure, 53
   synthesis of, 529
      inhibition by ionizing radiations, 187
      by ultraviolet radiations, 178
rods, retinal, 101–103, *103*, 167, *168*
roentgen, definition, 165
root pressure, 248

SALINITY, relation to chlorinity, 156
salts, 155–158. See also under specific salts, e.g., *sodium.*
   antagonism, 238, *238*

salts, cellular, 36, *36*, 37T
  definition, 144
  effect on enzyme activity, 316
    on permeability, 236–239
  in cell membranes, 270
  in induction of pinocytosis, 257, *258*
  in natural waters, 155, 156T
  relative amounts in different organisms, 34T
saltatory conduction, 463
    of nerve impulse, 440, *441*
salting out, of proteins, 72
Sanger, 41, 568
sap, nuclear, constituents, 112
sarcomeres, of myofibrils, 500, *501–503*
sarcoplasm, 499
Schleiden, 1, 563
Schoenheimer, 567
Scholander-Wennesland respirometer, *372*
Schwann, 1, 563
Schwann cell, 277, *278*
sclerenchyma, 18
scleroproteins, solubility of, 41
secretory granule, *11, 96*
semipermeable membrane, definition, 212
sense receptors, 463
sensitization, photodynamic, 165–167
sensory fibers, action potentials in, 463–465, *464, 465*
serum albumin, absorption spectra, *59*
shear zone, in ameboid movement, 476, *477*
Sherrington, 465, 569
shivering, 380
shock, chemical and physical, use to achieve synchrony in cell suspensions, 542, *545*
short-night plants, 175
shunt, pentose, 341, *343*
sinoauricular node, 486
sinus venosus, 486, *487, 488*
size, effect on respiration rate, 371T, *372, 373, 374*
  of cells, range in, 9T
    regulation of, 522–524, *522*
skeletal muscle. See *muscle, skeletal.*
skeletons, of plants, 18
sliding filament theory, of muscular contraction, 509–511, *512*
slime molds, movement in, 478, *479*
slow neutrons, 190
smooth muscle. See *muscle, visceral.*
snow blindness, 177
soaps, as emulsion stabilizers, 67
sodium chloride, effects on permeability, 236, 237
sodium ions, concentrations in cells and bathing media, 453, 453T
  movement through cell membrane, 248
  pump, 248, 459
  x-ray diffraction diagrams, *44*
solubility, of cellular compounds, 33T
  of proteins, 41
solutes, movement through cell membrane, 223–243
solutions, colligative properties of, 217
specific heat, 133
specificity, of hydrolytic enzymes, 306–308

spectrophotometry, use in identification of nucleic acids, 59, *59*
spectrum, absorption correspondence to action spectrum, *413, 415*
  of chlorophyll and carotenoids, 410, *411*
  of phycocyanin and phycoerythrin, *414*
  action, 168
    correspondence to absorption spectrum, *413, 415*
    for Blinks effect, *415*
    for Emerson effect, *415*
  of sunlight, 161, *162*
sperm, use in study of nucleic acids, 52
spermatozoa, centrioles, 101
  tails, 99, *101*
spike potential, 431
  formation, 459, *460*
  relation to local potential in neuron, 458, *459*
spin resonance, electron, 363, *364*
spinal ganglion cell, cervical, *12*
spindle elongation theory, of cleavage, 558, *559*
  mitotic, 554
splitting enzymes, 311
spores, 18, 197
staining techniques, 21
starch, 51
  digestion of, 305
steady state, of cell, 295
sterols, 50, *50*
stigma, *11*
stimulation, threshold and subthreshold, definitions, 435
stimulus artifact, 432
  definition, 423
Strasburger, 564
stratification, of ground substance, by means of centrifuge, 13, *13*
streaming birefringence, 276
  cytoplasmic, 475
strength-duration curve, *436*
  definition, 435
  relationship, 434–438
streptomycin, effect on bacterial cell wall, 269
striated muscle. See *muscle, skeletal.*
striations, in myofibrils, 500, *501, 502*
stromatin, 269
strong acids and bases. See *acids* and *bases.*
strong electrolytes, 227
substrate(s), concentration, effect on enzyme action, 314, *316*
  union with enzymes, 318
subthreshold stimulation, definition, 435
sucrose, *51*
sugars, active transport in gut, 250
  osmotic pressure at different concentrations, 215
summation, 436
sun, surface temperature, 161
sunburn, 177, *178*
sunlight, radiations of, 161–163, *162*
surface energy, 65
  tension, 79, *79*, 80T
    in heterogeneous systems, 65, *65*

surface energy, tension, of cell membrane, 271
  of water, 136
suspensions, 66–68
  size ranges of, 68T
sympathin, 468
synapses, facilitation at, 471
  inhibition at, 469–471
  polarization of, 465
  structure, 465, *466*
  variations in, 465
synaptic transmission, chemical theory, 466–469
  electrical theory, 466
  of action potentials, 465–471
  role of acetylcholine, 467
synchrony, in cell division, 540–544, *541*
Szent-Györgyi, 571

TACTOIDS, 73, *73*
Tatum, 524, 570
television camera, as attachment for ultraviolet microscope, 27
temperature, as factor in cell environment, 193–207
  characteristic, 205
  coefficient, 199
    and limiting reactions, 203
    for denaturation of protein and thermal death of
      cells, 201
    variation over temperature range, 204T
  effects of exercise, 380
    on active transport, 254
    on carbon dioxide solubility, 137T
    on enzyme activity, 315, *317*
    on oxygen solubility, 139T
    on permeability, 235
    on potassium ion concentration, 247
    on rate of photosynthesis, 399, 399T, *400*
    on respiration rate, 375, *375*, *376*
  lethal, 194
  measurement by thermocouples, 218, *218*
  of plants, 381
  of sun, 161
  use as physical shock to achieve synchrony, 543,
    545
template, of DNA, 125
tendon, connective tissue of, composition, *17*
tension, interfacial. See *interfacial tension.*
tension, surface. See *surface tension.*
tetanus, 493, *494*
Theorell, 567
thermal death of cells, temperature coefficient for, 201
thermal resistance, of dormant cells, 197–199
thermal shock, use to achieve synchrony, 543, *545*
thermobarometer, 390
thermochemical reactions, rate of, 199–201, 200T, *201*
  in photosynthesis, 404–407
thermocouples, 164, 218, *218*
thermodynamics, first law of, 287–289
  laws of, and the cell, 287–302

thermodynamics, second law of, 66, 289–291
  entropy and, 293
thermophilic organisms, 193
thermostabilizer, water as, 133–135
threshold current, in stimulation of neurons, 434
  stimulation, definition, 435
Thunberg, 569
Thunberg tube, 339, *341*
thymine, formula, *48*
time-lapse photography. See *photography.*
tissues, animal, classification, 16
  connective, composition, 16, *17*
  culture, growth in, 519–522
  definition, 16
  plant, classification of, 17
titration, 144
tonus, in skeletal muscle, 493
  in visceral muscle, 485
touch receptors, 463
transducer, biological, 463
transduction, in bacteria, 124
transferring enzymes, 311
transmission, synaptic. See *synaptic transmission.*
transmitter substance, in synaptic transmission, 467
transport, active. See *active transport.*
trans-retinene, 170
transition states, 206
trans-vitamin A, 169
Traube, 211
tricarboxylic acid cycle. See *Krebs cycle.*
triglycerides, 49, *49*
tripalmitin, formula, *49*
tropisms, 424
tropomyosin, 503
  structure, 505
trypsin, 306
tryptophan, 525, *526*
  formula, *39*
Tswett, 418
tumor cells, growth in, 519–522
  metabolic pathways in, 345
turgor movements, 424
twitch, muscle, 428, 493
  in visceral muscle, 484
Tyndall cone, 68

ULTRACENTRIFUGE microscope. See *microscope, centrifuge.*
ultraviolet absorption spectra, 178, *179*
ultraviolet light, effects on cells, 177–182
ultraviolet microscope. See *microscope.*
ultraviolet photomicrographs. See *photomicrographs.*
ultraviolet radiations, compared with ionizing radiations, 182, 183T
  effects on DNA synthesis, 549
  of sun, 161, 163
ultraviolet spectrophotometry, use in identification of
  nucleic acids, 59, *59*

unbalanced growth, 534–536
uptake measurements, in permeability studies, 225
uracil, formula, *48*
urethan, as respiratory inhibitor, 377
utilization time, 435

VACUOLAR function, as example of active transport, 249, *249*
vacuole(s), 11, 12, 97, 98
  pinocytotic, 258, *259, 260*
Van Allen belts, 161, *162*
Van Niel, 398
Van't Hoff, 215
Van't Hoff equation, 204
vapor pressure, determination of, 217, *217*
vaporization, latent heat of, 133
vertebrates, body structure, 4
Verworn, 566
viruses, as possible cause of cancer, 521
  compared with bacteria, 19
  organization of, 19–21
visceral muscle. See *muscle.*
viscosity, 80–82, 81T, *82*
  definition, 69
  of cytoplasm, 77, *77*
  of ground substance, 74
vision, 167–172
visual cycle, 171, *171*
visual purple, 169
vital dyes, 21
vitalistic interpretation of life activities, 5
vitamins, 56, 56T
vitamin A, role in vision, 169
vitamin A_1, structure, *412*
vitamin B_2, oxidation-reduction of, 361, *362*
vitelline membrane, of sea urchin egg, 265, *266*
Volta, 446
volume change, as method for studying permeability, 224, *224*
von Helmholtz, 432

WALLS, of bacterial cells, 18, 268
  of plant cells, 266–269
Warburg, 345, 416, 569
water, active transport of, 253
  as factor in cell environment, 133–137
  as solvent, 135, *136*
  as temperature stabilizer, 133–135
  bound, 36
  cellular, 35
  dielectric constant, 135
  dissociation of, 145
  effect on respiration, 377, *379, 380*
  free, 36
  heat of fusion, 134
    of vaporization, 133

water, hydrogen bonds of, 137
  in brain cells, 36
  movement across cell membrane, 211–222
  percentage of cell, 133
  permeability of cell membrane to, 213
  pH of, 150
  relative amounts in different organisms, 34T
  relative number of molecules in cell, 35T
  salts in, 155, 156T
  sea, cations in, 157, *158*
    ionic content compared to blood, 156, 157T
  solubility of oxygen in, 138
  special properties of, 136
  specific heat, 133
  structure of, 136, *136*
  surface tension, 136
  transparency, 136
  uptake, by proteins, 70, *71*
  vapor, in atmosphere, 134
Watson-Crick hypothesis, 53, *55*
wavelengths, of radiations, 164T
  x-ray, relation to voltage, 189
waxes, 50
weak acids and bases. See *acids* and *bases.*
weak electrolytes, 227
weight, as factor in cell division, 553
  molecular, of cellular materials, 35T
    of DNA and RNA, 53
white blood cells, 17. See also under specific white cells, e.g., *lymphocytes.*
white matter, water content, 36
Wieland, 346, 569
Wilson, E. B., 566
Wöhler, 565
work and heat relations, in contraction of muscle, 496

XANTHOPHYLLS, 50, 410
x-rays. See also under *ionizing radiations.*
  absorption of, 184
  diffraction, of DNA, 53
    of fibrous proteins, 43, *44*
  use in inhibition of cell division, 549
  wavelength, relation to voltage, 189
xylem, 18

YEAST, fermentation, *334*
  as vital process, 5
  formula, *48*
yield value, 70, *70*

ZERNICKE, 567
zones, in ameboid movement, 476, *477*
zwitterions, 152
  proteins as, 41, *42,* 42T